# Finite Mathematics

# Finite Mathematics

**Steven C. Althoen**
**University of Michigan—Flint**

**Robert J. Bumcrot**
**Hofstra University**

W • W • Norton & Company • New York • London

ACKNOWLEDGEMENTS:

*Page 8* MONOPOLY® is the registered trademark of Parker Brothers division of General Mills Fun Group, Inc., for its real estate trading game equipment and is used by its permission.

*Page 52* Trademark reproduced with the consent of Wendy's International, Inc.

*Pages 387, 392, 393, 397* SCRABBLE® is the registered trademark of Selchow and Righter Company, New York, New York, for a line of crossword games and as used in the text, it refers to the crossword game produced and marketed under the name "SCRABBLE® Brand Crossword Game by Selchow and Righter." Permission obtained.

*Pages 394–396* Specified excerpt from pp. 140–142 of NICK THE GREEK, KING OF THE GAMBLERS by Cy Rice. Copyright © 1969 by Cy Rice. Used by permission of Thomas Y. Crowell Company, Inc.

Library of Congress Cataloging in Publication Data

Althoen, Steven C.
  Finite mathematics.

  Includes index.
  1. Mathematics—1961–  I. Bumcrot, Robert J.,
1936–  joint author.  II. Title.
QA39.2.A48     510     78–326
ISBN 0-393-09046-9

# Contents

**Preface**                                                              ix

**How to Use
This Book**                                                              xi

**Introduction**                                                        xiii

**Chapter 1  Probability**                                                1

  1.1   Sorting and the Principle of Multiplication              1
  1.2   Outcomes and Events                                       8
  1.3   Probability Distributions                                17
  1.4   Equally Likely Outcomes                                   26
  1.5   Conditional Probability                                   37
  1.6   Summary                                                   47
       **Review Exercises**                               49
       **Supplementary Exercises**                        49

**Chapter 2  Systems of Linear Equations**                               54

  2.1   Introduction to Coordinates and Linear Equations         55
  2.2   Systems of Two Linear Equations in Two Unknowns          64
  2.3   Gauss-Jordan Reduction                                   77
  2.4   Shortcuts in Gauss-Jordan Reduction                      93
  2.5   The Geometry of Linear Equations in Three Variables     102
  2.6   Matrix Arithmetic                                       107
  2.7   Summary                                                 135
       **Review Exercises**                              137
       **Supplementary Exercises**                       139

## Chapter 3 Multistage Processes    149

3.1 Tree Diagrams    149
3.2 Bayes' Theorem    153
3.3 Markov Chains    169
3.4 Regular and Absorbing Markov Chains    183
3.5 Periodic and Ergodic Markov Chains    202
3.6 Summary    225
    **Review Exercises**    **226**
    **Supplementary Exercises**    **228**

## Chapter 4 Random Variables and Probability Distributions    232

4.1 Random Variables    232
4.2 Expectation    249
4.3 Mean and Standard Deviation    257
4.4 The Binomial and Geometric Distributions    264
4.5 The Normal Distribution    273
4.6 The Poisson Distribution    288
4.7 Summary    292
    **Review Exercises**    **292**
    **Supplementary Exercises**    **293**

## Chapter 5 Linear Programming    297

5.1 Introduction to Linear Programming    297
5.2 The Simplex Method    313
5.3 The Algebra of the Simplex Method    328
5.4 Phase I, Mixed Constraints, and Minimization    334
5.5 Linear Programming at Appalachian Creations    349
5.6 The Dual Variable Check and Unrestricted Variables    360
5.7 Summary    377
    **Review Exercises**    **382**
    **Supplementary Exercises**    **383**

## Chapter 6 Further Topics    387

6.1 Poker, Scrabble® Brand Crossword Game, and Odds    387
6.2 Matrix Inversion and Leontief Models    397

6.3   Game Theory                                                    428
6.4   Applications to Biology                                         441
6.5   Maximal Flows in Networks                                       449
6.6   Computers, Hand Calculators, and Finite Mathematics            475
      **Supplementary Exercises**                                     **492**

# Appendices

A   Review of Arithmetic and Algebra                                  503
B   Tables                                                            514
C   Answers to Odd-numbered and Starred Exercises,
    with Selected Comments and Solutions                              518

# Index                                                               **583**

To
      Marcia
       Christopher
      Francesca
    David
   Michael
Tosca

# Preface

This introductory text is intended for students of business, economics, or biology as well as for others who may want to broaden their understanding of mathematics and its uses. As explained in the next section, very little facility with high school mathematics will be assumed.

In this book, each concept and method is illustrated with examples based upon the hypothetical problems of imaginary business organizations. While a few of these examples are quite complicated, none is as involved as those generally encountered in real life, so that readers are not overwhelmed with data. We hope that the occasionally lighthearted nature of some of these examples will help make the learning process a pleasant one.

To make the text as accessible as possible to beginning students, mathematical abstraction is held to a minimum. The instructor may be surprised to find that nearly all traditional set theory *is* included. However, it is not presented as a separate subject but as a language that helps to express the concepts of probability as they are introduced. Otherwise technical notation and terminology are used sparingly; ideas are expressed in plain English whenever possible. Certainly rather sophisticated mathematical machinery would be needed to provide rigorous proofs of some of our assertions. Yet a student can understand these assertions, even see why they are true, without such proofs.

We have drawn connections between probability and linear mathematics wherever possible. This has been done in such a way that the instructor may either emphasize or ignore such relationships. The following diagram indicates the interdependence of the various sections of the book. It also gives our assessment of their relative difficulty, the bottom level being the most difficult. As this diagram shows, a number of different courses can be taught from this book, ranging in length from one quarter to a full academic year. Several courses are suggested below. The length of each course will depend on the students' abilities and the number of topics selected.

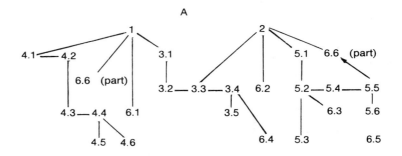

**Finite Mathematics for Business Students**

Sections 1.1–1.4, 2.1–2.3, 3.1–3.4, 5.1, 5.2, 5.3–5.5, 6.3, 6.6 with the emphasis on problem-solving techniques.

**Finite Mathematics for Liberal Arts Students**

Sections 1.1–1.5, 2.1–2.3, 2.6, 3.1–3.3, 4.1–4.3, 5.1 (with some mention of 2.5); topics from the rest of the book, chosen by the instructor (or perhaps by the class!).

**Introduction to Probability**

Sections 1.1–1.5, 2.6, 3.1–3.3, 4.1–4.5; topics from: 2.2–2.4, 3.4, 3.5, 4.6, 6.1, parts of 6.4, 6.6.

**Introduction to Linear Programming**

Sections 2.1–2.5, 5.1–5.7; topics from: 6.2, 6.3, 6.5, part of 6.6.

A preliminary edition of this book was used in classes at Hofstra University, the University of Michigan—Flint, and Nassau Community College. We are grateful to the students for their patience and to the instructors for their comments. As with our first book, the penetrating remarks of John Weidner were especially valuable. Useful criticism of parts of the revised manuscript was provided by Daniel Cullen, Larry Kugler, and Stephen Maurer. The extremely thorough and detailed comments on the entire work provided separately by Leonard Gillman and Leroy Meyers contributed corrections and other improvements to virtually every page. Thanks are due to Angelo Panoff and Nallapu Reddy for help with some technical economic details. Thanks are also tendered to Joseph B. Janson, II, Mary Shuford, and Ruth H. Bergman of W. W. Norton & Company for their many helpful contributions. Ms. Bergman also designed the cover of the preliminary version of this text. Kathleen O'Malley did an outstanding job in reworking all of the exercises. Finally, once again, a special thanks to Marcia Althoen, our typist and friend.

Flint, Michigan                                                      S. A.
New York, New York                                                   R. B.

# How to Use This Book

You have only to follow our directions to learn all of the computational techniques described in this book. No mathematical background beyond elementary algebra is required. The only requirement is that you be willing to practice each technique by working an appropriate number of exercises. It would be helpful if you were proficient in working with fractions and negative numbers. If you feel unsure in these areas, try the exercises in Appendix A, all of which are answered in Appendix C. If you have trouble, work through this appendix before starting the book. Otherwise, merely refer to it as needed.

While most of the ideas presented are fully explained in the text, a few facts are needed that are not obvious and that cannot be fully justified without using mathematics beyond the scope of this book. We have consistently introduced such facts with the phrase "it can be shown that." You should have no trouble understanding and accepting these facts, even without proper justification.

Nearly all the concepts in the text are illustrated in worked examples, called Problems. The problems are also models for the exercises which follow each section. If you can work several of the hardest numerical exercises in a set, you probably don't need to work all the easier ones. If a section contains some word problems (called Practical Problems in the text), be sure to work some of them, too. This will help develop your ability to apply the techniques you are learning.

The odd-numbered exercises are answered in Appendix C. A <sup>c</sup> precedes the number of an exercise if there is a hint or comment given in Appendix C. An * before an exercise number means that we think the exercise is more difficult than most. All these exercises are answered in Appendix C.

Additional practice may be obtained by working some of the supplementary exercises following each chapter. These exercises are not arranged by section; you must decide which technique to use in solving each one.

It is also a good idea to create and solve your own exercises. One reason the instructor is so far ahead of the class is that he or she is frequently required to make up good problems for the tests. Often you can learn more from making up one good problem than from solving many.

All the chapters except the last end with summaries and review exercises. In reviewing for an examination on one of these chapters, begin by going through the summary and the flow charts to which it refers. Then give yourself a "closed-book" examination consisting of the review exercises. All these exercises are answered in Appendix C.

An unusually complete index is provided to help locate specific terms, topics, techniques, and applications.

Sometimes students waste hours in confusion because of a typographical error in the text. We've tried hard to eliminate these errors, but if you find yourself stuck on what you think should be an easy point, please allow for the possibility that you're right and we're wrong!

# Introduction

In the following pages you will learn several mathematical techniques, which we will apply to decision-making problems in business. You should realize that the basic techniques are more important than our particular examples. If you thoroughly understand these methods, you should be able to apply them to situations that differ greatly from those presented here. In fact, most of these techniques also have important applications in the social and natural sciences. The following four problems illustrate the kinds of applications we have in mind. As you study this text and its examples, try to imagine other uses that may be particularly interesting to you.

**Problem 1**

This problem reappears as Exercise 32 in Section 4.5.

I plan to buy a truckload of electrical equipment from a manufacturer who claims that at most 5% of the items are defective. I select 100 items at random and find 7 to be defective. If I assume the manufacturer is telling the truth, what are the chances of my selecting such a sample?

**Answer**

Of every 100 such samples of 100, I should expect about 24 to contain 7 or more defective items. The chances are 24%.

**Problem 2**

This problem reappears as Exercise 14 in Section 3.4.

My taxi company is in competition with another taxi company in a small town with a population of 5,574. An independent survey reveals that most residents do not use a taxi 2 days in a row. In fact, 95% of the persons who use my taxi on one day will not use a taxi the next day and 92% of the competitor's customers will not use a taxi the next day. Furthermore, 10% of the people who did not use a taxi on a given day select me on the next day and 12% select him. Of course, a few people do use a taxi on 2 consecutive days. However, I lose 20% of my customers to him and get 25% of his customers. Yesterday I happened to have had 800 customers and he had 300 customers. How many customers will we each have 90 days from today?

**Answer**

If we assume that the trends predicted by the survey persist, then, on that day, I will have 482 customers and he will have 581.

**Problem 3**

This problem reappears as Exercise 8 in Section 5.5.

I am in charge of three chemical factories which each produce four chemicals: narcolase, enervate, aureate, and coprolite. The Bismuth, North Dakota, factory produces 300 liters of narcolase, 100 of enervate, 200 of aureate, and 700 of coprolite per hour at a cost of $2,400 per hour. The liter-per-hour figures for the Wilkes-Barium, Pennsylvania, factory are 300 of narcolase, 600 of enervate, 100 of aureate, and 200 of coprolite, at an operating cost of $700 per hour. The corresponding figures for the Indiumapolis, Indiana, plant are: 500, 800, 200, and 400 at a cost of $1,800. I have orders for 51,000 liters of narcolase and 20,000 liters of aureate, although I could produce more of either chemical. While I have no orders for enervate this week, it is an unavoidable by-product. I have storage space for 86,000 liters of it, but I could produce less. I have orders for 46,000 liters of coprolite. Unfortunately, this chemical deteriorates rapidly, so I must produce exactly 46,000 liters. My problem is this: What is the cheapest way for me to meet my orders, yet not exceed the storage restriction on enervate?

**Answer** Operate the Bismuth factory for 20 hours, the Wilkes-Barium factory for 100 hours, and the Indiumapolis factory for 30 hours. The total cost will be $17,200.

**Problem 4**

This problem reappears as Exercise 26 in Section 3.2.

I may have a disease believed present in only 1% of the population. Rather than send me to the hospital for an extensive examination, my doctor administers a simple and inexpensive test. While the results are negative (that is, do not indicate that I have the disease), he warns me that 10% of persons with the disease test negatively. Also, only 80% of persons without the disease test negatively. Given these data, what are the chances that I have the disease?

**Answer** The chances are about 1 in 1,000.

# Finite Mathematics

# Chapter 1
# Probability

Appalachian Creations, Inc., (or AC) is the largest (fictitious) maker and retailer of sporting goods on the East Coast.

Their earnings were up nearly 316%.

Operations research (OR) is a collection of mathematical techniques that is of primary importance in modern business decision making. Most of the topics in this text relate to OR, although they also have other uses.

The weather was so bad that the old warehouse was closed. Alan V. Gregory sat at home glancing over the day's mail: two bills, a card informing him that he might already be a winner, and a letter from the president of AC. Alan had just started work as a warehouse laborer at AC, so he read with interest the open letter to all employees:

```
The president of Appalachian Creations,
Inc., is pleased to announce record
earnings for the company in the last
quarter.
```

She went on to say that the company's success was due largely to good products, fair prices, effective advertising, and a rekindled national interest in the outdoors. She also pointed out that increased use of operations research had done much to make AC the leader among East Coast sporting goods companies. Alan was proud to be part of a growing company and looked forward to the time when he would be eligible to participate in the company's profit-sharing program.

The second page of the letter mentioned two other items of interest to us. The first had to do with the completion of the office-warehouse complex, which would become the new corporate headquarters in just three weeks. The second concerned several promotions, which would become effective immediately after the move. The biggest surprise was the announcement that Janet Witherspoon, a young member of the corporate staff, was to be made head of the newly organized planning department.

Janet's rapid rise at AC was of great interest to Alan. Three weeks later, when he began his first day in the new warehouse, Alan thought about their respective careers. Janet had conducted the orientation session that he attended when he was hired. She explained that AC would pay the tuition for one or two evening courses at Local College for any employee seeking to increase his or her practical knowledge and skills. Tired of the series of dead-end jobs he had held since leaving the army and before joining AC, Alan had registered for one course, Introduction to Finite Probability. Although he was unsure of the practical value of the course, he had enjoyed the first lecture, which began,

Fractions are reviewed in Appendix A, Section 4.

"Why do we say that the probability of flipping a coin and having it come up heads is $\frac{1}{2}$? We know there are two possible outcomes: heads or tails. The event "coming up heads" has one possible outcome: heads. We get the probability $\frac{1}{2}$ by dividing the number of possible outcomes in the event (one) by the total number of possible outcomes (two). Is $\frac{1}{2}$ the right answer? That depends. If the coin is balanced, in the sense that each face is equally likely to come up, and if the coin never lands on edge (well, almost never), then the proabability of heads is indeed $\frac{1}{2}$.

"Suppose we toss a balanced die. What is the probability that the number on top is greater than 4? There are six possible outcomes: 1, 2, 3, 4, 5, 6. The event in question has two possible outcomes: 5, 6. Thus, the probability of the event is $\frac{2}{6} = \frac{1}{3}$.

The die (plural: dice) dates back to at least 1370 B.C. and may be descended from a device called the astragalus, which was in use by 3500 B.C. in Egypt. Modern casino dice are made with extreme accuracy so as to insure that each face has the same probability of coming up. To further insure this, casinos require that when the dice are thrown they must bounce off the back wall of the dice table. Also the casino reserves the right to replace the dice at any time.

Of the many colloquial terms about dice we mention three: A one on a die is an **ace**; a pair of aces is **snake eyes**; a pair of sixes is **boxcars**.

"How do we check that these probabilities are correct for a particular coin or die? We could flip the coin or throw the die many times, although even then we would not be absolutely certain that our probabilities are correct. For an ordinary coin or die, it does seem that the probability of an event is the number of possible outcomes in the event divided by the total number of possible outcomes. That this method of calculation is not always correct is illustrated by the following problem.

Problem 1

Suppose I take a balanced die, cover the spots on its faces, and write 1 on three faces, 2 on two other faces, and 3 on the other face. If I throw the die, is the probability that 1 will come up equal to $\frac{1}{3}$? If not, what is it?

Solution

The outcomes 1, 2, and 3 are clearly not equally likely; the probability of 1 will not be $\frac{1}{3}$. Imagine that the faces of the die containing 1 are marked a, b, c, the faces containing 2 are marked d, e, and the face containing 3 is marked f. Since the die is balanced the six possible outcomes a, b, c, d, e, f are equally likely. The event 1 has three possible outcomes: a, b, c. Thus the probability of 1 is $\frac{3}{6} = \frac{1}{2}$, not $\frac{1}{3}$.

"We see from these examples that in calculating probabilities we must often begin by counting the possible outcomes. Before we go on with probability itself we must learn to count. This is not always easy. Counting is filled with pitfalls and can be very tricky. We will learn a few useful techniques and handy notations, but the only way to become a good counter is to study a lot of examples and work a lot of exercises.

"The fundamental technique of counting is

SORTING."

At this point the lecture ended. Next morning at the new AC warehouse, the foreman told Alan to find out how many wooden tent stakes were in a big pile of stakes that had been dumped in a corner during the move. It looked like a long, boring task. Alan poked around in the pile. He noticed that most of the stakes were tied in bundles. The bundles tied with blue twine had 8 stakes, those tied with red twine had 12 stakes, and those tied with white rope had 24 stakes. He sorted the bundles into piles, counting the blue bundles as he went. There were 35 blue bundles; so there were $35 \cdot 8 = 280$ stakes in the blue pile. He counted 43 red bundles; so there were $43 \cdot 12 = 516$ stakes in the red pile. The white pile had 37 bundles and therefore $37 \cdot 24 = 888$ stakes. Finally, he collected the loose stakes lying around, counting them as he put them in a fourth pile. There were 102. The total number of stakes in the original pile was then $280 + 516 + 888 + 102 = 1,786$. Sorting had made the job of counting easier.

The principle of sorting into piles that are easy to work with, counting each pile, and adding the results to get the total count is very useful in counting things, even when they cannot be physically sorted into piles. However, when we mentally sort things into piles we must be especially careful that: (1) each thing goes into one of the piles, and (2) we do not put any of the things into more than one pile. Of these two possibilities for error, the second is the more troublesome, as we shall see. As always, experience and practice will help in avoiding these pitfalls.

Here are two examples of counts that use a mental sorting process.

**Problem 2**
The digits in our system of numeration are: 0, 1, 2, 3, 4, 5, 6, 7, 8, 9. There are 10 of them. The letters in our system of writing are: A, B, C, D, E, F, G, H, I, J, K, L, M, N, O, P, Q, R, S, T, U, V, W, X, Y, Z. There are 26 of them.

Alan's daughter, Annie, was making little cardboard license plates for her collection of toy cars and trucks. Each plate consisted of one letter followed by one digit. Annie asked her father how many different plates she could make.

First Solution

Imagine all possible plates in a big pile. Put all the plates that begin with A in one pile, all that begin with B in a second pile, and so on down to Z. There are 26 piles. Each pile has 10 plates in it. For instance, the M pile has

$$M0, M1, M2, M3, M4, M5, M6, M7, M8, M9$$

This is the origin of the word "times" in multiplication: $26 \cdot 10$ means that 26 times you add 10.

Thus, the total number of plates possible is $10 + 10 + 10 + \ldots + 10$, where 26 tens are added. In other words there are $26 \cdot 10 = 260$ possible plates.

Second Solution

Put all plates that end with zero in the first pile, all that end with 1 in the second pile, and so on, finishing with the tenth pile, which consists of all plates that end with 9. Then there are 10 piles, each with 26 plates, for a total of $10 \cdot 26 = 260$ possible plates.

Problem 3

Information on cards is contained in Section 6.1.

You and I are each dealt 1 card from a 52-card deck. How many possible outcomes are there?

Solution

Outcomes need not be physical cards but may be slips of paper listing the deals.

In the first pile put all outcomes in which you receive the ace of hearts. Since you have the ace of hearts, I could not have been dealt it, although I could have been dealt any one of the 51 remaining cards. Thus, there are 51 possible outcomes in the first pile. Now make a second pile of all possible outcomes in which you get the two of hearts. There are 51 possible outcomes in this pile too. Continue in this way through all 52 cards in the deck. There are now 52 piles, each containing 51 possible outcomes. Every possible outcome is in one and only one of the piles; so the sorting is complete. There are $52 \cdot 51 = 2,652$ possible outcomes in all.

In each of these two problems the count involved two choices. In Problem 2, first solution, the first choice was the letter and the second choice was the digit. In Problem 3 the first choice was your card and the second choice was my card. In Problem 2 the first choice did not affect the possible outcomes of the second choice, while in Problem 3 it did. But in each problem the *number* of possible outcomes of the second choice was not affected by the first choice. This allowed us to do the final counts in each problem with a single multiplication, which was a considerable shortcut. This counting technique occurs so frequently that it is worth stating in general:

---

THE PRINCIPLE OF MULTIPLICATION IN COUNTING

Suppose that each possible outcome is, in one and only one way, the result of two choices. Suppose the first choice has m possible results and, after any first choice has been made, the second choice has n possible results. Then the total number of possible outcomes is mn.

---

As we have seen, this statement is a consequence of the fundamental technique of sorting. In the next three problems we will show how to apply the principle of multiplication to situations involving more than two choices.

Problem 4

A sack containing 5 candies is passed among 3 boys, each boy taking 1 candy. How many possible outcomes are there?

Solution

Here we use the principle of multiplication twice.

The first boy has 5 choices; then the second boy has 4 choices. Thus the first 2 boys have $5 \cdot 4 = 20$ choices. After this, the third boy has 3 choices. Hence there are $20 \cdot 3 = 60$ possible outcomes.

Problem 5

I take an ordinary 52-card deck and deal 1 card to each of 5 people. How many outcomes are possible?

Solution

Here we use the principle of multiplication four times.

I have 52 choices for the first, 51 for the second, 50 for the third, 49 for the fourth, and 48 for the fifth person. Altogether there are then $52 \cdot 51 \cdot 50 \cdot 49 \cdot 48 = 311,875,200$ possible deals (outcomes).

Problem 6

Each AC department is to be assigned a four-digit identification number, using only the digits 1, 2, 3, and 4. How many different identification numbers can be made under each of the following rules?
(a) Each digit may be used as often as desired.
(b) Each digit may be used only once.
(c) The first digit must be 3.
(d) The first two digits must be even and the last two must be odd.

Solution

In each case each ID number is the result of four choices: first digit, second digit, third digit, fourth digit.

1234, 1243, 1324, 1342, 1423, 1432,
2134, 2143, 2314, 2341, 2413, 2431,
3124, 3142, 3214, 3241, 3412, 3421,
4123, 4132, 4213, 4231, 4312, 4321.

If we also require the digits to be different, there would be only $1 \cdot 3 \cdot 2 \cdot 1$ $=6$ different ID numbers, namely, 3124, 3142, 3214, 3241, 3412, 3421.

The odd digits are 1, 3, 5, 7, 9. The even digits are 0, 2, 4, 6, 8. Zero is even because twice zero is zero.

(a) Each choice has four possible results; so there are $4 \cdot 4 \cdot 4 \cdot 4 = 256$ possible ID numbers.

(b) The first choice has four possible results, the second choice has three, the third has two, and the fourth has one; so there are $4 \cdot 3 \cdot 2 \cdot 1 = 24$ possible ID numbers under this rule. (They are listed in the margin.)

(c) The first choice has only one possible result (namely 3), and the second, third, and fourth choices each have four possible results; so there are $1 \cdot 4 \cdot 4 \cdot 4 = 64$ possibilities for ID numbers.

(d) The first and second choices each have two possible results (namely, 2 or 4), and the third and fourth choices each have two possible results (namely, 1 or 3); so there are $2 \cdot 2 \cdot 2 \cdot 2 = 16$ possible ID numbers.

**Exercises 1.1**

Throughout this book the answers to odd-numbered exercises appear in Appendix C. If a $^c$ precedes the exercise number it indicates that a comment or hint appears in Appendix C. An * before an exercise number indicates that the authors feel that the exercise is more difficult than most. Answers to all such exercises are given in Appendix C.

1. A balanced coin with one face heads and one face tails is flipped. Suppose it does not land on edge. What is the probability that
   (a) the coin lands with tails up?
   (b) the coin lands with tails down?
   (c) the coin lands with either heads up or tails up?
   (d) the coin lands with heads down and tails up?
   (e) the coin lands with heads up or tails down?
   (f) the coin lands with heads up and tails up?

2. A balanced coin with both faces heads is flipped. Suppose it does not land on edge. What is the probability that:
   (a) the coin lands with heads up?
   (b) the coin lands with heads up and heads down?
   (c) the coin lands with heads up or heads down?
   (d) the coin lands with heads up and tails down?
   (e) the coin lands with heads up or tails down?

3. A balanced die with faces marked 1, 2, 3, 4, 5, 6 is tossed. What is the probability of each of the following events?
   (a) 5   (b) 2 or 6   (c) an odd number   (d) not 3

4. A balanced die with two faces marked 3, three faces marked 5, and one face blank is tossed. What is the probability of each of the following events?
   (a) 5   (b) 2 or 6   (c) an odd number   (d) not 3

The Petaluma Hamburger Emporium Corporation (PHE) has grown tremendously since it started with one

5. The PHE warehouse in Houston contains 180 cases of boxes of hamburger buns. Sixty-five cases each contain 20 boxes of 12 buns each, and the other cases each contain 40 boxes of 8 buns each.

roadside stand in a small California town in 1936. Originally the stand sold only hamburgers, cheeseburgers, French fries, and three types of soft drink. By dint of careful scientific planning and management, PHE now controls a chain of 5,724 "mini-restaurants" located in every state, every Canadian province, and many countries in Europe.

We will be following this company throughout the exercises of this book.

Alan would have to stamp and mail a card to find out if he had won a photo or one of the other prizes, which he did regard as valuable.

(a) How many boxes of buns do they have?

(b) How many buns do they have?

6. Besides the warehouse, PHE has 7 stores in Houston. The downtown store has 10 cases of hamburger buns of the first type mentioned in Exercise 5 and 12 cases of the second type, while each of the other stores has 8 cases of each type. How many hamburger buns does PHE have in its stores in Houston?

7. How many different two-letter license plates can be made under each of these rules?
   (a) no restrictions
   (b) the letters must be different
   (c) neither the letter O nor the letter I may be used
   (d) the letters O and I cannot occur in the same plate
   (e) only the letters O and I may be used

8. Each of 3 people is dealt 1 card from an ordinary 52-card deck; then 2 more people are each dealt 1 card from another ordinary 52-card deck. How many different outcomes are possible?

9. Each of 4 people, in turn, picks a card from an ordinary 52-card deck, notes what it is, and returns it to the deck. How many different outcomes are possible?

10. In order to get from his area of the warehouse to the AC lunchroom without leaving the building, Alan has to take 1 of the 3 service elevators to the third floor, walk down a hall, and take 1 of the 5 main elevators to the lunchroom. It is snowing again, so Alan does not want to leave the building.
    (a) In how many ways can he get to the lunchroom?
    (b) In how many ways can he go to lunch and return?
    (c) Actually, while he was at lunch, 2 of the main elevators and 1 of the service elevators were shut down for the rest of the day. Now what is the answer to part (b)?

11. The card that Alan received (on page 1) informed him that he had a "good chance" of being a winner, since 100,000 people had been selected to receive prizes. However 94,650 of these prizes were autographed photos of Sonny Tufts, which Alan (in contrast with the authors) did not consider valuable. Assuming that 21,000,000 cards were mailed out, what is the probability that Alan was selected to receive a valuable prize?

12. Each AC employee has a four-digit ID number made from the digits 0, 5, 6, 7, 8, 9. How many different numbers are possible under each of the following rules?
    (a) No digit may appear more than once.
    (b) The first digit cannot be zero.
    (c) The last digit must be zero.
    (d) The first digit must be odd and the last digit must be even.

13. Janet knows that each department in Pocono Productions (PP), a small competitor of AC, has its own two-digit code number in which the first digit cannot be zero and the last digit must be odd. Is there

any truth in her boss's statement that PP, though small, has a complicated office structure involving at least 47 departments? Explain your answer.

14. My friend S. Uncopyrightable, a restaurateur I know, dislikes repetition and naturally would like his car license plate to have all different letters and numbers. His state makes license plates with any 3 letters followed by any 3 numbers.
    (a) How many license plates would be to his liking?
    (b) What is the probability he receives a plate he likes?

There is a 15-letter English word with no repeated letters and a 12-letter English word in which each letter is repeated. What are they?

## Section 1.2
## Outcomes and Events

In probability we study actions that may result in any one of a number of possible outcomes. Let's agree to call such actions experiments. When Alan throws a pair of dice or deals a poker hand, he is performing an experiment. In most dice games the outcome of a throw is the total number of dots showing on the tops of the dice. For example, if one die comes up 2 and the other comes up 4, the outcome is $2+4=6$. Since each die can show 1, 2, 3, 4, 5, or 6 dots, this experiment has eleven possible outcomes: $2, 3, 4, 5, 6, 7, 8, 9, 10, 11, 12$. In some dice games, however, special importance is attached to whether or not a pair is thrown. In such games the experiment of tossing two dice would have 15 possible outcomes: Pair of 1s, 3, pair of 2s, 4 but not a pair, 5, pair of 3s, 6 but not a pair, 7, pair of 4s, 8 but not a pair, 9, pair of 5s, 10 but not a pair, 11, pair of 6s. We could even imagine a game in which one red die and one green die are thrown and it is necessary to know which die has which number. We could record the possible outcomes of such a game with ordered pairs (red die, green die). For example, $(2, 5)$ means the dice were tossed, the red die came up 2, and the green die came up 5. This experiment has 36 possible outcomes:

In MONOPOLY®, for example, if each die comes up the same, you get an extra turn; but three pairs in a row lands you in jail.

We call these **ordered pairs** because the items are given in a specific order. For example, the pair $(3, 5)$ is to be considered as distinct from the pair $(5, 3)$.

$$
\begin{array}{cccccc}
(1,1) & (1,2) & (1,3) & (1,4) & (1,5) & (1,6) \\
(2,1) & (2,2) & (2,3) & (2,4) & (2,5) & (2,6) \\
(3,1) & (3,2) & (3,3) & (3,4) & (3,5) & (3,6) \\
(4,1) & (4,2) & (4,3) & (4,4) & (4,5) & (4,6) \\
(5,1) & (5,2) & (5,3) & (5,4) & (5,5) & (5,6) \\
(6,1) & (6,2) & (6,3) & (6,4) & (6,5) & (6,6)
\end{array}
$$

In order to apply probability theory to an experiment we need to count all the possible outcomes. This will be easier if we develop a good notation for the possible outcomes. For example, when Alan was asked in class to write down all possible outcomes of the red die-green die experiment, he wrote, "Red die comes up 1 and green die comes up 1" and so on. Later he shortened this to "red 1, green 1" and so on. Finally, at the teacher's suggestion, he used the ordered pair notation above.

This took 10 minutes and a whole page of writing.

This took 1 minute and a quarter-page of writing. Besides, it was easier to read.

For some experiments it is not possible to know all the possible outcomes in advance. For example, consider what happened at Appalachian Creations when Research and Development decided to run a series of strength tests on rip-stop nylon mending tapes. A strip of tape was stuck to a standard piece of nylon cloth that was clamped to a stand. The free end of the tape was attached to a hanging pan. Kilogram weights were placed on the pan. The weight required to pull the tape off the cloth was the outcome of the experiment. Now the testing lab had 12 ten-kg. weights, so they decided that the list of possible outcomes should be: 10, 20, 30, 40, 50, 60, 70, 80, 90, 100, 110, 120. That this was not a complete list became apparent on the first day when they tested a very poor quality tape: the weight of the pan was enough to pull it loose! Sheepishly, the lab people added zero to their list of possible outcomes. Later they were experimenting with a very good tape. At 90 kg. and at 100 kg. it still held. Some began to wonder if the list of possible outcomes should be extended beyond 120. Then, at 110 kg. the tape held but the cloth itself ripped. The outcomes 110 and 120 were impossible. There is no harm in keeping them in the list, but there is no reason to do so.

> Of course, the pan does have some weight, so zero is not quite correct. However, the pan weighs so much less than 10 kg. that the testers felt that zero was a reasonable approximation.

> The testers did add the letter e to the list of possible outcomes, where e stood for the sentence, "Tape strength exceeds cloth strength."

The set of all possible outcomes of an experiment is called the **sample space** of the experiment. The sample space is usually written by enclosing a list of possible outcomes in braces: { }. The sample space for the ordinary dice game is

$$\{2, 3, 4, 5, 6, 7, 8, 9, 10, 11, 12\}$$

It does not matter in which order we list the possible outcomes. For example, the sample space for the ordinary dice game could also be written $\{11, 8, 5, 4, 9, 7, 6, 10, 12, 3, 2\}$. As we remarked above, it is permissible to include some impossible "outcomes" in a sample space, but it is not permissible to exclude any possible outcomes. When the instructor first asked Alan to write the sample space for the ordinary dice game, Alan wrote $\{1, 2, 3, 4, 5, 6, 7, 8, 9, 10, 11, 12\}$. The instructor remarked, "That's certainly *a* sample space for the experiment, but it's not *the* sample space. You can't throw two dice and get a total of 1." We will follow this informal convention in this book: *The* sample space for an experiment is the set of all possible outcomes, no more. *A* sample space may contain some outcomes that are actually impossible.

> It may be useful, however, to use some principle of ordering in writing out a sample space so as to be sure to include everything. For one example of another principle of ordering, see Exercise 34.

Problem 1   Write the sample space for each of the following experiments.
(a) A die is tossed.
(b) A coin is flipped.
(c) A two-headed coin is flipped.

(a) {1, 2, 3, 4, 5, 6}
(b) {H, T} where H means heads and T means tails.
(c) {H} (The set {H, T} is a sample space.)

Problem 2

Alan, Betty, and Carl are being considered for promotion. What are the sample spaces for each of the following situations?
(a) There is 1 opening and 1 of them will be promoted to it.
(b) There is 1 opening.
(c) There are 2 identical openings and 2 of the candidates will be promoted to them.
(d) There are 4 identical openings.

Solution

Let A, B, and C stand for the statements, "Alan is promoted," "Betty is promoted," "Carl is promoted," respectively.
(a) The sample space is {A, B, C}.
(b) The sample space is {A, B, C, none are promoted}.
(c) *First solution.* {A and B, A and C, B and C}.

*Second solution.* Describe each outcome by an ordered triple, where the first letter describes what happens to Alan, the second describes Betty's fate, and third gives the decision on Carl. Let p mean "promoted" and n mean "not promoted." Then the sample space can be written {(p, p, n), (p, n, p), (n, p, p)}.

An ordered triple is an extension of the concept of an ordered pair from two entries to three. Here we are considering ordered triples of letters instead of numbers. For example, the ordered triple (p, n, p) is *not* the same as the ordered triple (p, n, n) because the third entries (p and n) are not the same.

(d) The A, B, C notation is inadequate. For example, in part (c) Alan knew that, if Betty and Carl were promoted, then he wasn't. Here "B and C" still means that Betty and Carl are promoted, but it doesn't say anything about Alan. If we agree that anyone not mentioned in an outcome is not promoted, then the sample space is

{none are promoted, A, B, C, A and B, A and C, B and C,

A and B and C}

There are many other equally good ways to express the answers to Problem 2.

However, it is simpler to use the ordered triple notation:

{(n, n, n), (p, n, n), (n, p, n), (n, n, p), (p, p, n), (p, n, p), (n, p, p), (p, p, p)}

Be sure you understand the phrases "at least," "at most," "less than," "greater than," "no more than," and "no less than." See Appendix A, Section 8, as required.

Now that we know how to describe experiments by writing the sample space, we want to study various events that may occur when an experiment is performed. In his regular Thursday night experiment (poker), Alan is very much interested in the event "royal flush." In certain dice games one is interested in the event "7 or 11." This event may be easily described by the set of its possible outcomes: {7, 11}. The event "royal flush" could be described by the set {spade: A K Q J 10; heart: A K Q J 10; diamond: A K Q J 10; club: A K Q J 10}. An **event** is any set of possible outcomes of an experiment. For example, in throwing dice, the set $\{9, 10, 11, 12\}$ describes the event "a number greater than 8." This event "occurs" whenever a number greater than eight is thrown.

**Problem 3**

Even the outcomes themselves may be considered as events with one element, as in part (e).

A die is thrown. Use sets to describe each of the following events.
(a) an even number
(b) a multiple of 3
(c) a number less than 4
(d) a number at least as large as 3
(e) an even number greater than 4

**Answer**

(a) $\{2, 4, 6\}$ (b) $\{3, 6\}$ (c) $\{1, 2, 3\}$ (d) $\{3, 4, 5, 6\}$ (e) $\{6\}$

We have said that any set of possible outcomes is an event. This includes the set of all possible outcomes, that is, the entire sample space. The sample space describes the **certain** event. At the other extreme we have the **impossible** event, which is described by a set with no elements, the **empty set** $\{\ \ \}$. The sample space of an experiment is usually denoted by S. The empty set is denoted by the symbol $\varnothing$.

**Problem 4**

**Solution**

A die is thrown. Use sets to describe each of the following events.
(a) a number less than 7
(b) a number greater than 7

(a) This event is certain to occur; it is the sample space $S = \{1, 2, 3, 4, 5, 6\}$.
(b) This event is impossible; it is $\varnothing$, the empty set.

In Section 6.1 we determine that there are 54,912 different "three-of-a-kind" poker hands. It would take at least 25 hours to write out the set T by hand. It would require over 100 pages of this text to display the list. More importantly, such a list would be worthless, except perhaps to a computer.

It is sometimes useful to denote the set describing an event by a capital letter. We have already done this for the certain event, S. This is particularly true for events with a large number of possible outcomes. It was an easy matter to list the possible outcomes in Alan's favorite event, "royal flush," but it would be a large task to do this for the event that actually occurred as his best hand last Thursday, "three-of-a-kind." It is better to call the set, say, T and hope that we never have to actually write out all the possible hands in it!

In mathematics, the things that make up a set are called the **elements** of the set. Thus, the elements of the sample space of an experiment are all the possible outcomes of the experiment. The hand "club 7, heart 7, diamond 7, club 5, heart 6" is an element of the sample space for the experiment "five-card poker." It is also an element of the set T of possible outcomes in the event "three-of-a-kind." We do not say, for example, that club 7, heart 7, diamond 7 is an element of T or of S. The elements of T as well as the elements of S must be complete poker hands. In fact, each element in T must also be an element of S. Mathematicians express this by saying that T must be a **subset** of S, or that T must be **contained** in S, or that S must **contain** T. All three statements mean the same thing: every element of T must be an element of S.

Notice that in our discussion of probability we have not bothered to distinguish between an event and the set of all possible outcomes of the event. An event *is* the set of all its possible outcomes. Thus, in the experiment of throwing a die, the real-life event "the die comes up an even number" is the set $\{2,4,6\}$. In this experiment the set $\{5,6\}$ is the real-life event "the die comes up a number greater than four" or "the die shows a number whose name in English contains the letter i," or any other equivalent description. In fact, we can even say that the real-life experiment "toss a die" is just the set $S = \{1,2,3,4,5,6\}$ and nothing more!

In real life, events are simply things that happen. They are not sets. We have here an example of mathematical modeling, which is done whenever mathematics is applied.

**Problem 5**

**Answer**

Use sets to write the experiment "flip a coin" and all its events. Denote heads by H and tails by T. The experiment is $S = \{H, T\}$. There are four events: S, $\{H\}$, $\{T\}$, and $\varnothing$.

**Problem 6**

**Answer**

One of the numbers 1, 2, or 3 is chosen. Use sets to describe this experiment and all its events.
The experiment is $S = \{1,2,3\}$. The events are: S, $\{1,2\}$, $\{1,3\}$, $\{2,3\}$, $\{1\}$, $\{2\}$, $\{3\}$, and $\varnothing$.

We have not told you *how* the number is chosen. That is relevant only if we want to know the probability of the events.

In the experiment of Problem 6 be sure you understand that, for example, the event $\{1,3\}$ does not refer to the choice of 1 and 3. That wouldn't make sense as the experiment involves choosing only one number. The event $\{1,3\}$ refers to the choice of 1 *or* 3.

One of the easiest and most useful approaches to probability is through the language and notations of sets. So far we have:

While Jerome Cardan (1501–1576) was probably the first to use mathematics extensively in the study of probability, credit for the invention of the theory of probability is usually given to Pierre de Fermat (1601–1665) and Blaise Pascal (1623–1662). There are three reasons that Cardan is ignored. (1) Nothing came of his work. (2) Pascal and Fermat were ignorant of it. (3) Modern probability had its origins in the work of Pascal and Fermat. Set theory was invented in 1874 by Georg Cantor (1845–1918) to study infinity. Set theory was applied to probability much later. Today, however, one can hardly describe probability theory without it.

| Probability | Sets | An example |
|---|---|---|
| An experiment | A set S, called the sample space | Five-card draw poker with no wild cards. |
| An outcome | An element of S | A hand |
| An event | A subset of S | A full house |
| A certain event | S | I have a card at least as high as a three. |
| An impossible event | $\varnothing$ | I have a royal flush and my opponent has four aces. |

The rest of this section contains a description of three other useful notions from the language of sets: complement, intersection, and union.

### Complement

The symbol ∼ was first used to denote "not" by Giuseppe Peano in 1893 (in theoretical arithmetic). Alfred Whitehead and Bertrand Russell introduced it into logic in 1910.

Consider the experiment of throwing a die: $S = \{1, 2, 3, 4, 5, 6\}$. Let A be the event that the die comes up an even number: $A = \{2, 4, 6\}$. The event "not A" is the event that the die does not come up an even number, that is, the event $\{1, 3, 5\}$. The set $\{1, 3, 5\}$ is called the **complement** of the set A, and we will use the notation $\sim A$ (read "not A" or "the complement of A") for it.

### Problem 7

In the game of craps success and failure are somewhat more difficult to define.

Two dice are thrown and the total number of spots that come up is recorded. Define "success" as getting 7 or 11 and "failure" as "not success." Use sets to express these events.

### Answer

Success is $A = \{7, 11\}$. Failure is $\sim A = \{2, 3, 4, 5, 6, 8, 9, 10, 12\}$.

For example, in Problem 7 the element "the coin comes up heads" is certainly not an element of A since it has nothing to do with a dice game. But for the same reason, it is not an element of the sample space for this experiment either. Thus, it is also not in $\sim A$.

Recall that in probability all events are subsets of the sample space S. Thus, the complement of an event A is the set of all elements of S that are not elements of A. It is *not* correct to say that $\sim A$ is the set of all elements that do not belong to A. We cannot use the word "elements" by itself like that; we must first answer the question "elements of what set?" In probability the answer to that question is always "elements of the sample space under consideration."

### Intersection

The symbol ∩ was first used by Peano in 1895 in logic to denote "and." In fact, it actually looks a little like the first letter in the word "∩ND."

We return now to the experiment of the thrown die. Let A be the event that the die comes up even: $A = \{2, 4, 6\}$, and let B be the event that it comes up at least 3: $B = \{3, 4, 5, 6\}$. The event "A and B," that is, "even and at least 3," is the set of all elements belonging to A and B: $\{4, 6\}$. This set is called the **intersection** of A and B and is denoted $A \cap B$ (read "A intersection B" or "A intersect B").

### Problem 8

In the experiment of Problem 7, besides "success": $A = \{7, 11\}$ and "failure": $\sim A = \{2, 3, 4, 5, 6, 8, 9, 10, 12\}$, consider the event "at least 9." Use sets to express the events "success and at least 9" and "failure, but at least 9."

### Solution

In probability the word "but" can usually be replaced by the word "and', without changing the meaning.

"At least 9" is the event $B = \{9, 10, 11, 12\}$. "Success and at least 9" is the event $A \cap B = \{7, 11\} \cap \{9, 10, 11, 12\} = \{11\}$. "Failure, but at least 9" is equivalent to the event "failure and at least 9," which is the set $(\sim A) \cap B = \{2, 3, 4, 5, 6, 8, 9, 10, 12\} \cap \{9, 10, 11, 12\} = \{9, 10, 12\}$.

### Union

If the phrase "but not both" were added, we would have the *exclusive or*.

Returning once more to one die and the events $A = \{2, 4, 6\}$ and $B = \{3, 4, 5, 6\}$, consider the event "A or B," that is, "the die comes up even or at least 3." There are two possible interpretations for this sentence. In mathematics, the most common interpretation is "even or at least 3 (or maybe both)." We will always use the word "or" in this *inclusive* sense unless we specifically add the words

The symbol ∪ was first used by Peano in 1895 in logic to denote "or." It looks a lot like the first letter in the word "∪nion," which means bringing together.

"but not both." Thus, the event "A or B" is the set $\{2,3,4,5,6\}$. This set is called the union of A and B and is denoted $A \cup B$ (read "A union B").

**Problem 9**  In the experiment of Problems 7 and 8 express the events "success or at least 9" and "failure or at least 9" in terms of sets.

**Solution**  Again we will let $A = \{7,11\}$ denote "success"; then $\sim A = \{2,3,4,5,6,8,9,10,12\}$ denotes "failure." Let $B = \{9,10,11,12\}$, that is, "at least 9." The event "success or at least 9" is the set

$$A \cup B = \{7,11\} \cup \{9,10,11,12\} = \{7,9,10,11,12\}.$$

By $\sim A \cup B$ we mean $(\sim A) \cup B$. This is not the same as $\sim(A \cup B)$. See Exercise 28a.

The event "failure or at least 9" is the set

$$\sim A \cup B = \{2,3,4,5,6,8,9,10,12\} \cup \{9,10,11,12\}$$
$$= \{2,3,4,5,6,8,9,10,11,12\}.$$

This last set may be more simply written as $\sim\{7\}$.

**Problem 10**  A single die is thrown. Let A denote the event "a number less than 4." Interpret the following events:
(a) $\sim A$
(b) $A \cap \sim A$
(c) $A \cup \sim A$
(d) $\sim(\sim A)$

**Solution**  (a) Since $S = \{1,2,3,4,5,6\}$ and $A = \{1,2,3\}$, we see that $\sim A = \{4,5,6\}$. This is the event "a number greater than 3."

(b) $A \cap \sim A = \{1,2,3\} \cap \{4,5,6\} = \varnothing$. This is the event "a number less than 4 and greater than 3." Since there are no numbers that are both less than four and greater than 3, this is an impossible event.

(c) $A \cup \sim A = \{1,2,3\} \cup \{4,5,6\} = S$. This is the event "a number that is less than 4 or greater than 3." For this experiment such an event is certain.

In general the same reasoning allows us to conclude that for any event A: $A \cap \sim A = \varnothing$, $A \cup \sim A = S$, and $\sim(\sim A) = A$.

(d) $\sim(\sim A) = \sim\{4,5,6\} = \{1,2,3\} = A$; that is, $\sim(\sim A) = A$. This is clear from the logic of the situation: if "not A" does not occur, then A must occur; if A occurs, then "not A" does not occur; hence "not (not A)" is logically the same as A.

**Exercises 1.2**

To write a set means to write all its elements, separated by commas, within braces: { }. The empty set, however, is written ∅.

In each of Exercises 1 through 6, write the sample space for the experiment described.
  1. Pick a card and note its suit.
  2. Pick a card and note whether or not it is a face card (jack, queen, king).
  3. (a) Flip two identical nickels.
     (b) Flip a nickel and flip a dime.

4. Flip a coin and toss a die.
5. Weigh a man to the nearest kilogram.
6. Measure the height of a mountain to the nearest meter above sea level.

7. What is the sample space for the tape strength experiment described on page 9?
8. Use ordered triples to write the sample space for the experiment of flipping a coin three times.

Consider the sample for the red die, green die experiment, p. 8, as a table of 6 rows numbered from top to bottom and 6 columns numbered from left to right. Describe the events given by those parts of the table mentioned in Exercises 9 through 12.

9. Row four.
10. Column five.
11. The diagonal from lower left to upper right.
12. The four entries nearest the center.

Return to Problem 2, in which Alan, Betty, and Carl are up for promotion. Write sample spaces for the situations in Exercises 13 through 18.

13. There are 2 identical openings.
14. There is 1 opening in sales and 1 in personnel.
15. There are 3 identical openings, but not everyone will be promoted.
16. There are 3 identical openings and at least 1 will be promoted.
17. There is 1 opening in sales and 1 in personnel, and Betty will be promoted.
18. There are 4 identical openings but the company will not promote more men than women.

19. Take a blank, six-faced die, mark two of its faces a, two b, and two x. Write all events in the experiment of throwing the die and noting what comes up.
20. Some PHE customers order their hamburgers with one or more of pickles, mustard, onion, ketchup. In an experiment it is noted what a customer orders with her hamburger. Write all the events.
21. (a) Is 2 an element of $\{1,2\}$?
    (b) Is $\{2\}$ an element of $\{1,2\}$?
    (c) Is 2 a subset of $\{1,2\}$?
    (d) Is $\{2\}$ a subset of $\{1,2\}$?
*22. (a) Is $\{1,2\}$ an element of $\{\{1,2\}, \{2,3\}\}$?
    (b) Is 1 or 2 an element of $\{\{1,2\}, \{2,3\}\}$?
    (c) Is $\{1,2\}$ a subset of $\{\{1,2\}, \{2,3\}\}$?
23. Two dice are thrown and the total number of spots that come up is recorded.
    (a) Let A be the event "a multiple of 4." Write the event $\sim A$.
    (b) Let B be the event "not a multiple of 3." Write the event $\sim B$.
    (c) Let C be the event "at least 7 and a multiple of 3." Write the event $\sim C$.
    (d) Let D be the event "at most 7 or not a multiple of 3." Write the event $\sim D$.

24. Let A be any event. What is the relationship between $\sim\sim$A and A?

25. If A is an event we may form the events $\sim$A, $\sim\sim$A, $\sim\sim\sim$A, and so on. What is the rule for simplifying the symbols for these events?

26. Two dice are thrown and the total number of spots that come up is recorded. Consider the events A = {2, 3, 4, 5}, B = {3, 5, 7, 9, 11}, C = {6, 8, 10, 11, 12}. Give a word description, in terms of A, B, C, "not," "or," and "and," of each of the following events, and write the events.

    (a) A∩B
    (b) B∪C
    (c) $\sim$A∩C
    (d) A∩C
    (e) $\sim$A∩$\sim$B
    (f) $\sim$A∪$\sim$C
    (g) A∩B∩C
    (h) A∪B∪C
    (i) A∪(B∩C)
    (j) A∩(B∪C)
    (k) $\sim$(A∩B)
    (l) $\sim$(B∪C)
    (m) $\sim$(A∩B∩C)
    (n) $\sim$($\sim$B∪$\sim$C)
    (o) $\sim$(A∪B∪C)
    (p) $\sim$($\sim$B∩$\sim$C)

27. Let A, B, C be any events.

    (a) Write A∩(B∪C) in terms of A∩B and A∩C.
    (b) Write A∪(B∩C) in terms of A∪B and A∪C.
    (c) Explain why your answers to (a) and (b) are correct.

The answers to parts (a) and (b) are called the **distributive** laws of set theory.

28. Let A and B be any events.

    (a) Write $\sim$(A∪B) in terms of $\sim$A and $\sim$B.
    (b) Write $\sim$(A∩B) in terms of $\sim$A and $\sim$B.
    (c) Explain why your answers to (a) and (b) are correct.

These results are called **De Morgan's Laws** of set theory, after the English mathematician Augustus De Morgan (1806–1871).

29. Two events, A and B, in a sample space S can be represented diagramatically as shown in Figure 1. The letters w, x, y, z are not part of the diagram but serve to label the four regions of the diagram.

    (a) What are these regions in terms of A, B, ∪, ∩, and $\sim$?
    (b) Which regions make up A, B, and A∪B?
    (c) Suppose S has 30 elements. If regions x and y contain 7 elements each and region w contains 4 elements, how many elements does region z contain?
    (d) If region w has 40% of S, x has 30%, and z has 20%, how much does y have?
    (e) If regions w and y each contain 40% of S and if region z contains 20%, what is the relation between A and B?

This and the following diagrams are named for the English mathematician John Venn (1834–1923), although Leonard Euler (1707–1783) originated the use of such diagrams.

**Figure 1**

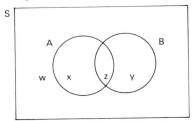

**Figure 2**

30. The Venn diagram for three sets A, B, C appears in Figure 2, with temporary labels for the regions.
    (a) What are these regions in terms of A, B, C, ∪, ∩, and ~?
    (b) Which regions make up A, B, B∪C, A∩C, and ~B?
    (c) Suppose S contains 47 elements; s has 16; t, u, v have 5 each; w is empty; and x and y together have 15. How many elements are in z?
    (d) If a survey reports that each of s, t, u, v, w, x, and y accounts for 15% of S, what can you conclude?

*31. Draw the Venn diagram for four sets. How many regions does it have?

In Exercises 32 and 33 use a Venn diagram to obtain the answer.

32. Of the 47 workers in Alan's division, 29 have been there at least five years and have at most a high school education, while 6 who have been there at least five years have more than a high school education. Of the employees who have not been there five years, only 3 have more than a high school education. How many employees in Alan's division have at most a high school education?

33. A survey of the Sasquatch forest indicates that 35% of the trees are immature, diseased, and not pines; 20% are mature diseased pines; 10% are mature, diseased, and not pines; 10% are mature, healthy, and not pines; 10% are healthy mature pines; 5% are diseased immature pines; and 5% are healthy, immature, and not pines. If 10,000 trees were surveyed, how many are healthy immature pines?

*34. What is the principle behind the following ordering of the possible outcomes of dice? {8, 11, 5, 4, 9, 7, 6, 10, 3, 12, 2}

35. How many events are there for an experiment with 3 outcomes? 4 outcomes? 5 outcomes? n outcomes?

**Section 1.3
Probability Distributions**

Alan's routine after supper is to collapse into his favorite chair, watch his favorite TV show, and eat AC Trail Candy, which is made from chocolate drops, peanuts, and raisins. He empties a packet into a bowl and eats the candy one piece at a time. However, last Tuesday Alan's set stopped working just as he filled his bowl. Perhaps it was his probability class, but, knowing Alan, it was more likely boredom that made him decide to count the candy. (See Table 1.)

Table 1

See Appendix A, Section 7, for the meaning of the symbol $\doteq$ (read "is approximately equal to").

| Ingredient | Actual number | Approximate percent |
|---|---|---|
| Chocolate drops | 153 | $153/338 \doteq 45\%$ |
| Peanuts | 107 | $107/338 \doteq 32\%$ |
| Raisins | 78 | $78/338 \doteq 23\%$ |
| Total | 338 | |

The data in Table 1 told Alan how AC had distributed each ingredient to his packet. It also told him the probability of his selecting each type of candy. In fact, we can view Alan's candy eating as an experiment with three possible outcomes {chocolate drop, peanut, raisin}. We might reasonably assign probabilities to each outcome according to Table 2.

Table 2

| Ingredient | Percent | Probability of selecting |
|---|---|---|
| Chocolate drops | 45% | 45/100 |
| Peanuts | 32% | 32/100 |
| Raisins | 23% | 23/100 |

If for some reason Alan couldn't actually count all the candy but only a sample of it, then he would be in a position similar to the lab's.

This is how oddsmakers make a living.

The following rule is a consequence of the three rules we have stated (and other remarks). *Rule*: No outcome may be assigned a probability greater than 1. See Exercise 22d.

Technicians in the testing lab at AC have a more difficult problem. They need to know the number of defective tent stakes in each lot of 1000. However, they cannot test them all, since their test ruins the stakes. Later in this book we will discuss how probability can be used to solve problems of this type. The application of probability to such a problem is called **statistics**.

In any experiment we can assign (or distribute) probabilities to the various outcomes in any way we choose. However, it is pointless to assign probabilities without considering the likelihood of each outcome. Before we look at particular examples, here are three general rules which any distribution of probabilities should obey.

Rule 1: No outcome may be assigned a negative probability.

Rule 2: Each impossible event must be assigned probability zero.

Rule 3: Each certain event must be assigned probability 1.

The reason for two of these rules is fairly obvious. An event that is impossible "happens" 0% of the time and $0\% = \frac{0}{100} = 0$. An event that is certain happens 100% of the time and $100\% = \frac{100}{100} = 1$. The reason for explicitly stating Rule 1 is not so apparent. However, it is certainly reasonable and it will turn out to be useful.

Aside from these rules we are free to assign any numbers we want as probabilities of the possible outcomes. Of course, some assignments of probabilities are more realistic than others.

Once probabilities have been assigned to each possible outcome we can define the probability of any event.

> HOW TO DETERMINE THE PROBABILITY OF AN EVENT
> Add the probabilities assigned to each possible outcome in the event.

Problem 1

We have chosen the most reasonable distribution for this particular experiment.

A balanced die is tossed. Suppose we assign probability $\frac{1}{6}$ to each possible outcome. Find the probabilities of each of the following events:

(a) $\{1,3,5,6\}$

(b) a power of two

(c) four

Solution

The sample space is $S = \{1,2,3,4,5,6\}$, and we have assigned the number $\frac{1}{6}$ to each element of S.

(a) The probability of the event $\{1,3,5,6\}$ is the number assigned to 1 plus the number assigned to 3 plus the number assigned to 5 plus the number assigned to 6; that is, $\frac{1}{6} + \frac{1}{6} + \frac{1}{6} + \frac{1}{6} = \frac{4}{6} \doteq 0.667$. In other words if we tossed the die many times we would expect to get a 1, 3, 5, or 6 about $\frac{4}{6}$ of the time, assuming that the assignment of probability $\frac{1}{6}$ to each possible outcome is a good model for the die.

One is a power of 2 since $2^0 = 1$. See Appendix A, Section 2, if needed.

(b) The probability of a power of 2 is the number assigned to 1 plus the number assigned to 2 plus the number assigned to 4; that is, $\frac{1}{6} + \frac{1}{6} + \frac{1}{6} = \frac{3}{6} = 0.5$.

(c) The probability of 4 is the number assigned to 4; that is, $\frac{1}{6} \doteq 0.167$.

The notation P(x) is sometimes called **functional notation**. A more familiar example might be a function such as $f(x) = x^3$. This function assigns numbers to numbers. For example, it assigns 8 to the number 2 since $f(2) = 2^3 = 8$. The probability function P assigns numbers to outcomes and events.

We can shorten calculations such as these by introducing some notation. Let P(x) denote the probability assigned to the possible outcome x. We read P(x) as "the probability of x" or simply as "P of x." For example, in Alan's candy problem P(chocolate drop) = $\frac{45}{100}$, P(peanut) = $\frac{32}{100}$, and P(raisin) = $\frac{23}{100}$. In the die example of Problem 1, P(1) is the probability of getting a 1. Hence P(1) = $\frac{1}{6}$. Likewise, P(2) = $\frac{1}{6}$. In fact P(x) = $\frac{1}{6}$ for each x in the sample space $\{1,2,3,4,5,6\}$.

If A is an event, then we will use P(A) to denote the probability of the event A. Our rule for determining the probability of an event says that P(A) is the sum of the probabilities of all the outcomes in A. To obtain P(A) we simply add the numbers P(x) for each x in A. For example in Problem 1 we have:

You may, if you wish, delete either the braces or parentheses and write P$\{1,3,5,6\}$ or P(1,3,5,6).

$$P(\{1,3,5,6\}) = P(1) + P(3) + P(5) + P(6) = \frac{4}{6}$$

$$P(\{1,2,4\}) = P(1) + P(2) + P(4) = \frac{1}{2}$$

$$P(\{4\}) = P(4) = \frac{1}{6}$$

We can also use this notation to shorten the statements of our rules:

Recall that $\geq$ means "is greater than or equal to."

The rule mentioned in the margin above becomes $P(x) \leq 1$ for all x in S.

Rule 1: $P(x) \geq 0$ for all x in S.

Rule 2: $P(\varnothing) = 0$

Rule 3: $P(S) = 1$

If two different assignments of numbers are under consideration in the same discussion, we will denote them by $P_1$ and $P_2$ (read "P one" and "P two").

Namely, 2,3,4,5,6,7,8,9,10,11,12.

Alan sometimes plays dice during his lunch hour. He has reasoned that, since each throw of two dice can have one of eleven possible outcomes, the probability of each should be $\frac{1}{11}$. But as we shall see in Section 1.4, the following probabilities are more realistic.

| Outcome | 2 | 3 | 4 | 5 | 6 | 7 | 8 | 9 | 10 | 11 | 12 |
|---|---|---|---|---|---|---|---|---|---|---|---|
| Probability | $\frac{1}{36}$ | $\frac{2}{36}$ | $\frac{3}{36}$ | $\frac{4}{36}$ | $\frac{5}{36}$ | $\frac{6}{36}$ | $\frac{5}{36}$ | $\frac{4}{36}$ | $\frac{3}{36}$ | $\frac{2}{36}$ | $\frac{1}{36}$ |

What are the probabilities, in Alan's opinion and in reality, of the event "7 or 11"?

In nonfinite probability, where an experiment may have an infinite number of possible outcomes, one cannot usually create a probability distribution by assigning a number to every possible outcome. Instead one must select a certain collection of subsets of S (not all subsets of S) as events and assign numbers to each of them. The result is called a **probability measure**. This concept is unnecessary in finite probability.

Let $P_1$ be Alan's assignment and let $P_2$ be the realistic assignment. Then $P_1(\{7, 11\}) = P_1(7) + P_1(11) = \frac{1}{11} + \frac{1}{11} = \frac{2}{11} \doteq 0.182$, while $P_2(\{7, 11\}) = P_2(7) + P_2(11) = \frac{6}{36} + \frac{2}{36} = \frac{8}{36} = \frac{2}{9} \doteq 0.222$. The real answer is about 20% larger than Alan's. No wonder he often lost his lunch money.

Any assignment of numbers to the possible outcomes in a sample space S that satisfies Rules 1, 2, and 3 is called a **probability distribution** for S. In Problem 2, both $P_1$ and $P_2$ are probability distributions for S.

Alan, Betty, and Carl are discussing the probabilities that they will be transferred to the warehouse in Orono, Maine. They know that exactly one of them will be transferred although each of them would really like to move out of the city. Comment on their statements.
(a) Alan said, "You two have the same chance of being transferred, but I'm so new here, my chance is minus 90%."
(b) Betty said, "No, we each have a 30% chance."
(c) Carl said, "I'd say Alan has a 10% chance, and you and I each have a 50% chance."

Let $a, b, c$ denote the possible outcomes that Alan, Betty, Carl, respectively, are transferred. Since exactly one will be transferred, the sample space for this experiment is $S = \{a, b, c\}$.
(a) Alan says that $P(a) = -90\% = -0.9$. This is absurd as it violates Rule 1.

Recall that $<$ means "is less than" and $>$ means "is greater than."

(b) With Betty's assignment of probabilities we would have $P(S) = P(a) + P(b) + P(c) = 0.3 + 0.3 + 0.3 = 0.9 < 1$. This violates Rule 3.
(c) Carl's assignment also violates Rule 3: $P(S) = P(a) + P(b) + P(c) = 0.1 + 0.5 + 0.5 = 1.1 > 1$.

Thus, none of their statements makes mathematical sense.

**Problem 4**

Alan has an antique die that belonged to his riverboat gambler ancestor Arlo V. Gregory. The die is worn and is unbalanced in such a way that the probabilities of the numbers are no longer $\frac{1}{6}$ each. In fact, a friend of Alan's father had a statistician check the die. Alan had written down the results of the statistical tests: P(1)=0.161, P(2)=0.170, P(3)=0.165, P(4)=■, P(5)=0.173, and P(6)=0.168. Unfortunately, the value for P(4) was smudged. What was it?

**Solution**

By Rule 3 we must have

$$P(1)+P(2)+P(3)+P(4)+P(5)+P(6)=1$$

that is,

$$0.161+0.170+0.165+P(4)+0.173+0.168=1$$

or

$$0.837+P(4)=1.000$$

Thus,

$$P(4)=1.000-0.837=0.163$$

Now we derive two results that will enable us to find the probability of an event if we know the probabilities of other related events. But first we must discuss mutually exclusive events. Two events A and B are **mutually exclusive** if they cannot both occur in the same performance of an experiment, that is, if there is no possible outcome that is in both A and B. In terms of sets, this means that A and B have no elements in common; that is, the set $A \cap B$ has no elements: $A \cap B = \varnothing$. In set theory sets whose intersection is the empty set are said to be **disjoint**. Since we regard an event as a set of possible outcomes, the terms "mutually exclusive" and "disjoint" mean the same thing in probability. We shall use them interchangeably.

**Problem 5**

Consider the experiment of throwing two dice and noting the total number of spots that come up. Let A be the event "the number is even," B be "the number is odd," C be "the number is less than 4," and D be "the number is greater than 11." Which pairs of these events are mutually exclusive?

**Solution**

A and B are mutually exclusive since the occurrence of one excludes the other and vice versa. If you know A has happened, you know for sure that B has not happened. On the other hand, the occurrence of event A does not exclude event C. If the outcome is 2, both events have occurred.

For reference: $A=\{2,4,6,8,10,12\}$, $B=\{3,5,7,9,11\}$, $C=\{2,3\}$, $D=\{12\}$. Since no number is simultaneously even and odd, $A \cap B = \varnothing$; so A and B are mutually exclusive. $A \cap C=\{2,4,6,8,10,12\} \cap \{2,3\}=\{2\}$; so A and C are not disjoint. $A \cap D=\{12\}$ so A and D are not mutually exclusive. $B \cap C=\{3\}$, so B and C are not disjoint. $B \cap D=\{3,5,7,9,11\} \cap \{12\}=\varnothing$, so B and D are mutually exclusive. Finally $C \cap D=\{2,3\} \cap \{12\}=\varnothing$, so C and D are mutually exclusive.

**Computation of P(A∪B)**

Recall that A∪B is the set of all outcomes that are in A or in B (or in both).

Let A and B be mutually exclusive events in an experiment. To compute P(A∪B) we must add all the numbers P(x) with x in A or x in B. We may do this by first adding the numbers P(x) for x in A, then adding the numbers P(x) for x in B, and then adding the results. The first addition gives P(A), the second addition gives P(B), and their sum is P(A)+P(B). Thus, if A and B are disjoint, P(A∪B)=P(A)+P(B). If A and B are not disjoint, this equation will generally not hold, because those P(x) for which x is in both A and B have been added twice: once because they are in A and once because they are in B. However, such outcomes occur only once in P(A∪B). To make them appear only once in P(A)+P(B) we must subtract (once) all the numbers P(x) for which x is in both A and B; that is, we must subtract P(x) for all x in the set A∩B. Consider, for example, the events A = {3,4,5} and B = {3,5,7,9} in the experiment of rolling two dice. The event A∪B = {3,4,5,7,9}. Now

$$P(A \cup B) = P(\{3,4,5,7,9\}) = P(3) + P(4) + P(5) + P(7) + P(9)$$

and

$$P(A) + P(B) = P(3) + P(4) + P(5) + P(3) + P(5) + P(7) + P(9)$$
$$= P(3) + P(3) + P(4) + P(5) + P(5) + P(7) + P(9)$$

The terms P(3) and P(5) each appear twice, since A∩B = {3,5}. To obtain P(A∪B) from P(A)+P(B) we must subtract P(3) and P(5); that is, we must subtract P(3)+P(5). But P(3)+P(5)= P({3,5})=P(A∩B). Thus, in order to get P(A∪B) we must subtract P(A∩B) from P(A)+P(B):

$$P(A \cup B) = P(A) + P(B) - P(A \cap B) \qquad \textbf{1}$$

Equation **1** holds for any two events in any experiment, not just for the two events listed above. The equation even holds if A and B happen to be disjoint, because then P(A∩B)=P(∅)=0 and equation **1** becomes P(A∪B)=P(A)+P(B)−0=P(A)+P(B), as before.

If we add P(A∩B) to both sides of equation **1** we obtain the following useful result.

If A and B are any two events in any experiment, and if P is any probability distribution for that experiment, then

$$P(A \cup B) + P(A \cap B) = P(A) + P(B)$$

**2**

If any three of the numbers $P(A \cup B)$, $P(A \cap B)$, $P(A)$, and $P(B)$ are known, then equation **2** can be used to find the fourth.

**Problem 6**  The consumer research department at AC has been running surveys in New England and in the Midwest to determine buyer preferences.

(a) In New England, 72% of those surveyed prefer AC sleeping bags, 64% prefer AC parkas, and 81% prefer at least one of these products over all others. What percentage prefer both products?

(b) In the Midwest, 62% prefer AC bags, 72% prefer at least one of the products, and 49% prefer both. What percentage prefer AC parkas?

**Solution**  Let $P_1$ give the New England distribution, and $P_2$ give the Midwest distribution. Let A be the event "prefer AC bags" and let B be the event "prefer AC parkas." Then $A \cup B$ is the event "prefer at least one of the AC products" and $A \cap B$ is the event "prefer both products."

If necessary see Appendix A, Section 11, on solving equations.

(a) We first convert the given percentages to probabilities: $P_1(A)$ $= 0.72$, $P_1(B) = 0.64$, and $P_1(A \cup B) = 0.81$. By equation **2**, $0.81$ $+ P_1(A \cap B) = 0.72 + 0.64 = 1.36$. Then $P_1(A \cap B) = 1.36 - 0.81 =$ $0.55$. Thus, 55% of the buyers surveyed in New England prefer both products.

(b) Here we are given $P_2(A) = 0.62$, $P_2(A \cup B) = .72$, and $P_2(A \cap B)$ $= 0.49$. Using equation **2** again yields $0.72 + 0.49 = 0.62 + P_2(B)$. Then $P_2(B) = 0.59$; so 59% in the Midwest prefer AC parkas.

We obtain a very useful special case of equation **2** by setting $B = {\sim}A$, the complement of A. By definition, ${\sim}A$ consists of all those outcomes in S that are not in A. Thus every outcome in S is necessarily in A or ${\sim}A$, and so $A \cup {\sim}A = S$. Since no outcomes are in A and not in A, we see that $A \cap {\sim}A = \varnothing$. These substitutions transform equation **2** as follows

$$P(A \cup B) + P(A \cap B) = P(A) + P(B)$$

Replace B by ${\sim}A$.

$$P(A \cup {\sim}A) + P(A \cap {\sim}A) = P(A) + P({\sim}A)$$

Recall $A \cup {\sim}A = S$ and $A \cap {\sim}A = \varnothing$.

$$P(S) + P(\varnothing) = P(A) + P({\sim}A)$$

We have used Rules 2 and 3.

$$1 + 0 = P(A) + P({\sim}A)$$

$$1 = P(A) + P({\sim}A)$$

All this really says is that it is certain that the event A will either happen or not happen. Although the idea is simple, it is nevertheless a powerful computational tool.

> If A is any event in any experiment and P is any
> probability distribution for that experiment, then
>
> $$P(A) + P(\sim A) = 1$$

**3**

One obvious way to use this result is to compute $P(\sim A)$ once
you are given (or have computed) $P(A)$:

$$P(\sim A) = 1 - P(A)$$

**Problem 7** Use the data of Problem 6 to determine the probability that a New
England customer will
(a) not prefer AC sleeping bags,
(b) not prefer AC parkas,
(c) not prefer both products (although perhaps prefer one of
them)
(d) prefer neither product.

**Solution** We will continue to use the notation of the solution to Problem 6.

We must use parentheses in $\sim(A \cap B)$
since it is not the same as $\sim A \cap B$.
See Exercise 28(b) in Chapter 1, Section 2.

(a) $P_1(\sim A) = 1 - P_1(A) = 1 - 0.72 = 0.28$.
(b) $P_1(\sim B) = 1 - P_1(B) = 1 - 0.64 = 0.36$.
(c) We are interested in the nonoccurrence of the event $A \cap B$ in
which both products are preferred; that is, we are interested in
the event $\sim(A \cap B)$. Then $P_1(\sim(A \cap B)) = 1 - P_1(A \cap B) = 1 - 0.55 = 0.45$.
(d) $P_1(\sim(A \cup B)) = 1 - P_1(A \cup B) = 1 - 0.81 = 0.19$.

The second way to use result **3** is a bit more subtle. Suppose
you are asked to calculate the probability of a complicated event
A. Before beginning to figure out $P(A)$, consider the event $\sim A$. It
might be that $\sim A$ is less complicated. If this is the case, then
compute $P(\sim A)$ and use result **3** to obtain $P(A) = 1 - P(\sim A)$.

**Problem 8** Use the realistic probability distribution for dice (given in Problem
2) to calculate the probability of getting a number between 3 and
11, inclusive.

**Tedious solution** $P(\{3, 4, 5, 6, 7, 8, 9, 10, 11\}) = P(3) + P(4) + P(5) + P(6) + P(7) + P(8) + P(9) + P(10) + P(11) = \frac{2}{36} + \frac{3}{36} + \frac{4}{36} + \frac{5}{36} + \frac{6}{36} + \frac{5}{36} + \frac{4}{36} + \frac{3}{36} + \frac{2}{36}$
$= \frac{34}{36} = \frac{17}{18} \doteq 0.944$.

**Quick solution** $P(\text{between 3 and 11}) = 1 - P(\text{not between 3 and 11}) = 1 - P(\{2, 12\})$
$= 1 - (\frac{1}{36} + \frac{1}{36}) = 1 - \frac{2}{36} = \frac{34}{36} = \frac{17}{18} \doteq 0.944$.

Exercises 1.3

Let the sample space for a certain experiment be $S = \{a,b,c,d\}$ and let $V = \{b,d\}$. For each of Exercises 1 through 6, determine whether or not the table gives a probability distribution for S and, if it does, find P(V).

1.

| a | b | c | d |
|---|---|---|---|
| $\frac{1}{4}$ | $\frac{1}{5}$ | $\frac{37}{60}$ | $\frac{1}{6}$ |

2.

| a | b | c | d |
|---|---|---|---|
| $\frac{1}{5}$ | $\frac{23}{60}$ | $\frac{1}{4}$ | $\frac{1}{6}$ |

3.

| a | b | c | d |
|---|---|---|---|
| $\frac{1}{3}$ | $\frac{1}{3}$ | $\frac{1}{2}$ | $-\frac{1}{6}$ |

4.

| a | b | c | d |
|---|---|---|---|
| $\frac{1}{3}$ | 0 | $\frac{1}{3}$ | $\frac{1}{3}$ |

5.

| a | b | c | d |
|---|---|---|---|
| 1 | 0 | 0 | 0 |

6.

| a | b | c | d |
|---|---|---|---|
| 0 | 0 | 0 | 0 |

In each of Exercises 7 through 12, figure out how to mark the faces of a blank balanced die so as to get distribution in the table.

7.

| a | b | c | d | e | f |
|---|---|---|---|---|---|
| $\frac{1}{6}$ | $\frac{1}{6}$ | $\frac{1}{6}$ | $\frac{1}{6}$ | $\frac{1}{6}$ | $\frac{1}{6}$ |

8.

| p | q | r | s | t | z |
|---|---|---|---|---|---|
| $\frac{1}{6}$ | $\frac{1}{6}$ | $\frac{1}{6}$ | $\frac{1}{6}$ | $\frac{1}{6}$ | $\frac{1}{6}$ |

9.

| 1 | 2 | 3 |
|---|---|---|
| $\frac{1}{3}$ | $\frac{1}{3}$ | $\frac{1}{3}$ |

10.

| 4 | 5 | 6 |
|---|---|---|
| $\frac{1}{3}$ | $\frac{1}{3}$ | $\frac{1}{3}$ |

11.

| u | v | w |
|---|---|---|
| $\frac{2}{3}$ | $\frac{1}{6}$ | $\frac{1}{6}$ |

12.

| x | y | z |
|---|---|---|
| $\frac{1}{2}$ | $\frac{1}{6}$ | $\frac{1}{3}$ |

13. The other die that Arlo had (Problem 4 of this section) has the same probabilities for 1, 2, 3, and 4 as the one now belonging to Alan. The probabilities of 5 and 6 are equal to each other. What are they?

14. An integer between 1 and 1000 is chosen. Which of the following pairs of events are disjoint?
    (a) even, at least 20,
    (b) odd, even,
    (c) ends in 7, multiple of 5,
    (d) ends in 2, multiple of 3,
    (e) ends in 14, multiple of 4.

15. In an experiment with sample space S, is there any event E such that S and E are disjoint?

In Exercises 16 through 20, find $P(A \cup B)$, $P(A \cap B)$, P(A), or P(B), whichever are not given.

16. $P(A) = 0.3281$, $P(B) = 0.2381$, $P(A \cap B) = 0.1299$.

17. $P(A \cup B) = 0.7727$, $P(A) = P(B) = 0.4359$.

18. $P(A \cup B) = \frac{2}{3}$, $P(A \cap B) = \frac{1}{4}$, $P(A) = P(B)$.

19. $P(A) = \frac{7}{10}$, $P(B) = \frac{1}{10}$, A and B are mutually exclusive.

20. $P(A \cup B) = \frac{1}{2}$, $P(A \cap B) = \frac{1}{4}$, $P(A) = \frac{1}{3}$,

21. On a typical day 65% of PHE customers world-wide buy a burger of some kind, 59% buy a burger and fries, and 30% do not buy fries (although they may buy other things). Of one million customers on a typical day, how many buy a burger or fries (or both)? How many buy a burger or fries but *not* both?

In this exercise we verify the rule given in the margin of page 18.

*22. Let A and B be events in an experiment and let P be a probability distribution for the experiment. Suppose that A is a subset of B (as defined in Section 1.2, p. 12).
(a) Explain why the sets A and $\sim A \cap B$ are disjoint.
(b) Explain why $B = A \cup (\sim A \cap B)$.
(c) Deduce from (a) and (b) that $P(A) \le P(B)$.
(d) Deduce from (c) that, for any event A, $P(A) \le 1$.

23. Suppose $P(A) = \frac{1}{3}$, $P(B) = \frac{1}{2}$, and $P(A \cup B) = \frac{2}{3}$.
(a) Find $P(A \cap B)$, $P(\sim A)$, $P(\sim B)$, $P(\sim(A \cup B))$, and $P(\sim(A \cap B))$.

Since De Morgan's Laws and result **2**, p. 22, are true for all events, we may be sure that this will check.

(b) By De Morgan's laws (Exercise 28, page 16), $\sim(A \cup B) = \sim A \cap \sim B$ and $\sim(A \cap B) = \sim A \cup \sim B$. Thus from (a) we know $P(\sim A \cup \sim B)$, $P(\sim A \cap \sim B)$, $P(\sim A)$, and $P(\sim B)$. Check that result **2** holds in this case.

24. In dice with the realistic probability distribution (see page 20), what is the probability of getting a multiple of 2, 3, 5, or 7?

## Section 1.4
## Equally Likely Outcomes

It is often reasonable to assign the same probability to each possible outcome in the sample space of an experiment. For example, whenever an experiment calls for something to be chosen at random we are to assume that no particular thing is more likely to be chosen than any other; the probability that any particular thing is chosen must therefore be the same for each thing. Such experiments are said to have **equally likely outcomes** and their probability distribution is called the equally likely distribution. The head of consumer research at AC wanted to be sure his surveyors in the field, when selecting people for questioning, were really selecting them at random. When he became aware that one of the surveyors was questioning only men between the ages of 18 and 24, he quickly had her transferred to the down-stuffing department. This incident made him adopt the approach used in many public opinion polls; *he* would randomly select individuals and then give each surveyor a specific assignment. In this way each person would have an equal probability of being selected.

While this is always the easiest assignment of probabilities, Alan has been discovering each lunch time that it is not always the most realistic assignment. See Problem 2, p. 20.

It is easy to assign equal probabilities to the possible outcomes in a sample space S. Since Rule 3, page 18, implies that the sum of all the assigned probabilities is 1, each outcome must be assigned the probability $1/n(S)$, where $n(S)$ denotes the number of elements in S. For example, the sample space for throwing a die is $S = \{1, 2, 3, 4, 5, 6\}$; so $n(S) = 6$. If we assume that the die is properly balanced, so that each outcome is equally likely, then $P(x) = 1/n(S) = \frac{1}{6}$ for each x in S; that is, $P(1) = P(2) = P(3) = P(4) = P(5) = P(6) = \frac{1}{6}$.

Problem 1

An urn is a container used only by crematoriums and writers of probability books. (Poets occasionally write on them.)

An urn holds three balanced dice: a red one, a white one, and a green one.

(a) A die is chosen at random. What is the probability that it is green?

(b) A die is chosen at random and tossed. What is the probability that it is the red die and it comes up 5?

Solution

(a) $S = \{red, white, green\}$. The phrase "at random" implies that we are to use the equally likely probability distribution. Thus, $P(green) = 1/n(S) = \frac{1}{3}$.

(b) Now $S = \{red\ comes\ up\ 1, red\ 2, \ldots, red\ 6, white\ 1, \ldots, white\ 6, green\ 1, \ldots, green\ 6\}$. Again, the phrases "at random" and "balanced die" imply that the equally likely probability distribution is appropriate. By the principle of multiplication (page 5), $n(S) = 3 \cdot 6 = 18$; hence $P(red\ 5) = \frac{1}{18}$.

There are three choices of dice. Once any die is selected there are six possible number outcomes.

Once we have assigned the equally likely probability distribution to an experiment, it is also easy to calculate the probability of any event. Suppose the experiment is "toss a balanced die" and consider the events $A = \{1, 3, 4, 5\}$ and $B = \{1, 2, 4, 6\}$. Since there are six possible outcomes in the sample space, each is assigned probability $\frac{1}{6}$. Then

$$P(A) = P(1) + P(3) + P(4) + P(5) = \tfrac{1}{6} + \tfrac{1}{6} + \tfrac{1}{6} + \tfrac{1}{6} = \tfrac{4}{6} = \tfrac{2}{3}$$

Similarly,

$$P(B) = P(1) + P(2) + P(4) + P(6) = \tfrac{1}{6} + \tfrac{1}{6} + \tfrac{1}{6} + \tfrac{1}{6} = \tfrac{2}{3}$$

Of course, $n(A)$ and $n(B)$ denote the number of elements in A and in B, respectively.

Events A and B have the same probability because they have the same number of possible outcomes, 4, and we add four $\frac{1}{6}$'s in each calculation. Recall that $\frac{1}{6} = 1/n(S)$, where $S = \{1, 2, 3, 4, 5, 6\}$ is the sample space. Thus, $P(A) = \frac{4}{6} = 4/n(S) = n(A)/n(S)$ and $P(B) = n(B)/n(S) = \frac{4}{6}$. In general we have the following result.

This works only if each outcome is equally likely.

> Let S be the sample space and P be the equally likely probability distribution for an experiment. Then the probability of any event A of the experiment is
> $$P(A) = \frac{n(A)}{n(S)}$$

1

This result holds for any event, not just the two mentioned above. This follows from the fact that, if A is any event, $P(x) = 1/n(S)$ for each x in A, so that the sum of all P(x) for which x is in A is the sum of n(A) numbers each equal to 1/n(S), that is,

n(A) times

$$P(A) = \overbrace{1/n(S) + \cdots + 1/n(S)} = n(A)(1/n(S)) = n(A)/n(S)$$

If $A = \emptyset$, the impossible event, then $n(\emptyset) = 0$ and $P(\emptyset) = n(\emptyset)/n(S) = 0/n(S) = 0$, in agreement with Rule 2, page 18. Also, if $A = S$, the certain event, then $P(S) = n(S)/n(S) = 1$, in agreement with Rule 3.

According to result **1**, to compute the probability of an event we have merely to count the number of outcomes in the experiment, count the number of outcomes in the event, and divide. Our use of the word "merely" here is highly questionable, since counting the number of elements in a complicated set can be very difficult. We will present here only a few techniques beyond those introduced in Section 1.1.

> A few more complicated counts appear in Section 6.1.

One night while driving home from class at Local College, Alan saw a car with the license plate DEF–3456. "Wow! Everything in order. I wonder what the chances of that are." If we assume that every license plate is equally likely, then the probability of DEF–3456 is 1 divided by the number of possible license plates. So we must find this number. In Alan's state, an ordinary license plate has 2 or 3 letters followed by a dash and 3 or 4 digits. We sort the plates into 4 piles: 2 letters, 3 digits; 2 letters, 4 digits; 3 letters, 3 digits; 3 letters, 4 digits; and then use the principle of multiplication to count each pile. There are 26 letters and 10 digits. Since no letters or digits are excluded and since repeated letters and/or digits are allowed, the first pile has $26 \cdot 26 \cdot 10 \cdot 10 \cdot 10 = 26^2 \cdot 10^3 = 676,000$ plates. The whole count is shown in Table 3.

> Actually, there are a few three-letter combinations that are deemed unacceptable for public display.

Table 3

| Letters | Digits | Plates | | |
|---------|--------|--------|---|---|
| 2 | 3 | $26^2 \cdot 10^3$ | = | 676,000 |
| 2 | 4 | $26^2 \cdot 10^4$ | = | 6,760,000 |
| 3 | 3 | $26^3 \cdot 10^3$ | = | 17,576,000 |
| 3 | 4 | $26^3 \cdot 10^4$ | = | 175,760,000 |
| | | Total | | 200,772,000 plates possible |

Thus, the probability of DEF–3456 is $1/200,772,000 \doteq 0.00000000498$. This is indeed a small number, but it is also the probability of seeing any other license plate, for example FTQ–7079, which is not likely to cause anyone to say "Wow!" What really impressed Alan was that the letters and numbers in the plate he saw were in consecutive order. Perhaps this is the probability we should have found.

Problem 2

What is the probability that a randomly chosen three-letter, four-digit license plate from Alan's state has distinct letters in consecutive alphabetical order and distinct digits in consecutive numerical order?

Solution

We assume that each of the 175,760,000 possible three-letter, four-digit plates is equally likely to be chosen. How many of these plates satisfy the required conditions? Once the first letter and the first digit of the plate is known, the plate is determined. For instance, if the first letter is T and the first digit is 6, then the plate must be TUV–6789. Now Y and Z cannot be the first letters and

Why not?

7, 8, and 9 cannot be the first digits. Thus there are 24 choices for first letter, and, for each such choice, there are 7 choices for first digit. Hence there are $24 \cdot 7 = 168$ such plates. The probability of such a plate is $168/175,760,000 = 21/21,970,000 \doteq 0.00000096$. This is certainly small enough to elicit a "Wow!" although it is almost 200 times larger than the probability found above.

With license plates, the order of the components (the letters and numbers) makes a difference. For example DEF–3456 is not the same as EDF–3465, although it does contain the same components. With some things, however, the order of the components does not matter. For example, the basketball team of Amy, Beth, Celeste, Dot, and Edith is the same as the team of Beth, Edith, Dot, Amy, and Celeste. There are of course situations in between these two extremes. For example, if the first person named is team captain, then the first team above (with Amy the captain) is different from the second team (with Beth the captain), although it is not different from the team of Amy, Edith, Dot, Celeste, and Beth. Outcomes in which the order of some (or all) the components does *not* matter cannot be counted by just one application of the principle of multiplication, as we see below.

When speaking of teams, committees, etc., we will assume that no member is to be distinguished as captain, chairperson, etc., unless we specifically say so.

Problem 3

Janet Witherspoon is to choose a basketball team of 5 from the 9 secretaries in her office. How many teams are possible?

Solution

Janet can choose the first team member in 9 ways, the second in 8, third in 7, fourth in 6, and fifth in 5 ways. By the principle of multiplication there are $9 \cdot 8 \cdot 7 \cdot 6 \cdot 5 = 15,120$ ways to choose a team. Are there this many different teams? Of course not. Each different team has been "counted" many times. How many times? Consider one of the possible teams. Any one of the 5 teammates could have been the first one chosen, then any of the other 4 could be next, any of the other 3 next, any of the other 2 next, and the other 1 would be last. Then, again by the principle of multiplication, this team was counted $5 \cdot 4 \cdot 3 \cdot 2 \cdot 1 = 120$ times. Each different team was "counted" 120 times in the total of 15,120. Thus, the number of different teams possible is $15,120/120 = 126$.

Another example: Alan had to choose three of his four nephews, Albert, Billy, Charles, David, to take on the picnic. Here is a list of the $24 = 4 \cdot 3 \cdot 2$ possible choices, assuming the order matters.

| | | | |
|---|---|---|---|
| ABC | ABD | ACD | BCD |
| ACB | ADB | ADC | BDC |
| BAC | BAD | CAD | CBD |
| BCA | BDA | CDA | CDB |
| CAB | DAB | DAC | DBC |
| CBA | DBA | DCA | DCB |

Since the order doesn't matter, all of

the choices in each box are the same. There are $3 \cdot 2 \cdot 1 = 6$ elements in each box, so there are $\frac{24}{6} = 4$ different selections.

In making this count Janet used another result of considerable usefulness, called the **principle of division**:

> THE PRINCIPLE OF DIVISION IN COUNTING
>
> Suppose you have "counted" the possible outcomes in some situation and obtained the number N. Suppose that in this "count" you have actually counted each different possible outcome exactly K times. Then the number of possible outcomes is N/K.

**Problem 4**

**Solution**

See Section 6.1 for information on cards.

We could theoretically make a list here just as we did for Alan's picnic above. In this case, there would be 2,598,960 boxes each with $5 \cdot 4 \cdot 3 \cdot 2 \cdot 1 = 120$ hands (all the same but each arranged differently).

How many 5-card poker hands are there?

There are $52 \cdot 51 \cdot 50 \cdot 49 \cdot 48$ ways to be dealt a poker hand. In this count each hand is counted $5 \cdot 4 \cdot 3 \cdot 2 \cdot 1$ times, so by the principle of division there are $52 \cdot 51 \cdot 50 \cdot 49 \cdot 48 / 5 \cdot 4 \cdot 3 \cdot 2 \cdot 1 = 2{,}598{,}960$ possible hands.

It is convenient at this point to introduce some standard general notation for counting.

Suppose we have n distinct objects (letters, digits, people, ...) from which we choose r distinct objects. Suppose we then list these r objects in some order. If each different order of listing the r choices is considered to be a different outcome (as with license plates), then each outcome is called a **permutation of n objects, r at a time**. The total number of possible permutations of n objects, r at a time, is denoted $P_r^n$ (read "nPr").

The letter P was first used to denote permutations by Harvey Goodwin by 1869. The particular notation used in this text was introduced by W. A. Whitworth in 1886.

**Problem 5**

**Answer**

How many four-letter license plates are possible with all letters different?

$P_4^{26} = 26 \cdot 25 \cdot 24 \cdot 23 = 358{,}800.$

An important special case: $P_n^n = n(n-1)\ldots 2 \cdot 1$ is often called n **factorial** and denoted n! It is convenient to define 0! to be 1.

For example, if $n = 26$ and $r = 4$, then $n = 26$, $n-1 = 25$, $n-2 = 24$ and $n-3 = 23$. To obtain $r = 4$ terms we must stop when we reach $n-3 = n-(4-1) = n-(r-1)$.

The general formula for $P_r^n$ is

$$P_r^n = n(n-1)\ldots(n-(r-1)) \qquad \textbf{2}$$

Note that the last factor is $(n-(r-1))$, not $n-r$, since there are r factors, beginning with n (*not* beginning with $n-1$).

If each choice of r particular distinct objects is considered as the same outcome, regardless of the order in which they were chosen (as with a poker hand), then each outcome is called a **combination of n objects, r at a time**. The total number of possible combinations of n objects, r at a time, is denoted $C_r^n$ (read "nCr",

The letter C was first used to denote combinations by George Peacock in 1830. The particular notation used in this text was introduced by W. A. Whitworth in 1886. The very pleasant idea of reading $C_r^n$ as "n choose r" is due to H. S. M. Coxeter. Another common symbol for $C_r^n$ is $\binom{n}{r}$.

In the factorial notation of the marginal note above, $C_r^n = \dfrac{n!}{r!(n-r)!}$.

**Problem 6**

The sort of cancellation that occurs in this answer will always be possible in any such calculation.

**Answer**

(See marginal note, page 29.) Since Alan only had room for only three nephews in this car, either Albert, Billy, Charles, or David had to stay home. Once he decided which of the four boys stayed home, the rest went. So he had four choices: A stays, BCD go; B stays, ACD go; C stays, ABD go; or D stays, ABC go.

Warning: there is no formula like formula **5** for $P_r^n$.

or "n choose r"). Any particular combination of r objects can be made in $P_r^r$ different ways. Hence, by the principle of division,

$$C_r^n = P_r^n / P_r^r \qquad\qquad\textbf{3}$$

or, by formula **2**,

$$C_r^n = \frac{n(n-1)\cdots(n-(r-1))}{r(r-1)\cdots 1} \qquad\qquad\textbf{4}$$

A grievance committee of 7 is to be chosen from 40 employees. How many different committees are possible?

$$C_7^{40} = \frac{\overset{10}{\cancel{40}}\cdot 39\cdot 38\cdot 37\cdot \cancel{36}\cdot \cancel{35}\cdot 34}{\cancel{7}\cdot\cancel{6}\cdot\cancel{5}\cdot\cancel{4}\cdot\cancel{3}\cdot\cancel{2}\cdot 1} = 18{,}643{,}560.$$

Suppose we want to calculate $C_6^8$. Formula **4** gives $C_6^8 = \frac{8\cdot 7\cdot 6\cdot 5\cdot 4\cdot 3}{6\cdot 5\cdot 4\cdot 3\cdot 2\cdot 1}$, and after much cancellation we obtain $C_6^8 = 28$. But there is an easier way to get this. Each time we choose 6 objects out of 8 there are 2 left out. Instead of choosing the 6 to go in the combination, it is easier to choose the 2 that do not go in. The number of ways to do this must be the same as the number of ways to choose the 6. Hence $C_6^8 = C_2^8 = \frac{8\cdot 7}{2\cdot 1} = 28$. In general we have

$$C_r^n = C_{n-r}^n \qquad\qquad\textbf{5}$$

Formula **5** will be useful whenever r is greater than half of n.

Obviously if we have n objects there is only one way to make a combination of all n of them; hence $C_n^n = 1$. Then by result **5** we should have $C_0^n = C_{n-0}^n = C_n^n = 1$, that is

$$C_0^n = 1 \qquad\qquad\textbf{6}$$

We cannot obtain result **6** from formula **4**, but it does seem reasonable to say that there is one and only one way to choose *no* objects from n objects: do nothing!

Given n objects we can choose any one of them to make a combination of one object. Thus,

$$C_1^n = n \text{ and } C_{n-1}^n = n, \qquad\qquad\textbf{7}$$

where we have used result **5** to get the second equality.

It does not make sense to have a negative number of objects, so we do not define $C_r^n$ or $P_r^n$ when $n < 0$ or $r < 0$. Also, you cannot take more objects than you have, since repetition is not allowed. Therefore, we do not define $C_r^n$ or $P_r^n$ when $r > n$.

We summarize our results about the important symbol $C_r^n$ in the following flow chart.

**How to Calculate $C_r^n$ by Hand**

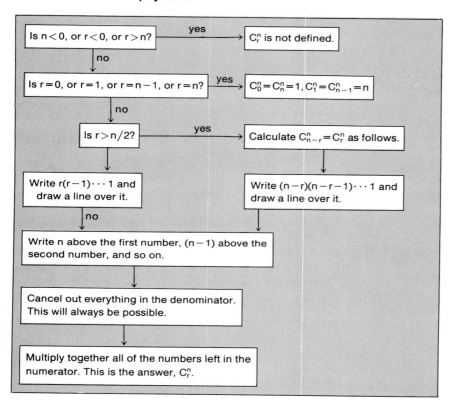

We return now to probability.

Problem 7 What is the probability that a license plate of the type described in Problem 5, selected at random, begins with A and ends with Z?

Solution The total number of license plates of the type described in Problem 5 is $P_4^{26}$. Of these, the total number beginning with A and ending with Z is $P_2^{24}$ since there are two middle letters to choose and neither A nor Z may be chosen. Thus, the probability we want is

$$P_2^{24}/P_4^{26} = 24 \cdot 23/26 \cdot 25 \cdot 24 \cdot 23 = 1/26 \cdot 25 = 1/650 \doteq 0.00154.$$

Problem 8 If the committee of Problem 6 is selected at random, what is the probability that it will contain the popular employees Sylvia and Stan?

Solution   If Sylvia and Stan are on the committee there are $C_5^{38}$ ways to select the remaining five members. Thus, the probability is

$$C_5^{38}/C_7^{40} = 6\cdot 7/40\cdot 39 = 7/260 \doteq 0.0269$$

Even if the possible outcomes of an experiment are not equally likely, it is sometimes possible to use the ideas of this section by thinking of an "artificial" sample space all of whose possible outcomes are equally likely. We illustrate this in the following problem.

Problem 9   Find the probabilities for the outcomes of the throw of two balanced dice.

Solution   The outcomes 2, 3, 4, 5, 6, 7, 8, 9, 10, 11, 12 are not equally likely. If we imagine one die to be Rose and one to be Violet we can record the outcomes with ordered pairs as shown below. Here the first number of the pair tells what Rose says and the second gives Violet's response:

$$
\begin{array}{cccccc}
(1,1) & (1,2) & (1,3) & (1,4) & (1,5) & (1,6) \\
(2,1) & (2,2) & (2,3) & (2,4) & (2,5) & (2,6) \\
(3,1) & (3,2) & (3,3) & (3,4) & (3,5) & (3,6) \\
(4,1) & (4,2) & (4,3) & (4,4) & (4,5) & (4,6) \\
(5,1) & (5,2) & (5,3) & (5,4) & (5,5) & (5,6) \\
(6,1) & (6,2) & (6,3) & (6,4) & (6,5) & (6,6)
\end{array}
$$

These artificial outcomes are equally likely; each has a probability of $\frac{1}{36}$. Each outcome in the original sample space is described by a set of outcomes in the artificial sample space. The "real" outcome 5, for example, becomes the set of artificial outcomes $\{(4,1),(3,2),(2,3),(1,4)\}$, as indicated by the line running through the tabulation above. Then $P(5) = \frac{4}{36} = \frac{1}{9} \doteq 0.111$. The other probabilities are obtained similarly.

Table 4

| Real outcome | Relevant artificial outcomes | Number | Probability |
|---|---|---|---|
| 2 | (1,1) | 1 | $\frac{1}{36}$ |
| 3 | (1,2), (2,1) | 2 | $\frac{2}{36}$ |
| 4 | (1,3), (2,2), (3,1) | 3 | $\frac{3}{36}$ |
| 5 | (1,4), (2,3), (3,2), (4,1) | 4 | $\frac{4}{36}$ |
| 6 | (1,5), (2,4), (3,3), (4,2), (5,1) | 5 | $\frac{5}{36}$ |
| 7 | (1,6), (2,5), (3,4), (4,3), (5,2), (6,1) | 6 | $\frac{6}{36}$ |
| 8 | (2,6), (3,5), (4,4), (5,3), (6,2) | 5 | $\frac{5}{36}$ |
| 9 | (3,6), (4,5), (5,4), (6,3) | 4 | $\frac{4}{36}$ |
| 10 | (4,6), (5,5), (6,4) | 3 | $\frac{3}{36}$ |
| 11 | (5,6), (6,5) | 2 | $\frac{2}{36}$ |
| 12 | (6,6) | 1 | $\frac{1}{36}$ |

The last column in Table 4 is the appropriate probability distribution whenever we assume that the dice are balanced.

We conclude this section by considering two cases of the celebrated birthday problem.

**Problem 10**  How many people must be in a room before it becomes a good bet that two of them were born on the same day of the week (Monday, Tuesday, and so on)?

**Solution**  Assumptions: (1) People are not more likely to be born on one day than another. (2) An event is a "good bet" if its probability exceeds $\frac{1}{2}$. Suppose there are, for example, five people in the room. Imagine a list with the names of the people and a space next to each name for the day of birth. The sample space S consists of all possible ways to fill out this list. So $n(S) = 7 \cdot 7 \cdot 7 \cdot 7 \cdot 7 = 7^5 = 16{,}807$. The event A = "2 or more days on the list are the same" looks complicated. Rather than attempt to describe it, we will follow the advice of Section 1.3 and consider the event $\sim$A = "no 2 days on the list are the same" = "all 5 days on the list are different." Then by the principle of multiplication,

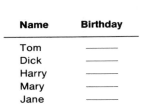

| Name | Birthday |
|------|----------|
| Tom | _____ |
| Dick | _____ |
| Harry | _____ |
| Mary | _____ |
| Jane | _____ |

$$n(\sim A) = 7 \cdot 6 \cdot 5 \cdot 4 \cdot 3 = 2{,}520$$

so

$$P(\sim A) = 2{,}520/16{,}807 = 360/2{,}401$$

Then

$$P(A) = 1 - P(\sim A) = 2{,}041/2{,}401 \doteq 0.850,$$

a very good bet. To actually answer the question we will use the following tabulation.

| Number of people | $P(\sim A)$ | $P(A)$ |
|------------------|-------------|--------|
| 1 | 1 | 0 |
| 2 | $7 \cdot 6/7^2 = \frac{6}{7}$ | $\frac{1}{7} \doteq 0.143$ |
| 3 | $7 \cdot 6 \cdot 5/7^3 = \frac{30}{49}$ | $\frac{19}{49} \doteq 0.388$ |
| 4 | $7 \cdot 6 \cdot 5 \cdot 4/7^4 = \frac{120}{343}$ | $\frac{223}{343} \doteq 0.650$ |
| 5 | $7 \cdot 6 \cdot 5 \cdot 4 \cdot 3/7^5 = \frac{360}{2,401}$ | $\frac{2,041}{2,401} \doteq 0.850$ |
| 6 | $7 \cdot 6 \cdot 5 \cdot 4 \cdot 3 \cdot 2/7^6 = \frac{720}{16,807}$ | $\frac{16,087}{16,807} \doteq 0.957$ |
| 7 | $7 \cdot 6 \cdot 5 \cdot 4 \cdot 3 \cdot 2 \cdot 1/7^7 = \frac{720}{117,649}$ | $\frac{116,929}{117,649} \doteq 0.994$ |
| 8 (or more) | 0 | 1 |

Thus, if there are 4 or more people in a room it is a good bet that 2 or more have the same birth day (of the week).

**Problem 11**  Janet belongs to the April Club, which requires only an April birthdate for membership. How many members must attend a

Solution

meeting before it is a good bet that 2 members at the meeting celebrate their birthdays on the same date?

We reason as in the previous problem. For example, if 5 people attend the meeting, $P(\sim A) = P(\text{all different dates}) = 30 \cdot 29 \cdot 28 \cdot 27 \cdot 26 / 30^5 = \frac{2,639}{3,750}$ and $P(A) = P(\text{at least two dates the same}) = 1 - \frac{2,639}{3,750} = \frac{1,111}{3,750} \doteq 0.296$. Here is part of the tabulation.

The notation 3D means that the entries are accurate to within one digit in the third decimal place.

| Number of people | P(A) 3D | Number of people | P(A) 3D |
|---|---|---|---|
| 1 | 0.000 | 7 | 0.531 |
| 2 | 0.033 | 8 | 0.640 |
| 3 | 0.098 | 9 | 0.736 |
| 4 | 0.188 | 10 | 0.815 |
| 5 | 0.296 | 11 | 0.877 |
| 6 | 0.414 | 12 | 0.922 |

The answer: at least 7 members must be present.

Comparison of the two tabulations suggests that the result for the month problem is likely to surprise more people than the result for the week problem. In Problem 7 it took 8 people to guarantee a sure thing and it took one-half that many to get a good bet. In Problem 8 it would take 31 people for a sure thing but less than one-fourth that many for a good bet. The corresponding problem for a year instead of a week or month should be even more surprising. Let's see, there are 365 or 366 days in a year; one-tenth of that is about 36. What odds would you give that in a class of 36 people at least 2 have the same birthdate, not including the year?

See Exercise 15.

Exercises 1.4

A whole number between 1 and 1,000 inclusive is chosen at random. Find the probabilities of the events in Exercises 1 through 10. The number

1. begins with 1.
2. ends in 0.
3. begins with 1 and ends in 0.
4. begins with 1 or ends in 0.
5. has exactly three digits.
6. has three even digits.
7. has three different even digits.
8. is a multiple of 5.
9. is a multiple of 6.
10. isn't a multiple of 6.

11. In this exercise you are to prove that, in an experiment with a finite sample space S, the equally likely probability distribution P is given by $P(x) = 1/n(S)$ for all x in S.

(a) Let $n = n(S)$. Choose an element a of S and let $p = P(a)$. Express $P(S)$ in terms of n and p.

(b) Use Rule 3, page 18, to complete the proof.

12. In how many ways can a baseball team of 9 be chosen from a summer camp of 17 kids?

13. How many different license plates consisting of three letters can be made under each of the following rules?

(a) no restrictions

(b) no two letters the same

*We decree that only A, E, I, O, U are vowels.*

(c) no vowels

(d) only vowels

(e) no Os or Is, and no two letters the same

(f) at least one vowel

(g) at most one vowel

(h) two letters the same, but not all three letters the same

(i) the letters distinct and in alphabetical order (for example, DEK)

(j) the letters in alphabetical order (for example, AAX)

14. In how many ways can a football team of 11 be chosen from a club of 15 kids?

15. You will need a computer, a hand calculator, or great patience to do all of this exercise. A group of high school students are entering the PHE store in suburban Oneonta, New York. They were all born in the same year (not a leap year), and there is no reason to expect more were born on any one day than on any other (though some probably were).

(a) Five students are now in the store. What is the probability that 2 or more have the same birthday?

(b) How many students have to be in the store before it is a good bet that 2 or more have the same birthday?

(c) Show that with 36 students the probability that at least 2 have the same birthday is about .832.

(d) How many students would have to be in the store to make the probability of 2 or more having the same birthday greater than $\frac{999}{1,000}$?

16. (a) In how many ways can a committee of 5 be formed from a society of 12 members?

(b) In how many ways can the committee be formed if one of the persons chosen is chosen to be the chairperson?

(c) In how many ways can the committee be formed if one of the persons chosen is chosen as the chair and another as vice-chair?

17. (a) For $2 a PHE customer at the Garden City, Kansas, store can choose from 3 kinds of salad, 4 kinds of potatoes, and 5 kinds of drinks. How many different meals can be chosen?

(b) The PHE store in Garden City, New York, has the same deal, except it costs $3 and they have more kinds of salads. They advertise that their customers have a choice of more than 300 different meals. How many kinds of salads must they stock in order to justify this claim?

## Section 1.5
## Conditional Probability

Often the probability of an event is affected by the occurrence (or nonoccurrence) of some other event. For instance, Alan knows that the chances of his doing a good job addressing the 977 packages to be shipped from the warehouse tomorrow will be affected by whether or not he stays up late tonight playing poker. Of course, he may do a good job even if he does stay up late, but he will be more likely to do a good job if he goes to bed on time. In some cases the probability of an event is drastically affected by another event. If Alan's daughter, Annie, is nominated for the presidency of her second-grade class, she has a good chance of being elected. However, if she is not nominated, she has no chance, since her teacher does not allow write-in votes. On the other hand, in some cases the probability of an event is not affected at all by another event. The chances that Alan loses his money in the candy machine are not affected by whether or not he goes to lunch early. For another example, if you flip a coin, the probability of heads on the second flip is not affected by the outcome of the first flip.

For another example, you have probably noticed that your performance on exams is affected by the number of homework exercises you work.

We will measure the effect of an event B on the event A by determining the probability of A under the condition that B occurs. We call this the probability of A **given** B and denote it by P(A|B). In our first example we were interested in comparing

This probability is called a **conditional probability** since it is determined subject to a condition.

$$P(\text{Alan does a good job})$$

to

$$P(\text{Alan does a good job}|\text{Alan goes to bed on time})$$

P(Alan does a good job|Alan goes to bed on time) is read "The probability that Alan does a good job given that Alan goes to bed on time."

and

$$P(\text{Alan does a good job}|\text{Alan stays up late})$$

In general, how do we calculate P(A|B)? Let's consider a simple experiment: flip a balanced penny and a balanced nickel. The sample space is $S = \{(H,H),(H,T),(T,H),(T,T)\}$ where the first entry of the ordered pair is the result of the penny flip. Here are two events: A = "two heads or two tails turn up"; B = "at least one head turns up." We first compute P(A|B), the probability that two heads or two tails turn up given that at least one head turns up. Since we know that B has occurred, our list of possible outcomes is just $B = \{(H,H),(H,T),(T,H)\}$. (The outcome (T, T) is now impossible.) Since the coins are balanced, each of these events is equally likely and we assign probability $\frac{1}{3}$ to each. Now what is the probability that A has occurred? Since B has occurred, the only way A can occur is if *both* A and B occur, that is, if $A \cap B$

Suppose a friend flips the coins, covers them up, and then asks you to bet. An onlooker annnounces that he saw that one of the coins was a head. What are the chances they are both heads?

occurs. Since $A \cap B = \{(H,H),(T,T)\} \cap \{(H,H),(H,T),(T,H)\} = \{(H,H)\}$, only one of the three possible outcomes is in the event $A \cap B$, and so the probability we want is $P(A|B) = \frac{1}{3}$. On the other hand $P(B|A) = \frac{1}{2}$ since $A = \{(H,H),(T,T)\}$, and exactly one of these two possible outcomes, namely $(H,H)$, is in the event B; that is, if you know that two heads or two tails have turned up, you know that the probability is $\frac{1}{2}$ that at least one head has turned up.

We can follow this same general procedure for any experiment: to compute $P(A|B)$, first reduce the sample space to B and then see what proportion $A \cap B$ is of this new sample space. Unfortunately, this will not quite work unless all the outcomes in B are equally likely. To avoid this difficulty we simply convert to probability: Add the probabilities of all outcomes in the event B (to get $P(B)$), add the probabilities of all outcomes in the event $A \cap B$ (to get $P(A \cap B)$), and divide.

> If A and B are events in an experiment with probability distribution P, and if $P(B) > 0$, then the probability of A given B is
>
> $$P(A|B) = \frac{P(A \cap B)}{P(B)}$$

**1**

There are two reasons for the stipulation that $P(B) > 0$ in definition **1**. In the first place if $P(B) = 0$, the definition would require us to divide by zero, which is impossible. Besides, if $P(B) = 0$ then B is impossible, so an assumption that B has occurred would be meaningless. Thus, we are not interested in defining $P(A|B)$ in this case anyway.

If the sample space is infinite, the relevant mathematical model may assign probability zero to outcomes which are possible. We shall not pursue this here.

If we take $A = B$ in formula **1**, we obtain $P(B|B) = P(B)/P(B) = 1$. Of course! If we are given that B has occurred, then it is certain that B has occurred.

Recall $B \cap B = B$.

**Problem 1**    A balanced die is thrown. Find
(a) P (three|odd)
(b) P (two|odd)
(c) P (greater than two|odd)

**Solution**    (a) By definition **1** we have

The calculation of conditional probabilities often involves division of fractions by fractions. See Appendix A, Section 4.4, if necessary.

$$P(\text{three}|\text{odd}) = P(\{3\}|\{1,3,5\}) = \frac{P(\{3\} \cap \{1,3,5\})}{P(\{1,3,5\})} = \frac{P(\{3\})}{P(\{1,3,5\})}$$

$$= \frac{\frac{1}{6}}{\frac{1}{6} + \frac{1}{6} + \frac{1}{6}} = \frac{\frac{1}{6}}{\frac{3}{6}} = \frac{1}{6} \cdot \frac{6}{3} = \frac{1}{3}$$

(b)  $P(\text{two}|\text{odd}) = P(\{2\}|\{1,3,5\}) = \dfrac{P(\{2\} \cap \{1,3,5\})}{P(\{1,3,5\})}$

$= \dfrac{P(\varnothing)}{P(\{1,3,5\})} = \dfrac{0}{\frac{1}{6}+\frac{1}{6}+\frac{1}{6}} = \dfrac{0}{\frac{3}{6}} = 0 \cdot \dfrac{6}{3} = 0$

This result was to be expected since, if we are given that the die has come up odd, it is impossible that it should have also come up two.

(c)  $P(\text{greater than two}|\text{odd}) = P(\{3,4,5,6\}|\{1,3,5\})$

$= \dfrac{P(\{3,4,5,6\} \cap \{1,3,5\})}{P(\{1,3,5\})} = \dfrac{\frac{1}{6}+\frac{1}{6}}{\frac{1}{6}+\frac{1}{6}+\frac{1}{6}} = \dfrac{\frac{2}{6}}{\frac{3}{6}} = \dfrac{2}{6} \cdot \dfrac{6}{3} = \dfrac{2}{3}$

If all outcomes in the sample space are equally likely, then there is an easier way to compute conditional probabilities. By result **1** on page 27, if P is the equally likely probability distribution, then $P(B) = n(B)/n(S)$ and $P(A \cap B) = n(A \cap B)/n(S)$. Thus,

Recall that n(B) denotes the number of elements in B and $n(A \cap B)$ denotes the number of elements in $A \cap B$.

$P(A|B) = \dfrac{P(A \cap B)}{P(B)} = \dfrac{\dfrac{n(A \cap B)}{n(S)}}{\dfrac{n(B)}{n(S)}} = \dfrac{n(A \cap B)}{n(S)} \cdot \dfrac{n(S)}{n(B)} = \dfrac{n(A \cap B)}{n(B)}$

> Suppose P is the equally likely probability distribution for an experiment. If A and B are events in that experiment (and B is not empty), then
>
> $$P(A|B) = \dfrac{n(A \cap B)}{n(B)}$$

**2**

Since the balanced die experiment of Problem 1 has the equally likely distribution, we can use equation **2** to rework this problem. For example, in part (c):  $P(\{3, 4, 5, 6\}|\{1, 3, 5\}) = n(\{3,4,5,6\} \cap \{1,3,5\})/n(\{1,3,5\}) = n(\{3,5\})/n(\{1,3,5\}) = \frac{2}{3}$. This is certainly easier than the first solution, but remember we can apply result **2** only to an experiment with the equally likely probability distribution.

Problem 2    Alan's friend, Carl, rolled a pair of balanced dice. Carl said, "What will you bet that the result was a multiple of 3, that is, 3, 6, 9, or 12?" Alan said, "Not much." Betty spoke up. "Well, Alan, I'll say this. I can't remember the outcome, but I do remember that it was an odd number." Does this fact increase the chances that the result was a multiple of 3?

**Solution** Let $A = \{3, 6, 9, 12\}$ and let $B = \{3, 5, 7, 9, 11\}$. We are asked to compare $P(A)$ with $P(A|B)$. The probability distribution for this experiment is given on page 33. Since it is not the equally likely distribution, we must use definition **1**.

$$P(A) = P(\{3, 6, 9, 12\}) = P(3) + P(6) + P(9) + P(12)$$
$$= \tfrac{2}{36} + \tfrac{5}{36} + \tfrac{4}{36} + \tfrac{1}{36} = \tfrac{12}{36} = \tfrac{1}{3}.$$
$$P(B) = P(\{3, 5, 7, 9, 11\}) = \tfrac{2}{36} + \tfrac{4}{36} + \tfrac{6}{26} + \tfrac{4}{36} + \tfrac{2}{36} = \tfrac{18}{36} = \tfrac{1}{2}.$$
$$P(A \cap B) = P(\{3, 9\}) = \tfrac{2}{36} + \tfrac{4}{36} = \tfrac{6}{36} = \tfrac{1}{6}.$$

$$P(A|B) = P(A \cap B)/P(B) = \frac{\tfrac{1}{6}}{\tfrac{1}{2}} = \tfrac{1}{6} \cdot \tfrac{2}{1} = \tfrac{1}{3}.$$

Since $P(A|B) = P(A)$ we see that Betty's information does not help Alan.

If we multiply both sides of equation **1** by $P(B)$ we obtain a very important result:

$$P(A \cap B) = P(A|B)P(B) \tag{3}$$

We state this in words: the probability that the events A and B both occur is equal to the conditional probability of A given B, times the probability of B.

**Problem 3** Alan is interested in local politics. Many of his friends are of Greek extraction; so the district Republican party leader tells Alan to ask his Greek friends if they plan to support the Republican candidate in the upcoming congressional election. Alan reports that 40% of them plan to do so. The party leader decides that Alan's report is typical of the local Greek voter population, which according to the latest census makes up 14% of the voters in the district. What is the probability that a voter selected at random from the district will be a Greek who plans to support the Republican candidate?

*A common tipoff that a conditional probability is being stated is the use of the word "of." When you read that 40% of Alan's Greek friends support Republicans, think: Given that a person is of Greek extraction, the probability he or she is Republican is 40%.*

**Solution** The experiment is to select a voter and determine his or her national origin and voting preference. The events of interest here are $G$ = "of Greek extraction" and $R$ = "supports Republican candidate." Alan found (or at least the party has assumed he found) that $P(R|G) = 0.40$. In other words, he restricted his sample space to G and within this new sample space he found the probability of R to be 0.40. The U.S. Census Bureau found that $P(G) = 0.14$. The event in question—being a Greek voter in favor of the Republican candidate—is $G \cap R$. If we substitute G for A and R for B in equation **3**, we obtain $P(G \cap R) = P(G|R)P(R)$. But this is of no use since we know neither $P(G|R)$ nor $P(R)$. What the party leader must realize is that the event in question can also be written $R \cap G$; that is, "the voter favors the Republican and is of Greek extraction." Then by equation **3** with R for A and G for B we have $P(R \cap G) = P(R|G)P(G) = (0.40)(0.14) = 0.056$. This is the probability we wanted: 0.056 or 5.6%.

There is a way to convert almost any conditional probability problem into numerical terms. Some individuals prefer to do this although the ideas and arithmetic are identical. *Pretend* there are 100 voters in Alan's neighborhood. Then 14 of these people will be of Greek extraction and 40% of these will vote Republican. Thus, $14 \times 40\% = 5.6$ people will be Greeks who also vote Republican. That is, 5.6 out of 100 will be Greeks and vote Republican. Our answer is $\frac{5.6}{100} = 0.056$. In this case we could avoid "fractions of people" by assuming that there are 1,000 voters in Alan's neighborhood. Then 140 will be Greek and $40\% \times 140 = 56$ will be Greeks who vote Republican. Thus, $\frac{56}{1,000} = 0.056$ is the desired probability. The general procedure is this: assign a number to the sample space and then calculate percentages based upon this number. While the number assigned will almost certainly be wrong, the percentages will be correct.

**Alternate Solution**

The conclusion that 14 of the 100 individuals will be of Greek extraction will be true if each individual in the population has the same probability of being chosen (that is, in the equally likely case). Otherwise, this conclusion may be false although the numerical technique presented here will still work.

In our first attempt to solve this problem we noticed an important fact. If $P(A) > 0$ and $P(B) > 0$, then besides equation **3** we also have $P(B \cap A) = P(B|A)P(A)$. Since $B \cap A = A \cap B$, we can write this result as

$$P(A \cap B) = P(B|A)P(A) \qquad \textbf{4}$$

In any practical application, it will always be clear, as it was in Problem 3, which of the formulas, **3** or **4**, is more useful.

Two events that are not independent could be termed **dependent**, but we shall avoid this usage.

Two events A and B are said to be **independent** if the occurrence of event B does not affect the probability of event A. For example, if we flip two coins, the probability of getting heads on the second coin is not affected by the outcome of the first coin. To check whether A and B are independent we first calculate the probability of A, that is, $P(A)$, and then we calculate the probability of A under the assumption that event B has occurred, that is, $P(A|B)$. If the occurrence of B does not affect the probability of A, then $P(A)$ and $P(A|B)$ will be the same. This observation is the basis for the following definition.

For example, in Problem 2 we determined that the events "multiple of 3" and "odd" are independent.

If $P(B)$ is zero, then $P(A|B)$ is not defined so equation **1** would be meaningless in this case. We will explain later why we require $P(A)$ to be nonzero as well.

Let A and B be events in an experiment with probability distribution P. We say that A and B are independent if $P(A)$ and $P(B)$ are not zero and

$$P(A|B) = P(A)$$

**5**

Even though A appears more often than B in equation **5**, one would hope that if A and B are independent then so are B and A. Let's consider an example.

Problem 4  A balanced die, marked as usual, is tossed. Which of the following pairs of events are independent?
(a) even; greater than two,
(b) even; greater than three,
(c) greater than two; even,
(d) greater than three; even.

Solution  Since the probability distribution for this experiment is the equally likely distribution, we may use result **2** to calculate the conditional probabilities.

(a)

P(even|greater than two)

$$= n(\text{even and greater than two})/n(\text{greater than two})$$

$$= \frac{n(\{4,6\})}{n(\{3,4,5,6\})} = \tfrac{2}{4} = \tfrac{1}{2},$$

and

$$P(\text{even}) = \tfrac{1}{2}.$$

These events satisfy equation **5** and are therefore independent.

(b)

P(even|greater than three)

$$= n(\text{even and greater than three})/n(\text{greater than three})$$

$$= n(\{4,6\})/n(\{4,5,6\}) = \tfrac{2}{3},$$

and

$$P(\text{greater than three}) = P(\{4,5,6\}) = \tfrac{3}{6} = \tfrac{1}{2}.$$

Since equation **5** is not satisfied, these events are not independent.

(c)

P(greater than two|even)

$$= P(\text{greater than two and even})/P(\text{even})$$

$$= n(\{4,6\})/n(\{2,4,6\}) = \tfrac{2}{3},$$

and

$$P(\text{greater than two}) = P(\{3,4,5,6\}) = \tfrac{2}{3}.$$

By definition **5**, these events are independent.

(d)

$$P(\text{greater than three}|\text{even}) = n(\{4,6\})/n(\{2,4,6\}) = \tfrac{2}{3},$$

and

$$P(\text{greater than three}) = P(\{4,5,6\}) = \tfrac{1}{2}.$$

These events are not independent.

On his second hour exam, Alan answered that the events "even" and "greater than two" were not independent. He reasoned that, if the event "greater than two" occurs, then the outcome 2 is no longer possible. Similarly, if the event "even" occurs, then the outcomes 3 and 5 are ruled out. Thus, each of these events has an effect on the other. Alan mentioned all this in his attempt to get his exam grade raised from a C to a B. However, his professor pointed out that neither event has any effect on the *probability* of the other. This is the sense in which the word "independent" is used in probability.

Despite this special use of the word "independent," one still has the feeling that, if the events A and B are independent, then the events B and A should also be independent. Fortunately, this does follow from our definition. We will verify this fact in the following paragraphs and derive some very useful equations along the way.

Suppose A and B are independent. Then by definition

$$P(A|B) = P(A). \qquad\qquad \textbf{6}$$

From the definition of conditional probability we see that

$$P(A|B) = \frac{P(A \cap B)}{P(B)} \qquad\qquad \textbf{7}$$

If we put equations **6** and **7** together we get

$$P(A) = \frac{P(A \cap B)}{P(B)}$$

or, multiplying both sides by P(B),

$$P(A)P(B) = P(A \cap B) \qquad\qquad \textbf{8}$$

This is one of the most important consequences of the assumption of independence.

This works both ways. Suppose $P(A \cap B) = P(A)P(B)$. Then

$$P(A|B) = \frac{P(A \cap B)}{P(B)} = \frac{P(A)P(B)}{P(B)} = P(A)$$

Of course if Alan had worked a few exercises before the test he would have caught and corrected his mistaken impression.

It is for this reason that we require P(A) to be nonzero in definition **5**. If P(A)=0, then equation **1** is satisfied, so that A and B would be independent. However, the corresponding equaton asserting the independence of B and A (namely P(B|A) = P(B)) is meaningless, so B and A would not be independent.

and

Recall $A \cap B = B \cap A$.

$$P(B|A) = \frac{P(B \cap A)}{P(A)} = \frac{P(A \cap B)}{P(A)} = \frac{P(A)P(B)}{P(A)} = P(B) \qquad \textbf{9}$$

(provided, of course, P(A) and P(B) are both non-zero). Putting all this together we obtain the following sequence of steps:

(1) Suppose A and B are independent. Then

(2) $P(A)P(B) = P(A \cap B)$ by equation **8**, so that

(3) $P(B|A) = P(B)$ by equation **9**, and

(4) the events B and A are independent.

We summarize these results as follows.

| |
|---|
| If the events A and B are independent, then so are the events B and A. |

**10**

| |
|---|
| If the events A and B are independent, then $P(A \cap B) = P(A)P(B)$ |

**11**

| |
|---|
| If P(A) and P(B) are not zero and if $P(A \cap B) = P(A)P(B)$, then the events A and B are independent. |

**12**

Some texts do exactly this. However, while result **12** is most useful, it is unclear why two events satisfying it should be called independent. The use of the word "independent" makes sense only in the light of equation **5**.

It follows from results **11** and **12** that we could have used result **12** as our original definition of independence.

We can also use these results to determine when two events are *not* independent. Suppose A and B are not independent. Then $P(A|B) \neq P(A)$ and $P(A \cap B) \neq P(A)P(B)$. Conversely, if $P(A \cap B) \neq P(A)P(B)$, then A and B cannot be independent, for in this case either P(B) = 0 or

$$P(A|B) = \frac{P(A \cap B)}{P(B)} \neq P(A).$$

We summarize:

| |
|---|
| If A and B are not independent, then neither are B and A. If A and B are not independent and P(A) and P(B) are not zero, then $P(A \cap B) \neq P(A)P(B)$. |

**13**

| |
|---|
| If $P(A \cap B) \neq P(A)P(B)$, then A and B are not independent. |

**14**

Problem 5    (a) At the moment, the probability that Jones will be elected canine control specialist next Tuesday is 0.30, the chances of Potanski's election as coroner are 2 in 5, and there is a 12% chance that both of them will be elected. Are the events "Jones is elected" and "Potanski is elected" independent?

(b) If Jones is not elected canine control specialist, then Chiu certainly will be. The chances that Brown is being elected coroner are the same as Potanski's, and there is a 10% chance that both Chiu and Brown will achieve office. Are the events "Brown is elected" and "Chiu is elected" independent?

Solution    Denote by $A, B, C, D$ the events of the election of Jones, Potanski, Chiu, Brown, respectively.

(a) We are given $P(A) = 0.30$, $P(B) = \frac{2}{5} = 0.40$, and $P(A \cap B) = 0.12$. Since $P(A)P(B) = (0.30)(0.40) = 0.12 = P(A \cap B)$, we have (by result **12**) that the events $A$ and $B$ are independent.

(b) We are given the further information that $P(C) = 1 - P(A) = 0.70$, $P(D) = P(B) = 0.40$, and $P(C \cap D) = 0.10$. Now $P(C)P(D) = (0.70)(0.40) = 0.28 \neq P(C \cap D)$. By result **14** the events $C$ and $D$ are not independent.

If we combine result **11** of this section with equation **1** of Section 3, we obtain the following useful result.

> If $A$ and $B$ are independent events, then
> $$P(A \cup B) = P(A) + P(B) - P(A)P(B)$$

**15**

Problem 6    I plan to go camping today, but there is a 30% chance my car will break down on the way and a 60% chance that the campground will be full when I arrive. I believe that neither of these events has any effect on the probability of the other. What is the probability that I will not be camping tonight?

Solution    Let $A$ be the event "my car breaks down" and let $B$ be the event "the campground is full." Then $P(A) = 0.30$ and $P(B) = 0.60$. We are interested in the event $A \cup B = $ "my car breaks down or the campground is full." By equation **15**

$$P(A \cup B) = 0.30 + 0.60 - (0.30 \cdot 0.60)$$
$$= 0.90 - 0.18$$
$$= 0.72$$

There is a 72% chance that I will not be camping tonight because of a broken-down car or a full campground.

**Exercises 1.5**  In each of Exercises 1 through 6, find the probability in the usual dice game of the first event, given the second event.

1. 7 or 11, greater than 5.
2. greater than 5, 7 or 11.
3. even, less than 9.
4. less than 9, even.
5. 7 or 11, less than 5.
6. less than 5, 7 or 11.

In pool there are balls numbered 1 through 15 and a white cue ball. Balls 9 through 15 are striped, balls 1 through 7 are solid colors, not black, and the 8 ball is solid black. A ball is chosen at random. In each of Exercises 7 through 10, find $P(A|B)$.

7. $A$ = solid color, $B$ = less than 8.
8. $A$ = less than 8, $B$ = solid color.
9. $A$ = cue ball, $B$ = solid color.
10. $A$ = numbered ball, $B$ = cue ball.
11. There will be three nominees for president of Annie's class; suppose each has an equal chance of being elected. If the probability of Annie's being nominated is $\frac{8}{10}$, what is the probability of her being elected?
12. Three percent of the voters in Alan's district are of Russian descent, and 62% of these support the Democratic candidate for senator. What are the chances that a district voter chosen at random will be a Russian-American who does not favor the Democrat?
13. When Joe gets in the car he buckles his seatbelt only one-third of the time. Of people injured in accidents, 90% do not have on seatbelts. What are chances that Joe will be injured in an accident?
14. Let $A_1$ and $A_2$ be mutually exclusive events in an experiment with probability distribution $P$ and let $B$ be an event in the experiment.
    (a) Why does $(A_1 \cup A_2) \cap B$ equal $(A_1 \cap B) \cup (A_2 \cap B)$?
    (b) Why are $A_1 \cap B$ and $A_2 \cap B$ disjoint?
    (c) Use (a) and (b) to prove that $P(A_1 \cup A_2|B) = P(A_1|B) + P(A_2|B)$.
    (d) Let $A$ be any event in the experiment. Use (c) to prove that $P(A|B) + P(\sim A|B) = 1$.
15. Let $P$ be a probability distribution for an experiment and let $B$ be an event in the experiment with $P(B) > 0$. Find:
    (a) $P(\varnothing|B)$
    (b) $P(S|B)$
    (c) $P(B|B)$

In Exercises 16 and 17 determine whether or not the events described are independent.

16. A balanced die, marked as usual, is tossed.
    (a) odd, at most five
    (b) at least three, at least five
    (c) odd, even
    (d) no more than four, at most two
    (e) five, at least one

17. Two dice, marked as usual, are tossed and the total number of spots that come up is counted.
    (a) even, at most eight
    (b) at least seven, a multiple of three
    (c) not seven and not eleven, odd
    (d) not six, not twelve
    (e) one, two

18. Nineteen percent of PHE customers order a hamburger without French fries and 62% make French fries a part of their order. If ordering a hamburger and ordering French fries are independent events, what percentage of PHE customers orders a hamburger?

19. Can an event and its complement ever be independent?

*20. (a) Show that, if A and B are independent events and if $P(A) \neq 1$, then $\sim$A and B are independent.
    (b) Show that, if A and B are independent events and if $P(A) \neq 1$ and $P(B) \neq 1$, then $\sim$A and $\sim$B are independent.

See Exercise 20.

21. If $P(A) = \frac{3}{5}$ and $P(B) = \frac{4}{7}$ and A and B are independent, find $P(\sim A \cap B)$, $P(A \cap \sim B)$, and $P(\sim A \cap \sim B)$.

22. If $P(A) = \frac{3}{4}$, $P(B) = \frac{1}{5}$, and $P(\sim A \cap \sim B) = \frac{1}{5}$, find $P(A \cap B)$.

23. I have two children. When I go to the park I label one child A and the other one B. They not only ignore each other completely, they also tend to get lost rather easily. I have found that the probability that A gets lost is 0.30 and the probability that B gets lost is 0.40. If we assume that these two events are independent, what is the probability that I will have to find at least one lost child (of my own)?

24. I figure that there is a 10% chance that the state will audit my income tax return and a 5% chance the federal government will audit my tax return. Assume that these two events are independent, and compute the probability that I will be audited.

25. At my store, 80% of my customers buy either milk or eggs (or both), 30% buy both milk and eggs, and 40% buy eggs. What is the probability that one of my customers, chosen at random, has bought milk?

26. The last time I was lost on Mount Everett, I knew that two rescue teams would be sent. Team A has a 60% success rate; Team B has an 80% success rate. Unfortunately, the teams refuse to acknowledge one another and so behave independently. What is the probability that I was rescued?

**Section 1.6 Summary**  At this point it might seem reasonable to expect a definitive answer to the question, "Just what *is* probability?" But this is actually a very difficult question, which has concerned mathematicians and philosophers for many years. We have suggested a relative frequency approach to the subject, which seems plausible for experiments that can be repeated endlessly. But if a die is tossed 6,000 times and comes up 3 exactly 1,005 times, can we really conclude anything? Another approach has to do with the degree of confidence a rational person may have, given a certain amount of evidence, in a possible outcome. Readers with a philosophical bent are urged to seek out and peruse the appropriate literature. For our present purposes it is perhaps best to simply proceed formally, leaving the "real" interpretation of P(A) to the individual student.

| TERM | SET THEORY DEFINITION |
|---|---|
| Experiment | A set S which is called a **sample space** |
| Possible outcome | An element of S |
| Event | A subset of S |
| Probability distribution P for an experiment | A rule P that assigns a non-negative number to each element of S so that the numbers assigned sum to one |
| The probability of the event A | $P(A) = $ the sum of the numbers assigned by P to the elements of A; $P(\varnothing) = 0$ |
| Let A and B be events. | |
| not A | $\sim A = $ the set of all elements of S that are not in A |
| A or B | $A \cup B = $ the set of all elements of S that are in A or in B (or in both) |
| A and B | $A \cap B = $ the set of all elements of S that are in A and in B |
| A and B are mutually exclusive. | $A \cap B = \varnothing$, i.e., A and B are disjoint |
| The equally likely distribution | $P(A) = n(A)/n(S)$, where n means "number of elements in" |
| Probability of A given that B has occurred | $P(A|B) = P(A \cap B)/P(B)$; defined only if $P(B) \neq 0$ |
| A and B are independent | $P(A) \neq 0$, $P(B) \neq 0$, and $P(A|B) = P(A)$ |

OTHER TERMS AND RESULTS

The principle of multiplication in counting, page 5
$P(A \cup B) + P(A \cap B) = P(A) + P(B)$, page 22
$P(A) + P(\sim A) = 1$, page 24
The principle of division in counting, page 30
Permutations, $P_r^n$, page 30
Combinations, $C_r^n$, page 30
$C_0^n = C_n^n = 1$, $C_1^n = C_{n-1}^n = n$, $C_r^n = C_{n-r}^n$, page 31
Events A and B are independent if, and only if,
   $P(A \cap B) = P(A)P(B)$, page 44.

**Review Exercises**
Reread Chapter 1. Then try to do all the following exercises without looking back. All these exercises are answered in Appendix C.

1. Let's count the number of possible phone numbers.
   (a) A phone number consists of a three-digit area code followed by a three-digit exchange and four more digits. That's 10 digits. How many 10-digit numbers are there?
   (b) An area code cannot start with zero but its second digit must be zero or one. How many 10-digit numbers are there like this?
   (c) An exchange cannot start with zero or have second digit zero or one (or else it would be confused with an area code). Now how many numbers are there?

2. Write the sample space for the following experiment. Pick a card; if it is a face card, flip a coin; if it is not a face card, toss a die.

3. For the experiment of Exercise 2, write the event "heads, or an even number on the die."

4. Let A and B be events in an experiment. Write the following events in set notation.
   (a) A or not B
   (b) The event A and B does not occur
   (c) It is not the case that the event not A does not occur

5. A dodecahedron is a regular solid with 12 faces, each of which is a pentagon. I have a small plastic dodecahedral calendar—each face is marked with a different month.
   (a) If I randomly place the calendar on my desk, what is the probability that it shows the correct month?
   (b) What is the probability it shows a month in this season?

6. If $S = \{a, b, c, d, e\}$ is a sample space, P is a probability distribution on S, $P(a) = \frac{1}{3}$, $P(b) = \frac{1}{4}$, $P(c) = \frac{1}{5}$, and $P(d) = \frac{1}{6}$, what is $P(e)$? If $A = \{b, c, d\}$, what are $P(A)$ and $P(\sim A)$?

7. If P is a probability distribution on a sample space S, A and B are events, and $P(A) = \frac{1}{2}$, $P(B) = \frac{2}{3}$, and $P(A \cap B) = \frac{5}{12}$, find $P(A \cup B)$.

8. If A and B are independent, $P(A \cup B) = \frac{3}{4}$, and $P(A) = \frac{1}{3}$, find $P(B)$.

9. An urn contains one flag for each state in the United States. The flags of the original 13 colonies have gold fringe; the others do not. A flag is drawn at random, and it has gold fringe. What is the probability that it represents a state whose name begins with one of the first 13 letters of the alphabet?

10. Find two events in the experiment of throwing a balanced die that are independent.

**Supplementary Exercises**

1. How many permutations of the letters in the word "permutation" are there?

2. In how many (legal) ways can the first four moves in chess be made (that is, White's first move, Black's first move, White's second move, and Black's second move)?

3. There are 8 buildings on Alan's block, each 4 stories tall, with 3 apartments on each floor. How many apartments are on Alan's block?

4. Here are some final configurations in tick-tack-toe.

(no reason to go on)

How many really different configurations are there? (The configuration below is the same, really, as one of those above.)

5. The parade is to have a column of 6 different horses who must stay together, a column of 8 jugglers who must stay together, 4 senators, no 2 of whom should be together, and 1 elephant. How many different parades can be presented?

*6. Of your staff of 18 salesmen you must assign at least 3 to Peoria, at most 9 to Chicago, and 2, 3, 4, or 5 to Des Moines. In how many ways can this be done?

*7. (a) Find four events in the toss of a die such that any two of them could occur in a single toss, but no three of them would occur in a single toss.

   (b) Can you find five events in the toss of a die that have property (a)?

8. Describe the sample spaces for each of the following experiments.

   (a) Harry, Mary, and Larry run a race. The winner is determined, unless there is a tie.

   (b) Harry, Mary, and Larry run a race. The order of finish, including ties if any, is determined.

   (c) Harry, Mary, and Larry each choose an integer from 1 to 4. The sum of the integers chosen is determined.

   (d) They repeat the action of (c), but the product is determined.

9. Make up any set of a finite number of positive rational numbers that total 1. (For instance $\frac{3}{8}$, $\frac{2}{7}$, $\frac{1}{5}$, $\frac{71}{2520}$, $\frac{1}{9}$.) Show how to devise an experiment with an urn and colored balls that has these numbers as its probability distribution.

10. Which of the following assignments of numbers to the possible outcomes of a toss of a die are probability distributions?

   (a) Assign $\frac{1}{6}$ to each outcome.

   (b) Assign $\frac{1}{4}$ to each outcome except 1, and assign zero to 1.

   (c) Assign $\frac{1}{7}$ to each outcome except 1, and assign $\frac{2}{7}$ to 1.

   (d) Add 2 to each outcome and divide 1 by the sum. Assign the result to the outcome.

*11. (a) Let A, B, C be events in an experiment with probability distribution P. Give examples and explain in general why $P(A \cup B \cup C) = P(A) + P(B) + P(C) - P(A \cap B) - P(A \cap C) - P(B \cap C) + P(A \cap B \cap C)$.

   (b) Let A, B, C, D be events in the experiment. What is the corresponding expression for the probability $P(A \cup B \cup C \cup D)$?

   (c) Let $A_1, A_2, \ldots, A_n$ be any finite number of events in the experiment. What is the corresponding expression for the probability $P(A_1 \cup A_2 \cup \ldots \cup A_n)$?

(d) What is the expression for $P(A \cap B \cap C)$? For the probability $P(A_1 \cap A_2 \cap \ldots \cap A_n)$?

12. If A and B are independent events, $P(\sim B \cup A) = \frac{4}{7}$, and $P(\sim A) = \frac{3}{5}$, find $P(B \cup \sim A)$.

13. Show that, if A, B, C are events, $P(C) \neq 0$, and $P(B \cap C) \neq 0$, then $P(A \cap B \cap C) = P(A|B \cap C)P(B|C)P(C)$.

In Exercises 14 through 17 assume $P(B \cap C) \neq 0$ and $P(C) \neq 0$.

14. If $P(A|B \cap C) = \frac{2}{3}$, $P(B|C) = \frac{1}{2}$, and $P(C) = \frac{3}{4}$, find $P(A \cap B \cap C)$.

15. If $P(A \cap B \cap C) = \frac{3}{7}$, $P(B|C) = \frac{4}{5}$, and $P(C) = \frac{5}{7}$, find $P(A|B \cap C)$.

16. If $P(A \cap B \cap C) = \frac{1}{3}$, $P(A|B \cap C) = \frac{3}{5}$, and $P(C) = \frac{7}{9}$, find $P(B|C)$.

17. If $P(A \cap B \cap C) = \frac{1}{8}$, $P(A|B \cap C) = \frac{3}{8}$, and $P(B|C) = \frac{2}{3}$, find $P(C)$.

Recall our hero's name is Alan V. Gregory.

We are using the definition of the term "word" that most probability books have adopted; namely, a **word** is any finite ordered list of letters, whether or not it makes sense.

In each part of this exercise assume all information given in the previous parts.

18. All members of the Gregory clan have the same seven-letter middle name.

(a) How many "words" would have to be written in order to be absolutely sure we have written the name?

(b) No two letters in the name are the same. Now how many words might be written?

(c) Exactly two of the letters are vowels. Now how many?

(d) The second and fifth letters are vowels. Now how many?

(e) The vowels are i and o (not necessarily in that order). Now how many?

(f) The middle letter is t. Now how many?

(g) The remaining unknown letters occur in alphabetical order. Now how many?

(h) The vowels are in alphabetical order, and the last letter in the name is y. Now how many?

(i) The name is a common English word. What is it?

19. A standard electronic keyboard digit display format has seven segments (Figure 3) which are lighted to produce the digits. For example: 1, 2, 4, 6, and 7 are lighted to make a 5.

(a) How many different symbols could be displayed?

(b) How many different symbols could be displayed if each symbol must involve at least three lighted segments? The answer to this part may require some interpretation.

*(c) How many different symbols could be displayed if at least three segments must be lighted and every lighted segment must be next to another lighted segment? (For example, if 2 is lighted then at least one of 1, 4, or 5 must be lighted.)

**Figure 3**

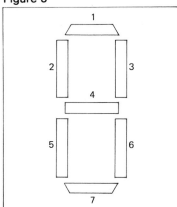

20. Necklaces are of two types: with clasp and without clasp as in Figures 4 and 5 on the next page. Both types can be flipped over. If I flip over the clasp necklace in Figure 4, I get the necklace in Figure 6. This is the same necklace as before. When being worn, the nonclasp necklace can be flipped too, and it can also be turned. If I turn the nonclasp necklace in Figure 5, I might get the necklace in Figure 7. This is the same necklace as before. The clasp necklace cannot be turned, because the clasp would show.

(a) How many different clasp necklaces can I make using five different beads?

**Figure 4**

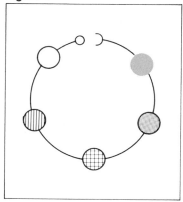

A very carefully designed survey might be accurate to within 3%.

**Figure 5**

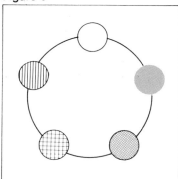

**Figure 6**

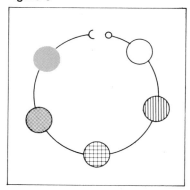

(b) How many different nonclasp necklaces can I make using five different beads?

*(c) How many different clasp necklaces and how many different non-clasp necklaces can I make using n different beads?

(d) How many different clasp necklaces and nonclasp necklaces can I make using three identical white beads and three identical brown beads?

21. How many different four-letter license plates can be made using only the letters SAAB?

*22. How many arrangements of the word MISSISSIPPI are possible?

23. How many different rearrangements do each of the following words have?
   (a) DO
   (b) DID
   (c) DODO
   (d) ODDS
   (e) DUMDEDUM
   (f) BEEKEEPER

*24. Surveys conducted by the AC consumer research department indicate that, among all New England buyers of camping equipment, 62% prefer AC parkas, 84% prefer AC sleeping bags, and 46% prefer both. Assuming that these surveys are accurate to within 3%, can it be concluded that these preferences are independent?

25. A giant office building has: 7 windows on the ground floor; 18 windows on each of its 4 sides on floors 2 through 33; 14 windows on each of the north and south sides, 8 on the east side, and 1 on the west on floors 34 through 79; 6 windows on the north, 5 on each of the east and west, and none on the south on floors 80 through 115; and 1 skylight. Each ground floor window has 4 panes, each window on floors 2 through 50 has 3 panes, the skylight has 9 panes, and the other windows each have 5 panes. How many panes does the building have?

26. My library contains 5 history books, 8 math books, and 10 novels. In how many ways can I arrange my library so that all the books in the same subject are kept together on one shelf?

27. Alan decided to take his family out to eat at a newly opened restaurant—Wendy's Old Fashioned Hamburgers. During their brief wait in line, Annie started to giggle: "Daddy, look at that sign. It says there are 256 ways to have your hamburger fixed. Isn't that silly—there are only eight possible relishes: catsup, onion, mustard, pickles, lettuce, tomato, mayonnaise, and relish."
   (a) Verify that the sign is correct.
   (b) Wendy's also serves five different soft drinks (each in two sizes, large and small): hot chocolate, coffee, tea, milk, and a thick dessert called a Frosty dairy dessert. How many different meals are possible, if a meal consists of a hamburger, drink, and may or may not include French fries or chili?
   (c) Actually, things are slightly more complicated. Wendy's serves

They also serve water.

Figure 7

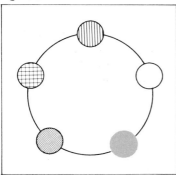

three basic sizes of hamburgers: the single, the double, and the triple. You can pay a little bit extra for cheese. Of course, you can get coffee with cream, sugar, both or neither. The same is true for tea. Suppose you eat a different meal every night. How long will it take you to eat every possible meal?

28. "I am confident that, of these five people chosen at random, at least four will prefer Fizz over the other cola," roared the president of Fizz, Inc., "because I know that 99% of the folks around here prefer it." In fact, only $\frac{3}{4}$ of the folks around here prefer it. What is the probability that the Fizz executive will be happy with the test?

29. (a) If $A = B$, what can we say about $A \cup B$ and $A \cap B$?
    (b) If $A \cup B = A \cap B$, what can we say about A and B?

30. (a) If A is a subset of B, what can we say about $A \cup B$ and $A \cap B$?
    (b) If $A \cup B = B$, what can we say about $A \cap B$?
    (c) If $A \cap B = A$, what can we say about $A \cup B$?

# Chapter 2
# Systems
# of Linear
# Equations

The managers of Appalachian Creations are professional decision makers. Janet Witherspoon is just one member of a large staff of applied mathematicians who help provide the data upon which each decision is based. There are basically two circumstances under which decisions are made:

**Certainty** All important data are known for sure. For example, AC knows its production costs and can try to minimize them.

**Uncertainty** Not all important data are known for sure. For example, AC is never sure exactly what the demand for its products will be, although information is continually collected to improve the accuracy of its staff's guesses.

The word "linear" contains the word "line," which denotes one of the simplest mathematical objects.

In many cases a linear model is appropriate for situations involving decisions under certainty. We cannot give a simple answer to the question, What is a linear model? It is a mathematical model that involves ideas and techniques such as those found in this chapter and in Chapter 5. If a linear model is not appropriate, then calculus can often be applied to change the problem into one in which linear methods are useful. In the case of decisions under uncertainty, a *probability* model must be used. If probabilities cannot be assigned directly to the possible outcomes, then *statistics* can be used to provide good guesses for them.

Calculus is completely avoided in this text.

The fact that this text treats linear models and probability models separately might lead one to think that there is no relationship between them. In fact most problems in real life involve a lot of each. We will see one example of this in our study of Markov chains (Chapter 3). However, it is easier to learn about each of these models when it is taken up separately. In this way the fundamental aspects of one model are not obscured by the other.

For example, if we assign a probability distribution to the outcomes of an experiment, we can regard these numbers as data known for sure and can perhaps apply linear methods.

## Section 2.1
### Introduction to Coordinates and Linear Equations

Figure 1

Insulation Requirements

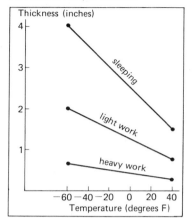

In advertising as well as at sales meetings and other presentations, the management at Appalachian Creations often finds a graphical presentation of data to be the most effective means of communication. For example, consider Figure 1, which appeared in AC's most recent catalog. This chart is typical in that it involves only straight lines. Except for a few technical reports on topics such as wind-chill at extreme altitudes, AC prepares and uses only straight-line graphs. Since improperly prepared graphs can ruin the reputation of any company, AC requires all its managers to understand the preparation and interpretation of such graphs.

The kinds of data that can be studied by coordinates and graphs are many and diverse. They range from fiscal information —for example, retirement incomes as a function of longevity—to knowledge about manufacturing—for example, tent life as a function of fabric quality. While some of these data may not be linear, understanding the following material is a necessary first step to understanding the presentation of any kind of data.

**Coordinates on a Line**

Figure 2

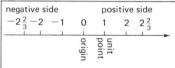

Figure 3

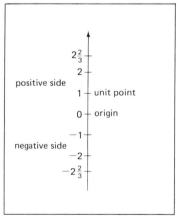

Our first geometric application involves lines and their points. It will be convenient to be able to refer to a point on a line, and we do this by assigning numbers to the points in a natural way. The number to be associated with a point is called its **coordinate**. We set up a system of coordinates on a line by assigning the coordinate 0 to some point on the line, called the **origin**, and assigning the coordinate 1 to some other point, called the **unit point**. It is traditional to choose the unit point to the right of the origin if the line is horizontal (Figure 2) and to choose the unit point above the origin if the line is vertical (Figure 3).

The arrow on the lines in Figures 2 and 3 and similar arrows in later figures indicate the "positive directions" established by these choices. The coordinate of a point on the positive side of the origin is simply the distance from the point to the origin in terms of the unit distance; the coordinate of a point on the negative side of the origin is the negative of the distance from the point to the origin.

Problem 1

(a) Set up a coordinate system on a horizontal line and indicate the points with coordinates $-2\frac{2}{3}$, $-2$, $-1$, 0, 1, 2, and $2\frac{2}{3}$.

(b) Repeat part (a) for a vertical line.

Answer

(a) See Figure 2.

(b) See Figure 3.

### Coordinates on a Plane

When only two variables are involved they are often called x and y, and the 1-axis and 2-axis are usually called the **x-axis** and **y-axis**, respectively. But since we will eventually be considering three, four, and more variables, we shall use the subscript notation $x_1, x_2, x_3, x_4, \ldots$ for variables and the corresponding notation for the axes. The term "1-axis" is merely a shortened form of "$x_1$-axis."

Following ideas of René Descartes (1596–1650), Pierre de Fermat (ca. 1601–1665), and John Wallis (1616–1703), we set up a system of coordinates in a plane by choosing a horizontal line and a vertical line in the plane. We call these lines the **1-axis** and the **2-axis**, respectively. We then set up systems of coordinates on each of these lines, as explained above, using the point 0 at which these lines intersect as the origin for both systems. Now suppose P is a point in the plane (Figure 4). Draw the horizontal and vertical lines through P. Suppose the vertical line crosses the 1-axis at a point with coordinate $x_1$ (read "x one"), and the horizontal line through P crosses the 2-axis at the point with coordinate $x_2$. We call these numbers the **coordinates** of P and we write

$$P = (x_1, x_2)$$

We have used this notation in Chapter 1 to express the outcomes in the experiment "two dice are tossed."

**Figure 4**

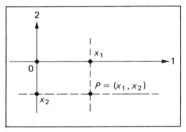

Axes is the plural of axis.

The expression $(x_1, x_2)$ is called an **ordered pair**. The first number tells how far P is to the left or right of the 2-axis. (A positive number indicates "right"; a negative number indicates "left.") The second number tells how far P is above or below the 1-axis. (A positive number indicates "above"; a negative number indicates "below.")

When the point $x_1$ in Figure 4 is considered as a point in the plane, its coordinates are $(x_1, 0)$, since the horizontal line through $x_1$ (namely, the 1-axis) crosses the 2-axis at the origin. In the same way we see that the point $x_2$ in Figure 4 has coordinates $(0, x_2)$, when considered as a point in the plane. In general, points on the 1-axis have coordinates in which the second number is zero; points on the 2-axis have coordinates in which the first number is zero. Since the origin is on both axes, it has coordinates $(0, 0)$.

**Problem 2**

In a plane with a coordinate system indicate the points with coordinates $(x_1, x_2)$, where $x_1$ and $x_2$ are either $-3$, 0, or 3.

**Answer**

See Figure 5.

**Figure 5**

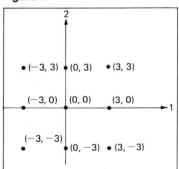

Problem 3

In a plane with a coordinate system, indicate the points with coordinates $(x_1, x_2)$, where both $x_1$ and $x_2$ are positive integers, $x_1 < x_2$, and $x_2 < 4$.

Solution

The second condition implies that $x_2$ can be only 1, 2, or 3. If $x_2 = 3$, then, since $x_1$ must be less than $x_2$, $x_1$ can be 1 or 2. Thus, the points $(1, 3)$ and $(2, 3)$ satisfy the conditions. If $x_2 = 2$, the only choice for $x_1$ is $x_1 = 1$, and we obtain the point $(1, 2)$. Finally, if $x_2 = 1$, then $x_1$ cannot be assigned any value, since there is no positive integer less than 1. These points are indicated in Figure 6.

**Figure 6**

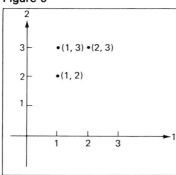

**Linear Equations in Two Variables**

We are now ready to discuss lines in the plane. Consider the equation

$$3x_1 - 2x_2 = 6 \qquad \mathbf{1}$$

This is an equation involving two variables, $x_1$ and $x_2$. There are many ordered pairs $(x_1, x_2)$ that satisfy equation **1**, as we see in the following problem.

Problem 4

Which of the ordered pairs $(4, 3)$, $(1, 1)$, $(2, 0)$, $(1, -\frac{3}{2})$, $(3, \frac{4}{3})$, and $(0, -3)$ satisfy equation **1**?

Solution

If you cannot simplify $3 \cdot 1 - 2 \cdot (-\frac{3}{2})$ to get 6, see Appendix A, Section 5.

$3 \cdot 4 - 2 \cdot 3 = 6$, so $(4, 3)$ satisfies the equation. $3 \cdot 1 - 2 \cdot 1 = 1 \neq 6$. Hence $(1, 1)$ does not satisfy the equation. $3 \cdot 2 - 2 \cdot 0 = 6$, $3 \cdot 1 - 2 \cdot (-\frac{3}{2}) = 6$, $3 \cdot 3 - 2(\frac{4}{3}) = 6\frac{1}{3}$, and $3 \cdot 0 - 2(-3) = 6$. It follows that $(4, 3)$, $(2, 0)$, $(1, -\frac{3}{2})$, and $(0, -3)$ satisfy the equation, but $(1, 1)$ and $(3, \frac{4}{3})$ do not.

**Figure 7**

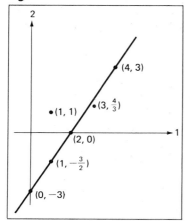

Each of the ordered pairs in Problem 4 can be plotted as a point in a plane with a coordinate system. It can be shown that all the solutions of equation **1** lie on a straight line and, conversely, that every point on this line has coordinates that are a solution of equation **1** (Figure 7). We call this line the **graph** of equation **1**, and we say that equation **1** is a **linear equation** in two variables $x_1$ and $x_2$. As we saw in Problem 4, the points $(1, 1)$ and $(3, \frac{4}{3})$ are not solutions of equation **1**, and therefore do not lie on the graph.

Problem 5

Consider the linear equation

$$4x_1 + 5x_2 = 10 \qquad \mathbf{2}$$

(a) For $x_1 = 2$, what value of $x_2$ satisfies this equation? Also, what is $x_2$ when $x_1 = -2$?

(b) For $x_2 = 2$, what value of $x_1$ satisfies this equation? Also, what is $x_1$ when $x_2 = -2$?

(c) Plot the points $(x_1, x_2)$ obtained in (a) and (b) and draw the graph of equation **2** through them.

Solution

Note that in part (c) coordinates are *ordered* pairs. None of the points $(\frac{18}{5}, -2), (2, 0), (\frac{2}{5}, 2), (-2, 5)$ is on the graph.

(a) For $x_1 = 2$, equation **2** becomes $4 \cdot 2 + 5x_2 = 10$, $8 + 5x_2 = 10$, $5x_2 = 2$, $x_2 = \frac{2}{5}$. For $x_1 = -2$ we have $4 \cdot (-2) + 5x_2 = 10$, from which $x_2 = \frac{18}{5}$.

(b) For $x_2 = 2$, we have $4x_1 + 5 \cdot 2 = 10$, $4x_1 = 0$, $x_1 = 0$. For $x_2 = -2$ we have $4x_1 - 10 = 10$, $x_1 = 5$.

(c) We plot the points $(2, \frac{2}{5})$, $(-2, \frac{18}{5})$, $(0, 2)$, and $(5, -2)$ and draw the straight line through them (Figure 8).

**Figure 8**

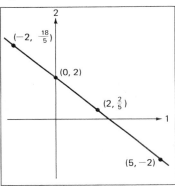

In general, it can be shown that any equation of the form

$$ax_1 + bx_2 = c \qquad \mathbf{3}$$

where a, b, and c are given numbers and not both a and b are zero, is a linear equation in the sense that its graph is a straight line. It is also the case, conversely, that every straight line in a plane with a coordinate system is the graph of some equation of the form of equation **3**, where not both a and b are zero.

**Graphing a Linear Equation in Two Variables**

What is the easiest way to draw the graph of equation **1**? We know that two points determine a line; so we need only find two solutions $(x_1, x_2)$ of equation **1**, plot them, and draw the line through them. Usually the easiest solutions to find are those in which either $x_1$ or $x_2$ is zero. These give, respectively, the points at which the line crosses the 2-axis and the 1-axis.

If $x_1 = 0$, equation **1** becomes $3 \cdot 0 - 2x_2 = 6$ or $-2x_2 = 6$; then $x_2 = -3$, so $(0, -3)$ is a solution. The point $(0, -3)$ is where the line we are seeking crosses the 2-axis. If $x_2 = 0$, equation **1** becomes $3x_1 - 2 \cdot 0 = 6$ or $3x_1 = 6$; then $x_1 = 2$, so $(2, 0)$ is a solution. This point is where our line crosses the 1-axis. We connect these two points to obtain the graph (Figure 7).

Problem 6

Graph the equation $4x_1 + 5x_2 = 10$.

Solution

If $x_1 = 0$, we have $5x_2 = 10$, or $x_2 = 2$, and we obtain the point $(0, 2)$ as we did in Problem 5. If $x_2 = 0$, we have $4x_1 = 10$, $x_1 = \frac{5}{2}$, and we

Figure 9

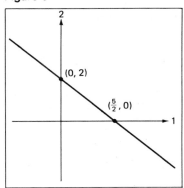

obtain $(\frac{5}{2}, 0)$. We draw the straight line through these two points to obtain the graph of this equation (Figure 9), which is the same as the graph in Problem 5 (Figure 8).

The above procedure is often the easiest way to obtain the graph of a linear equation. But there are some cases in which the procedure must be modified. We give examples of these cases below.

**Problem 7**

Graph the equation $3x_1 + 0x_2 = -5$.

**Solution**

We have $3x_1 = -5$, so $x_1 = -\frac{5}{3}$. Thus, the graph crosses the 1-axis at $(-\frac{5}{3}, 0)$. Since there is a zero multiplying $x_2$, the value we choose for $x_2$ is irrelevant—whatever it is, it will be multiplied by zero. Thus, while each solution must have $x_1 = -\frac{5}{3}$, its $x_2$ value may be any number whatsoever. It follows that the graph must be the vertical line through the point $x_1 = -\frac{5}{3}$ (Figure 10).

Our previous procedure fails here, since setting $x_1 = 0$ yields the impossibility $3 \cdot 0 = -5$ or $0 = -5$.

Figure 10

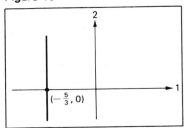

**Problem 8**

Graph the equation $0x_1 - \frac{2}{3}x_2 = -\frac{4}{5}$.

**Solution**

We have $-\frac{2}{3}x_2 = -\frac{4}{5}$, so $x_2 = \frac{6}{5}$. Thus, the graph crosses the 2-axis at $(0, \frac{6}{5})$. In this case the value of $x_1$ may be any number we choose, so the graph must be the horizontal line through the point $(0, \frac{6}{5})$ (Figure 11).

Here setting $x_2 = 0$ would give $(-\frac{2}{3}) \cdot 0 = -\frac{4}{5}$, or $0 = -\frac{4}{5}$, which is absurd.

Figure 11

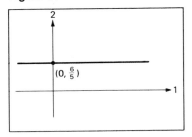

These last two problems illustrate the following general situation. In the linear equation $ax_1 + bx_2 = c$, we may have $a = 0$ or $b = 0$, but not both $a = 0$ and $b = 0$. If $a = 0$, the equation becomes $0x_1 + bx_2 = c$. This is usually written simply as $bx_2 = c$, or $x_2 = c/b$. If $b = 0$, the equation becomes $ax_1 + 0x_2 = c$, or $ax_1 = c$, or $x_1 = c/a$. To correctly interpret an equation such as $x_1 = 2$, it is necessary to know from the context of the problem how many variables are being considered. If two variables are involved, then the equation $x_1 = 2$ is to be interpreted as the equation $x_1 + 0x_2 = 2$, whose graph is the vertical line through the point $(2, 0)$.

Problem 9   Graph the equation $4x_1 + 5x_2 = 0$.

Solution   The graph crosses both axes at the origin, $(0,0)$, and at no other point. We have to find another solution. An easy solution is obtained by switching the 4 and 5 and changing the sign of the 4. Since $4 \cdot 5 + 5(-4) = 0$, the point $(5, -4)$ is on the graph. We connect these points to obtain the graph (Figure 12).

Setting $x_1 = 0$ yields $x_2 = 0$ and vice versa.

**Figure 12**

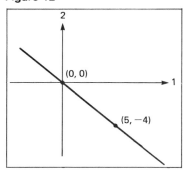

The flow chart below summarizes these procedures and applies to any linear equation in two variables.

Now we are ready to describe a simple example of the use of linear models at AC. Janet Witherspoon's supervisor had given her a problem which involved the intersection of lines. Janet knows that equations such as $x_1 - x_2 = 1$ and $x_1 + x_2 = 5$, for example, each represent lines in the plane. Two lines will intersect in a point, unless they are parallel. The mathematical question involved in the problem at hand was: What are the coordinates of the point where these two lines intersect? In other words, she was required to find a pair of numbers $(x_1, x_2)$ which satisfies both equations in the *system*

$$\begin{bmatrix} x_1 - x_2 = 1 \\ x_1 + x_2 = 5 \end{bmatrix} \qquad \textbf{4}$$

**To Graph the Equation**
$$ax_1 + bx_2 = c$$
**Where Not Both a and b Are Zero**

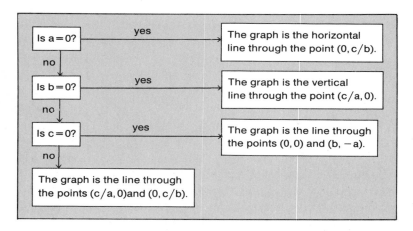

Janet was called upon to consider this particular system because the vice-president in charge of freeze-dried foods had decided to hire a new chief nutritionist and an assistant nutritionist. After checking existing salaries, she decided to pay the chief nutritionist $10,000 more than the assistant. Her budget allowed for a total expenditure of only \$50,000. The problem was to determine the salary of each of the new employees. If we let $x_1$ denote the salary of the chief and $x_2$ denote the salary of the assistant, then the fact that the chief is paid \$10,000 more is expressed by the equation

$$x_1 = x_2 + 10,000$$

or

$$x_1 - x_2 = 10,000$$

The budget allocation translates into the equation

$$x_1 + x_2 = 50,000$$

Finally, if we simplify matters by measuring salaries in units of \$10,000, we obtain system **4** above.

If on the same coordinate plane we draw a careful graph of the two lines represented by the equations in our system, they appear to cross at the point $(3, 2)$ (Figure 13). Sure enough, this possible solution, $x_1 = 3, x_2 = 2$, checks in both equations of system **4**:

$$\begin{bmatrix} 3 - 2 = 1 \\ 3 + 2 = 5 \end{bmatrix} \begin{matrix} \checkmark \\ \checkmark \end{matrix}$$

Thus, the chief nutritionist's salary will be \$30,000 and the assistant's, \$20,000.

In general, of course, a graph will not be accurate enough to make guessing effective, especially if the actual answer involves a fraction. What is needed is an algebraic technique to provide the answer without recourse to graphs. This chapter is devoted to just this type of problem. By way of introduction, notice that the first equation may be rewritten

$$x_1 = x_2 + 1. \qquad\qquad \textbf{5}$$

Substituting this expression for $x_1$ into the second equation yields:

$$(x_2 + 1) + x_2 = 5$$

or

$$2x_2 + 1 = 5$$
$$2x_2 = 4$$
$$x_2 = 2.$$

Now if we substitute this back into equation **5** we obtain

$$x_1 = 2 + 1$$
$$x_1 = 3$$

just as we had guessed.

**Figure 13**

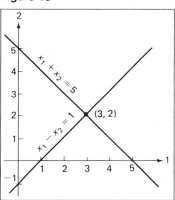

**Problem 10**   Solve the system

$$\begin{bmatrix} 3x_1 - 2x_2 = 7 \\ 2x_1 + 3x_2 = -4 \end{bmatrix}$$

**Solution**   The first equation tells us that

$$3x_1 - 2x_2 = 7$$
$$3x_1 = 7 + 2x_2$$
$$x_1 = (7 + 2x_2)/3 \qquad\qquad \textbf{6}$$

The second equation says

$$2x_1 + 3x_2 = -4$$
$$2((7 + 2x_2)/3) + 3x_2 = -4$$

We multiply both sides by 3 to obtain

$$2(7 + 2x_2) + 9x_2 = -12$$
$$14 + 4x_2 + 9x_2 = -12$$
$$13x_2 = -26$$
$$x_2 = -2$$

Now equation **6** becomes

$$x_1 = (7 + 2(-2))/3$$
$$x_1 = (7 - 4)/3$$
$$x_1 = \tfrac{3}{3}$$
$$x_1 = 1$$

See Appendix A if needed.

Don't worry if this algebra seems too fancy. The method to be presented later is easier from a purely algebraic standpoint.

**Figure 14**

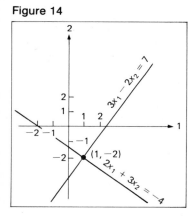

The answer is $(1, -2)$.

**Check**

$$\begin{bmatrix} 3(1) - 2(-2) = 7 \\ 2(1) + 3(-2) = -4 \end{bmatrix} \begin{matrix} \surd \\ \surd \end{matrix}$$

The point is, in fact, on both lines (see Figure 14.)

**Exercises 2.1**

1. (a) Set up a coordinate system on a horizontal line and indicate the points with coordinates $-3$, $1$, $4$, $-\tfrac{4}{3}$, and $\tfrac{5}{2}$.
   (b) Repeat part (a) for a vertical line.
2. Set up a coordinate system in a plane and indicate the points with

The $^C$ signifies that there is a comment on this exercise in Appendix C.

coordinates $(0,0)$, $(1,0)$, $(0,1)$, $(2,3)$, $(\frac{1}{2},\frac{1}{3})$, $(-3,2)$, $(-2,-3)$, and $(-\frac{1}{2},\frac{8}{3})$.

3. What are the coordinates of the vertices of a square with lower left vertex $(-2,3)$, sides parallel to the coordinate axes, and sides of length 5?

$^C$4. A baseball diamond is actually a square 90 feet on a side. If we let 1 unit equal 1 foot and place home base at the origin and second base on the 2-axis, what are the coordinates of third base?

In Problems 5 through 22, graph each equation.

5. $4x_1 + 5x_2 = 20$

6. $-3x_1 + x_2 = 6$

7. $6x_1 + 3x_2 = 18$

8. $-2x_1 + 4x_2 = 5$

9. $3x_1 - 7x_2 = -4$

10. $\frac{2}{3}x_1 + \frac{3}{4}x_2 = \frac{7}{12}$

11. $\frac{1}{2}x_1 - \frac{2}{3}x_2 = \frac{3}{4}$

12. $-\frac{5}{2}x_1 + \frac{3}{8}x_2 = \frac{1}{16}$

13. $\frac{2}{3}x_1 - \frac{1}{2}x_2 = \frac{5}{6}$

14. $-\frac{2}{5}x_1 + \frac{2}{3}x_2 = \frac{1}{3}$

15. $1\frac{2}{3}x_1 + 3\frac{1}{8}x_2 = 5\frac{5}{24}$

16. $4x_1 + 0x_2 = 16$

17. $0x_1 - 5x_2 = 9$

18. $3x_1 + 4x_2 = 0$

19. $\frac{3}{4}x_1 - \frac{4}{5}x_2 = 0$

20. $7x_1 + 0x_2 = 0$

21. $0x_1 - \frac{64}{9}x_2 = 0$

22. $2.3x_1 + 3.4x_2 = 7.82$

23. Suppose the line labeled "sleeping" in the graph on p. 55 is given by the equation $x_1 + 40x_2 = 100$. How much insulation is required for each of the following temperatures?
(a) $-10°$  (b) $30°$  $^C$(c) $80°$  $^C$(d) $-80°$

24. Given $3x_1 - 4x_2 = 8$, find the value of the other variable when
(a) $x_1 = 0$  (b) $x_1 = -2$  (c) $x_2 = 3$  (d) $x_2 = -4$

25. Find four solutions to the equation $\frac{1}{2}x_1 + \frac{2}{3}x_2 = 20$.

\*26. Let P be a point and L a line in a plane. The **reflection** of P in L is the point $P'$ such that the line through P and $P'$ is perpendicular to L and such that P and $P'$ have the same distance from L. (Figure 15). (If P is on L we take $P' = P$.) Suppose the plane has a coordinate system and $P = (x_1, x_2)$. What are the coordinates of each of the following?
(a) The reflection of P in the 1-axis.
(b) The reflection of P in the 2-axis.
(c) The reflection in the 2-axis of the reflection of P in the 1-axis.
(d) The reflection in the 1-axis of the reflection of P in the 2-axis.
(e) The reflection of P in the line with equation $x_1 - x_2 = 0$.

$^C$27. At a meeting in Ames, Iowa, of the managers of PHE's Midwestern stores, the PHE directors want to show just how daily hamburger sales are related to profits. Each hamburger sold gives a profit of 15 cents. Hamburger profits are expected to contribute $105 toward daily overhead costs. Let $x_1$ be the daily sale of hamburgers and let $x_2$ be the hamburger net profit after paying overhead. Deduce the relation between $x_1$ and $x_2$ and prepare a graph showing the relation for the sales meeting.

Figure 15

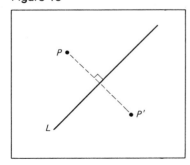

Solve the following systems of equations. That is, find the point each pair of lines has in common. Graph the lines.

28. $\begin{bmatrix} x_1 - 2x_2 = -1 \\ x_1 + x_2 = 2 \end{bmatrix}$

29. $\begin{bmatrix} 2x_1 + x_2 = 3 \\ x_1 - 3x_2 = -9 \end{bmatrix}$

30. $\begin{bmatrix} 3x_1 - 2x_2 = -8 \\ x_1 - x_2 = -3 \end{bmatrix}$

31. $\begin{bmatrix} 2x_1 - 3x_2 = 0 \\ -4x_1 + 5x_2 = 2 \end{bmatrix}$

*32. Why must we assume that not both a and b are zero in the general equation of a line?

## Section 2.2
## Systems of Two Linear
## Equations in Two Unknowns

We have already solved several systems of equations. For example, in Section 1 we solved the system

$$\begin{bmatrix} x_1 - x_2 = 1 \\ x_1 + x_2 = 5 \end{bmatrix} \qquad \textbf{1}$$

graphically (see Figure 13, page 61) and by substitution.

There are at least four other equally efficient methods of solution. Unfortunately, real problems often lead to systems with more than two variables and more than two equations. For these larger systems there are only two easy and efficient solution methods. The fastest technique for computers is called **Gaussian reduction** and will be described in Section 4. The fast method for hand calculation is only slightly different. It is called **Gauss-Jordan reduction** after the mathematician C. F. Gauss (1777–1855) and W. Jordan (1819–1904). In this section we will illustrate Gauss-Jordan reduction in the simplest case of a system with two equations and two variables. It is worth learning this technique now otherwise you will have difficulty when we apply it to larger systems.

We introduce this technique by considering the following system.

$$\begin{bmatrix} 3x_1 + 2x_2 = 6 \\ 4x_1 + 3x_2 = 12 \end{bmatrix} \qquad \textbf{2}$$

Do not expect to understand immediately the reasons for each of the steps involved in the following solution. These reasons will become clearer as you work through more examples. However, you should check that the arithmetic in each step is properly done.

Multiply the first equation by $\frac{4}{3}$: $(\frac{4}{3})(3x_1 + 2x_2 = 6)$ gives $(\frac{4}{3})(3x_1) + (\frac{4}{3})(2x_2) = (\frac{4}{3})6$, that is, $4x_1 + \frac{8}{3}x_2 = 8$. Now we have the system

$$\left(\tfrac{4}{3} \text{ equation 1}\right) \quad \begin{bmatrix} 4x_1 + \frac{8}{3}x_2 = 8 \\ 4x_1 + 3x_2 = 12 \end{bmatrix} \qquad \textbf{3}$$

Now subtract equation 1 of system **3** from equation 2: $(4x_1 + 3x_2) - (4x_1 + \frac{8}{3}x_2) = 12 - 8$, that is, $0x_1 + \frac{1}{3}x_2 = 4$. We now have

$$(\text{eqn. } 2 - \text{eqn. } 1) \quad \begin{bmatrix} 4x_1 + \frac{8}{3}x_2 = 8 \\ 0x_1 + \frac{1}{3}x_2 = 4 \end{bmatrix} \qquad \textbf{4}$$

Now multiply equation 2 of system **4** by 8:

$$(8 \text{ eqn. } 2) \quad \begin{bmatrix} 4x_1 + \frac{8}{3}x_2 = 8 \\ 0x_1 + \frac{8}{3}x_2 = 32 \end{bmatrix} \qquad \textbf{5}$$

Subtract equation 2 of system **5** from equation 1:

$$(\text{eqn. } 1 - \text{eqn. } 2) \quad \begin{bmatrix} 4x_1 + 0x_2 = -24 \\ 0x_1 + \frac{8}{3}x_2 = 32 \end{bmatrix} \qquad \textbf{6}$$

In system **6** multiply equation 1 by $\frac{1}{4}$ and equation 2 by $\frac{3}{8}$:

$$\begin{array}{l}\left(\tfrac{1}{4} \text{ eqn. } 1\right) \\ \left(\tfrac{3}{8} \text{ eqn. } 2\right)\end{array} \quad \begin{bmatrix} 1x_1 + 0x_2 = -6 \\ 0x_1 + 1x_2 = 12 \end{bmatrix} \qquad \textbf{7}$$

System **7** is the solution to system **2**: $x_1 = -6$ and $x_2 = 12$.

$$\begin{bmatrix} 3(-6) + 2(12) = 6 \\ 4(-6) + 3(12) = 12 \end{bmatrix} \begin{array}{l}\checkmark \\ \checkmark\end{array}$$

Thus, the two lines that are the graphs of the equations, $3x_1 + 2x_2 = 6$ and $4x_1 + 3x_2 = 12$ intersect at the point $(-6, 12)$ (Figure 16).

In solving this system, we first eliminated $x_1$ from equation 2 and then eliminated $x_2$ from equation 1. This resulted in the extremely simple equations of system **7**.

The manipulations carried out above to solve system **2** do not really change the symbols $x_1$, $x_2$, the plus signs, or the equals signs; they just change the numbers. So let us leave out the signs and symbols in system **2**. We are left with the **matrix** of system **2**:

$$\begin{bmatrix} 3 & 2 & 6 \\ 4 & 3 & 12 \end{bmatrix} \qquad \textbf{2'}$$

**Figure 16**

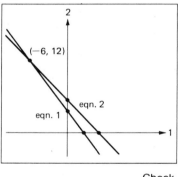

Check

A **matrix** is any rectangular (perhaps square) array of numbers. The plural of matrix is **matrices**. The English mathematician Arthur Cayley (1821–1895) is credited with the invention of matrices. The particular notation used in this text was introduced by C. E. Cullis in 1913.

In this example only, we have inserted arrows to indicate the order in which these matrices were obtained: left to right, moving down.

In this setting, the references above to equation 1 and 2 of system **2** become references to *rows* **1** and **2** of matrix **2'**. The steps carried out to solve system **2** can now be described in terms of manipulations with rows as follows:

$$\begin{bmatrix} 3 & 2 & 6 \\ 4 & 3 & 12 \end{bmatrix} \xrightarrow{\frac{4}{3}R_1} \begin{bmatrix} 4 & \frac{8}{3} & 8 \\ 4 & 3 & 12 \end{bmatrix} \rightarrow$$

$$\begin{matrix} \\ R_2 - R_1 \end{matrix} \begin{bmatrix} 4 & \frac{8}{3} & 8 \\ 0 & \frac{1}{3} & 4 \end{bmatrix} \xrightarrow{8R_2} \begin{bmatrix} 4 & \frac{8}{3} & 8 \\ 0 & \frac{8}{3} & 32 \end{bmatrix} \rightarrow$$

$$\begin{matrix} R_1 - R_2 \\ \\ \end{matrix} \begin{bmatrix} 4 & 0 & -24 \\ 0 & \frac{8}{3} & 32 \end{bmatrix} \xrightarrow[\frac{3}{8}R_2]{\frac{1}{4}R_1} \begin{bmatrix} 1 & 0 & -6 \\ 0 & 1 & 12 \end{bmatrix} \qquad \mathbf{3'}$$

In this display each time $R_1$ or $R_2$ occurs it refers to the corresponding row of the *preceding* matrix. The result of a row calculation is entered in the *following* matrix in the row next to where the expression describing the calculation is written. If no expression is written in front of a row of a matrix, then the corresponding row of the preceding matrix is simply copied. Thus, the second matrix above is obtained from the first as follows. We see $\frac{4}{3}R_1$, so we take $R_1$ of the preceding matrix, 3   2   6, and multiply each number in it by $\frac{4}{3}$: $(\frac{4}{3})3$, $(\frac{4}{3})2$, $(\frac{4}{3})6$, giving 4   $\frac{8}{3}$   8. Since the expression $\frac{4}{3}R_1$ is next to row one of the following matrix, this is where we enter our 4   $\frac{8}{3}$   8. The second row of the following matrix has no expression in front of it, so we simply copy the corresponding row (the second row) of the preceding matrix, 4   3   12. Going on we read $R_2 - R_1$, so we subtract $R_1$ of the preceding matrix, 4   $\frac{8}{3}$   8, from $R_2$ of the preceding matrix, 4   3   12, to obtain:

$$\begin{array}{rccc} R_2: & 4 & 3 & 12 \\ R_1: & 4 & \frac{8}{3} & 8 \\ \hline R_2 - R_1: & 0 & \frac{1}{3} & 4 \end{array}$$

The result, 0   $\frac{1}{3}$   4, is entered next to the expression $R_2 - R_1$, that is, in the second row of the following matrix. The first row is copied. Now continue reading through display **3'** to the end.

We can compress the first two steps of the above procedure into one: replace row two by row two minus $\frac{4}{3}$ times row one. This is displayed as follows:

$$\begin{bmatrix} 3 & 2 & 6 \\ 4 & 3 & 12 \end{bmatrix} R_2 - \frac{4}{3}R_1 \begin{bmatrix} 3 & 2 & 6 \\ 0 & \frac{1}{3} & 4 \end{bmatrix}$$

Note that this step changes only $R_2$. The row $R_1$ stays the same. We next "eliminate" the $\frac{1}{3}$; that is, we change it to zero, by the following step:

$$R_1: \quad 3 \quad 2 \quad 6$$
$$6R_2: \quad 0 \quad 2 \quad 24$$
$$R_1 - 6R_2: \quad 3 \quad 0 - 18$$

$$\begin{bmatrix} 3 & 2 & 6 \\ 0 & \frac{1}{3} & 4 \end{bmatrix} \begin{matrix} R_1 - 6R_2 \\ \ \end{matrix} \begin{bmatrix} 3 & 0 & -18 \\ 0 & \frac{1}{3} & 4 \end{bmatrix}$$

Note that this step changes only one row, $R_1$, and that $R_2$, the row used to make this change, is not itself changed at all.

How did we arrive at the $-\frac{4}{3}$ in the expression $R_2 - \frac{4}{3}R_1$? We wanted to multiply $R_1$ by some number x and add it to $R_2$ so as to make the 4 become zero. Thus, we needed to find a number x such that $3x + 4 = 0$. Hence, $x = -\frac{4}{3}$. In the case of the $-6$ in the expression $R_1 - 6R_2$, we wanted to multiply $R_2$ by some number x and add it to $R_1$ so as to make the 2 become zero. Thus, we needed the number x to be such that $(\frac{1}{3})x + 2 = 0$. Hence $x = -6$. We use the simpler but equivalent expression $R_1 - 6R_2$ in place of $R_1 + (-6)R_2$.

See Appendix A, Section 11.

Now to complete our work we write

$$\begin{bmatrix} 3 & 0 & -18 \\ 0 & \frac{1}{3} & 4 \end{bmatrix} \begin{matrix} \frac{1}{3}R_1 \\ 3R_2 \end{matrix} \begin{bmatrix} 1 & 0 & -6 \\ 0 & 1 & 12 \end{bmatrix}$$

This gives the same answer as in system **7** and system **3'**, but in three steps instead of five.

Here is another example.

Problem 1

What is the point of intersection of the lines $2x_1 + 3x_2 = 4$ and $-3x_1 + x_2 = 3$?

Solution

We must solve the system $\begin{bmatrix} 2x_1 + 3x_2 = 4 \\ -3x_1 + \ x_2 = 3 \end{bmatrix}$, which we do in matrix notation as follows.

$$\begin{bmatrix} 2 & 3 & 4 \\ -3 & 1 & 3 \end{bmatrix} \begin{matrix} R_2 + \frac{3}{2}R_1 \\ \ \end{matrix} \begin{bmatrix} 2 & 3 & 4 \\ 0 & \frac{11}{2} & 9 \end{bmatrix}$$

$$R_1 - \frac{6}{11}R_2 \begin{bmatrix} 2 & 0 & -\frac{10}{11} \\ 0 & \frac{11}{2} & 9 \end{bmatrix} \begin{matrix} \frac{1}{2}R_1 \\ \frac{2}{11}R_2 \end{matrix} \begin{bmatrix} 1 & 0 & -\frac{5}{11} \\ 0 & 1 & \frac{18}{11} \end{bmatrix}$$

Thus, we conclude that $x_1 = -\frac{5}{11}, x_2 = \frac{18}{11}$. The point is $(-\frac{5}{11}, \frac{8}{11})$.

Check

$$\begin{bmatrix} 2\left(-\frac{5}{11}\right) + 3\left(\frac{18}{11}\right) = \frac{44}{11} = 4 \ \checkmark \\ -3\left(-\frac{5}{11}\right) + \ \frac{18}{11} \ = \frac{33}{11} = 3 \ \checkmark \end{bmatrix}$$

The idea behind each of the solutions above is the same: we write down the matrix of the system to be solved and we work with the rows to "reduce" the matrix to the form

$$\begin{bmatrix} 1 & 0 & a \\ 0 & 1 & b \end{bmatrix}$$  **8**

The solution of the system is just $x_1 = a$ and $x_2 = b$. In working with the rows we are allowed to perform two types of operations: (1) add a multiple of one row to another row (this includes the possibility of adding a negative multiple of one row to another); or (2) multiply a row by a nonzero number (this includes the possibility of multiplying a row by the reciprocal of a nonzero number, that is, dividing a row by a nonzero number.)

There are many ways to reduce a matrix to the form of system **8**, but it can be shown that for a given problem all these ways lead to the same numbers $a$ and $b$ in system **8**. Here, for example, is another way to reduce the matrix of the previous problem:

$$\begin{bmatrix} 2 & 3 & 4 \\ -3 & 1 & 3 \end{bmatrix} \begin{matrix} \frac{1}{2}R_1 \\ \frac{1}{3}R_2 \end{matrix} \begin{bmatrix} 1 & \frac{3}{2} & 2 \\ -1 & \frac{1}{3} & 1 \end{bmatrix} R_2 + R_1 \begin{bmatrix} 1 & \frac{3}{2} & 2 \\ 0 & \frac{11}{6} & 3 \end{bmatrix}$$

$$\frac{6}{11}R_2 \begin{bmatrix} 1 & \frac{3}{2} & 2 \\ 0 & 1 & \frac{18}{11} \end{bmatrix} R_1 - \frac{3}{2}R_2 \begin{bmatrix} 1 & 0 & -\frac{5}{11} \\ 0 & 1 & \frac{18}{11} \end{bmatrix}$$

The final matrix is the same as before.

One other type of row operation is sometimes of use: switching the rows. This is certainly an allowable operation when working with a system of equations, since it amounts to writing down the equations in a different order. This operation is not essential in solving a system, but it can save steps. Here is an example.

*See Supplementary Exercise 62 for example.*

**Problem 2** Find the intersection point of the lines $2x_2 = -6$ and $3x_1 + x_2 = 0$.

**Solution**

$$\begin{bmatrix} 0 & 2 & -6 \\ 3 & 1 & 0 \end{bmatrix} \begin{matrix} R_2 \\ R_1 \end{matrix} \begin{bmatrix} 3 & 1 & 0 \\ 0 & 2 & -6 \end{bmatrix} R_1 - \frac{1}{2}R_2 \begin{bmatrix} 3 & 0 & 3 \\ 0 & 2 & -6 \end{bmatrix}$$

$$\frac{1}{3}R_1 \begin{bmatrix} 1 & 0 & 1 \\ 0 & 1 & -3 \end{bmatrix}$$
$$\frac{1}{2}R_2$$

**Answer** $(1, -3)$

Check: $2x_2 = 2(-3) = -6$ ✓ and
$3x_1 + x_2 = 3(1) - 3 = 0$ ✓

Not all problems of this kind result in a unique solution. Some problems have no solution at all; others have infinitely many solutions. The method developed above also covers these cases, as we see in the following examples.

**Problem 3**

Find the point of intersection of the lines $-2x_1 + x_2 = 2$ and $6x_1 - 3x_2 = 4$.

**Solution**

$$\begin{bmatrix} -2 & 1 & 2 \\ 6 & -3 & 4 \end{bmatrix} R_2 + 3R_1 \begin{bmatrix} -2 & 1 & 2 \\ 0 & 0 & 10 \end{bmatrix}$$

$$-\tfrac{1}{2}R_1 \begin{bmatrix} 1 & -\tfrac{1}{2} & -1 \\ 0 & 0 & 10 \end{bmatrix}$$

One step is really all you need to perform in order to tell that this system has no solution.

The second row of the final matrix corresponds to the equation $0x_1 + 0x_2 = 10$, which obviously has no solution. The original problem has no solution either. This means that lines $-2x_1 + x_2 = 2$ and $6x_1 - 3x_2 = 4$ have no intersection and are thus parallel. (You should graph these lines to see this.)

**Problem 4**

Find the point of intersection of the lines $4x_1 - 6x_2 = 8$ and $-6x_1 + 9x_2 = -12$.

**Solution**

$$\begin{bmatrix} 4 & -6 & 8 \\ -6 & 9 & -12 \end{bmatrix} R_2 + \tfrac{3}{2}R_1 \begin{bmatrix} 4 & -6 & 8 \\ 0 & 0 & 0 \end{bmatrix} \tfrac{1}{4}R_1 \begin{bmatrix} 1 & -\tfrac{3}{2} & 2 \\ 0 & 0 & 0 \end{bmatrix}$$

Whenever a row of zeros occurs, it can be ignored.

The second row of the last matrix corresponds to the equation $0x_1 + 0x_2 = 0$, which holds for all numbers $x_1$ and $x_2$. Unlike the situation in Problem 3, this poses no difficulty. It indicates that the original system has many solutions, all of which are given by the equation corresponding to the other row—in this case, $x_1 - \tfrac{3}{2}x_2 = 2$. To facilitate finding particular solutions, we solve this equation for $x_1$ in terms of $x_2$: $x_1 = 2 + \tfrac{3}{2}x_2$. If, say, $x_2 = 0$, we obtain the point $(2,0)$; if $x_2 = 2$, we obtain $(5,2)$; if $x_2 = -\tfrac{4}{3}$, we obtain $(0, -\tfrac{4}{3})$. Each of these points, and an infinite number of other points, are solutions of the system. Since the lines $4x_1 - 6x_2 = 8$ and $-6x_1 + 9x_2 = -12$ have more than one point in common, they are in fact *identical*, as you can easily see by drawing their graphs. We indicate the solution to the problem by the formula

$$\left(2 + \tfrac{3}{2}x_2, \ x_2\right)$$

where the presence of the variable $x_2$ indicates that we are free to assign it any value we wish to obtain a particular solution. This answer does, in fact, check:

$$4\left(2 + \tfrac{3}{2}x_2\right) - 6x_2 = 8 + 6x_2 - 6x_2$$

$$= 8 \ \checkmark$$

$$-6\left(2 + \tfrac{3}{2}x_2\right) + 9x_2 = -12 - 9x_2 + 9x_2$$

$$= -12 \ \checkmark$$

It is of course possible to rewrite the equation $x_1 - \frac{3}{2}x_2 = 2$ as $-\frac{3}{2}x_2 = 2 - x_1$ or $x_2 = \frac{2}{3}x_1 - \frac{4}{3}$. Doing this results in writing the solutions as all points of the form $(x_1, \frac{2}{3}x_1 - \frac{4}{3})$. Since this solution turns out to be equivalent to the other one, we do not actually need to give the answer in this form as well.

We conclude by presenting our general method of solution in flow chart form. First we introduce some new notation. The **position** or **address** of an entry in a matrix is an ordered pair giving first the row and second the column of the entry. For example, in the matrix $\begin{bmatrix} 1 & 2 & 3 \\ 4 & 5 & 6 \end{bmatrix}$ the entry 2 is in position $(1, 2)$ and the entry at address $(2, 1)$ is 4. In the following chart we have eliminated the phrase "the entry in position" before each ordered pair. For instance, the box "Is $(1, 1)$ zero?" is an abbreviation for

We also sometimes express this by calling 2 the $(1, 2)$-entry and 4 the $(2, 1)$-entry.

**To Solve Any System
of Two Linear Equations
In Two Variables**

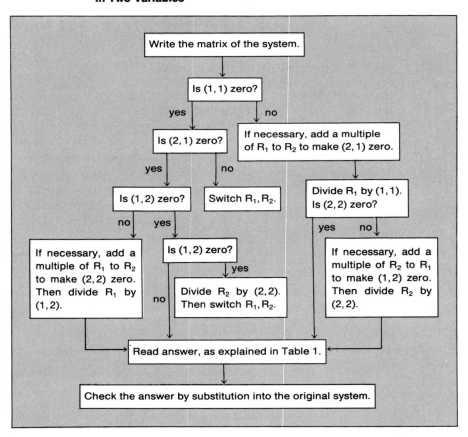

"Is the entry in position $(1, 1)$ zero?" The word "divide" is used in four places in the chart. In actual practice we multiply by the reciprocal of the number in question. This has the same effect. Table 1 summarizes the various forms that the reduced matrix may take.

Table 1
Solving Systems:
How to Read the Answer

| Reduced matrix | Answer |
|---|---|
| $\begin{bmatrix} 1 & 0 & a \\ 0 & 1 & b \end{bmatrix}$ | $(a, b)$ |
| $\begin{bmatrix} 1 & c & a \\ 0 & 0 & b \end{bmatrix}$ where $b \neq 0$ | no solution |
| $\begin{bmatrix} 1 & c & a \\ 0 & 0 & 0 \end{bmatrix}$ | $(a - cx_2, x_2)$, where $x_2$ may be any number |
| $\begin{bmatrix} 0 & 1 & a \\ 0 & 0 & b \end{bmatrix}$ where $b \neq 0$ | no solution |
| $\begin{bmatrix} 0 & 1 & a \\ 0 & 0 & 0 \end{bmatrix}$ | $(x_1, a)$, where $x_1$ may be any number |
| $\begin{bmatrix} 0 & 0 & a \\ 0 & 0 & b \end{bmatrix}$ where $a \neq 0$ or $b \neq 0$ | no solution |
| $\begin{bmatrix} 0 & 0 & 0 \\ 0 & 0 & 0 \end{bmatrix}$ | $(x_1, x_2)$, where $x_1$ and $x_2$ may be any numbers |

The last two cases in this table never occur in a problem about intersecting lines, although they can occur in other contexts.

In the remainder of this section we present some production and supply problems at Appalachian Creations that Janet solved by these methods.

We then go on to some problems involving a larger number of producers, suppliers, or receivers, which seem similar to the previous problems but that we cannot solve at the moment. We will show how to solve these problems and all problems of the same general type in Section 3.

Problem 5

The Appalachian Creations outlet in Bangor, Maine, has ordered 29 jackets and 52 pairs of down booties. In one day of operation, the Springfield, Massachusetts, factory can make 3 jackets and 6 pairs of booties and the Waterbury, Connecticut, factory can make 4 jackets and 5 pairs of booties. How many days should AC operate the two factories to exactly fill the order from Bangor?

Solution

Let $x_1$ be the number of days AC operates the Springfield factory. In this time this factory will make $3x_1$ jackets and $6x_1$ pairs of booties. Let $x_2$ be the number of days AC operates the Waterbury factory. In this time this factory will make $4x_2$ jackets and $5x_2$ pairs of booties. The total number of jackets made will then be $3x_1 + 4x_2$, and the total number of pairs of booties will be $6x_1 + 5x_2$. The order from Bangor leads, then, to the following system of two linear equations in two unknowns.

$$\begin{bmatrix} 3x_1 + 4x_2 = 29 \\ 6x_1 + 5x_2 = 52 \end{bmatrix}$$

**9**

We solve this system by Gauss-Jordan reduction:

$$\begin{bmatrix} 3 & 4 & 29 \\ 6 & 5 & 52 \end{bmatrix} \begin{array}{c} \\ R_2 - 2R_1 \end{array} \begin{bmatrix} 3 & 4 & 29 \\ 0 & -3 & -6 \end{bmatrix} \begin{array}{c} R_1 + \frac{4}{3}R_2 \\ \\ \end{array} \begin{bmatrix} 3 & 0 & 21 \\ 0 & -3 & -6 \end{bmatrix}$$

$$\begin{array}{c} \frac{1}{3}R_1 \\ -\frac{1}{3}R_2 \end{array} \begin{bmatrix} 1 & 0 & 7 \\ 0 & 1 & 2 \end{bmatrix}$$

Answer   (7,2) So Janet tells the factory managers to operate the Springfield factory for 7 days and the Waterbury factory for 2 days.

Check: $\begin{bmatrix} 3 \cdot 7 + 4 \cdot 2 = 29 \\ 6 \cdot 7 + 5 \cdot 2 = 52 \end{bmatrix}$ ✓ ✓

**Problem 6**   The Springfield factory can make 9 cups and 3 canteens per hour while the Danbury, Connecticut, factory can make 12 cups and 4 canteens per hour. AC regularly receives an order from Falmouth, Massachusetts, for 108 cups and 36 canteens, which it has been filling by operating the Springfield factory 8 hours and the Danbury factory for 3. But AC is worried about labor problems at both factories. In case of strikes, can they find other ways to fill this order exactly, either by cutting down on the Springfield operation or by cutting down on the Danbury operation?

**Solution**   Let $x_1$ be the number of hours AC operates the Springfield plant, and let $x_2$ be the number of hours AC operates the Danbury plant. As in the previous problem, AC is led to a system:

$$\begin{bmatrix} 9x_1 + 12x_2 = 108 \\ 3x_1 + 4x_2 = 36 \end{bmatrix} \qquad \textbf{10}$$

We solve the system:

$$\begin{bmatrix} 9 & 12 & 108 \\ 3 & 4 & 36 \end{bmatrix} \begin{array}{c} \\ R_2 - \frac{1}{3}R_1 \end{array} \begin{bmatrix} 9 & 12 & 108 \\ 0 & 0 & 0 \end{bmatrix} \begin{array}{c} \frac{1}{9}R_1 \\ \\ \end{array} \begin{bmatrix} 1 & \frac{4}{3} & 12 \\ 0 & 0 & 0 \end{bmatrix}$$

**Answer**   $(12 - \frac{4}{3}x_2, x_2)$, where $x_2$ may be any number. Note that if $x_2 = 3$ this gives the solution (8,3), which has been used before. Now if AC wanted to eliminate the Danbury operation altogether, they would make $x_2 = 0$ to obtain the solution (12,0). If AC wanted to eliminate the Springfield operation, they would make $12 - \frac{4}{3}x_2 = 0$ (that is, $12 = \frac{4}{3}x_2$, $x_2 = (\frac{3}{4})12 = 9$) and obtain the solution (0,9). If $x_2$ exceeded 9, the Danbury factory would be overproducing; besides, $x_1$ would become negative, which is meaningless. Similarly, $x_1$ cannot exceed 12. So $x_2$ may vary from zero to 9 and $x_1$ may vary from zero to 12, in accordance with the formula

$$x_1 = 12 - \frac{4}{3}x_2 \qquad \textbf{11}$$

Janet's answer to the problem posed by management might take the form of Tables 2 and 3.

| Table 2 Operation Schedules (time at Danbury reduced from the usual 3 hours) | Danbury | 2 hr. | 1 hr. | closed |
| | Springfield | 9 hr. 20 min. | 10 hr. 40 min. | 12 hr. |

| Table 3 Operating Schedules (time at Springfield reduced from the usual 8 hours) | Springfield | 7 hr. | 6 hr. | 5 hr. |
| | Danbury | 3 hr. 45 min. | 4 hr. 30 min. | 5 hr. 15 min. |
| | Springfield | 4 hr. | 3 hr. | 2 hr. |
| | Danbury | 6 hr. | 6 hr. 45 min. | 7 hr. 30 min. |
| | Springfield | 1 hr. | closed | |
| | Danbury | 8 hr. 15 min. | 9hr. | |

While Table 3 could have been calculated from formula **11**, Janet first rewrote this formula as follows:

$$\tfrac{4}{3}x_2 = 12 - x_1, x_2 = \left(\tfrac{3}{4}\right)(12 - x_1) = 9 - \tfrac{3}{4}x_1, \text{ that is,}$$

$$x_2 = 9 - \tfrac{3}{4}x_1 \qquad\qquad \textbf{12}$$

This formula made the preparation of Table 3 easier.

**Problem 7**

The labor problems in the cup and canteen divisions of Springfield and Danbury have been cleared up, but Falmouth has changed its regular order to 90 cups and 40 canteens. How does AC fill the order exactly?

**Solution**

As in Problem 6, Janet is led to the system

$$\begin{bmatrix} 9x_1 + 12x_2 = 90 \\ 3x_1 + 4x_2 = 40 \end{bmatrix} \qquad\qquad \textbf{13}$$

She applies Gauss-Jordan reduction:

$$\begin{bmatrix} 9 & 12 & 90 \\ 3 & 4 & 40 \end{bmatrix} R_2 - \tfrac{1}{3}R_1 \begin{bmatrix} 9 & 12 & 90 \\ 0 & 0 & 10 \end{bmatrix} \tfrac{1}{9}R_1 \begin{bmatrix} 1 & \tfrac{4}{3} & 10 \\ 0 & 0 & 10 \end{bmatrix}$$

**Answer**

No solution. Janet must tell management that the order cannot be filled exactly with existing facilities; they must plan for a surplus of either cups or canteens. We shall have more to say on problems of this type in later chapters.

See Supplementary Exercise 30, p. 385.

**Problem 8**

(See Problem 5.) Bangor has reduced its order to 26 jackets and 28 pairs of booties. Can this be filled exactly?

**Solution**

We seek a solution for the system

$$\begin{bmatrix} 3x_1 + 4x_2 = 26 \\ 6x_1 + 5x_2 = 28 \end{bmatrix} \qquad\qquad \textbf{14}$$

We reduce the matrix:

$$\begin{bmatrix} 3 & 4 & 26 \\ 6 & 5 & 28 \end{bmatrix} R_2 - 2R_1 \begin{bmatrix} 3 & 4 & 26 \\ 0 & -3 & -24 \end{bmatrix}$$

$$R_1 + \tfrac{4}{3}R_2 \begin{bmatrix} 3 & 0 & -6 \\ 0 & -3 & -24 \end{bmatrix} \begin{matrix} \tfrac{1}{3}R_1 \\ -\tfrac{1}{3}R_2 \end{matrix} \begin{bmatrix} 1 & 0 & -2 \\ 0 & 1 & 8 \end{bmatrix}$$

Answer

$(-2, 8)$ This is the only answer for system **14**, but it makes no sense for us, since AC cannot operate the Springfield factory for $-2$ days! Thus, Janet must announce that the order cannot be filled exactly.

Problem 9

(See Problem 5.) There is some material left over from the jacket and booties operations, which the Springfield and Waterbury factories make into mittens and pillows. In one day of operation, Springfield makes 2 pairs of mittens and 1 pillow, and Waterbury makes 3 pairs of mittens and 2 pillows. Bangor orders, in addition to its usual order for jackets and booties, 20 pairs of mittens and 11 pillows. How does AC fill this order exactly?

Solution

Using the notation of Problem 5, AC will produce $2x_1 + 3x_2$ pairs of mittens and $x_1 + 2x_2$ pillows. Thus, we are asked to solve the system

$$\begin{bmatrix} 3x_1 + 4x_2 = 29 \\ 6x_1 + 5x_2 = 52 \\ 2x_1 + 3x_2 = 20 \\ x_1 + 2x_2 = 11 \end{bmatrix} \qquad \textbf{15}$$

We have not yet developed a systematic method for solving such a large system; we will do so in the next section. However, it happens that we can manage to solve system **15** now. Any solution of this system must, in particular, satisfy the first two equations. But these two equations comprise system **9**, which, as we learned in the solution to Problem 5, has only one solution: $(7, 2)$. Thus, the only possible solution of system **15** is $(7, 2)$. This actually is a solution, since this answer checks in the last two equations as well: $2 \cdot 7 + 3 \cdot 2 = 20 \checkmark$ and $7 + 2 \cdot 2 = 11 \checkmark$. Thus, we repeat our instruction of Problem 5: run Springfield for 7 days and Waterbury for 2.

Problem 10

In an attempt to get a solution to Problem 7, management has opened a new factory in Mystic, which makes 6 cups and 4 canteens per hour. Can AC now fill the order exactly?

Solution

As before, we let $x_1$ be the number of hours AC operates the Springfield plant and $x_2$ be the number of hours AC operates the Danbury plant. Also, let $x_3$ be the number of hours AC operates the Mystic factory. Then total cup production is $9x_1 + 12x_2 + 6x_3$ and total canteen production is $3x_1 + 4x_2 + 4x_3$. Thus, we are to solve the system

$$\begin{bmatrix} 9x_1 + 12x_2 + 6x_3 = 90 \\ 3x_1 + 4x_2 + 4x_3 = 40 \end{bmatrix} \qquad \textbf{16}$$

Try $x_1 = 4, x_2 = 2, x_3 = 5$.

Again, we must wait until the next section for a method of solving such a system, although we might be able to guess a solution.

One final remark: Gauss-Jordan reduction is simply a concise matrix form of the substitution technique, which we presented in Section 2.1. For example, here is system **2** solved again by substitution and by Gauss-Jordan reduction:

$$\begin{bmatrix} 3x_1 + 2x_2 = 6 \\ 4x_1 + 3x_2 = 12 \end{bmatrix}$$

$$\underline{\textit{Substitution}} \qquad\qquad\qquad \textit{Gauss-Jordan}$$

$$3x_1 + 2x_2 = 6 \qquad\qquad\qquad \begin{bmatrix} 3 & 2 & 6 \\ 4 & 3 & 12 \end{bmatrix}$$

$$3x_1 = 6 - 2x_2$$
$$x_1 = 2 - \tfrac{2}{3}x_2$$

$$4(2 - \tfrac{2}{3}x_2) + 3x_2 = 12 \qquad\qquad R_2 - \tfrac{4}{3}R_1 \begin{bmatrix} 3 & 2 & 6 \\ 0 & \tfrac{1}{3} & 4 \end{bmatrix}$$

$$8 - \tfrac{8}{3}x_2 + 3x_2 = 12$$
$$\tfrac{1}{3}x_2 = 4 \qquad\qquad \text{same equation}$$

$$x_2 = 12 \qquad\qquad R_1 - 6R_2 \begin{bmatrix} 3 & 0 & -18 \\ 0 & \tfrac{1}{3} & 4 \end{bmatrix}$$
$$x_1 = 2 - \tfrac{2}{3}(12)$$
$$x_1 = 2 - 8 \qquad\quad \text{same equation}$$
$$x_1 = -6$$

$$\tfrac{1}{3}R_1 \begin{bmatrix} 1 & 0 & -6 \\ 0 & 1 & 12 \end{bmatrix}$$
$$3R_2$$

Answer    $(-6, 12)$.

**Exercises 2.2**   In the following 20 exercises, find the coordinates of the points of intersection of the two lines with the given equations.
$^c$1. $x_1 + 2x_2 = 3$ and $3x_1 + 8x_2 = 13$
2. $3x_1 - x_2 = -11$ and $x_1 + 4x_2 = 18$

C3. $0x_1 + 3x_2 = 16$ and $x_1 - 6x_2 = 0$

4. $3x_1 + 2x_2 = 4$ and $x_1 + 2x_2 = 3$

C5. $4x_1 - x_2 = 2$ and $-20x_1 + 5x_2 = -1$

6. $2x_1 - x_2 = 5$ and $-3x_1 + 4x_2 = 7$

C7. $-2x_1 + x_2 = 3$ and $4x_1 - 2x_2 = -6$

8. $2x_1 + x_2 = 4$ and $3x_1 - 2x_2 = -1$

9. $-\frac{1}{2}x_1 + \frac{1}{3}x_2 = 1$ and $x_1 - \frac{1}{4}x_2 = 2$

10. $\frac{2}{3}x_1 + \frac{3}{5}x_2 = 3$ and $\frac{1}{3}x_1 - \frac{1}{2}x_2 = -2$

11. $-3x_1 + 4x_2 = 2$ and $-2x_1 + 5x_2 = 1$

12. $x_1 + 2x_2 = 4$ and $-2x_1 - 4x_2 = 7$

13. $-\frac{2}{3}x_1 + \frac{3}{2}x_2 = -1$ and $4x_1 - 9x_2 = 8$

14. $x_1 + 2x_2 = 4$ and $-2x_1 - 4x_2 = 8$

15. $\frac{1}{3}x_1 - \frac{1}{4}x_2 = \frac{1}{2}$ and $\frac{2}{3}x_1 + \frac{3}{4}x_2 = -\frac{3}{5}$

16. $\frac{1}{3}x_1 + \frac{1}{2}x_2 = 5$ and $\frac{2}{5}x_1 + \frac{3}{5}x_2 = 6$

17. $x_1 + 0x_2 = 0$ and $3x_1 + 0x_2 = 0$

18. $\frac{3}{7}x_1 - \frac{15}{7}x_2 = 1$ and $-2x_1 + 10x_2 = -14$

19. $4x_1 + 0x_2 = 6$ and $0x_1 - 3x_2 = -\frac{9}{2}$

20. $\frac{9}{5}x_1 - 9x_2 = \frac{24}{5}$ and $-x_1 + 5x_2 = -\frac{7}{3}$

See Exercise 27, p. 63 and, if necessary, its solution.

**Figure 17**

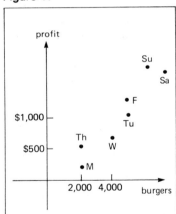

C21. Some of the really big PHE stores represented at the Ames conference—for instance, the downtown Minneapolis and Chicago stores—have a relation between the daily burger sale $x_1$ and net daily burger profit $x_2$ that is different from the smaller stores. At a private meeting with PHE board members, the manager of store 894 in the Chicago Loop, one of the most successful stores in the chain, asked that his store's figures (see Figure 17) be compared with the presentation given at the conference. He had checked his daily burger sales and profit for several days. The resulting data were plotted, and, while they did not lie on a straight line, a statistical technique called the **method of least squares** yielded the line of best fit. This line was $x_1 - 3x_2 = 1,500$. Present his figures, and make the comparison.

C22. Given the production data of Problem 5, how does AC fill each of the following orders exactly?

(a) Kansas City wants 11 jackets and 16 pairs of booties.

(b) Eureka, California, wants 12 jackets and 15 pairs of booties.

(c) Elmont, New York, wants 18 jackets and 2 dozen pairs of booties.

(d) Gerster, Missouri, wants 1 jacket, no booties.

23. The Williams Motor Company, with plants at Dearborn and Oshkosh, produces two models of its car: the Civet and the Wildebeest. In one week the Dearborn plant can produce 4,200 Civets and 3,400 Wildebeests, while Oshkosh can make 2,100 Civets and 1,700 Wildebeests. We have a production goal of 16,800 Civets and 13,600 Wildebeests. There is a possibility of a strike at either plant. Prepare a table of possible production schedules for each plant, assuming that the struck plant will operate a whole number of weeks, if it operates at all.

[c]24. AC has been asked to make up packets of freeze-dried food for the American expedition to Sagarmatha. Each packet must contain exactly 86 grams of protein, 88 grams of fats, and 90 grams of carbohydrates. AC has a supply of three types of freeze-dried food, in 12-gram packets, having the following nutritional composition (in grams per package):

| Type | Protein | Fats | Carb. | Other |
|------|---------|------|-------|-------|
| 1    | 3       | 2    | 3     | 4     |
| 2    | 4       | 1    | 3     | 4     |
| 3    | 2       | 5    | 3     | 2     |

Write the system that must be solved in order to determine how many packets of each type should go into each expedition packet. (This system will be solved in the last example problem of Section 2.3.)

25. PHE is considering an ad campaign for selected stores in the South, West, and East based on the slogan, "Look what you can buy for $____!" They want to offer various combinations of items for a fixed total price. The possible combinations must be the same in every region but the total price will vary, because the prices per item vary from region to region. The items they want to push, with prices shown by region are:

| | Hamburger | Superburger | Fishfeast | Root beer |
|-------|-----------|-------------|-----------|-----------|
| South | $0.30     | $0.40       | $1.00     | $0.25     |
| West  | 0.40      | 0.60        | 1.40      | 0.30      |
| East  | 0.50      | 0.70        | 1.70      | 0.35      |

The total prices they have in mind, that is, the prices to be used in the slogan, are: South $3.50; West, $4.80; East, $5.70. How many different combinations can they offer? Just introduce the notation and set up this problem as a system. You will be asked to solve this problem in Exercise 38 in the next section.

## Section 2.3
## Gauss-Jordan Reduction

In the previous section we learned how to solve any system of two linear equations in two variables, but we saw that we are going to need to solve some systems in which there are more than two equations and/or more than two variables. In this section we extend the method of Gauss-Jordan reduction to larger systems of equations.

We call an equation such as $3x_1 - 4x_2 = 5$ a linear equation because its graph is a straight line. The equations to be studied here, some of which we met in the last section, are of the same type as this, but they may contain more than two variables. We shall also call these new equations linear equations, although we will not show how to graph them. For example, we say that the equation $-2x_1 + \frac{2}{3}x_2 - 3x_3 = 7$ is a linear equation in three vari-

We will say a little bit about the geometric interpretation of the three-variable case in Section 2.5.

ables, and that

$$x_1 - 2x_2 + \tfrac{3}{4}x_3 + 5x_4 + x_5 = 4$$

is a linear equation in five variables.

Consider now the large systems encountered in Section 2.2. System **15** in that section is a system of four linear equations in two variables; system **16** is a system of two linear equations in three variables. The matrices of these systems are, respectively,

$$\begin{bmatrix} 3 & 4 & 29 \\ 6 & 5 & 52 \\ 2 & 3 & 20 \\ 1 & 2 & 11 \end{bmatrix} \qquad \mathbf{1}$$

and

$$\begin{bmatrix} 9 & 12 & 6 & 90 \\ 3 & 4 & 4 & 40 \end{bmatrix} \qquad \mathbf{2}$$

These matrices are of different sizes. We describe the **size** of a matrix by giving first its number of rows and second its number of columns. A matrix with m rows and n columns is said to be an m×n matrix (read "m by n matrix"). Matrices **1** and **2** are of size 4×3 and 2×4, respectively. The number of rows equals the number of equations in the system. The number of columns is *one more than* the number of unknowns in the system, because the last column is used for the numbers on the right-hand side of the equations.

Let us apply the techniques of the previous section to system **15** of that section. We are going to manipulate the rows of matrix **1** above according to the following rules.

(1) We may add (or subtract) a multiple of one row to (or from) another.
(2) We may multiply (or divide) a row by a nonzero number.
(3) We may switch any two rows.

Remember each R refers to a row in the matrix to its *left*.

Consider the following manipulations of matrix **1**:

$$\begin{bmatrix} 3 & 4 & 29 \\ 6 & 5 & 52 \\ 2 & 3 & 20 \\ 1 & 2 & 11 \end{bmatrix} \begin{matrix} \tfrac{1}{3}R_1 \\ R_2 - 2R_1 \\ R_3 - \tfrac{2}{3}R_1 \\ R_4 - \tfrac{1}{3}R_1 \end{matrix} \begin{bmatrix} 1 & \tfrac{4}{3} & \tfrac{29}{3} \\ 0 & -3 & -6 \\ 0 & \tfrac{1}{3} & \tfrac{2}{3} \\ 0 & \tfrac{2}{3} & \tfrac{4}{3} \end{bmatrix} \begin{matrix} R_1 + \tfrac{4}{9}R_2 \\ -\tfrac{1}{3}R_2 \\ R_3 + \tfrac{1}{9}R_2 \\ R_4 + \tfrac{2}{9}R_2 \end{matrix} \begin{bmatrix} 1 & 0 & 7 \\ 0 & 1 & 2 \\ 0 & 0 & 0 \\ 0 & 0 & 0 \end{bmatrix} \qquad \mathbf{3}$$

The final matrix of sequence **3** represents the system

$$\begin{bmatrix} 1x_1 + 0x_2 = 7 \\ 0x_1 + 1x_2 = 2 \\ 0x_1 + 0x_2 = 0 \\ 0x_1 + 0x_2 = 0 \end{bmatrix} \qquad \mathbf{4}$$

that is, $x_1 = 7$ and $x_2 = 2$. The last two equations in system **4** give no additional information. The solution is $(7,2)$, as found in Problem 9, Section 2.2.

In the first four steps of sequence **3** we used $R_1$, the first row, in various ways to change $C_1$, the first column, from its original form $\begin{bmatrix} 3 \\ 6 \\ 2 \\ 1 \end{bmatrix}$ into $\begin{bmatrix} 1 \\ 0 \\ 0 \\ 0 \end{bmatrix}$. We briefly describe this procedure by saying

Just as we denote the rows of a matrix by $R_1, R_2,$ etc., reading from top to bottom, so we denote the columns of a matrix by $C_1, C_2,$ etc., reading from left to right.

that we have used $R_1$ to clear $C_1$. Speaking generally, to use a row R to **clear** a column C means to add or subtract the proper multiples of R to or from all the other rows of the matrix so that each entry in C except the entry in R becomes zero. Next, divide R by whatever number will produce a 1 in column C.

In the next four steps of series **3** we used $R_2 = [0 \ -3 \ -6]$ to clear

$$C_2 = \begin{bmatrix} \frac{4}{3} \\ -3 \\ \frac{1}{3} \\ \frac{2}{3} \end{bmatrix}, \text{ that is, to change } C_2 \text{ to } \begin{bmatrix} 0 \\ 1 \\ 0 \\ 0 \end{bmatrix}$$

As a further illustration, consider the matrix

$$\begin{bmatrix} -2 & 1 & 3 & 2 \\ 4 & 0 & 2 & -2 \\ 0 & -6 & -4 & 0 \\ -5 & -1 & -6 & 3 \end{bmatrix} \qquad \mathbf{5}$$

Notice that we cannot, for example, use $R_2$ of matrix **5** to clear $C_2$, because the entry at the intersection of $R_2$ and $C_2$ (that is, at address $(2,2)$) is 0, and 0 cannot be changed to $-1, 6, 1$ (or any other number) by multiplication. We can however use $R_1$ to clear $C_2$:

$$\begin{bmatrix} -2 & 1 & 3 & 2 \\ 4 & 0 & 2 & -2 \\ 0 & -6 & -4 & 0 \\ -5 & -1 & -6 & 3 \end{bmatrix} \begin{matrix} \\ \\ R_3 + 6R_1 \\ R_4 + R_1 \end{matrix} \begin{bmatrix} -2 & 1 & 3 & 2 \\ 4 & 0 & 2 & -2 \\ -12 & 0 & 14 & 12 \\ -7 & 0 & -3 & 5 \end{bmatrix}$$

We now describe the method of Gauss-Jordan reduction in flow chart form. This chart is the generalized version of the chart given in Section 2.2 for systems of two linear equations in two variables. Note that the paragraph following the flow chart entitled "How to Read the Answer" is actually part of the flow chart. It might not apply to other methods of solution such as those presented in the material on shortcuts in Section 4.

**Gauss-Jordan Reduction of a System of Linear Equations**

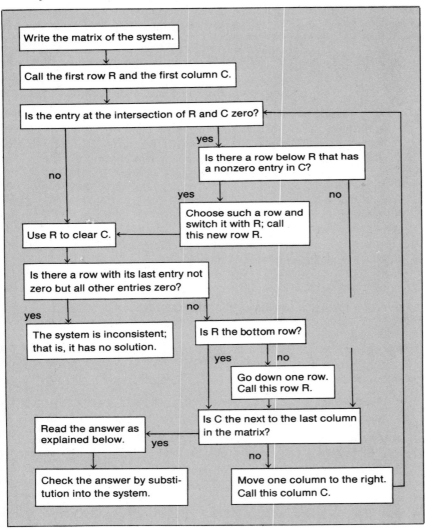

### How to Read the Answer after
### Gauss-Jordan Reduction

If the final matrix obtained from Gauss-Jordan reduction contains a row with its last entry not zero but all other entries zero, then the system has no solution.

Suppose we have carried out Gauss-Jordan reduction and the final matrix does not contain a row with all entries zero except the last. Each row that does not consist entirely of zeros corresponds to an equation from which we obtain the value of one variable. This value may be a single number. Suppose, for example, one of the rows is 0 1 0 0 0 0 −5. This corresponds to the equations $0x_1 + 1x_2 + 0x_3 + 0x_4 + 0x_5 + 0x_6 = -5$, that is, $x_2 = -5$. On the other hand, some rows may yield an expression for a variable that involves one or more **free variables**, that is, variables whose values are not determined by the problem. These variables are free in the sense that we may assign to them any values whatsoever. Suppose, for example, that one of the rows of the final matrix is

$$0 \quad 0 \quad 1 \quad 0 \quad 2 \quad -4 \quad 3 \qquad\qquad \textbf{6}$$

Then the corresponding equation is

$$x_3 + 2x_5 - 4x_6 = 3 \qquad\qquad \textbf{7}$$

The first variable occurring in equation **7** is $x_3$. We solve equation **7** for $x_3$:

$$x_3 = 3 - 2x_5 + 4x_6 \qquad\qquad \textbf{8}$$

This is the final expression for $x_3$ in this case. The variables $x_5$ and $x_6$ are free, and they will appear in the answer simply as $x_5$ and $x_6$, with the comment that they may be any numbers whatever. In the final matrix each uncleared column, except the last, corresponds to a free variable. In practice it is easy to write the answer immediately after inspecting each row, without writing any intermediate steps (such as equation **7**).

For our first illustration of Gauss-Jordan reduction, we solve Problem 10 from Section 2.2. The matrix of system **10** in that section is

$$
\begin{array}{c}
\phantom{R}\quad C \\
R \begin{bmatrix} 9 & 12 & 6 & 90 \\ 3 & 4 & 4 & 40 \end{bmatrix}
\end{array}
\qquad\qquad \textbf{9}
$$

We have indicated the first row to be called R and column to be called C. The entry at the intersection of R and C, namely 9, is not zero, so we use R to clear C:

$$
\begin{array}{c}
\phantom{R}\quad C \\
R \begin{bmatrix} 9 & 12 & 6 & 90 \\ 3 & 4 & 4 & 40 \end{bmatrix}
\end{array}
\quad
\begin{array}{c}
\tfrac{1}{9}R_1 \\
R_2 - \tfrac{1}{3}R_1
\end{array}
\begin{bmatrix} 1 & \tfrac{4}{3} & \tfrac{2}{3} & 10 \\ 0 & 0 & 2 & 10 \end{bmatrix}
$$

We move down one row to the new R and move to the right one

column to the new column C:

$$\begin{array}{c} & \text{C} & \\ & \begin{bmatrix} 1 & \frac{4}{3} & \frac{2}{3} & 10 \\ 0 & 0 & 2 & 10 \end{bmatrix} \\ \text{R} & & \end{array}$$

Since the entry at the intersection of R and C is zero, since there is no row below R, and since C is not the next to the last column, the flow chart instructs us to move one column to the right to the new column C:

$$\begin{array}{c} & & \text{C} & \\ & \begin{bmatrix} 1 & \frac{4}{3} & \frac{2}{3} & 10 \\ 0 & 0 & 2 & 10 \end{bmatrix} \\ \text{R} & & \end{array}$$

The new C is $C_3$. The entry at the intersection of R and C, 2, is not zero; so we use R to clear C:

$$\begin{array}{c} & \text{C} & & \\ & \begin{bmatrix} 1 & \frac{4}{3} & \frac{2}{3} & 10 \\ 0 & 0 & 2 & 10 \end{bmatrix} & \begin{array}{c} R_1 - \frac{1}{3}R_2 \\ \frac{1}{2}R_2 \end{array} & \begin{bmatrix} 1 & \frac{4}{3} & 0 & \frac{20}{3} \\ 0 & 0 & 1 & 5 \end{bmatrix} \\ \text{R} & & & \end{array}$$

This is the final matrix, from which we read the answer: $x_1 = \frac{20}{3} - \frac{4}{3}x_2$, $x_2$ is free, $x_3 = 5$. Notice that, if we take $x_2 = 2$, we get the solution $x_1 = 4$, $x_2 = 2$, $x_3 = 5$, as suggested in Problem 10 of Section 2.2. So, with the new factory at Mystic, there are many ways to fill the order from Bangor exactly.

Before continuing with more examples, we offer some explanation of why Gauss-Jordan reduction works. Let us consider the effect of the three types of row operations (p. 78) on a system of equations.

(1) If an equation is multiplied by a nonzero number, the resulting equation will have the same solutions as the original equation. For example, every solution of the equation

$$-3x_1 + 4x_2 = -5 \qquad \qquad \textbf{10}$$

will also be a solution of $-\frac{1}{3}$ times that equation

$$x_1 - \frac{4}{3}x_2 = \frac{5}{3} \qquad \qquad \textbf{11}$$

Conversely, any solution of equation **11** will also be a solution of equation **10**, since equation **10** can be obtained from equation **11** by multiplying the latter by $-3$.

(2) If we are given two equations and a number k, the system consisting of the first equation and the second equation plus k times the first equation will have the same solutions, if any, as the

original system. For example, any solution of the system

$$\text{(eqn. 1 )} \quad \begin{bmatrix} 4x_1 - 3x_2 + x_3 = 6 \\ -x_1 + 2x_2 - 3x_3 = 4 \end{bmatrix} \qquad \textbf{12}$$

will also be a solution of the system

Here $R = R_1$ and $k = \frac{1}{4}$

$$\text{(eqn. 1 )} \quad \begin{bmatrix} 4x_1 - 3x_2 + x_3 = 6 \\ 0x_1 + \frac{5}{4}x_2 - \frac{11}{4}x_3 = \frac{11}{2} \end{bmatrix} \qquad \textbf{13}$$
$$\left(\text{eqn. } 2 + \tfrac{1}{4} \text{ eqn. 1 }\right)$$

Conversely, any solution of system **13** will also be a solution of system **12**, since system **12** can be obtained from system **13** by subtracting $\frac{1}{4}$ times the first equation of system **13** from the second equation of system **13**.

(3) Given a system of equations, it is obvious that switching the order in which we write the equations will in no way affect the solutions, if any, of the system. Thus, for example, systems **12** and

$$\begin{bmatrix} -x_1 + 2x_2 - 3x_3 = 4 \\ 4x_1 - 3x_2 + x_3 = 6 \end{bmatrix} \qquad \textbf{14}$$

have exactly the same solutions.

Gauss-Jordan reduction is just a sequence of the three types of operations described above. Since none of these operations affects the solutions of a system, it follows that the solutions, if any, of a given system will be the same as the solutions of the system with the final matrix obtained by Gauss-Jordan reduction. But as we have seen, it is very easy to read the solutions from the final matrix of a Gauss-Jordan reduction. This is why the flow chart above is an effective and practical method for solving systems of equations.

We close this section with more examples and exercises. As you work through these exercises, you may notice some cases in which you can save labor by doing the steps in another order. By all means do so. The Gauss-Jordan method always works, but, as we shall see in Section 2.4, it is not always the quickest way.

Problem 1 Solve:

$$\begin{bmatrix} & & 3x_3 & & = & 9 \\ & & & 4x_4 + 8x_5 = & 0 \\ -2x_1 - & 6x_2 + 3x_3 & + 2x_5 = & 13 \\ -2x_1 - & 6x_2 & + 2x_5 = & 4 \\ 4x_1 + & 12x_2 - 9x_3 & - 4x_5 = & -35 \end{bmatrix} \qquad \textbf{15}$$

Solution

$$\begin{bmatrix} 0 & 0 & 3 & 0 & 0 & 9 \\ 0 & 0 & 0 & 4 & 8 & 0 \\ -2 & -6 & 3 & 0 & 2 & 13 \\ -2 & -6 & 0 & 0 & 2 & 4 \\ 4 & 12 & -9 & 0 & -4 & -35 \end{bmatrix}$$

$$\begin{array}{c} R_3 \\ \\ R_1 \\ \\ \\ \end{array} \begin{bmatrix} -2 & -6 & 3 & 0 & 2 & 13 \\ 0 & 0 & 0 & 4 & 8 & 0 \\ 0 & 0 & 3 & 0 & 0 & 9 \\ -2 & -6 & 0 & 0 & 2 & 4 \\ 4 & 12 & -9 & 0 & -4 & -35 \end{bmatrix} \text{(now } R = R_1, C = C_1\text{)}$$

$$\begin{array}{c} -\frac{1}{2}R_1 \\ \\ \\ R_4 - R_1 \\ R_5 + 2R_1 \end{array} \begin{bmatrix} 1 & 3 & -\frac{3}{2} & 0 & -1 & -\frac{13}{2} \\ 0 & 0 & 0 & 4 & 8 & 0 \\ 0 & 0 & 3 & 0 & 0 & 9 \\ 0 & 0 & -3 & 0 & 0 & -9 \\ 0 & 0 & -3 & 0 & 0 & -9 \end{bmatrix}$$

$$\begin{array}{c} \\ R_3 \\ R_2 \\ \\ \\ \end{array} \begin{bmatrix} 1 & 3 & -\frac{3}{2} & 0 & -1 & -\frac{13}{2} \\ 0 & 0 & 3 & 0 & 0 & 9 \\ 0 & 0 & 0 & 4 & 8 & 0 \\ 0 & 0 & -3 & 0 & 0 & -9 \\ 0 & 0 & -3 & 0 & 0 & -9 \end{bmatrix} \text{(now } R = R_2, C = C_3\text{ )}$$

$$\begin{array}{c} R_1 + \frac{1}{2}R_2 \\ \frac{1}{3}R_2 \\ \\ R_4 + R_2 \\ R_5 + R_2 \end{array} \begin{bmatrix} 1 & 3 & 0 & 0 & -1 & -2 \\ 0 & 0 & 1 & 0 & 0 & 3 \\ 0 & 0 & 0 & 4 & 8 & 0 \\ 0 & 0 & 0 & 0 & 0 & 0 \\ 0 & 0 & 0 & 0 & 0 & 0 \end{bmatrix} \text{(now } R = R_3, C = C_4\text{)}$$

$$\begin{array}{c} \\ \\ \frac{1}{4}R_3 \\ \\ \\ \end{array} \begin{bmatrix} 1 & 3 & 0 & 0 & -1 & -2 \\ 0 & 0 & 1 & 0 & 0 & 3 \\ 0 & 0 & 0 & 1 & 2 & 0 \\ 0 & 0 & 0 & 0 & 0 & 0 \\ 0 & 0 & 0 & 0 & 0 & 0 \end{bmatrix} \text{(This is the final matrix.)}$$

Answer $\quad x_1 = -2 - 3x_2 + x_5$

$x_2$ is free

$x_3 = 3$

$x_4 = -2x_5$

$x_5$ is free

Check

$$\begin{bmatrix} & 3(3) & = & 9 \\ & 4(-2x_5)+8(x_5)= & 0 \\ -2(-2-3x_2+x_5)- 6(x_2)+3(3) & +2(x_5)= & 13 \\ -2(-2-3x_2+x_5)- 6(x_2) & +2(x_5)= & 4 \\ 4(-2-3x_2+x_5)+12(x_2)-9(3) & -4(x_5)=-35 \end{bmatrix} \begin{matrix} \checkmark \\ \checkmark \\ \checkmark \\ \checkmark \\ \checkmark \end{matrix}$$

Problem 2    Solve:

$$\begin{bmatrix} 3x_1- x_2+2x_3= 7 \\ x_1- x_2+ x_3=-2 \\ 4x_1-2x_2+3x_3= 3 \end{bmatrix}$$

Solution

$$\begin{bmatrix} 3 & -1 & 2 & 7 \\ 1 & -1 & 1 & -2 \\ 4 & -2 & 3 & 3 \end{bmatrix} \begin{matrix} \frac{1}{3}R_1 \\ R_2-\frac{1}{3}R_1 \\ R_3-\frac{4}{3}R_1 \end{matrix} \begin{bmatrix} 1 & -\frac{1}{3} & \frac{2}{3} & \frac{7}{3} \\ 0 & -\frac{2}{3} & \frac{1}{3} & -\frac{13}{3} \\ 0 & -\frac{2}{3} & \frac{1}{3} & -\frac{19}{3} \end{bmatrix}$$

$$\begin{matrix} R_1-\frac{1}{2}R_2 \\ -\frac{3}{2}R_2 \\ R_3-R_2 \end{matrix} \begin{bmatrix} 1 & 0 & \frac{1}{2} & \frac{9}{2} \\ 0 & 1 & -\frac{1}{2} & \frac{13}{2} \\ 0 & 0 & 0 & -2 \end{bmatrix}$$

Answer    No solution.

Problem 3    Solve Exercise 24 in Section 2.2.

Solution    Let $x_1$, $x_2$, $x_3$, respectively, be the number of packets of types 1, 2, and 3 used to make an expedition packet. We must solve:

$$\begin{bmatrix} 3x_1+4x_2+2x_3=86 \\ 2x_1+ x_2+5x_3=88 \\ 3x_1+3x_2+3x_3=90 \end{bmatrix}$$

$$\begin{bmatrix} 3 & 4 & 2 & 86 \\ 2 & 1 & 5 & 88 \\ 3 & 3 & 3 & 90 \end{bmatrix} \begin{matrix} \frac{1}{3}R_1 \\ R_2-\frac{2}{3}R_1 \\ R_3 -R_1 \end{matrix} \begin{bmatrix} 1 & \frac{4}{3} & \frac{2}{3} & \frac{86}{3} \\ 0 & -\frac{5}{3} & \frac{11}{3} & \frac{92}{3} \\ 0 & -1 & 1 & 4 \end{bmatrix}$$

$$\begin{matrix} R_1+\frac{4}{5}R_2 \\ -\frac{3}{5}R_2 \\ R_3-\frac{3}{5}R_2 \end{matrix} \begin{bmatrix} 1 & 0 & \frac{18}{5} & \frac{266}{5} \\ 0 & 1 & -\frac{11}{5} & -\frac{92}{5} \\ 0 & 0 & -\frac{6}{5} & -\frac{72}{5} \end{bmatrix}$$

$$\begin{matrix} R_1+3R_3 \\ R_2-\frac{11}{6}R_3 \\ -\frac{5}{6}R_3 \end{matrix} \begin{bmatrix} 1 & 0 & 0 & 10 \\ 0 & 1 & 0 & 8 \\ 0 & 0 & 1 & 12 \end{bmatrix}$$

Answer     Use 10 packets of type 1, 8 of type 2, and 12 of type 3 to make one expedition packet.

Check

$$\begin{bmatrix} 3(10)+4(8)+2(12)=86 \\ 2(10)+1(8)+5(12)=88 \\ 3(10)+3(8)+3(12)=90 \end{bmatrix} \begin{array}{c} \checkmark \\ \checkmark \\ \checkmark \end{array}$$

Inventory control is an important operations research topic, which we will unfortunately have to skip, because it requires calculus. The main problem of inventory control is to find the most economical level of inventory for each item stocked by a given company.

The fuel shortage of 1974 hurt the sales of AC as much as it hurt those of any other company. Certainly, the dedicated backpackers were as active as ever. But the bulk of the AC customers had been using motorized recreational vehicles (RVs); their response was to stay home rather than risk being stranded. Sales dropped so sharply that the AC inventory control specialist warned that they would soon be spending more on storage than they were earning in profits. He said, "You had better quit producing until people start buying sporting goods again." The president reluctantly agreed. AC would receive orders, fill them from inventory, and then produce only enough to replenish the supply. Their first order arrived on July 15 and read in part:

| Item | Quantity |
| --- | --- |
| Light sleeping bag | 99 |
| Heavy sleeping bag | 25 |
| Down jacket | 47 |
| Two-person tent | 84 |
| Four-person tent | 64 |

The question for Janet's department was: How many days should each factory be operated to fill this order exactly?

AC's daily production of these items is given in Table 4.

Table 4
Production
Table for a
Day in July

| Item | Factory | | |
| --- | --- | --- | --- |
| | Danbury, CT | Springfield, MA | Rutland, VT |
| Light sleeping bags | 11 | 13 | 7 |
| Heavy sleeping bags | 3 | 4 | 0 |
| Down jackets | 5 | 7 | 2 |
| Two-person tents | 8 | 15 | 0 |
| Four-person tents | 0 | 14 | 4 |

If we let $x_1$, $x_2$, $x_3$ denote the number of days we operate the Danbury, Springfield, and Rutland factories, respectively, then according to Table 4 AC will produce

$$11x_1 + 13x_2 + 7x_3$$

LIGHT SLEEPING BAGS    To fill the order exactly we must have

$$11x_1 + 13x_2 + 7x_3 = 99$$

We have four similar equations for the other items:

HEAVY SLEEPING BAGS

$$3x_1 + 4x_2 \qquad = 25$$

DOWN JACKETS

$$5x_1 + 7x_2 + 2x_3 = 47$$

TWO-PERSON TENTS

$$8x_1 + 15x_2 \qquad = 84$$

FOUR-PERSON TENTS

$$14x_2 + 4x_3 = 64$$

We are thus led to a system of equations:

$$\begin{bmatrix} 11x_1 + 13x_2 + 7x_3 = 99 \\ 3x_1 + 4x_2 \qquad = 25 \\ 5x_1 + 7x_2 + 2x_3 = 47 \\ 8x_1 + 15x_2 \qquad = 84 \\ 14x_2 + 4x_3 = 64 \end{bmatrix}$$

We solve system **1** by Gauss-Jordan reduction, using a technique for avoiding fractions that will be discussed in Section 2.4.

$$\begin{bmatrix} 11 & 13 & 7 & 99 \\ 3 & 4 & 0 & 25 \\ 5 & 7 & 2 & 47 \\ 8 & 15 & 0 & 84 \\ 0 & 14 & 4 & 64 \end{bmatrix} \begin{matrix} R_1 - 2R_3 \\ \\ \\ R_4 - 2R_2 \\ \\ \end{matrix} \begin{bmatrix} 1 & -1 & 3 & 5 \\ 3 & 4 & 0 & 25 \\ 5 & 7 & 2 & 47 \\ 2 & 7 & 0 & 34 \\ 0 & 14 & 4 & 64 \end{bmatrix}$$

$$\begin{matrix} R_2 - 3R_1 \\ R_3 - 5R_1 \\ R_4 - 2R_1 \\ \\ \end{matrix} \begin{bmatrix} 1 & -1 & 3 & 5 \\ 0 & 7 & -9 & 10 \\ 0 & 12 & -13 & 22 \\ 0 & 9 & -6 & 24 \\ 0 & 14 & 4 & 64 \end{bmatrix} \begin{matrix} \\ \\ \\ R_4 - R_2 \\ R_5 - 2R_2 \end{matrix} \begin{bmatrix} 1 & -1 & 3 & 5 \\ 0 & 7 & -9 & 10 \\ 0 & 12 & -13 & 22 \\ 0 & 2 & 3 & 14 \\ 0 & 0 & 22 & 44 \end{bmatrix}$$

$$\begin{matrix} R_2 - 3R_4 \\ R_3 - 6R_4 \\ \\ \tfrac{1}{22}R_5 \end{matrix} \begin{bmatrix} 1 & -1 & 3 & 5 \\ 0 & 1 & -18 & -32 \\ 0 & 0 & -31 & -62 \\ 0 & 2 & 3 & 14 \\ 0 & 0 & 1 & 2 \end{bmatrix} \begin{matrix} R_1 + R_2 \\ \\ R_3 + 31R_5 \\ R_4 - 2R_2 \\ \end{matrix} \begin{bmatrix} 1 & 0 & -15 & -27 \\ 0 & 1 & -18 & -32 \\ 0 & 0 & 0 & 0 \\ 0 & 0 & 39 & 78 \\ 0 & 0 & 1 & 2 \end{bmatrix}$$

$$\begin{matrix} R_1 + 15R_5 \\ R_2 + 18R_5 \\ \\ R_4 - 39R_5 \\ \end{matrix} \begin{bmatrix} 1 & 0 & 0 & 3 \\ 0 & 1 & 0 & 4 \\ 0 & 0 & 0 & 0 \\ 0 & 0 & 0 & 0 \\ 0 & 0 & 1 & 2 \end{bmatrix}$$

Check:

$$\begin{bmatrix} 11\cdot3 + 13\cdot4 + 7\cdot2 = 99 \\ 3\cdot3 + 4\cdot4 + 0\cdot2 = 25 \\ 5\cdot3 + 7\cdot4 + 2\cdot2 = 47 \\ 8\cdot3 + 15\cdot4 + 0\cdot2 = 84 \\ 0\cdot3 + 14\cdot4 + 4\cdot2 = 64 \end{bmatrix} \begin{matrix} \checkmark \\ \checkmark \\ \checkmark \\ \checkmark \\ \checkmark \end{matrix}$$

The answer: operate the Danbury factory for 3 days, the Springfield factory for 4 days, and the Rutland Factory for 2 days.

Actually, the problem for AC is not quite this simple. This is really a *linear programming* situation, in which we must take into account the cost of operating each factory. It costs \$3,000 a day to operate the Danbury factory, \$2,000 to operate the Springfield factory, and \$5,000 to operate the Rutland factory. Of real interest then is the problem:

Minimize $3x_1 + 2x_2 + 5x_3 =$ total daily cost subject to

$$\begin{aligned}
11x_1 + 13x_2 + 7x_3 &= 99 \\
3x_1 + 4x_2 \phantom{+ 7x_3} &= 25 \\
5x_1 + 7x_2 + 2x_3 &= 47 \\
8x_1 + 15x_2 \phantom{+ 7x_3} &= 84 \\
14x_2 + 4x_3 &= 64
\end{aligned}$$

We shall learn how to solve problems of this type in Chapter 5. Notice, however, that we have already solved this particular linear programming problem. Since the collection of equations has only one solution, we have no choice. No matter what the cost, there is only one way to meet the demand exactly.

It is easy to create a system with *no* solution simply by altering the orders. For example, if we change the 64 above to a 65, the problem would have no solution. In such a case, it may be sensible to replace some or all of the equations by inequalities. If we do that, then the more general techniques of Chapter 5 become necessary.

**Why?**

**Exercises 2.3**   In Exercises 1 through 27, solve the systems of equations.

1. $\begin{bmatrix} x_1 + x_2 \phantom{+ x_3} = 2 \\ \phantom{x_1 +} x_2 + x_3 = 2 \\ x_1 \phantom{+ x_2} + x_3 = 2 \end{bmatrix}$

2. $\begin{bmatrix} x_1 + 2x_2 + x_3 = 7 \\ 2x_1 + 3x_2 + 3x_3 = 16 \\ 2x_1 + 3x_2 + 4x_3 = 19 \end{bmatrix}$

3. $\begin{bmatrix} x_1 + 3x_2 + x_3 = 3 \\ 3x_1 + 8x_2 + 3x_3 = 7 \\ 2x_1 - 3x_2 + x_3 = -10 \end{bmatrix}$

4. $\begin{bmatrix} 3x_1 + 3x_2 + 5x_3 = 14 \\ x_1 + 6x_2 + 8x_3 = 20 \\ 2x_1 + x_2 + 2x_3 = 6 \end{bmatrix}$

5. $\begin{bmatrix} 9x_1 + 2x_2 + 3x_3 = -40 \\ 2x_1 + x_2 + x_3 = 8 \\ 4x_1 - x_2 + x_3 = 68 \end{bmatrix}$

6. $\begin{bmatrix} 2x_1 + x_2 + 3x_3 = 9 \\ 3x_1 - 6x_2 - 4x_3 = 7 \\ 5x_1 + 2x_2 + 7x_3 = 22 \end{bmatrix}$

7. $\begin{bmatrix} 5x_1 + 9x_2 + 5x_3 = 27 \\ 3x_1 + 3x_2 + 2x_3 = 8 \\ 4x_1 + 5x_2 + 3x_3 = 14 \end{bmatrix}$

8. $\begin{bmatrix} 2x_1 + 5x_2 + 2x_3 = 4 \\ 2x_1 - 3x_2 + 3x_3 = 6 \\ 3x_1 + 7x_2 + 3x_3 = 6 \end{bmatrix}$

9. $\begin{bmatrix} 5x_1 + 4x_2 + 6x_3 = 0 \\ 2x_1 + 5x_2 + 2x_3 = 0 \\ 2x_1 - 4x_2 + 3x_3 = 0 \end{bmatrix}$   10. $\begin{bmatrix} 3x_1 + 3x_2 + 2x_3 = 22 \\ 4x_1 + 5x_2 + 3x_3 = 39 \\ 8x_1 + 9x_2 + 9x_3 = 69 \end{bmatrix}$

11. $\begin{bmatrix} x_1 + x_2 - x_3 = 0 \\ x_1 + x_2 + x_3 = 6 \\ x_1 - x_2 - x_3 = -4 \end{bmatrix}$   12. $\begin{bmatrix} 8x_1 + 7x_2 + 2x_3 = 14 \\ 3x_1 + 2x_2 + 5x_3 = 2 \\ x_1 + x_2 - x_3 = -3 \end{bmatrix}$

13. $\begin{bmatrix} 2x_1 + 3x_2 + x_3 = 5 \\ 2x_1 + 7x_2 + x_3 = 5 \\ 3x_1 + 2x_2 + x_3 = 0 \end{bmatrix}$   14. $\begin{bmatrix} 4x_1 + 7x_2 + 2x_3 = -2 \\ 4x_1 \qquad\quad + 5x_3 = -3 \\ 7x_1 + 6x_2 + 7x_3 = 12 \end{bmatrix}$

15. $\begin{bmatrix} 7x_1 + 3x_2 + 3x_3 = 10 \\ 2x_1 + x_2 + x_3 = 8 \\ 3x_1 + 7x_2 + 2x_3 = -5 \end{bmatrix}$   16. $\begin{bmatrix} x_1 + 2x_2 + 2x_3 = -5 \\ 6x_1 + 5x_2 + 4x_3 = 9 \\ 3x_1 + 3x_2 + 2x_3 = -7 \end{bmatrix}$

17. $\begin{bmatrix} x_1 \qquad\quad - 4x_3 = 2 \\ 2x_1 + 2x_2 + 3x_3 = 5 \\ -2x_1 + 4x_2 + x_3 = 6 \end{bmatrix}$   18. $\begin{bmatrix} 5x_1 + 5x_2 + 9x_3 = 0 \\ 2x_1 - 5x_2 - 2x_3 = 7 \\ 6x_1 + 2x_2 + 4x_3 = 5 \end{bmatrix}$

19. $\begin{bmatrix} -2x_1 + x_2 + 9x_3 = 8 \\ -6x_1 - 3x_2 + 2x_3 = -6 \\ x_1 - 8x_2 + 4x_3 = 4 \end{bmatrix}$   20. $\begin{bmatrix} x_1 + x_2 + x_3 = 5 \\ 2x_1 - x_2 + 2x_3 = 1 \\ -x_1 + 2x_2 - x_3 = 4 \end{bmatrix}$

21. $\begin{bmatrix} 2x_1 - x_2 - x_3 = 0 \\ x_1 + 2x_2 - 3x_3 = 0 \\ 3x_1 - x_2 - 2x_3 = 0 \end{bmatrix}$   22. $\begin{bmatrix} -2x_1 + x_2 + x_3 = 3 \\ x_2 + x_3 = 1 \\ x_1 + x_2 - 2x_3 = -3 \end{bmatrix}$

23. $\begin{bmatrix} -\frac{2}{3}x_1 + x_2 - x_3 = \frac{1}{6} \\ \frac{1}{2}x_1 - x_2 - \frac{1}{2}x_3 = -1 \\ \frac{3}{4}x_1 - \frac{1}{2}x_2 + \frac{1}{4}x_3 = \frac{5}{4} \end{bmatrix}$   24. $\begin{bmatrix} -\frac{3}{4}x_1 - \frac{4}{3}x_2 + x_3 = \frac{2}{3} \\ 9x_1 + 16x_2 - 12x_3 = -8 \\ -3x_1 - \frac{16}{3}x_2 + 4x_3 = \frac{8}{3} \end{bmatrix}$

25. $\begin{bmatrix} 3x_1 + x_2 - 2x_3 + 4x_4 = 7 \\ x_1 - x_2 + 3x_3 - x_4 = 6 \\ 2x_1 - 3x_2 + x_3 - 2x_4 = 5 \end{bmatrix}$   26. $\begin{bmatrix} 5x_1 + 4x_2 + x_3 = 0 \\ 7x_1 + 5x_2 + 6x_3 = 0 \\ x_1 + 8x_2 - 3x_3 = 0 \end{bmatrix}$

27. $\begin{bmatrix} x_1 + x_2 + x_3 + x_4 + x_5 = 15 \\ x_1 - x_2 + x_3 - x_4 - x_5 = 3 \\ x_1 + x_2 + x_3 - x_4 - x_5 = -3 \\ -x_1 - x_2 + x_3 - x_4 + x_5 = 1 \\ x_1 - x_2 - x_3 - x_4 - x_5 = -5 \end{bmatrix}$

28. Given the information in Exercise 24 of Section 2.2, how does AC make up the high-altitude expedition packets, which consist of 28 grams of protein, 37 grams of fats, and 33 grams of carbohydrates?

29. Find the solutions to Problem 10 of Section 2, page 74, in which the factory at Danbury is used (a) as little as possible, (b) as much as possible.

30. The ACME Company makes three kinds of toys: toy A, toy B and the other toy. It makes $2.00 profit on toy A, $5.00 profit on toy B,

and \$6.00 profit on the other toy. It takes 4 person-hours to make toy A, 3 to make toy B, and 12 to make the other toy. It takes 1 hour to check each toy A for safety, 1 hour to check each toy B, and 3 hours to check each other toy. The management decides to use 100 person-hours and 50 safety-check hours to make \$40 profit. How many of each toy should ACME make?

31. A manufacturer makes 4 types of pocket calculators: A, B, C, and D. Each calculator must pass through 3 separate assembly procedures: memory assembly (M), arithmetic unit assembly (U), and final assembly (F). The time in person-hours for each type of calculator is shown in Table 5.

Table 5

| Calculator | Procedure | | |
|---|---|---|---|
| | **M** | **U** | **F** |
| A | 7 | 1 | 9 |
| B | 3 | 2 | 7 |
| C | 4 | 3 | 10 |
| D | 1 | 4 | 9 |

The manufacturer has available 80 person-hours of memory assembly time, 40 of arithmetic unit assembly, and 100 of final assembly time. Can she use up all of this time?

$^C$32. I was happy when I thought I had solved the system

$$\begin{bmatrix} -3x_1 - 4x_2 & & =1 \\ & 2x_2 + 3x_3 =1 \\ -2x_1 & +4x_3 =2 \end{bmatrix}$$

by the following sequence of steps:

$$\begin{bmatrix} -3 & -4 & 0 & 1 \\ 0 & 2 & 3 & 1 \\ -2 & 0 & 4 & 2 \end{bmatrix} \begin{array}{c} -\frac{1}{3}R_1 \\ \\ R_3 - \frac{2}{3}R_1 \end{array} \begin{bmatrix} 1 & \frac{4}{3} & 0 & -\frac{1}{3} \\ 0 & 2 & 3 & 1 \\ 0 & \frac{8}{3} & 0 & -\frac{4}{3} \end{bmatrix}$$

$$\begin{array}{c} R_1 - \frac{2}{3}R_2 \\ \frac{1}{2}R_2 \\ R_3 - \frac{4}{3}R_2 \end{array} \begin{bmatrix} 1 & 0 & -2 & -1 \\ 0 & 1 & \frac{3}{2} & \frac{1}{3} \\ 0 & 0 & -4 & -\frac{8}{3} \end{bmatrix} \begin{array}{c} R_1 - \frac{1}{2}R_3 \\ R_2 + \frac{3}{8}R_3 \\ -\frac{1}{4}R_3 \end{array} \begin{bmatrix} 1 & 0 & 0 & \frac{1}{3} \\ 0 & 1 & 0 & -\frac{1}{2} \\ 0 & 0 & 1 & \frac{2}{3} \end{bmatrix}$$

Answer: $x_1 = \frac{1}{3}$, $x_2 = -\frac{1}{2}$, $x_3 = \frac{2}{3}$

$$\begin{bmatrix} -3(\frac{1}{3}) - 4(-\frac{1}{2}) & = -1 + 2 = 1 \\ 2(-\frac{1}{2}) + 3(\frac{2}{3}) = -1 + 2 = 1 \\ -2(\frac{1}{3}) & +4(\frac{2}{3}) = -\frac{2}{3} + \frac{8}{3} = 2 \end{bmatrix} \begin{array}{c} \checkmark \\ \checkmark \\ \checkmark \end{array}$$

Find my error and give the correct solution.

De gustibus non disputandum est.

Many people like to read in bed.

33. I want to publish a book of my poetry containing a selection of my odes, cantos, and epics. Aesthetic considerations impel me to demand that the book contain exactly 108 stanzas, 45 allusions to Greek mythology, and 128 Latin phrases. Each of my odes contains 12 stanzas, makes 3 allusions, and has 9 Latin phrases. Each canto has 8 stanzas, makes 1 allusion (always in the penultimate stanza), and contains 7 Latin phrases. Each epic has 4 stanzas (of 800 lines each), 5 allusions, and 12 Latin phrases. My Table of Contents will list 4 poems per page, with fewer listed on the final page if the number of poems is not a multiple of 4. How many pages will my Table of Contents have?

34. Esther is going out of the jewelry business. She wants to use up her stock of 775 diamonds, 736 rubies, and 1,061 opals by making necklaces (9 diamonds, 8 rubies, 11 opals each), bracelets (7, 8, 10 each) and brooches (3, 5, 15 each), which she will sell for a profit of $700 per necklace, $600 per bracelet, and $500 per brooch. When they are all sold she will spend $2,400 to move from Ft. Lauderdale, Florida, to a retirement village in Juneau, Alaska. How much of her profits will she have when she arrives?

35. This is Daryl's chance of a lifetime! Her Grace has asked him to furnish the 27 rooms on the third floor of the new palace, in any way he wants. Oh, there are a few stipulations: each room furnished as a bedroom must have 2 sofas, 6 chamber pots, 4 tables, and 7 beds; each game room must have 1 sofa, 2 chamber pots, 5 tables, and 2 beds; each reading room must have 3 sofas, 1 chamber pot, 8 tables, and 6 beds; and each parlor must have 5 sofas, 7 chamber pots, 9 tables, and 1 bed. Because of the great cost of the new palace, he can only use the furniture in the *old* palace: 73 sofas, 116 chamber pots, 170 tables, and 107 beds. How many of each room should Daryl create?

36. I want to plan a concert of pieces by certain (justifiably) unknown composers for a quartet consisting of horn, cello, violin, and kettledrum. My musicians insist on precise working times: the horn player will play for 73 minutes, the cellist 116, the violinist 170, and the tympanist 107. Each of my overtures has 2 minutes of horn time, 6 of cello, 4 of violin, and 7 of kettledrum; each prelude has 1 minute of horn, 2 of cello, 5 of violin, and 2 of drum; each concertino has 3 minutes of horn, 1 of cello, 8 of violin, and 6 of drum; each symphonette has 5 minutes of horn, 7 of cello, 9 of violin, and 1 of drum. The overtures, lasting 10 minutes each, will be played without interruption first, followed by a 15-minute intermission. Then the preludes, 5 minutes each, and concertinos, 10 minutes each, will be played without interruption, followed by a 20-minute intermission. Finally, the symphonettes, 15 minutes a piece, will be played, separated by 1-minute intervals. The concert starts at 2 P.M. When does it end?

37. The Friendship Grocery chain has donated 10 boxes of each of its 3 kinds of biscuit mixes to my skydiving club for our annual parachute breakfast outing. I figure that to feed its members I'll need a mixture of 6.8 lbs. sugar, 83 lbs. shortening, and 118 lbs. flour. Each box of Lite mix contains 0.4 lbs. sugar, 0.1 lbs. shortening, and 3.1 lbs. flour; each box of Jiffy mix has 0.3 lbs. sugar, 1.3 lbs. shortening, and 4.3 lbs. flour; each box of He-man mix has 0.2 lbs. sugar, 7.2 lbs. shortening, and 6.5 lbs. flour. I can auction off unused Lites at $2 per box, Jiffys at $3, and He-mans at $7. How much will I make from the auction?

38. Solve the PHE problem of Exercise 25, Section 2.2; that is, give all possible "meaningful" combinations. Note: PHE stores will sell half-orders of superburgers (called "semiburgers") and of fishfeasts.

39. A friend of mine has had bit parts in several movies. He also likes to go to the movies with me but only if he's not in the picture. Once he said to me, "Did you notice that last year every movie you went to had me in the theater, either on the screen or in a seat next to you (but not both)? Furthermore, I went to twice as many movies with you as the number I was in. And the number of times you went without me was equal to three times the number of movies I was in." "Very funny," I replied. How many movies did I go to last year?

*40. After the robbery the 3 criminals were able to split the loot according to the following conditions. Since Jimmy drove the car and planned the job, he got twice as much as Lefty and Spike put together. Since Spike did the talking, Lefty got $10,000 less than the difference of the cuts for Jimmy and Spike. How much did they steal and what was each individual's take, assuming that Lefty got $1,000 more than Spike?

The following matrices arose in an attempt to solve a system of equations. For each matrix, determine if further reduction is required. If so, further reduce the matrix and read the answer. Otherwise, read the answer from the matrix as it stands.

41. $\begin{bmatrix} 1 & 0 & 3 \\ 0 & 1 & 2 \\ 0 & 0 & 3 \end{bmatrix}$
42. $\begin{bmatrix} 1 & 0 & 1 & 3 \\ 0 & 1 & 0 & 2 \\ 0 & 0 & 1 & 2 \end{bmatrix}$

43. $\begin{bmatrix} 1 & 0 & 0 & 0 & 2 \\ 0 & 0 & 1 & 0 & 3 \\ 0 & 0 & 0 & 1 & 2 \\ 0 & 0 & 0 & 0 & 0 \end{bmatrix}$
44. $\begin{bmatrix} 1 & 1 & 0 & 0 & 0 & 2 \\ 0 & 0 & 1 & 1 & 0 & 3 \\ 0 & 0 & 0 & 0 & 1 & 4 \\ 0 & 0 & 0 & 0 & 0 & 0 \end{bmatrix}$

45. $\begin{bmatrix} 0 & 0 & 0 & 1 & 0 & 4 \\ 0 & 1 & 0 & 0 & 2 & 3 \\ 1 & 0 & 3 & 0 & 0 & 2 \end{bmatrix}$
46. $\begin{bmatrix} 2 & 3 & 0 & 2 & 4 \\ 1 & 0 & 1 & 0 & 2 \\ 0 & 0 & 0 & 1 & 3 \\ 0 & 0 & 0 & 0 & 1 \end{bmatrix}$

47. $\begin{bmatrix} 2 & 3 & 0 & 2 & 4 \\ 1 & 0 & 1 & 0 & 2 \\ 0 & 0 & 0 & 1 & 3 \\ 0 & 0 & 0 & 0 & 0 \end{bmatrix}$    48. $\begin{bmatrix} 1 & 1 & 1 & 1 \\ 1 & 1 & 1 & 2 \\ 1 & 1 & 1 & 3 \\ 1 & 1 & 1 & 4 \end{bmatrix}$

49. $\begin{bmatrix} 1 & 0 & 2 & 0 & 1 & 3 \\ 0 & 1 & 1 & 0 & 0 & 2 \\ 0 & 0 & 0 & 1 & 3 & 4 \\ 0 & 0 & 0 & 0 & 1 & 2 \end{bmatrix}$    50. $\begin{bmatrix} 1 & 0 & 1 & 0 & 3 \\ 2 & 1 & 0 & 0 & 4 \\ 3 & 0 & 0 & 1 & 5 \end{bmatrix}$

51. An experiment has three possible outcomes, a, b, c. Suppose we know from experience that $P(\{a,b\}) = \frac{7}{11}$ and $P(\{b,c\}) = \frac{6}{11}$. What is $P(a)$?

52. I ran an experiment with sample space $\{a, b, c, d\}$ several times. I am convinced that $P(a,d) = \frac{1}{2}$, $P(a,c) = \frac{1}{8}$, and $P(c,d) = \frac{1}{4}$. Given this information, what is the probability of the outcome b?

53. An experiment has four possible outcomes, a, b, c, d. Determine the probability distribution for the sample space given that $P(a,b) = \frac{4}{7}$, $P(b,c) = \frac{1}{2}$, and $P(c,d) = \frac{3}{7}$.

## Section 2.4
## Shortcuts in
## Gauss-Jordan Reduction

Gaussian elimination (Shortcut 3) is faster for computers by a ratio of 3 to 2.

While other techniques for solving systems of equations are known, none are nearly as fast or efficient for hand calculation as Gauss-Jordan reduction. As efficient as Gauss-Jordan reduction is, however, it often can be improved significantly by several slight modifications, which we are about to describe. Since these shortcuts depend upon Gauss-Jordan reduction, you cannot use them properly without first having a good command of the technique described in the flow chart on p. 80. In fact, the unconsidered use of these techniques is totally ineffective. The effective use of shortcuts depends on taking advantage of the particular arrangement of numbers in a given problem. Thus the following methods could not be included in the flow chart.

Once you begin to understand the way in which Gauss-Jordan reduction successively eliminates variables, you will be ready to begin to use the following tricks. It should be stated, however, that none of these tricks is needed to solve any system; they merely help to shorten the work for some students. If you are confused by this section, retreat to the flow chart on p. 80.

Some of these shortcuts are of greater psychological value than actual computational value; it is a matter of personal taste whether or not you will want to use them. Others actually do shorten the work.

**Shortcut 1**  Do not routinely require there to be a 1 in a cleared column.

**Problem 1**  Solve: $\begin{bmatrix} 3x_1 + x_2 = 7 \\ 2x_1 + 3x_2 = 9 \end{bmatrix}$

**Solution**

$$\begin{bmatrix} 3 & 1 & 7 \\ 2 & 3 & 9 \end{bmatrix} R_2 - \tfrac{2}{3}R_1 \begin{bmatrix} 3 & 1 & 7 \\ 0 & \tfrac{7}{3} & \tfrac{13}{3} \end{bmatrix}$$

$$R_1 - \tfrac{3}{7}R_2 \begin{bmatrix} 3 & 0 & \tfrac{36}{7} \\ 0 & \tfrac{7}{3} & \tfrac{13}{3} \end{bmatrix}$$

The first row corresponds to $3x_1 = \tfrac{36}{7}$ or $x_1 = \tfrac{12}{7}$

The second row corresponds to $\tfrac{7}{3}x_2 = \tfrac{13}{3}$ or $x_2 = \tfrac{13}{7}$.

The point here is that after a little practice the answer can simply be read from the final matrix. Do the division in your head. As a further example, suppose the final matrix is:

$$\begin{bmatrix} 4 & 3 & 0 & 7 & 2 \\ 0 & 0 & 3 & -8 & 5 \end{bmatrix}$$

Again, we divide mentally and simply write the answer:

$$x_1 = \tfrac{1}{4}(2 - 3x_2 - 7x_4)$$

$$x_2 \text{ is free}$$

$$x_3 = \tfrac{1}{3}(5 + 8x_4)$$

$$x_4 \text{ is free}$$

**Shortcut 2**  Multiply to avoid fractions.

**Problem 2**  Solve:

$$\begin{bmatrix} 2x_1 - x_2 + x_3 = -2 \\ x_1 + 2x_2 - x_3 = 3 \\ -x_1 + x_2 + 2x_3 = 2 \end{bmatrix}$$

**Solution**

$$\begin{bmatrix} 2 & -1 & 1 & -2 \\ 1 & 2 & -1 & 3 \\ -1 & 1 & 2 & 2 \end{bmatrix} \begin{matrix} \\ 2R_2 - R_1 \\ 2R_3 + R_1 \end{matrix} \begin{bmatrix} 2 & -1 & 1 & -2 \\ 0 & 5 & -3 & 8 \\ 0 & 1 & 5 & 2 \end{bmatrix}$$

$$\begin{matrix} 5R_1 + R_2 \\ \\ 5R_3 - R_2 \end{matrix} \begin{bmatrix} 10 & 0 & 2 & -2 \\ 0 & 5 & -3 & 8 \\ 0 & 0 & 28 & 2 \end{bmatrix} \begin{matrix} 14R_1 - R_3 \\ 28R_2 + 3R_3 \\ \\ \end{matrix} \begin{bmatrix} 140 & 0 & 0 & -30 \\ 0 & 140 & 0 & 230 \\ 0 & 0 & 28 & 2 \end{bmatrix}$$

Thus $x_1 = -\frac{3}{14}$, $x_2 = \frac{23}{14}$, $x_3 = \frac{1}{14}$.

Check

$$\begin{bmatrix} 2\left(-\frac{3}{14}\right) - 1\left(\frac{23}{14}\right) + 1\left(\frac{1}{14}\right) = -2 \\ 1\left(-\frac{3}{14}\right) + 2\left(\frac{23}{14}\right) - 1\left(\frac{1}{14}\right) = \phantom{-}3 \\ -1\left(-\frac{3}{14}\right) + 1\left(\frac{23}{14}\right) + 2\left(\frac{1}{14}\right) = \phantom{-}2 \end{bmatrix} \begin{matrix} \checkmark \\ \checkmark \\ \checkmark \end{matrix}$$

Shortcut 3    Substitute to find the other variables.

This technique is called **Gaussian elimination**. While this method is quicker for computers, for hand computation it is generally more time consuming than Gauss-Jordan reduction. To use it, clear only the part of column C that is below R.

Problem 3

Solve: $\begin{bmatrix} x_1 + 2x_2 - x_3 = \phantom{0}3 \\ 2x_1 + \phantom{2}x_2 + x_3 = \phantom{0}0 \\ 3x_1 + 6x_2 + 2x_3 = 14 \end{bmatrix}$

Solution

$$\begin{bmatrix} 1 & 2 & -1 & 3 \\ 2 & 1 & 1 & 0 \\ 3 & 6 & 2 & 14 \end{bmatrix} \begin{matrix} \\ R_2 - 2R_1 \\ R_3 - 3R_1 \end{matrix} \begin{bmatrix} 1 & 2 & -1 & 3 \\ 0 & -3 & 3 & -6 \\ 0 & 0 & 5 & 5 \end{bmatrix}$$

From the last row we see that $x_3 = 1$. Substitution into the equation corresponding to row 2 yields

$$-3x_2 + 3 \cdot 1 = -6$$
$$-3x_2 = -9$$
$$x_2 = \phantom{-}3$$

Finally, substituting the two known values into the equation corresponding to row 1 yields

$$x_1 + 2 \cdot 3 - 1 \cdot 1 = \phantom{-}3$$
$$x_1 + 5 = \phantom{-}3$$
$$x_1 = -2$$

Check

$$\begin{bmatrix} 1(-2) + 2(3) - 1(1) = \phantom{1}3 \\ 2(-2) + 1(3) + 1(1) = \phantom{1}0 \\ 3(-2) + 6(3) + 2(1) = 14 \end{bmatrix} \begin{matrix} \checkmark \\ \checkmark \\ \checkmark \end{matrix}$$

Shortcut 4    Combine row operations.

Problem 4

Solve: $\begin{bmatrix} 3x_1 + 2x_2 - x_3 = \phantom{-}1 \\ 2x_1 + 4x_2 - 2x_3 = -1 \\ 4x_1 - 5x_2 + x_3 = \phantom{-}3 \end{bmatrix}$

Solution

$$\begin{bmatrix} 3 & 2 & -1 & 1 \\ 2 & 4 & -2 & -1 \\ 4 & -5 & 1 & 3 \end{bmatrix} \begin{matrix} \\ 3R_2-2R_1 \\ 3R_3-4R_1 \end{matrix} \begin{bmatrix} 3 & 2 & -1 & 1 \\ 0 & 8 & -4 & -5 \\ 0 & -23 & 7 & 5 \end{bmatrix}$$

For the third matrix, the operation $4R_1-R_2$, instead of $8R_1-2R_2$, would yield smaller numbers: a shortcut within the shortcut.

$$\begin{matrix} 8R_1- 2R_2 \\ \\ 8R_3+23R_2 \end{matrix} \begin{bmatrix} 24 & 0 & 0 & 18 \\ 0 & 8 & -4 & -5 \\ 0 & 0 & -36 & -75 \end{bmatrix}$$

$$9R_2-R_3 \begin{bmatrix} 24 & 0 & 0 & 18 \\ 0 & 72 & 0 & 30 \\ 0 & 0 & -36 & -75 \end{bmatrix}$$

Thus $x_1=\frac{9}{12}$, $x_2=\frac{5}{12}$, $x_3=\frac{25}{12}$. Rather than reduce $\frac{9}{12}$ to $\frac{3}{4}$ it is easier to keep a common denominator for checking:

$$\begin{bmatrix} 3\left(\frac{9}{12}\right)+2\left(\frac{5}{12}\right)- & \frac{25}{12} & = & 1 \\ 2\left(\frac{9}{12}\right)+4\left(\frac{5}{12}\right)-2\left(\frac{25}{12}\right)= & & & -1 \\ 4\left(\frac{9}{12}\right)-5\left(\frac{5}{12}\right)+ & \frac{25}{12} & = & 3 \end{bmatrix} \begin{matrix} \checkmark \\ \checkmark \\ \checkmark \end{matrix}$$

Shortcut 5    Use 1's effectively.
Shortcut 6    Never switch rows.

These techniques work together and are by far the most useful shortcuts available. They are easy to use when the system has a unique solution.

Problem 5

Solve:
$$\begin{bmatrix} 2x_1+3x_2+7x_3= & 15 \\ 5x_1+4x_2-4x_3= & -9 \\ -2x_1+ x_2+2x_3= & 7 \end{bmatrix}$$

Solution    Instead of using the $(1,1)$ entry to clear the first column, we use the $(3,2)$ entry to clear the second column. This is an allowable operation and, since it uses a 1 to clear the column, it will not involve fractions:

$$\begin{bmatrix} 2 & 3 & 7 & 15 \\ 5 & 4 & -4 & -9 \\ -2 & 1 & 2 & 7 \end{bmatrix} \begin{matrix} R_1-3R_3 \\ R_2-4R_3 \\ \\ \end{matrix} \begin{bmatrix} 8 & 0 & 1 & -6 \\ 13 & 0 & -12 & -37 \\ -2 & 1 & 2 & 7 \end{bmatrix}$$

We now use the $(1,3)$ entry to clear the third column:

$$\begin{matrix} \\ R_2+12R_1 \\ R_3-2R_1 \end{matrix} \begin{bmatrix} 8 & 0 & 1 & -6 \\ 109 & 0 & 0 & -109 \\ -18 & 1 & 0 & 19 \end{bmatrix}$$

We now perform $\frac{1}{109}R_2$ and then use the $(2,1)$ entry to clear the

It is important to remember that, once you have used a row to clear a column, you should never use that row again. It would not be mathematically wrong to do so; it just would not help.

first column.

$$\tfrac{1}{109}R_2 \begin{bmatrix} 8 & 0 & 1 & -6 \\ 1 & 0 & 0 & -1 \\ -18 & 1 & 0 & 19 \end{bmatrix} \begin{matrix} R_1 - 8R_2 \\ \\ R_3 + 18R_2 \end{matrix} \begin{bmatrix} 0 & 0 & 1 & 2 \\ 1 & 0 & 0 & -1 \\ 0 & 1 & 0 & 1 \end{bmatrix}$$

Without switching rows, we obtain the answer: $x_3 = 2$, $x_1 = -1$, $x_2 = 1$; that is, $x_1 = -1$, $x_2 = 1$, $x_3 = 2$.

Check

$$\begin{bmatrix} 2(-1) + 3(1) + 7(2) = & 15 \\ 5(-1) + 4(1) - 4(2) = & -9 \\ -2(-1) + 1(1) + 2(2) = & 7 \end{bmatrix} \begin{matrix} \checkmark \\ \checkmark \\ \checkmark \end{matrix}$$

This same idea can be used even though the initial matrix does not contain a 1.

Problem 6

Solve:
$$\begin{bmatrix} 3x_1 + 4x_2 + 3x_3 = & 7 \\ 4x_1 + 6x_2 - 3x_3 = & -11 \\ 2x_1 - 8x_2 + 4x_3 = & 0 \end{bmatrix}$$

Solution

The matrix of the system is

$$\begin{bmatrix} 3 & 4 & 3 & 7 \\ 4 & 6 & -3 & -11 \\ 2 & -8 & 4 & 0 \end{bmatrix}$$

There are many ways to proceed. We decide to use a preliminary operation, $R_2 - R_1$, to obtain a 1 at address $(2, 1)$:

$$R_2 - R_1 \begin{bmatrix} 3 & 4 & 3 & 7 \\ 1 & 2 & -6 & -18 \\ 2 & -8 & 4 & 0 \end{bmatrix}$$

Using this 1 as before, we obtain

$$\begin{matrix} R_1 - 3R_2 \\ \\ R_3 - 2R_2 \end{matrix} \begin{bmatrix} 0 & -2 & 21 & 61 \\ 1 & 2 & -6 & -18 \\ 0 & -12 & 16 & 36 \end{bmatrix}$$

In this case having a $-2$ at address $(1, 2)$ is even better than having a 1 there.

We now use the $(1, 2)$ entry to clear the second column and continue

$$\begin{matrix} \\ R_2 + R_1 \\ R_3 - 6R_1 \end{matrix} \begin{bmatrix} 0 & -2 & 21 & 61 \\ 1 & 0 & 15 & 43 \\ 0 & 0 & -110 & -330 \end{bmatrix}$$

$$-\tfrac{1}{110}R_3 \begin{bmatrix} 0 & -2 & 21 & 61 \\ 1 & 0 & 15 & 43 \\ 0 & 0 & 1 & 3 \end{bmatrix} \begin{matrix} R_1 - 21R_3 \\ R_2 - 15R_3 \\ \end{matrix} \begin{bmatrix} 0 & -2 & 0 & -2 \\ 1 & 0 & 0 & -2 \\ 0 & 0 & 1 & 3 \end{bmatrix}$$

Thus $x_1 = -2$, $x_2 = 1$, $x_3 = 3$.

Check

$$\begin{bmatrix} 3(-2)+4\cdot1+3\cdot3= & 7 \\ 4(-2)+6\cdot1-3\cdot3= & -11 \\ 2(-2)-8\cdot1+4\cdot3= & 0 \end{bmatrix} \begin{matrix} \checkmark \\ \checkmark \\ \checkmark \end{matrix}$$

Preliminary row operations are useful not only for obtaining 1's but also for reducing the size of the numbers in the matrix. A row that is used in such a preliminary operation may, of course, be used later to clear a column.

Shortcuts 5 and 6 can also be used when the system has multiple answers. However, in this case the answer is not read according to the instructions on page 81. While one can give a formal description of how to read the answer, we will limit ourselves to some general advice.

(a) It is never necessary to clear more columns than rows.
(b) Keeping this in mind, clear columns until further reduction no longer simplifies the matrix.

Here we are using Shortcut 1; a cleared column need not contain 1.

(c) A column is cleared if it is not the last column and if it contains exactly one nonzero entry. Choose as many cleared columns as possible subject to the condition that no two chosen columns have their nonzero entry in the same row.
(d) The variables corresponding to the columns chosen in (c) are determined by the remaining variables (which are free).

Problem 7

Here is the final matrix that arose in trying to solve a system of equations. Read the answer.

$$\begin{bmatrix} 3 & 0 & 0 & 2 & 0 & -11 \\ 2 & -3 & 4 & 0 & 0 & 7 \\ 1 & 0 & 0 & 0 & 1 & 18 \end{bmatrix}$$

Solution

Columns $C_2$, $C_3$, $C_4$, and $C_5$ are cleared. According to (c) above, we may choose either $C_2$, $C_4$, and $C_5$ or else $C_3$, $C_4$, and $C_5$. The first choice determines the variables $x_2$, $x_4$, $x_5$ in terms of the other variables, $x_1$ and $x_3$:

$x_1$ is free

$x_2$ is given by $R_2$: $x_2 = -\frac{1}{3}(7-2x_1-4x_3)$

$x_3$ is free

$x_4$ is given by $R_1$: $x_4 = \frac{1}{2}(-11-3x_1)$

$x_5$ is given by $R_3$: $x_5 = 18-x_1$

The second choice determines the variables $x_3$, $x_4$, and $x_5$ in terms of the other variables, $x_1$ and $x_2$:

$$x_1 \text{ is free}$$
$$x_2 \text{ is free}$$
$$x_3 \text{ is given by } R_2: x_3 = \tfrac{1}{4}(7 - 2x_1 + 3x_2)$$
$$x_4 \text{ is given by } R_1: x_4 = \tfrac{1}{2}(-11 - 3x_1)$$
$$x_5 \text{ is given by } R_3: x_5 = 18 - x_1$$

In general, problems with multiple answers will have many equivalent answers, which appear in quite different forms. However, any two equivalent answers will have the same number of free variables.

**Shortcut 7** Use "Error Chasing."

This technique can save a lot of time. Let us consider the following sequence of steps to "solve" Problem 2:

**Problem 2'** Solve:

$$\begin{bmatrix} 2x_1 - x_2 + x_3 = -2 \\ x_1 + 2x_2 - x_3 = 3 \\ -x_1 + x_2 + 2x_3 = 2 \end{bmatrix}$$

**Solution**

$$\begin{bmatrix} 2 & -1 & 1 & -2 \\ 1 & 2 & -1 & 3 \\ -1 & 1 & 2 & 2 \end{bmatrix} \begin{matrix} \\ 2R_2 \\ 2R_3 \end{matrix} \begin{bmatrix} 2 & -1 & 1 & -2 \\ 2 & 4 & -2 & 6 \\ -2 & 2 & 4 & 4 \end{bmatrix}$$

$$\begin{matrix} \\ R_2 - R_1 \\ R_3 + R_1 \end{matrix} \begin{bmatrix} 2 & -1 & 1 & -2 \\ 0 & 5 & -3 & 8 \\ 0 & 1 & 5 & 2 \end{bmatrix} \begin{matrix} 5R_1 \\ \\ 5R_3 \end{matrix} \begin{bmatrix} 10 & -5 & 5 & -10 \\ 0 & 5 & -3 & 8 \\ 0 & 5 & 25 & 10 \end{bmatrix}$$

$$\begin{matrix} R_1 + R_2 \\ \\ R_3 - R_2 \end{matrix} \begin{bmatrix} 10 & 0 & 2 & -2 \\ 0 & 5 & -3 & 8 \\ 0 & 0 & 28 & 2 \end{bmatrix} \begin{matrix} 14R_1 \\ 28R_2 \\ \\ \end{matrix} \begin{bmatrix} 140 & 0 & 28 & -28 \\ 0 & 140 & -84 & 234 \\ 0 & 0 & 28 & 2 \end{bmatrix}$$

$$\begin{matrix} R_1 - R_3 \\ R_2 + 3R_3 \\ \\ \end{matrix} \begin{bmatrix} 140 & 0 & 0 & -30 \\ 0 & 140 & 0 & 240 \\ 0 & 0 & 28 & 2 \end{bmatrix}$$

Thus, $x_1 = -\tfrac{3}{14}$, $x_2 = \tfrac{24}{14}$, $x_3 = \tfrac{1}{14}$.

**Check**

$$\begin{bmatrix} 2\left(-\tfrac{3}{14}\right) - 1\left(\tfrac{24}{14}\right) + 1\left(\tfrac{1}{14}\right) = -\tfrac{29}{14} \end{bmatrix} \text{Oops!}$$

Most people would grit their teeth and start over again. This approach is generally a mistake. Most of this "solution" is probably all right. To do these seven steps over again might just introduce *new* errors. Even rechecking the arithmetic is not as good as substituting the answer into each matrix starting with the last. The answer obviously checks in the last matrix. The next to last matrix corresponds to the system

$$\begin{bmatrix} 140x_1 & +28x_3 = -28 \\ 140x_2 - 84x_3 = 234 \\ 28x_3 = 2 \end{bmatrix}$$

Since this system must have the same answer as each system in the chain, our answer must check here as well:

$$\begin{bmatrix} 140(-\frac{3}{14}) & +28(\frac{1}{14}) = -30+2 = -28 \,\checkmark \\ 140(\frac{24}{14}) - 84(\frac{1}{14}) = 240-6 = 234 \,\checkmark \\ 28(\frac{1}{14}) = 2 & \checkmark \end{bmatrix}$$

Thus no error was made in reducing this system. We check our answers in the following matrix:

$$\begin{bmatrix} 10(-\frac{3}{14}) & +2(\frac{1}{14}) = \frac{(-30+2)}{14} = -2 \\ 5(\frac{24}{14}) - 3(\frac{1}{14}) = & \frac{117}{14} = 8\frac{5}{14} \quad \text{Wrong!} \\ \\ \end{bmatrix}$$

An error has been caught. A mistake was made in going from this matrix to the next. The correct step is

$$\begin{bmatrix} 10 & 0 & 2 & -2 \\ 0 & 5 & -3 & 8 \\ 0 & 0 & 28 & 2 \end{bmatrix} \begin{matrix} 14R_1 \\ 28R_2 \end{matrix} \begin{bmatrix} 140 & 0 & 28 & -28 \\ 0 & 140 & -84 & 224 \\ 0 & 0 & 28 & 2 \end{bmatrix}$$

We complete the solution

$$\begin{matrix} R_1 - R_3 \\ R_2 + 3R_3 \end{matrix} \begin{bmatrix} 140 & 0 & 0 & -30 \\ 0 & 140 & 0 & 230 \\ 0 & 0 & 28 & 2 \end{bmatrix}$$

find that $x_1 = -\frac{3}{14}$, $x_2 = \frac{23}{14}$, and $x_3 = \frac{1}{14}$, and check again.

**Check**

$$\begin{bmatrix} 2(-\frac{3}{14}) - 1(\frac{23}{14}) + 1(\frac{1}{14}) = -2 \,\checkmark \\ 1(-\frac{3}{14}) + 2(\frac{23}{14}) - 1(\frac{1}{14}) = 3 \,\checkmark \\ -1(-\frac{3}{14}) + 1(\frac{23}{14}) + 2(\frac{1}{14}) = 2 \,\checkmark \end{bmatrix}$$

This time we have the correct answer. If it failed to check again, we would proceed as before until we found another error.

Obviously, if you have made ten arithmetic mistakes, this procedure is slower than starting over. However, it is often the

case that a wrong answer occurs because of a single mistake near
the end of the process.

**Exercises 2.4**

Making up and solving exercises is
actually the best way to learn
mathematics.

1. Select five phone numbers at random from the directory. Discarding
   the prefixes, write four of the remaining four-digit numbers as the
   first four entries of rows and the fifth four-digit number as the last
   column of the matrix of a system. For example, the numbers
   999–3838, 555–1212, QU3–7629, 312–8207, ZY5–3291 result in the
   matrix

$$\begin{bmatrix} 3 & 8 & 3 & 8 & 3 \\ 1 & 2 & 1 & 2 & 2 \\ 7 & 6 & 2 & 9 & 9 \\ 8 & 2 & 0 & 7 & 1 \end{bmatrix}$$

   Solve the resulting system of equations.
2. Repeat Exercise 1 a few times. An easier problem results if you use
   only four phone numbers, decide upon an answer, say $x_1 = -1$,
   $x_2 = 3$, $x_3 = -2$, $x_4 = 1$, and substitute to find the last column. For
   example, in the previous problem take

$$\begin{bmatrix} 3 & 8 & 3 & 8 \\ 1 & 2 & 1 & 2 \\ 7 & 6 & 2 & 9 \\ 8 & 2 & 0 & 7 \end{bmatrix}$$

   and substitute an answer picked at random. For example, $x_1 = -1$,
   $x_2 = 3$, $x_3 = -2$, $x_4 = 1$:

$$\begin{bmatrix} 3(-1) + 8(3) + 3(-2) + 8(1) = 23 \\ 1(-1) + 2(3) + 1(-2) + 2(1) = 5 \\ 7(-1) + 6(3) + 2(-2) + 9(1) = 16 \\ 8(-1) + 2(3) + 0(-2) + 7(1) = 5 \end{bmatrix}$$

   Now solve the system

$$\begin{bmatrix} 3x_1 + 8x_2 + 3x_3 + 8x_4 = 23 \\ x_1 + 2x_2 + x_3 + 2x_4 = 5 \\ 7x_1 + 6x_2 + 2x_3 + 9x_4 = 16 \\ 8x_1 + 2x_2 \qquad + 7x_4 = 5 \end{bmatrix}$$

   In this way you will have a problem for which you will know the
   answer. More than that, the answer will not involve fractions
   (although the reduction may).
3. As a variation of Problem 2, introduce some minus signs in the
   phone numbers.
4. PHE is preparing to ship some display materials to an exhibitor who
   requires 181 flags, 150 banners, 142 shields, 155 windmills, and 106
   pennants. It has on hand 5 types of packets of display materials,
   stocked as shown in Table 6. How many of each type do they ship?

Table 6

| Packet type | Flags | Banners | Shields | Windmills | Pennants |
|---|---|---|---|---|---|
| I | 20 | 5 | 11 | 7 | 16 |
| II | 16 | 12 | 4 | 10 | 5 |
| III | 4 | 11 | 15 | 12 | 7 |
| IV | 3 | 10 | 12 | 13 | 4 |
| V | 8 | 11 | 19 | 11 | 2 |

*5. Solve:

$$\begin{bmatrix}
& & & & x_5 & & +x_7-x_8 & = & 2 \\
& x_2 & & -x_4+x_5 & & & & = & 1 \\
& & x_3 & & +x_5 & & -x_7 & = & 0 \\
x_1+x_2 & & & & & & & = & -1 \\
& & x_3 & & -x_5+x_6 & & & = & -2 \\
& & & x_4 & -x_6 & & +x_8 & = & 0 \\
& x_2-x_3+x_4 & & & & & & = & -1 \\
& & & & -x_5 & & +x_7-x_8 & = & 2 \\
x_1-x_2+x_3 & -x_4+x_5-x_6 & & & & & & = & -1 \\
& & -x_3 & & +x_5+x_6 & -x_7 & & = & 1
\end{bmatrix}$$

6. An experiment has six possible outcomes: $x_1$, $x_2$, $x_3$, $x_4$, $x_5$, $x_6$. Direct observation leads me to believe that the following probabilities are correct: $P(x_1, x_3, x_5, x_6) = 0.7$, $P(x_2, x_3, x_4) = 0.7$, $P(x_4, x_5, x_6) = 0.3$, $P(x_1, x_2, x_6) = 0.35$, $P(x_3, x_4, x_5) = 0.65$. What is the probability of each outcome?

7. An experiment has sample space $S = \{a, b, c, d, e\}$. Suppose $P(a, b, c) = \frac{4}{7}$, $P(b, c, d) = \frac{4}{7}$, $P(a, c) = P(b, d)$, $P(c, d, e) = \frac{4}{7}$. What is $P(a, d, e)$?

**Section 2.5**
**The Geometry of**
**Linear Equations in**
**Three Variables**

This section is designed to increase your understanding of the various possible outcomes of Gauss-Jordan reduction. It will also be helpful in your study of the simplex method (Chapter 5). There are no new techniques of practical importance in this section; you are not necessarily expected to become proficient at drawing two-dimensional renditions of three-dimensional graphs. Linear equations in four, five, or more variables also have geometrical interpretations as graphs (called "hyperplanes") in four-dimensional, five-dimensional, or higher dimensional "space," but since no one can draw higher dimensional pictures, we will not explore that topic!

**Coordinates and**
**Planes in Space**

Just as we extended our discussion of coordinates for a line (the one-variable case) to a discussion of coordinates for the plane (the two-variable case), we will now go further, setting up a coordinate system in space (the three-variable case) by taking three lines through a point O, each line perpendicular to the other two (Figure 18). Establish a coordinate system on each of these lines,

Figure 18

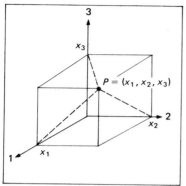

Here again we meet ordered triples. Compare with Problem 2 of Chapter 1, Section 2, p. 10.

Figure 19

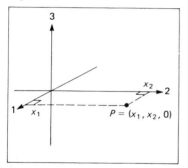

Figure 20

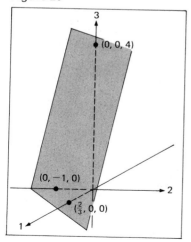

each with origin O, and call these lines, in some order, the 1-axis, 2-axis, and 3-axis. Now suppose P is a point in space. Draw the lines from P that are perpendicular to each of the three axes.

Say these lines meet the 1-, 2-, and 3-axes at points with coordinates $x_1$, $x_2$, and $x_3$, respectively. These numbers are called the **coordinates** of P, and we write

$$P = (x_1, x_2, x_3) \qquad \qquad 1$$

Points on the 1-, 2-, and 3-axis have coordinates of the form $(x_1, 0, 0)$, $(0, x_2, 0)$, and $(0, 0, x_3)$, respectively. In particular, the origin has coordinates

$$(0, 0, 0) \qquad \qquad 2$$

The plane containing the 1-axis and the 2-axis is called the **1-2-plane**. The points in the 1-2-plane all have coordinates of the form $(x_1, x_2, 0)$ (Figure 19). Similarly, the points in the **1-3-plane** and the **2-3-plane** all have coordinates of the form $(x_1, 0, x_3)$ and $(0, x_2, x_3)$, respectively.

Consider the linear equation

$$3x_1 - 2x_2 + \tfrac{1}{2}x_3 = 2 \qquad \qquad 3$$

The *graph* of this equation consists of all points $(x_1, x_2, x_3)$ whose coordinates satisfy equation **3**. Are there any such points on the 1-axis? To find out, set $x_2 = 0$ and $x_3 = 0$ in equation **3**. Then equation **3** becomes $3x_1 = 2$; that is, $x_1 = \tfrac{2}{3}$. So there is one such point on the 1-axis: $(\tfrac{2}{3}, 0, 0)$. On the 2-axis we set $x_1 = 0$ and $x_3 = 0$ in equation **3**, to obtain $-2x_2 = 2$, $x_2 = -1$; the point $(0, -1, 0)$ is on the graph. On the 3-axis we set $x_1 = 0$ and $x_2 = 0$ in equation **3** to obtain $\tfrac{1}{2}x_3 = 2$, $x_3 = 4$; the point $(0, 0, 4)$ is on the graph. These three points determine a plane (Figure 20). It can be shown that this plane is the graph of equation **3**. In general, it can be shown that the graph of any linear equation in three variables,

$$ax_1 + bx_2 + cx_3 = d \qquad \qquad 4$$

where a, b, c, and d are given numbers and a, b, and c are not all zero, is always a plane. (Compare this with the statement made about equation **3** of Section 2.1.)

If in equation **4** it happens that $a = 0$, $b = 0$, or $c = 0$, then the plane is parallel to the 1-axis, 2-axis, or 3-axis, respectively. For example, the plane with equation

$$2x_1 - 3x_3 = 6 \qquad \qquad 5$$

crosses the 1-axis at $(3, 0, 0)$, is parallel to the 2-axis, and crosses the 3-axis at $(0, 0, 2)$ (Figure 21). Another example: the plane with

Figure 21

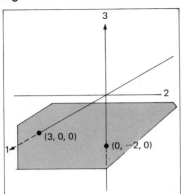

equation

$$x_2 = 4 \qquad\qquad \textbf{6}$$

is parallel to the 1-axis and the 3-axis (and hence is parallel to the 1-3-plane), and it crosses the 2-axis at $(0,4,0)$ (Figure 22). Note that the cautions given in the last paragraph on p. 59 regarding missing variables also apply here.

Now a system of two linear equations in three variables represents two planes in space. There are three possibilities:

(i) the planes are parallel,
(ii) the planes intersect in a line, or
(iii) the planes are identical; that is, the two equations represent the same plane.

These possibilities correspond to the possible solutions of the system:

(i′) no solution,
(ii′) a solution involving one free variable, or
(iii′) a solution involving two free variables.

Figure 22

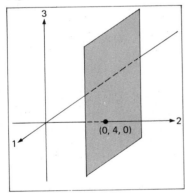

**Problem 1** Solve and interpret geometrically the following systems.

$$\text{(a)} \begin{bmatrix} 2x_1 - x_2 + x_3 = 1 \\ 4x_1 - 2x_2 + 2x_3 = -4 \end{bmatrix}$$

$$\text{(b)} \begin{bmatrix} x_1 - 2x_2 + x_3 = -2 \\ 2x_1 + 4x_2 + x_3 = 0 \end{bmatrix}$$

$$\text{(c)} \begin{bmatrix} x_1 - 2x_2 + x_3 = -2 \\ 2x_1 - 4x_2 + 2x_3 = -4 \end{bmatrix}$$

**Solution**

From now on we will usually omit the notation for the row operations used in Gauss-Jordan reduction. If you have practiced this technique enough, it should be obvious which operations we are using.

(a) $\begin{bmatrix} 2 & -1 & 1 & 1 \\ 4 & -2 & 2 & -4 \end{bmatrix}$ $\qquad$ $\begin{bmatrix} 1 & -\frac{1}{2} & \frac{1}{2} & \frac{1}{2} \\ 0 & 0 & 0 & -6 \end{bmatrix}$

No solution. The planes are parallel (Figure 23).

(b) $\begin{bmatrix} 1 & -2 & 1 & -2 \\ 2 & 4 & 1 & 0 \end{bmatrix}$ $\qquad$ $\begin{bmatrix} 1 & -2 & 1 & -2 \\ 0 & 8 & -1 & 4 \end{bmatrix}$

$\begin{bmatrix} 1 & 0 & \frac{3}{4} & -1 \\ 0 & 1 & -\frac{1}{8} & \frac{1}{2} \end{bmatrix}$

Answer

$(-1-\frac{3}{4}x_3, \frac{1}{2}+\frac{1}{8}x_3, x_3)$ where $x_3$ is free. The planes intersect in a line (Figure 24).

(c) $\begin{bmatrix} 1 & -2 & 1 & -2 \\ 2 & -4 & 2 & -4 \end{bmatrix}$ $\quad$ $\begin{bmatrix} 1 & -2 & 1 & -2 \\ 0 & 0 & 0 & 0 \end{bmatrix}$

Answer

$(-2+2x_2-x_3, x_2, x_3)$, where $x_2$ and $x_3$ are free. The planes are identical (both are the lower plane in Figure 23).

**Figure 23**

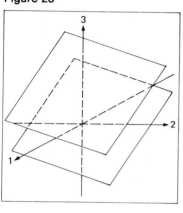

If we consider three or more planes in space, then there are two further cases.

(iv) the planes intersect in one point. This corresponds to the following possibility for a system of three or more equations in three variables.

(iv') the system has exactly one solution; that is, there are no free variables.

The final case is

(v) the planes are not all parallel, but they have no common point. Case (v) can occur in many different ways. (See, for example, Figure 25, p. 106.)

Fortunately we do not have to worry about these possibilities in connection with the corresponding system of three or more linear equations in three variables, because they all correspond to possibility (i') above: the system has no solution.

Problem 2

Solve and interpret geometrically:

$$\begin{bmatrix} x_1 - 2x_2 + x_3 = -2 \\ x_1 - 2x_2 - x_3 = \phantom{-}0 \\ x_1 + 2x_2 + x_3 = \phantom{-}1 \end{bmatrix}$$

**Figure 24**   Solution

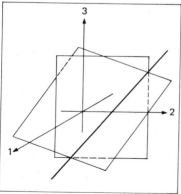

$\begin{bmatrix} 1 & -2 & 1 & -2 \\ 1 & -2 & -1 & 0 \\ 1 & 2 & 1 & 1 \end{bmatrix}$ $\quad$ $\begin{bmatrix} 1 & -2 & 1 & -2 \\ 0 & 0 & -2 & 2 \\ 0 & 4 & 0 & 3 \end{bmatrix}$

$\begin{bmatrix} 1 & -2 & 1 & -2 \\ 0 & 4 & 0 & 3 \\ 0 & 0 & -2 & 2 \end{bmatrix}$ $\quad$ $\begin{bmatrix} 1 & 0 & 1 & -\frac{1}{2} \\ 0 & 1 & 0 & \frac{3}{4} \\ 0 & 0 & -2 & 2 \end{bmatrix}$

$\begin{bmatrix} 1 & 0 & 0 & \frac{1}{2} \\ 0 & 1 & 0 & \frac{3}{4} \\ 0 & 0 & 1 & -1 \end{bmatrix}$

Answer   $(\frac{1}{2}, \frac{3}{4}, -1)$

The planes meet in one point (Figure 26).

**Figure 25**

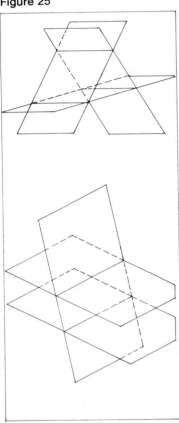

**Exercises 2.5**

In Exercises 1 through 8 solve and interpret geometrically each of the systems. You need not actually draw any planes.

1. $\begin{bmatrix} x_1 - x_2 + x_3 = 4 \\ -2x_1 + 12x_2 - 2x_3 = -6 \end{bmatrix}$

2. $\begin{bmatrix} 4x_1 - 3x_2 + 6x_3 = 12 \\ \frac{1}{3}x_1 - \frac{1}{4}x_2 + \frac{1}{2}x_3 = 1 \end{bmatrix}$

3. $\begin{bmatrix} -\frac{2}{3}x_1 + x_3 = 1 \\ 3x_1 - 2x_2 = 0 \end{bmatrix}$

4. $\begin{bmatrix} x_1 + 2x_2 + 3x_3 = 1 \\ 4x_1 + 5x_2 + 6x_3 = 2 \\ 7x_1 + 8x_2 + 9x_3 = 3 \end{bmatrix}$

5. $\begin{bmatrix} x_1 + 2x_2 + 3x_3 = 3 \\ 4x_1 + 5x_2 + 6x_3 = 2 \\ 7x_1 + 8x_2 + 9x_3 = 2 \end{bmatrix}$

6. $\begin{bmatrix} 2x_1 + x_2 + x_3 = 0 \\ x_1 - x_2 + x_3 = 1 \\ x_1 + x_2 - 2x_3 = -1 \\ 4x_1 + x_2 = 0 \end{bmatrix}$

7. $\begin{bmatrix} 2x_1 + x_2 + x_3 = 0 \\ x_1 - x_2 + x_3 = 1 \\ x_1 + x_2 - 2x_3 = -1 \\ 3x_1 + 2x_2 + x_3 = 0 \end{bmatrix}$

8. $\begin{bmatrix} 2x_1 + x_2 + x_3 = 0 \\ x_1 - x_2 + x_3 = 1 \\ 3x_1 + 2x_3 = 1 \\ x_1 + 2x_2 = -1 \end{bmatrix}$

**Figure 26**

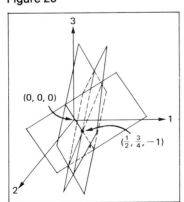

*9. Proceeding by analogy with the discussion in this section, give a geometrical interpretation of the system of equations and its solution resulting from the PHE advertising campaign (Exercise 25 in Section 2.2 and Exercise 38 in Section 2.3).

**Section 2.6**
**Matrix Arithmetic**

The workers had just finished painting

PLANNING DEPARTMENT
J. Witherspoon
Vice-President

on the door as Janet noticed the date on the appointment calendar her secretary had placed on the desk. Suddenly she realized that she had been at Appalachian Creations for exactly seven years. She recalled joining the staff just after completing her advanced degree in management science. It was her first real job. She had shared a small office with four other executives who together were responsible for computerizing many aspects of the company's affairs. Janet's specific assignment was to tabulate the production data. In this section we will see how matrix operations helped Janet answer many of the questions which came to her department.

*Her bachelor's degree was, of course, in mathematics.*

It is convenient for AC to use only three production schedules. These schedules reflect the different consumer demands in the winter, summer, and off seasons. They are:

*We are considering only a very small part of the complete production table.*

**Table 7**
**Daily Production**
**Table for June,**
**July, and August**

| Item | Factory | | |
|---|---|---|---|
| | Danbury | Springfield | Rutland |
| Light sleeping bags | 11 | 13 | 7 |
| Heavy sleeping bags | 3 | 4 | 0 |
| Down jackets | 5 | 7 | 2 |
| Two-person tents | 8 | 15 | 0 |
| Four-person tents | 0 | 14 | 4 |

**Table 8**
**Daily Production**
**Table for December,**
**January, and February**

| Item | Factory | | |
|---|---|---|---|
| | Danbury | Springfield | Rutland |
| Light sleeping bags | 2 | 5 | 0 |
| Heavy sleeping bags | 7 | 9 | 4 |
| Down jackets | 11 | 15 | 5 |
| Two-person tents | 12 | 18 | 0 |
| Four-person tents | 0 | 22 | 5 |

**Table 9**
**Daily Production**
**Table for March,**
**April, May, September,**
**October, November**

| Item | Factory | | |
|---|---|---|---|
| | Danbury | Springfield | Rutland |
| Light sleeping bags | 7 | 8 | 4 |
| Heavy sleeping bags | 4 | 6 | 3 |
| Down jackets | 8 | 9 | 0 |
| Two-person tents | 10 | 16 | 0 |
| Four-person tents | 0 | 19 | 6 |

These tables were immediately stored in matrix form in the computer's memory bank:

THE SUMMER PRODUCTION MATRIX

$$S = \begin{bmatrix} 11 & 13 & 7 \\ 3 & 4 & 0 \\ 5 & 7 & 2 \\ 8 & 15 & 0 \\ 0 & 14 & 4 \end{bmatrix}$$

THE WINTER PRODUCTION MATRIX

$$W = \begin{bmatrix} 2 & 5 & 0 \\ 7 & 9 & 4 \\ 11 & 15 & 5 \\ 12 & 18 & 0 \\ 0 & 22 & 5 \end{bmatrix}$$

THE OFF SEASON PRODUCTION MATRIX

$$O = \begin{bmatrix} 7 & 8 & 4 \\ 4 & 6 & 3 \\ 8 & 9 & 0 \\ 10 & 16 & 0 \\ 0 & 19 & 6 \end{bmatrix}$$

**Multiplication of a Matrix by a Number**

Janet's first request was for the production figures for the entire month of July. Since July of the year in question had 22 workdays, she simply had the computer multiply each entry in the production matrix S by 22. The result was the matrix

$$22S = \begin{bmatrix} 242 & 286 & 154 \\ 66 & 88 & 0 \\ 110 & 154 & 44 \\ 176 & 330 & 0 \\ 0 & 308 & 88 \end{bmatrix}$$

The actual report contained Table 10.

**Table 10
Production
Table for July**

| Item | Factory | | |
|---|---|---|---|
| | **Danbury** | **Springfield** | **Rutland** |
| Light sleeping bags | 242 | 286 | 154 |
| Heavy sleeping bags | 66 | 88 | 0 |
| Down jackets | 110 | 154 | 44 |
| Two-person tents | 176 | 330 | 0 |
| Four-person tents | 0 | 308 | 88 |

On August 17 the company switched from a 7-hour day to a 9-hour day due to increased demand. Instead of making 8 two-person tents daily at Danbury, for example, the company now produced $\frac{9}{7} \times 8 = 10\frac{2}{7}$ tents. Here the fraction $\frac{2}{7}$ refers to the fact that the last tent of the day is only partially completed. To obtain the new production figures, Janet had the computer multiply each entry of matrix S by $\frac{9}{7}$ and obtained Table 11.

Table 11
Production Table
for August 17
(increased production schedule)

| Item | Factory | | |
|---|---|---|---|
| | **Danbury** | **Springfield** | **Rutland** |
| Light sleeping bags | $14\frac{1}{7}$ | $16\frac{5}{7}$ | 9 |
| Heavy sleeping bags | $3\frac{6}{7}$ | $5\frac{1}{7}$ | 0 |
| Down jackets | $6\frac{3}{7}$ | 9 | $2\frac{4}{7}$ |
| Two-person tents | $10\frac{2}{7}$ | $19\frac{2}{7}$ | 0 |
| Four-person tents | 0 | 18 | $5\frac{1}{7}$ |

We say that matrix 22S was obtained from matrix S by *multiplying matrix S by 22*:

$$22 \begin{bmatrix} 11 & 13 & 7 \\ 3 & 4 & 0 \\ 5 & 7 & 2 \\ 8 & 15 & 0 \\ 0 & 14 & 4 \end{bmatrix} = \begin{bmatrix} 242 & 286 & 154 \\ 66 & 88 & 0 \\ 110 & 154 & 44 \\ 176 & 330 & 0 \\ 0 & 308 & 88 \end{bmatrix}$$

Similarly we obtain the matrix of Table 11 by multiplying matrix S by $\frac{9}{7}$:

$$\frac{9}{7} \begin{bmatrix} 11 & 13 & 7 \\ 3 & 4 & 0 \\ 5 & 7 & 2 \\ 8 & 15 & 0 \\ 0 & 14 & 4 \end{bmatrix} = \begin{bmatrix} 14\frac{1}{7} & 16\frac{5}{7} & 9 \\ 3\frac{6}{7} & 5\frac{1}{7} & 0 \\ 6\frac{3}{7} & 9 & 2\frac{4}{7} \\ 10\frac{2}{7} & 19\frac{2}{7} & 0 \\ 0 & 18 & 5\frac{1}{7} \end{bmatrix}$$

Obviously, this operation, multiplication of a matrix by a number, can be performed with any matrix and any number. The result will be a matrix of the same size as the original matrix.

**Problem 1**

Multiply the matrix $\begin{bmatrix} -1 & 4 & 7 & 2 \\ 3 & 8 & -6 & 1 \\ 0 & 9 & 3 & 5 \end{bmatrix}$ by $\frac{1}{2}$.

**Solution**

$$\frac{1}{2} \begin{bmatrix} -1 & 4 & 7 & 2 \\ 3 & 8 & -6 & 1 \\ 0 & 9 & 3 & 5 \end{bmatrix} = \begin{bmatrix} -\frac{1}{2} & 2 & \frac{7}{2} & 1 \\ \frac{3}{2} & 4 & -3 & \frac{1}{2} \\ 0 & \frac{9}{2} & \frac{3}{2} & \frac{5}{2} \end{bmatrix}$$

Janet's second big assignment was the preparation of the yearly production tables for the annual report. This was complicated by the fact that the company used three different production schedules. First she determined the total summer, winter, and off season production matrices. Since there were 64 production days under the summer schedule, 63 under the winter schedule, and 128 under the off season schedule, the results were obtained by multiplying.

TOTAL SUMMER PRODUCTION MATRIX

$$64\begin{bmatrix} 11 & 13 & 7 \\ 3 & 4 & 0 \\ 5 & 7 & 2 \\ 8 & 15 & 0 \\ 0 & 14 & 4 \end{bmatrix} = \begin{bmatrix} 704 & 832 & 448 \\ 192 & 256 & 0 \\ 320 & 448 & 128 \\ 512 & 960 & 0 \\ 0 & 896 & 256 \end{bmatrix}$$

TOTAL WINTER PRODUCTION MATRIX

$$63\begin{bmatrix} 2 & 5 & 0 \\ 7 & 9 & 4 \\ 11 & 15 & 5 \\ 12 & 18 & 0 \\ 0 & 22 & 5 \end{bmatrix} = \begin{bmatrix} 126 & 315 & 0 \\ 441 & 567 & 252 \\ 693 & 945 & 315 \\ 756 & 1,134 & 0 \\ 0 & 1,386 & 315 \end{bmatrix}$$

TOTAL OFF SEASON PRODUCTION MATRIX

$$128\begin{bmatrix} 7 & 8 & 4 \\ 4 & 6 & 3 \\ 8 & 9 & 0 \\ 10 & 16 & 0 \\ 0 & 19 & 6 \end{bmatrix} = \begin{bmatrix} 896 & 1,024 & 512 \\ 512 & 768 & 384 \\ 1,024 & 1,152 & 0 \\ 1,280 & 2,048 & 0 \\ 0 & 2,432 & 768 \end{bmatrix}$$

Now to obtain the total *yearly* production Janet simply had the computer add the corresponding entries in these three matrices. For example, according to the matrices, the Springfield factory produced 960 two-person tents in the summer, 1,134 in the winter, and 2,048 in the off season. Accordingly, the factory's total production of tents for the year was $960+1,134+2,048=4,142$. Each of the other entries in the total yearly production table was obtained in the same way.

**Table 12
Total Yearly
Production**

| Item | Factory | | |
|---|---|---|---|
| | **Danbury** | **Springfield** | **Rutland** |
| Light sleeping bags | 1,726 | 2,171 | 960 |
| Heavy sleeping bags | 1,145 | 1,591 | 636 |
| Down jackets | 2,037 | 2,545 | 443 |
| Two-person tents | 2,548 | 4,142 | 0 |
| Four-person tents | 0 | 4,714 | 1,339 |

Another problem arose. Each of the factories consigns a certain part of its daily output to a small factory outlet shop. The number of items sent to the store changes every day depending upon sales. The rest of the day's production is sent to the main store in Portsmouth, New Hampshire. Every day each factory fills out a form indicating how much of that day's production is to be retained for local sale. This information is tabulated by the company in Table 13.

**Table 13**
**Factory Outlet Consignment,**
**July 17**

| Item | Factory | | |
| --- | --- | --- | --- |
| | Danbury | Springfield | Rutland |
| Light sleeping bags | 3 | 5 | 2 |
| Heavy sleeping bags | 1 | 2 | 0 |
| Down jackets | 0 | 2 | 2 |
| Two-person tents | 6 | 3 | 0 |
| Four-person tents | 0 | 3 | 0 |

Refer to Table 7, p. 107. For example, of the 7 jackets produced on July 17 by the Springfield factory, 2 are sent to the factory outlet store in Springfield and the remaining 5 are sent to Portsmouth.

In order for Janet to tell the manager of the Portsmouth store how many of the items produced on July 17 will be available for sale at his store, she has merely to ask the computer to subtract each entry of the daily consignment matrix from the corresponding entry of the daily production matrix. Table 14 results.

**Table 14**
**Available Production,**
**July 17**

| Item | Factory | | |
| --- | --- | --- | --- |
| | Danbury | Springfield | Rutland |
| Light sleeping bags | 8 | 8 | 5 |
| Heavy sleeping bags | 2 | 2 | 0 |
| Down jackets | 5 | 5 | 0 |
| Two-person tents | 2 | 12 | 0 |
| Four-person tents | 0 | 11 | 4 |

This type of addition and subtraction of matrices can be done without regard to the tables from which they originate. To add two matrices, simply add corresponding entries.

**Problem 2**   Add the matrices $\begin{bmatrix} 1 & 7 \\ 3 & 5 \end{bmatrix}$ and $\begin{bmatrix} 4 & 0 \\ 6 & 2 \end{bmatrix}$

**Solution**
$$\begin{bmatrix} 1 & 7 \\ 3 & 5 \end{bmatrix} + \begin{bmatrix} 4 & 0 \\ 6 & 2 \end{bmatrix} = \begin{bmatrix} 1+4 & 7+0 \\ 3+6 & 5+2 \end{bmatrix} = \begin{bmatrix} 5 & 7 \\ 9 & 7 \end{bmatrix}$$

To subtract matrices, simply subtract corresponding entries.

**Problem 3**  Perform the indicated subtraction:

$$\begin{bmatrix} 9 & 7 & 5 \\ 10 & 6 & 3 \end{bmatrix} - \begin{bmatrix} 5 & 4 & 1 \\ 7 & 2 & 3 \end{bmatrix}$$

**Solution**

$$\begin{bmatrix} 9 & 7 & 5 \\ 10 & 6 & 3 \end{bmatrix} - \begin{bmatrix} 5 & 4 & 1 \\ 7 & 2 & 3 \end{bmatrix} = \begin{bmatrix} 9-5 & 7-4 & 5-1 \\ 10-7 & 6-2 & 3-3 \end{bmatrix}$$

$$= \begin{bmatrix} 4 & 3 & 4 \\ 3 & 4 & 0 \end{bmatrix}$$

Notice that since addition and subtraction of matrices involves the addition and subtraction of corresponding entries, two matrices can be added or subtracted only if they are the same size. To help keep this in mind we will occasionally provide exercises in which matrices of different sizes are to be added.

**Problem 4**  Add: $\begin{bmatrix} 1 & 3 \\ 3 & 4 \end{bmatrix} + \begin{bmatrix} 5 \\ 6 \end{bmatrix}$

**Solution**  They cannot be added because they are not the same size.

Addition and subtraction can just as easily be performed with negative or fractional entries.

**Problem 5**  Perform the indicated operations:

(a) $\begin{bmatrix} -2 & 3 & -1 \\ 4 & -5 & 2 \end{bmatrix} + \begin{bmatrix} 3 & -2 & -4 \\ -2 & 3 & -1 \end{bmatrix}$

(b) $\begin{bmatrix} 7 & 3 \\ -2 & 5 \\ -4 & -1 \end{bmatrix} - \begin{bmatrix} 2 & 5 \\ 4 & -2 \\ 2 & 3 \end{bmatrix}$

(c) $\begin{bmatrix} \frac{1}{2} & \frac{3}{4} \\ 1 & \frac{1}{4} \end{bmatrix} + \begin{bmatrix} \frac{1}{4} & \frac{1}{2} \\ \frac{3}{4} & 1 \end{bmatrix}$

(d) $\begin{bmatrix} \frac{2}{3} & -\frac{1}{5} & \frac{1}{2} \end{bmatrix} - \begin{bmatrix} \frac{1}{5} & \frac{3}{4} & \frac{1}{3} \end{bmatrix}$

**Solution**

(a) $\begin{bmatrix} -2 & 3 & -1 \\ 4 & -5 & 2 \end{bmatrix} + \begin{bmatrix} 3 & -2 & -4 \\ -2 & 3 & -1 \end{bmatrix} = \begin{bmatrix} 1 & 1 & -5 \\ 2 & -2 & 1 \end{bmatrix}$

(b) $\begin{bmatrix} 7 & 3 \\ -2 & 5 \\ -4 & -1 \end{bmatrix} - \begin{bmatrix} 2 & 5 \\ 4 & -2 \\ 2 & 3 \end{bmatrix} = \begin{bmatrix} 5 & -2 \\ -6 & 7 \\ -6 & -4 \end{bmatrix}$

(c) $\begin{bmatrix} \frac{1}{2} & \frac{3}{4} \\ 1 & \frac{1}{4} \end{bmatrix} + \begin{bmatrix} \frac{1}{4} & \frac{1}{2} \\ \frac{3}{4} & 1 \end{bmatrix} = \begin{bmatrix} \frac{3}{4} & \frac{5}{4} \\ \frac{7}{4} & \frac{5}{4} \end{bmatrix}$

(d) $\begin{bmatrix} \frac{2}{3} & -\frac{1}{5} & \frac{1}{2} \end{bmatrix} - \begin{bmatrix} \frac{1}{5} & \frac{3}{4} & \frac{1}{3} \end{bmatrix} = \begin{bmatrix} \frac{7}{15} & -\frac{19}{20} & \frac{1}{6} \end{bmatrix}$

We can even combine the three operations of addition, subtraction, and multiplication by a number:

**Problem 6**   Perform the indicated operations:

$$3\begin{bmatrix} 2 & 1 & 4 \\ -1 & 3 & 5 \end{bmatrix} + 2\begin{bmatrix} -1 & 2 & -3 \\ 2 & 1 & 2 \end{bmatrix} - 5\begin{bmatrix} 1 & 3 & 2 \\ 2 & 1 & -1 \end{bmatrix}$$

**Solution**

$$3\begin{bmatrix} 2 & 1 & 4 \\ -1 & 3 & 5 \end{bmatrix} + 2\begin{bmatrix} -1 & 2 & -3 \\ 2 & 1 & 2 \end{bmatrix} - 5\begin{bmatrix} 1 & 3 & 2 \\ 2 & 1 & -1 \end{bmatrix}$$

$$= \begin{bmatrix} 6 & 3 & 12 \\ -3 & 9 & 15 \end{bmatrix} + \begin{bmatrix} -2 & 4 & -6 \\ 4 & 2 & 4 \end{bmatrix} - \begin{bmatrix} 5 & 15 & 10 \\ 10 & 5 & -5 \end{bmatrix}$$

$$= \begin{bmatrix} 6-2-5 & 3+4-15 & 12-6-10 \\ -3+4-10 & 9+2-5 & 15+4+5 \end{bmatrix}$$

$$= \begin{bmatrix} -1 & -8 & -4 \\ -9 & 6 & 24 \end{bmatrix}$$

**Matrix Multiplication**

After Janet had programmed the computer to record production data, multiply a matrix by a number, and add and subtract two matrices, her department was able to answer almost any reasonable question quickly and efficiently. In fact, things quieted down so much that Janet was able to spend time working with the women's group at the plant. But then it happened. In November there was a strike at the Danbury plant that closed it down for 10 days; in Rutland, a steam pipe failed and the factory there was closed for five days. The Springfield factory was the only one of the three that was open for the entire month. Before this trouble, when Janet was asked to provide the total November production figures, she merely had the computer multiply the November production matrix by the number of workdays in November. For example, to obtain the total November production of light sleeping bags, the computer multiplied $R_1$ of the November daily production matrix (see Table 9, p. 107) by 18 (the number of working days in November) and then added the entries in the row:

$$18 \cdot 7 + 18 \cdot 8 + 18 \cdot 4 = 342$$

But now to get the total production they had to multiply the Danbury daily production by 8, the Rutland daily production by 13 and the Springfield daily production by 18. The total November light sleeping bag production was

$$8 \cdot 7 + 13 \cdot 8 + 18 \cdot 4 = 232.$$

This was a hard problem for Janet since the entire AC production matrix is really a $519 \times 20$ matrix.

Janet quickly realized that this problem could easily be solved once the computer was programmed to perform *matrix multiplication*. Since the other members of her department were not familiar with matrix operations, she first had to explain how to multiply a row matrix by a column matrix.

By a **row matrix** we mean a matrix with only one row. A **column matrix** is a matrix with only one column.

She began by presenting three examples...

**Problem 7**

Multiply $[3 \quad -1]$ by $\begin{bmatrix} -2 \\ -1 \end{bmatrix}$

**Solution**

$$[3 \quad -1]\begin{bmatrix} -2 \\ -1 \end{bmatrix} = 3\cdot(-2)+(-1)\cdot(-1) = -6+1 = -5$$

**Problem 8**

Multiply $[1 \quad 2 \quad 3]$ by $\begin{bmatrix} 4 \\ 5 \\ 6 \end{bmatrix}$.

**Solution**

$$[1 \quad 2 \quad 3]\begin{bmatrix} 4 \\ 5 \\ 6 \end{bmatrix} = 1\cdot4+2\cdot5+3\cdot6$$

$$= 4+10+18 = 32$$

**Problem 9**

Multiply $[2 \quad 1 \quad 3 \quad 4]$ by $\begin{bmatrix} 5 \\ 0 \\ -1 \\ 6 \end{bmatrix}$.

**Solution**

$$[2 \quad 1 \quad 3 \quad 4]\begin{bmatrix} 5 \\ 0 \\ -1 \\ 6 \end{bmatrix} = 2\cdot5+1\cdot0+3\cdot(-1)+4\cdot6$$

$$= 10+0-3+24 = 31$$

The next page shows a flow chart for this operation. The idea is simply to multiply the corresponding entries and then add the results. AC's problem was easily solved by the single matrix multiplication

$$[7 \quad 8 \quad 4]\begin{bmatrix} 8 \\ 13 \\ 18 \end{bmatrix} = 7\cdot8+8\cdot13+4\cdot8 = 232 \qquad \textbf{1}$$

The product of two matrices, if it is defined, is always a matrix. Thus the answers to Problems 1, 2, and 3 are really the $1\times1$ matrices [32], [31], and [−5], respectively. But for our purposes it will be convenient to omit the matrix brackets for $1\times1$

matrices and pretend that they are numbers. Notice that the number of entries in the row matrix must equal the number of entries in the column matrix, or else the matrices cannot be multiplied. Here are two more examples.

Problem 10   Multiply

$$\begin{bmatrix} 2 & 1 & 4 & 6 \end{bmatrix} \begin{bmatrix} 3 \\ 1 \\ 2 \\ 4 \\ 5 \end{bmatrix}$$

Solution   Since the first matrix has fewer entries than the second, they cannot be multiplied.

Problem 11   Multiply

$$\begin{bmatrix} -\frac{1}{3} & \frac{3}{4} & -\frac{1}{8} & 0 \end{bmatrix} \text{ by } \begin{bmatrix} 3 \\ \frac{1}{3} \\ \frac{5}{8} \\ -1 \end{bmatrix}$$

**Multiplication of a Row Matrix
by a Column Matrix**

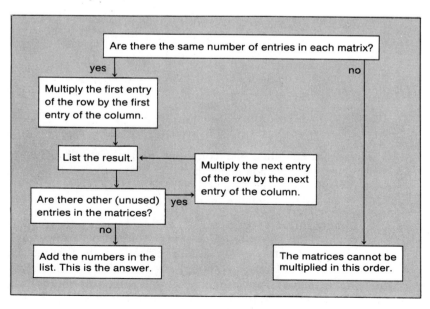

Solution

$$\begin{bmatrix} -\frac{1}{3} & \frac{3}{4} & -\frac{1}{8} & 0 \end{bmatrix} \begin{bmatrix} 3 \\ \frac{1}{3} \\ \frac{5}{8} \\ -1 \end{bmatrix} = -\frac{1}{3} \times 3 + \frac{3}{4} \times \frac{1}{3} - \frac{1}{8} \times \frac{5}{8} + 0 \times -1$$

$$= -1 + \frac{1}{4} - \frac{5}{64} + 0 = -\frac{64}{64} + \frac{16}{64} - \frac{5}{64} = -\frac{53}{64}$$

When we speak of multiplying a row matrix by a column matrix, we mean that the row matrix is on the left and the column matrix is on the right. As we shall see, the result will not be the same as when we multiply a column matrix by a row matrix.

Of course, AC makes 519 items, and to calculate the total November production of each item requires multiplication of many row matrices by the same column matrix. To complete our table there are four multiplications left to do:

HEAVY SLEEPING BAG PRODUCTION

$$\begin{bmatrix} 4 & 6 & 3 \end{bmatrix} \begin{bmatrix} 8 \\ 13 \\ 18 \end{bmatrix} = 164 \qquad\qquad \mathbf{2}$$

DOWN JACKET PRODUCTION

$$\begin{bmatrix} 8 & 9 & 0 \end{bmatrix} \begin{bmatrix} 8 \\ 13 \\ 18 \end{bmatrix} = 181 \qquad\qquad \mathbf{3}$$

TWO-PERSON TENT PRODUCTION

$$\begin{bmatrix} 10 & 16 & 0 \end{bmatrix} \begin{bmatrix} 8 \\ 13 \\ 18 \end{bmatrix} = 288 \qquad\qquad \mathbf{4}$$

FOUR-PERSON TENT PRODUCTION

$$\begin{bmatrix} 0 & 19 & 6 \end{bmatrix} \begin{bmatrix} 8 \\ 13 \\ 18 \end{bmatrix} = 355 \qquad\qquad \mathbf{5}$$

Janet programmed the computer to perform all of these operations at a single command thus saving time by requiring only one submission of data. The necessary procedure involved multiplying a matrix by a column matrix.

**How to Multiply a Matrix by a Column Matrix**

The result of this operation is always a column matrix with the same number of entries as the number of rows in the first matrix. Its first entry is obtained by multiplying $R_1$ of the first matrix by the column matrix. The second entry is obtained by multiplying $R_2$ of the first matrix by the column matrix, and so on. A flow chart for this type of multiplication appears on the next page.

Problem 12

Multiply the matrix $\begin{bmatrix} 1 & 2 & 4 \\ 3 & 1 & 2 \\ 0 & 1 & 4 \\ 1 & 2 & 1 \end{bmatrix}$ by the matrix $\begin{bmatrix} 2 \\ 1 \\ 2 \end{bmatrix}$

Solution   The answer will be a column matrix. We compute the product:

$$[1 \quad 2 \quad 4]\begin{bmatrix} 2 \\ 1 \\ 2 \end{bmatrix} = 1\cdot 2 + 2\cdot 1 + 4\cdot 2 = 12;$$ so the first entry in the col-

umn matrix is 12. Continuing, we compute the products:

$$[3 \quad 1 \quad 2]\begin{bmatrix} 2 \\ 1 \\ 2 \end{bmatrix} = 11, \quad [0 \quad 1 \quad 4]\begin{bmatrix} 2 \\ 1 \\ 2 \end{bmatrix} = 9, \text{ and } [1 \quad 2 \quad 1]\begin{bmatrix} 2 \\ 1 \\ 2 \end{bmatrix} = 6$$

Thus, the answer is

$$\begin{bmatrix} 1 & 2 & 4 \\ 3 & 1 & 2 \\ 0 & 1 & 4 \\ 1 & 2 & 1 \end{bmatrix}\begin{bmatrix} 2 \\ 1 \\ 2 \end{bmatrix} = \begin{bmatrix} 12 \\ 11 \\ 9 \\ 6 \end{bmatrix}$$

**Multiplication of a Matrix
by a Column Matrix**

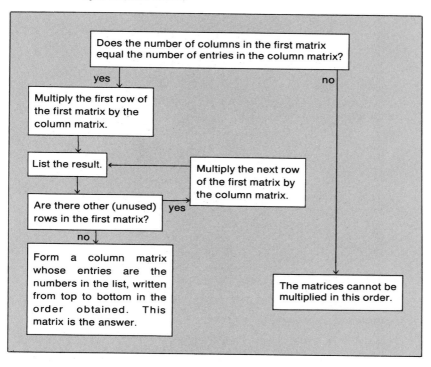

**Problem 13**

$$\text{Multiply} \begin{bmatrix} 3 & 1 & 4 \\ 2 & 8 & 1 \\ 0 & 1 & 2 \\ 3 & 1 & 5 \end{bmatrix} \text{by} \begin{bmatrix} 1 \\ 3 \\ 1 \\ 4 \end{bmatrix}$$

**Solution** Since the first matrix has only 3 columns and the column matrix has 4 entries, they cannot be multiplied.

**Problem 14** Multiply

$$\begin{bmatrix} \frac{3}{2} & -\frac{1}{3} & \frac{7}{8} \\ \frac{2}{5} & -\frac{4}{5} & -\frac{4}{15} \end{bmatrix} \text{by} \begin{bmatrix} \frac{2}{3} \\ \frac{3}{8} \\ -\frac{1}{4} \end{bmatrix}$$

**Solution**

$$\begin{bmatrix} \frac{3}{2} & -\frac{1}{3} & \frac{7}{8} \\ \frac{2}{5} & -\frac{4}{5} & -\frac{4}{15} \end{bmatrix} \begin{bmatrix} \frac{2}{3} \\ \frac{3}{8} \\ -\frac{1}{4} \end{bmatrix}$$

$$= \begin{bmatrix} \frac{3}{2} \times \frac{2}{3} + -\frac{1}{3} \times \frac{3}{8} + \frac{7}{8} \times -\frac{1}{4} \\ \frac{2}{5} \times \frac{2}{3} + -\frac{4}{5} \times \frac{3}{8} + -\frac{4}{15} \times -\frac{1}{4} \end{bmatrix}$$

$$= \begin{bmatrix} 1 - \frac{1}{8} - \frac{7}{32} \\ \frac{4}{15} - \frac{3}{10} + \frac{1}{15} \end{bmatrix} = \begin{bmatrix} \frac{21}{32} \\ \frac{1}{30} \end{bmatrix}$$

In the AC example each entry in the answer has already been computed (equations **1** through **5**):

$$\begin{bmatrix} 7 & 8 & 4 \\ 4 & 6 & 3 \\ 8 & 9 & 0 \\ 10 & 16 & 0 \\ 0 & 19 & 6 \end{bmatrix} \begin{bmatrix} 8 \\ 13 \\ 18 \end{bmatrix} = \begin{bmatrix} 232 \\ 164 \\ 181 \\ 288 \\ 355 \end{bmatrix}$$

This result is interpreted as Table 15.

**Table 15**
**Total November Production**

| Item | Production |
|---|---|
| Light sleeping bags | 232 |
| Heavy sleeping bags | 164 |
| Down jackets | 181 |
| Two-person tents | 288 |
| Four-person tents | 355 |

### Matrix Multiplication and Systems of Equations

We can use matrix multiplication to write a system of linear equations as a single matrix equation. For example, the system

$$\begin{bmatrix} 4x_1 - 3x_2 + x_3 = -7 \\ -2x_1 \qquad + 6x_3 = \phantom{-}8 \end{bmatrix} \qquad \textbf{6}$$

can be written

$$\begin{bmatrix} 4 & -3 & 1 \\ -2 & 0 & 6 \end{bmatrix} \begin{bmatrix} x_1 \\ x_2 \\ x_3 \end{bmatrix} = \begin{bmatrix} -7 \\ 8 \end{bmatrix} \qquad \textbf{7}$$

The first entry of the matrix product in **7** is $4x_1 - 3x_2 + x_3$. This must equal the first entry in the matrix $\begin{bmatrix} -7 \\ 8 \end{bmatrix}$: $4x_1 - 3x_2 + x_3 = -7$. This is the first equation in system **6**. Similarly we obtain the second equation of system **6** and thus see that equation **7** is an equivalent way to write system **6**. The matrix $\begin{bmatrix} 4 & -3 & 1 \\ -2 & 0 & 6 \end{bmatrix}$ is called the **coefficient matrix** of system **6**; the matrix $\begin{bmatrix} x_1 \\ x_2 \\ x_3 \end{bmatrix}$ is called the **unknown matrix** of system **6**; and the matrix $\begin{bmatrix} -7 \\ 8 \end{bmatrix}$ is called the **requirement matrix** of system **6**.

If we call the coefficient, unknown, and requirement matrices of system **6** A, X, and B, respectively, then equation **7** becomes $AX = B$. If we had an operation of matrix *division* we could try to solve the equation $AX = B$ by dividing both sides by A. We shall consider this in Section 6.2.

### Multiplication of Matrices

We return now to the problems at Appalachian Creations. In December, the Springfield factory was only open for 2 days because of a truckers' strike. To help meet the orders, Rutland stayed open for 25 days and Danbury for 30 days. To obtain the total December production Janet had the computer multiply the winter production schedule matrix (obtained from Table 8, p. 107) by the column matrix $\begin{bmatrix} 30 \\ 2 \\ 25 \end{bmatrix}$:

$$\begin{bmatrix} 2 & 5 & 0 \\ 7 & 9 & 4 \\ 11 & 15 & 5 \\ 12 & 18 & 0 \\ 0 & 22 & 5 \end{bmatrix} \begin{bmatrix} 30 \\ 2 \\ 25 \end{bmatrix} = \begin{bmatrix} 70 \\ 328 \\ 485 \\ 396 \\ 169 \end{bmatrix}$$

In Table 16 the headings are restored to this array of numbers:

**Table 16**
**Total December Production**

| Item | Production |
|---|---|
| Light sleeping bags | 70 |
| Heavy sleeping bags | 328 |
| Down jackets | 485 |
| Two-person tents | 396 |
| Four-person tents | 169 |

As it turned out, each month that winter each factory was open a different number of days, as Table 17 shows.

Table 17
Days of Factory
Operation per Month

| | Dec. | Jan. | Feb. |
|---|---|---|---|
| Danbury | 30 | 5 | 20 |
| Springfield | 2 | 28 | 24 |
| Rutland | 25 | 15 | 0 |

To obtain a table listing total production for each month it appeared that three separate problems would have to be fed into the machine:

DECEMBER PRODUCTION

$$\begin{bmatrix} 2 & 5 & 0 \\ 7 & 9 & 4 \\ 11 & 15 & 5 \\ 12 & 18 & 0 \\ 0 & 22 & 5 \end{bmatrix} \begin{bmatrix} 30 \\ 2 \\ 25 \end{bmatrix} = \begin{bmatrix} 70 \\ 328 \\ 485 \\ 396 \\ 169 \end{bmatrix}$$  8

JANUARY PRODUCTION

$$\begin{bmatrix} 2 & 5 & 0 \\ 7 & 9 & 4 \\ 11 & 15 & 5 \\ 12 & 18 & 0 \\ 0 & 22 & 5 \end{bmatrix} \begin{bmatrix} 5 \\ 28 \\ 15 \end{bmatrix} = \begin{bmatrix} 150 \\ 347 \\ 550 \\ 564 \\ 691 \end{bmatrix}$$  9

FEBRUARY PRODUCTION

$$\begin{bmatrix} 2 & 5 & 0 \\ 7 & 9 & 4 \\ 11 & 15 & 5 \\ 12 & 18 & 0 \\ 0 & 22 & 5 \end{bmatrix} \begin{bmatrix} 20 \\ 24 \\ 0 \end{bmatrix} = \begin{bmatrix} 160 \\ 356 \\ 580 \\ 672 \\ 528 \end{bmatrix}$$  10

But this was not the case. Since the computer had actually been programmed to multiply *any* two matrices, Janet simply fed the winter production matrix:

$$\begin{bmatrix} 2 & 5 & 0 \\ 7 & 9 & 4 \\ 11 & 15 & 5 \\ 12 & 18 & 0 \\ 0 & 22 & 5 \end{bmatrix}$$  11

and the matrix from Table 17:

$$\begin{bmatrix} 30 & 5 & 20 \\ 2 & 28 & 24 \\ 25 & 15 & 0 \end{bmatrix}$$  12

If your computer doesn't have such a button, see the flow chart on the next page.

and pressed the "multiply" button. Of course, the result was a matrix. To obtain the first column of the answer, the machine multiplied the production matrix by the first (December) column of the factory day matrix, matrix **12**. The second column involved the production matrix and the January column. The third column was the product of the production matrix and the February column. The result was the winter production matrix, consisting of the three column matrices obtained above equations **8**, **9**, and **10**:

$$
\begin{bmatrix} 2 & 5 & 0 \\ 7 & 9 & 4 \\ 11 & 15 & 5 \\ 12 & 8 & 0 \\ 0 & 22 & 5 \end{bmatrix}
\begin{bmatrix} 30 & 5 & 20 \\ 2 & 28 & 24 \\ 25 & 15 & 0 \end{bmatrix}
=
\begin{bmatrix} 70 & 150 & 160 \\ 328 & 347 & 356 \\ 485 & 550 & 580 \\ 396 & 564 & 672 \\ 169 & 691 & 528 \end{bmatrix}
$$

This yielded Table 18.

**Table 18**
**Total Winter Production**

| Item | Dec. | Jan. | Feb. |
|---|---|---|---|
| Light sleeping bags | 70 | 150 | 160 |
| Heavy sleeping bags | 328 | 347 | 356 |
| Down jackets | 485 | 550 | 580 |
| Two-person tents | 369 | 564 | 672 |
| Four-person | 169 | 691 | 528 |

**Problem 15**

Multiply $\begin{bmatrix} 1 & 2 & 3 \\ 1 & 1 & 2 \\ 2 & 1 & 1 \end{bmatrix}$ by $\begin{bmatrix} 3 & 1 \\ 1 & 2 \\ 2 & 3 \end{bmatrix}$

**Solution**

This problem will involve six multiplications of rows by columns. Generally one does these multiplications on scratch paper and records the result in the answer matrix. However, this time we will show all the steps involved in the flow chart procedure.

The first column is

$$
\begin{bmatrix} 1 & 2 & 3 \\ 1 & 1 & 2 \\ 2 & 1 & 1 \end{bmatrix}
\begin{bmatrix} 3 \\ 1 \\ 2 \end{bmatrix}
=
\begin{bmatrix} 1\cdot3+2\cdot1+3\cdot2 \\ 1\cdot3+1\cdot1+2\cdot2 \\ 2\cdot3+1\cdot1+1\cdot2 \end{bmatrix}
=
\begin{bmatrix} 11 \\ 8 \\ 9 \end{bmatrix}
$$

The second column is

$$
\begin{bmatrix} 1 & 2 & 3 \\ 1 & 1 & 2 \\ 2 & 1 & 1 \end{bmatrix}
\begin{bmatrix} 1 \\ 2 \\ 3 \end{bmatrix}
=
\begin{bmatrix} 1\cdot1+2\cdot2+3\cdot3 \\ 1\cdot1+1\cdot2+2\cdot3 \\ 2\cdot1+1\cdot2+1\cdot3 \end{bmatrix}
=
\begin{bmatrix} 14 \\ 9 \\ 7 \end{bmatrix}
$$

Hence, the answer is

$$\begin{bmatrix} 1 & 2 & 3 \\ 1 & 1 & 2 \\ 2 & 1 & 1 \end{bmatrix} \begin{bmatrix} 3 & 1 \\ 1 & 2 \\ 2 & 3 \end{bmatrix} = \begin{bmatrix} 11 & 14 \\ 8 & 9 \\ 9 & 7 \end{bmatrix}$$

**Multiplication of
One Matrix by
Another Matrix**

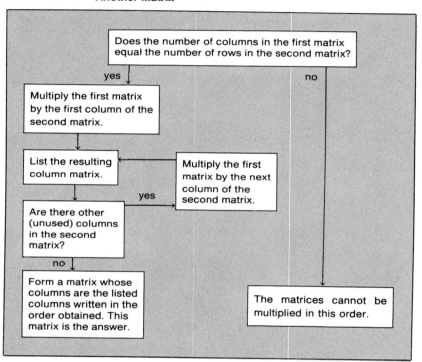

**Problem 16**

Multiply the matrix $\begin{bmatrix} 1 & 3 & 4 & 1 \\ 2 & 1 & 8 & 0 \\ 1 & 0 & 2 & 5 \end{bmatrix}$ by the matrix $\begin{bmatrix} 2 & 0 & 3 \\ 3 & 1 & -1 \\ 1 & 2 & 2 \end{bmatrix}$

**Solution**  Since the first matrix has 4 columns and the second matrix has 3 rows, the matrices cannot be multiplied.

**Problem 17**

Multiply $\begin{bmatrix} \frac{1}{2} & -\frac{1}{3} \\ \frac{2}{3} & \frac{3}{4} \\ \frac{5}{6} & \frac{1}{4} \end{bmatrix}$ by $\begin{bmatrix} 12 & -12 \\ 24 & 36 \end{bmatrix}$

Solution

$$\begin{bmatrix} \frac{1}{2} & -\frac{1}{3} \\ \frac{2}{3} & \frac{3}{4} \\ \frac{5}{6} & \frac{1}{4} \end{bmatrix} \begin{bmatrix} 12 & -12 \\ 24 & 36 \end{bmatrix}$$

If we denote the first and second matrices in this problem by A and B, respectively, we may write

$$AB = \begin{bmatrix} -2 & -18 \\ 26 & 19 \\ 16 & -1 \end{bmatrix}$$

$$= \begin{bmatrix} \frac{1}{2} \times 12 + -\frac{1}{3} \times 24 & \frac{1}{2} \times -12 + -\frac{1}{3} \times 36 \\ \frac{2}{3} \times 12 + \frac{3}{4} \times 24 & \frac{2}{3} \times -12 + \frac{3}{4} \times 36 \\ \frac{5}{6} \times 12 + \frac{1}{4} \times 24 & \frac{5}{6} \times -12 + \frac{1}{4} \times 36 \end{bmatrix}$$

$$= \begin{bmatrix} 6-8 & -6-12 \\ 8+18 & -8+27 \\ 10+6 & -10+9 \end{bmatrix} = \begin{bmatrix} -2 & -18 \\ 26 & 19 \\ 16 & -1 \end{bmatrix}$$

Matrix multiplication is not hard to remember once you have learned how to multiply a row by a column. For example, to obtain the (3,2) entry of the answer, multiply the third row of the first matrix by the second column of the second matrix:

The rows of the matrix, reading from top to bottom, are denoted by $R_1$, $R_2$, $R_3$, and so on. The columns of a matrix, reading from left to right, are denoted by $C_1$, $C_2$, $C_3$, and so on.

$$R_3 \text{ (first matrix)} \times C_2 \text{ (second matrix)} =$$
$$\text{the (3,2) entry of the answer.}$$

In Problem 17 the first matrix has

$$R_3 = \begin{bmatrix} \frac{5}{6} & \frac{1}{4} \end{bmatrix}$$

and the second matrix has

$$C_2 = \begin{bmatrix} -12 \\ 36 \end{bmatrix}$$

so their product,

$$R_3 C_2 = \begin{bmatrix} \frac{5}{6} & \frac{1}{4} \end{bmatrix} \begin{bmatrix} -12 \\ 36 \end{bmatrix} = -1$$

is the (3,2) entry of the answer.

In general, to obtain the entry in a particular row and column of the answer, multiply the row of the first matrix corresponding to the row of the entry by the column of the second matrix corresponding to the column of the entry.

Problem 18   What is the (4,5) entry of the following product?

$$\begin{bmatrix} 2 & 0 & 3 & 4 \\ 4 & 0 & 8 & 2 \\ 3 & 2 & 1 & 4 \\ 2 & 8 & 6 & 4 \end{bmatrix} \begin{bmatrix} 1 & 3 & 7 & 2 & 3 \\ 4 & 2 & 1 & 1 & 2 \\ 2 & 1 & 4 & 9 & 1 \\ 5 & 6 & 8 & 6 & 5 \end{bmatrix}$$

Solution   In the first matrix

$$R_4 = \begin{bmatrix} 2 & 8 & 6 & 4 \end{bmatrix}$$

In the second matrix

$$C_5 = \begin{bmatrix} 3 \\ 2 \\ 1 \\ 5 \end{bmatrix}$$

The (4, 5) entry of the product is

$$R_4 C_5 = \begin{bmatrix} 2 & 8 & 6 & 4 \end{bmatrix} \begin{bmatrix} 3 \\ 2 \\ 1 \\ 5 \end{bmatrix} = 48$$

Another helpful hint: before multiplying two matrices, write their sizes side by side. If you are asked to multiply a $3 \times 4$ matrix by a $4 \times 2$ matrix, write:

$$3 \times 4 \quad 4 \times 2$$

First look at the inside numbers (the 4s). If they are the same, the matrices can be multiplied; otherwise, they cannot. And if the inside numbers are the same, then the outside numbers (the 3 and the 2) indicate the size of the answer: in this case, a $3 \times 2$ matrix.

**Problem 19**

What size matrix results when a $3 \times 5$ and a $5 \times 4$ matrix are multiplied?

**Solution**

Same: they can be multiplied

$$3 \times 5 \quad 5 \times 4$$

The result is a $3 \times 4$ matrix.

**Problem 20**

What size matrix results when a $5 \times 6$ and a $7 \times 4$ matrix are multiplied?

**Solution**

not the same

$$5 \times 6 \quad 7 \times 4$$

They cannot be multiplied.

**Problem 21**

What size matrix results when a $1 \times 3$ and a $3 \times 1$ matrix are multiplied?

**Solution**

Same: they can be multiplied.

$$1 \times 3 \quad 3 \times 1$$

The result is a $1 \times 1$ matrix.

Thus, the result is a number, as we would expect from multiplying a row matrix by a column matrix.

**Problem 22**

What size matrix results when a $3 \times 1$ matrix and a $1 \times 3$ matrix are multiplied?

**Solution**

——Same: they can be multiplied.

$3 \times 1 \quad 1 \times 3$

——The result is a $3 \times 3$ matrix.

This last problem raises an interesting question. If you multiply the $3 \times 1$ column matrix $\begin{bmatrix} 1 \\ 3 \\ 2 \end{bmatrix}$ by the $1 \times 3$ row matrix [4  5  6], the rule says that you will get a $3 \times 3$ matrix as a result. Just how does this happen? The $(1,1)$ entry of the answer is obtained by multiplying $R_1$ of $\begin{bmatrix} 1 \\ 3 \\ 2 \end{bmatrix}$ by $C_1$ of [4  5  6]. $R_1$ is just the number 1; $C_1$ is just the number 4. Thus, the $(1,1)$ entry of the answer is $1 \cdot 4 = 4$. To obtain the $(2,3)$ entry, we multiply $R_2$ of $\begin{bmatrix} 1 \\ 3 \\ 2 \end{bmatrix}$ by $C_3$ of [4  5  6]. Since $R_2 = 3$ and $C_3 = 6$, the $(2,3)$ entry of the answer matrix is $3 \cdot 6 = 18$. The other seven entries are found in exactly the same way:

$$\begin{bmatrix} 1 \\ 3 \\ 2 \end{bmatrix} [4 \quad 5 \quad 6] = \begin{bmatrix} 1 \cdot 4 & 1 \cdot 5 & 1 \cdot 6 \\ 3 \cdot 4 & 3 \cdot 5 & 3 \cdot 6 \\ 2 \cdot 4 & 2 \cdot 5 & 2 \cdot 6 \end{bmatrix} = \begin{bmatrix} 4 & 5 & 6 \\ 12 & 15 & 18 \\ 8 & 10 & 12 \end{bmatrix}$$

Notice that the product of these two matrices in the other order is

$$[4 \quad 5 \quad 6] \begin{bmatrix} 1 \\ 3 \\ 2 \end{bmatrix} = 4 \cdot 1 + 5 \cdot 3 + 6 \cdot 2$$

$$= 4 + 15 + 12 = 31$$

The product in one order is a $3 \times 3$ matrix and in the other order a $1 \times 1$ matrix, that is, a number. With numbers, the order of multiplication is immaterial: for instance, $3 \cdot 6 = 18 = 6 \cdot 3$. With matrices, the order matters quite a lot. Sometimes two matrices can be multiplied only in one order. For example, a $2 \times 3$ matrix can be multiplied by a $3 \times 4$ matrix:

—— same

$2 \times 3 \quad 3 \times 4$;   but not the other way around:   $3 \times 4 \quad 2 \times 3$. ——different

We will explore this facet of matrix multiplication in some of the problems at the end of this section.

Janet found many uses for matrix multiplication at Appalachian Creations. One summer, for example, the president asked for a table listing the daily raw material requirements of each of the various plants. While AC actually uses several hundred different components in its products, we will again limit our discussion to the use of goose down, type 1 nylon, and type 2 nylon. Table 19 lists the various requirements and, incidently, the profit on each item produced.

Table 19

| Material | Item | | | | |
|---|---|---|---|---|---|
| | | | | Two-person | Four-person |
| | Lt. bags | Heavy bags | Jackets | tents | tents |
| Down (in lbs.) | 2 | 4 | 3 | 0 | 0 |
| Type 1 nylon (in yds.) | 2 | 2 | 2 | 4 | 8 |
| Type 2 nylon (in yds.) | 2 | 2 | 0 | 2 | 4 |
| Profit (in $) | 1 | 1 | 2 | 2 | 3 |

To obtain the material requirements, Janet had the computer multiply the matrix obtained from Table 19 by the daily summer production matrix (from Table 7, p. 107).

$$\begin{bmatrix} 2 & 4 & 3 & 0 & 0 \\ 2 & 2 & 2 & 4 & 8 \\ 2 & 2 & 0 & 2 & 4 \\ 1 & 1 & 2 & 2 & 3 \end{bmatrix} \begin{bmatrix} 11 & 13 & 7 \\ 3 & 4 & 0 \\ 5 & 7 & 2 \\ 8 & 15 & 0 \\ 0 & 14 & 4 \end{bmatrix} = \begin{bmatrix} 49 & 63 & 20 \\ 70 & 220 & 50 \\ 44 & 120 & 30 \\ 40 & 103 & 23 \end{bmatrix}$$

The result of this multiplication is tabulated in Table 20:

Table 20

| | Danbury | Springfield | Rutland |
|---|---|---|---|
| Down | 49 lbs. | 63 lbs. | 20 lbs. |
| Type 1 nylon | 70 yds. | 220 yds. | 50 yds. |
| Type 2 nylon | 44 yds. | 120 yds. | 30 yds. |
| Profit | $40 | $103 | $23 |

Note that in this table the row headings correspond to the row headings in Table 19 and the column headings correspond to the column headings in Table 7. In fact, if the matrices in any multiplication problem arise from a practical situation, the column headings on the first matrix must correspond to the row headings on the second matrix. The resulting table inherits its row headings from the first matrix and its column headings from the second matrix. The repeated headings disappear.

As another application consider the problems of determining the total production per factory for a day and the total production of each item for a day in July.

The answers to these questions are provided by the respective multiplications:

$$\begin{bmatrix} 1 & 1 & 1 & 1 & 1 \end{bmatrix} \begin{bmatrix} 11 & 13 & 7 \\ 3 & 4 & 0 \\ 5 & 7 & 2 \\ 8 & 15 & 0 \\ 0 & 14 & 4 \end{bmatrix} = \begin{bmatrix} 27 & 53 & 13 \end{bmatrix}$$

and

$$\begin{bmatrix} 11 & 13 & 7 \\ 3 & 4 & 0 \\ 5 & 7 & 2 \\ 8 & 15 & 0 \\ 0 & 14 & 4 \end{bmatrix} \begin{bmatrix} 1 \\ 1 \\ 1 \end{bmatrix} = \begin{bmatrix} 31 \\ 7 \\ 14 \\ 23 \\ 18 \end{bmatrix}$$

(If you perform the arithmetic involved in each matrix multiplication, you will see that you are doing exactly the computation you would do to obtain the answers directly from the tables.)

Finally, for purposes of Chapters 5 and 6, we introduce the identity matrices. An **identity matrix** is a square matrix with ones on the main diagonal (the diagonal from upper left to lower right) and zeros everywhere else. Thus, the $1 \times 1$, $2 \times 2$, $3 \times 3$, and $4 \times 4$ identity matrices are: $[1]$, $\begin{bmatrix} 1 & 0 \\ 0 & 1 \end{bmatrix}$, $\begin{bmatrix} 1 & 0 & 0 \\ 0 & 1 & 0 \\ 0 & 0 & 1 \end{bmatrix}$, and $\begin{bmatrix} 1 & 0 & 0 & 0 \\ 0 & 1 & 0 & 0 \\ 0 & 0 & 1 & 0 \\ 0 & 0 & 0 & 1 \end{bmatrix}$ respectively. It can be shown that, if I is an identity matrix and A is any matrix with the same number of rows as I, then $IA = A$. It can also be shown that, if B is any matrix with the same number of columns as I, then $BI = B$. The reader may easily check, for example, that

> **A square matrix** is a matrix with the same number of rows as columns.

> If a and b are numbers then, of course, $1 \cdot a = a$ and $b \cdot 1 = b$. Thus, the identity matrices are a matrix analog to the multiplicative identity number, 1. Indeed, this is why these matrices are called identity matrices.

$$\begin{bmatrix} 1 & 0 \\ 0 & 1 \end{bmatrix} \begin{bmatrix} -2 & 3 & \frac{1}{2} \\ 0 & 2 & -4 \end{bmatrix} = \begin{bmatrix} -2 & 3 & \frac{1}{2} \\ 0 & 2 & -4 \end{bmatrix},$$

$$\begin{bmatrix} -2 & 3 & \frac{1}{2} \\ 0 & 2 & -4 \end{bmatrix} \begin{bmatrix} 1 & 0 & 0 \\ 0 & 1 & 0 \\ 0 & 0 & 1 \end{bmatrix} = \begin{bmatrix} -2 & 3 & \frac{1}{2} \\ 0 & 2 & -4 \end{bmatrix}$$

$$\begin{bmatrix} 4 & 5 & 6 & 7 \\ 3 & 4 & 5 & 6 \\ 2 & 1 & 0 & -1 \\ -5 & -4 & -3 & -2 \end{bmatrix} \begin{bmatrix} 1 & 0 & 0 & 0 \\ 0 & 1 & 0 & 0 \\ 0 & 0 & 1 & 0 \\ 0 & 0 & 0 & 1 \end{bmatrix}$$

$$= \begin{bmatrix} 1 & 0 & 0 & 0 \\ 0 & 1 & 0 & 0 \\ 0 & 0 & 1 & 0 \\ 0 & 0 & 0 & 1 \end{bmatrix} \begin{bmatrix} 4 & 5 & 6 & 7 \\ 3 & 4 & 5 & 6 \\ 2 & 1 & 0 & -1 \\ -5 & -4 & -3 & -2 \end{bmatrix} = \begin{bmatrix} 4 & 5 & 6 & 7 \\ 3 & 4 & 5 & 6 \\ 2 & 1 & 0 & -1 \\ -5 & -4 & -3 & -2 \end{bmatrix}$$

**Exercises 2.6**  In Exercises 1 through 6 calculate the indicated product.

1. $2 \begin{bmatrix} -1 & 0 & 3 \\ 2 & 4 & 7 \\ 3 & 8 & 5 \end{bmatrix}$

2. $-3 \begin{bmatrix} 2 & -1 \\ 0 & 3 \\ -4 & 1 \end{bmatrix}$

3. $\frac{1}{2} \begin{bmatrix} 2 & 0 & -4 & 6 \\ 8 & 4 & -6 & 2 \\ 2 & -2 & 0 & 4 \end{bmatrix}$

4. $-\frac{2}{3} \begin{bmatrix} -3 \\ 6 \\ 0 \end{bmatrix}$

5. $6 \begin{bmatrix} \frac{2}{3} & -1 & \frac{5}{6} \\ 0 & \frac{1}{2} & -\frac{4}{3} \end{bmatrix}$

6. $-\frac{3}{4} \begin{bmatrix} -2 & \frac{3}{8} & -\frac{4}{3} \\ 0 & 4 & 7 \\ -\frac{1}{4} & -\frac{2}{3} & \frac{3}{4} \end{bmatrix}$

7. Since 1958 the vaccination clinic in Addis Ababa, Ethiopia, has administered shots for typhus, typhoid, yellow fever, and cholera to men, women, and children every day, seven days a week, as shown in Table 21.

**Table 21**
**Number of Shots**
**Given per Day**

|  | Men | Women | Children |
|---|---|---|---|
| Typhus | 80 | 60 | 201 |
| Typhoid | 60 | 70 | 184 |
| Yellow fever | 42 | 24 | 97 |
| Cholera | 145 | 163 | 88 |

Denote by V (for vaccination) the matrix obtained from the table. Write, in terms of V, the matrices that give:
(a) the number of shots given in 1973.
C(b) the number of shots given in 1972.
C(c) the number of shots given in the 1960s.

8. Suppose that each of 1,000 workers at a factory does the same amount of work. If the company reduces its staff by 200 but increases its workday from 10 to 15 hours, by what fraction should it multiply its production matrix to obtain the new daily production matrix?

*Assume that the reduction in staff does not affect individual productivity.*

9. Find a $2 \times 2$ matrix X such that

$$2X - \begin{bmatrix} 1 & 2 \\ 3 & 4 \end{bmatrix} = \begin{bmatrix} 5 & 6 \\ 7 & 8 \end{bmatrix}$$

10. What is the total daily production of bags, jackets, and tents by Appalachian Creations for the months of February, July, and September?

11. It happened that in November the daily consignment table was the same for each one of the 18 workdays (Table 22).

**Table 22**
**November Daily**
**Consignment Table**

| Item | Factory | | |
|---|---|---|---|
|  | Danbury | Springfield | Rutland |
| Light sleeping bags | 2 | 3 | 0 |
| Heavy sleeping bags | 3 | 5 | 3 |
| Down jackets | 6 | 7 | 0 |
| Two-person tents | 3 | 5 | 0 |
| Four-person tents | 0 | 3 | 2 |

Use the figures in Table 22 to obtain the available-output table for the entire month of November.

In Exercises 12 through 20 perform the indicated operations.

12. $\begin{bmatrix} 1 & 2 \\ 3 & 1 \end{bmatrix} + \begin{bmatrix} 2 & 2 \\ 1 & 4 \end{bmatrix}$
$\qquad$
13. $\begin{bmatrix} -1 & 2 \\ 3 & -4 \end{bmatrix} + \begin{bmatrix} 2 & 5 \\ -1 & 9 \end{bmatrix}$

14. $\begin{bmatrix} 3 & 1 & -1 \\ 2 & -1 & 0 \end{bmatrix} + \begin{bmatrix} 1 & 2 \\ -1 & 3 \end{bmatrix}$
$\qquad$
15. $\begin{bmatrix} -1 \\ 3 \\ -2 \end{bmatrix} + \begin{bmatrix} 3 \\ -2 \\ 4 \end{bmatrix}$

16. $[-1 \quad 2 \quad -3] + \begin{bmatrix} 3 \\ -1 \\ 4 \end{bmatrix}$

17. $\begin{bmatrix} -\frac{1}{3} & \frac{1}{5} & -\frac{1}{7} \\ \frac{2}{3} & \frac{1}{7} & \frac{3}{8} \end{bmatrix} - \begin{bmatrix} \frac{2}{3} & -\frac{1}{5} & \frac{3}{2} & 1 \\ -\frac{1}{5} & \frac{1}{9} & \frac{2}{3} & -\frac{1}{2} \end{bmatrix}$

18. $\begin{bmatrix} \frac{2}{3} & \frac{1}{8} \\ \frac{3}{4} & \frac{1}{2} \end{bmatrix} + \begin{bmatrix} 0 & 0 \\ 0 & 0 \end{bmatrix}$
$\qquad$
19. $\begin{bmatrix} \frac{3}{8} \\ \frac{2}{3} \end{bmatrix} - \begin{bmatrix} \frac{3}{8} \\ \frac{2}{3} \end{bmatrix}$

20. $\begin{bmatrix} 1 & -2 & \frac{2}{3} & -\frac{1}{7} \\ 2 & -\frac{1}{5} & -\frac{1}{4} & \frac{1}{8} \\ \frac{1}{3} & \frac{3}{8} & -2 & \frac{1}{4} \\ -\frac{2}{9} & \frac{1}{4} & -\frac{1}{5} & -\frac{1}{3} \end{bmatrix} - \begin{bmatrix} \frac{1}{2} & -\frac{1}{4} & -\frac{1}{3} & \frac{3}{7} \\ -\frac{1}{3} & -3 & 1 & \frac{3}{8} \\ 2 & -\frac{1}{4} & \frac{1}{2} & -2 \\ -\frac{4}{9} & \frac{1}{8} & -\frac{2}{3} & \frac{1}{2} \end{bmatrix}$

In Exercises 21 through 25 perform the indicated operations.

21. $3 \begin{bmatrix} 2 & -1 & 3 \\ 1 & 0 & 2 \\ -1 & 4 & 1 \end{bmatrix} + 5 \begin{bmatrix} 1 & -2 & 3 \\ 2 & 1 & 4 \\ 3 & 2 & 1 \end{bmatrix}$

22. $2 \begin{bmatrix} 1 & 2 \\ 4 & 2 \end{bmatrix} - \begin{bmatrix} 3 & 2 \\ 1 & 0 \end{bmatrix}$
$\qquad$
23. $\frac{1}{2} \begin{bmatrix} 3 & 4 \\ -1 & 2 \end{bmatrix} - \frac{1}{3} \begin{bmatrix} 7 & -6 \\ 2 & -4 \end{bmatrix}$

24. $2 \begin{bmatrix} 2 & 1 & 3 \\ 0 & 2 & 3 \\ 1 & 1 & 1 \end{bmatrix} + \begin{bmatrix} 1 & 1 & 3 \\ 3 & 1 & 0 \\ 7 & 4 & 6 \end{bmatrix} - 3 \begin{bmatrix} 1 & 1 & 3 \\ 1 & 1 & 2 \\ 3 & 2 & 2 \end{bmatrix}$

25. $\frac{1}{2} \begin{bmatrix} 1 & 2 \\ 0 & 3 \\ -1 & 2 \end{bmatrix} + \frac{1}{3} \begin{bmatrix} 2 & 1 \\ 3 & 2 \\ -1 & 4 \end{bmatrix} - \frac{1}{5} \begin{bmatrix} 1 & 2 & -1 \\ 0 & 3 & 4 \\ 1 & 2 & 3 \end{bmatrix}$

*26. Determine what matrix should be added to the first matrix to obtain the second matrix.

$$\begin{bmatrix} 2 & 1 & 3 \\ 1 & 2 & 3 \end{bmatrix}, \begin{bmatrix} 7 & 0 & 4 \\ 5 & 5 & 1 \end{bmatrix}$$

*27. Determine what matrix should be subtracted from the first to obtain the second.

$$\begin{bmatrix} 7 \\ 3 \\ 2 \end{bmatrix}, \begin{bmatrix} 3 \\ 3 \\ 1 \end{bmatrix}$$

See Exercise 7 above.

28. Recently a second clinic opened in Addis Ababa. This one is closed on Saturday and Sunday each week, but on the other days it gives shots as shown in Table 23.

Table 23
Number of Shots
Given per Day

| | Men | Women | Children |
|---|---|---|---|
| Typhus | 30 | 30 | 40 |
| Typhoid | 20 | 30 | 96 |
| Yellow fever | 8 | 6 | 0 |
| Cholera | 205 | 107 | 212 |

(a) Write the matrix obtained from a table that shows the number of shots given on any Thursday by the two clinics combined.

*(b) Let U denote the matrix obtained from Table 23. Let W be the matrix obtained from a table that shows the number of shots per week given by the combined clinics. Express W in terms of U and V.

V is obtained from Table 21, Exercise 7, above.

*(c) For some time the World Health Organization was using a matrix F for weekly shots for the combined clinics that was based on the false assumption that both clinics were operating every day. Show how to obtain W from F and U.

29. Like many sophisticated modern corporations, Petaluma Hamburger Emporium has created, on paper, a small "model" company for use in planning. The data related to the Petaluma Hamburger Emporium Model (PHEM) company are supplied by the PHE market-research department based on surveys of MacDougal's, PHE's arch competitor, as well as PHE itself. PHEM has three stores, called simply store 1, store 2, and store 3, each selling four items: item 1, hamburger; item 2, cheeseburger; item 3, French fries; item 4, milkshake. Production matrices for PHEM are monthly, not weekly. The production matrices for July (J), August (A), September (S), and October (O), are

$$J = \begin{bmatrix} 40 & 30 & 60 & 60 \\ 50 & 20 & 60 & 70 \\ 30 & 40 & 50 & 60 \end{bmatrix} \quad S = \begin{bmatrix} 30 & 30 & 70 & 75 \\ 60 & 25 & 80 & 50 \\ 35 & 55 & 65 & 45 \end{bmatrix}$$

$$A = \begin{bmatrix} 45 & 35 & 65 & 70 \\ 45 & 30 & 40 & 65 \\ 40 & 60 & 70 & 35 \end{bmatrix} \quad O = \begin{bmatrix} 40 & 35 & 70 & 60 \\ 50 & 30 & 80 & 70 \\ 30 & 60 & 65 & 60 \end{bmatrix}$$

(a) Denote by Q the PHEM production matrix for the third quarter. Express Q in terms of J, A, S, and O.

(b) Write out Q.

(c) The PHEM production matrix for the fourth quarter was

$$F = \begin{bmatrix} 120 & 100 & 190 & 185 \\ 145 & 65 & 170 & 160 \\ 110 & 145 & 195 & 155 \end{bmatrix}$$

Denote by T the production matrix for the last two months of the year. Express T in terms of the matrices above.

(d) Write out T.

30. Write

$$[2 \quad -3 \quad 4]\begin{bmatrix} x_1 \\ x_2 \\ x_3 \end{bmatrix} = 7$$

as a numerical equation.

In Exercises 31 and 32 write the given matrix equation as a system of linear equations.

31. $\begin{bmatrix} 2 & 0 & 1 \\ -3 & 1 & -4 \end{bmatrix}\begin{bmatrix} x_1 \\ x_2 \\ x_3 \end{bmatrix} = \begin{bmatrix} 8 \\ -25 \end{bmatrix}$    32. $\begin{bmatrix} 3 & 2 \\ -1 & 4 \\ 2 & 8 \end{bmatrix}\begin{bmatrix} x_1 \\ x_2 \end{bmatrix} = \begin{bmatrix} 2 \\ 4 \\ 3 \end{bmatrix}$

In Exercises 33 and 34 write the given system of linear equations as a matrix equation.

33. $\begin{bmatrix} 3x_1 + 2x_2 - x_3 = -2 \\ x_1 - 2x_2 + 3x_3 = 12 \\ 4x_1 - x_2 + 2x_3 = 11 \end{bmatrix}$    34. $\begin{bmatrix} x_1 - 2x_2 + x_3 = 0 \\ 3x_1 - x_2 - 3x_3 = -7 \end{bmatrix}$

In Exercises 35 through 38 find the indicated entries in the product

$$\begin{bmatrix} 2 & -1 & 3 & 0 & 2 \\ 1 & 1 & 2 & 1 & 4 \\ 3 & 2 & 8 & 0 & -9 \\ 1 & -4 & 6 & -2 & 1 \\ -1 & 2 & -1 & 4 & 9 \end{bmatrix}\begin{bmatrix} 1 & 3 & -1 \\ 4 & -8 & 2 \\ 2 & 1 & -3 \\ 6 & -7 & 4 \\ 8 & 6 & 6 \end{bmatrix}$$

35. $(2,1)$    36. $(6,3)$    37. $(5,2)$    38. $(3,3)$

In Exercises 39 through 42, do not multiply the pairs of matrices; simply give the size of the answer.

$^c$39. $\begin{bmatrix} 2 & 1 & 0 \\ 3 & 1 & 4 \\ 6 & 7 & 8 \end{bmatrix}\begin{bmatrix} 2 & 1 & 7 & 8 & 4 \\ 1 & -1 & 3 & 8 & 6 \\ 2 & 4 & 8 & 9 & 5 \end{bmatrix}$

40. $\begin{bmatrix} 2 & 0 \\ 1 & -1 \\ 4 & 6 \\ 3 & 1 \\ 5 & 8 \end{bmatrix}\begin{bmatrix} 2 & 4 & 7 & 3 & 8 \\ 1 & 5 & 0 & 7 & 4 \end{bmatrix}$

41. $\begin{bmatrix} 3 & 1 & 2 & 4 \\ 0 & 1 & 1 & 2 \\ 2 & -1 & 3 & 6 \\ 4 & 2 & 1 & 8 \\ 7 & 6 & 0 & 5 \end{bmatrix} \begin{bmatrix} 3 & 2 & 7 & 6 & 1 \\ 2 & 1 & 0 & 2 & 1 \\ 4 & 5 & 7 & 8 & -1 \\ 6 & 1 & 9 & 3 & -1 \\ 3 & 2 & 0 & 2 & 5 \end{bmatrix}$

42. $\begin{bmatrix} 3 \\ 1 \\ 2 \\ 4 \\ 6 \\ 8 \end{bmatrix} [2 \quad 1 \quad 7 \quad 8 \quad 9]$

43. Multiplication of two matrices results in a $5 \times 7$ matrix. What can be said about the sizes of the two matrices that were multiplied to produce this result?

In Exercises 44 through 62 perform the matrix multiplications:

44. $[3 \quad 2] \begin{bmatrix} 1 \\ 4 \end{bmatrix}$

45. $\begin{bmatrix} 3 & 2 \\ 1 & 2 \end{bmatrix} \begin{bmatrix} 1 \\ 4 \end{bmatrix}$

46. $[1 \quad 4] \begin{bmatrix} 3 & 2 \\ 1 & 2 \end{bmatrix}$

47. $\begin{bmatrix} 1 & 4 \\ 3 & 1 \end{bmatrix} \begin{bmatrix} 3 & 2 \\ 1 & 2 \end{bmatrix}$

48. $\begin{bmatrix} 1 & 4 \\ 3 & 1 \\ 0 & 2 \end{bmatrix} \begin{bmatrix} 3 & 2 & 1 \\ 1 & 2 & 2 \end{bmatrix}$

49. $\begin{bmatrix} 1 & 1 \\ 0 & 1 \end{bmatrix} \begin{bmatrix} 1 & 0 \\ 1 & 1 \end{bmatrix}$

$^c$50. $\begin{bmatrix} 1 & 0 \\ 1 & 1 \end{bmatrix} \begin{bmatrix} 1 & 1 \\ 0 & 1 \end{bmatrix}$

51. $\begin{bmatrix} 3 & 2 \\ 4 & -1 \end{bmatrix} \begin{bmatrix} 3 & 1 \\ 2 & 1 \end{bmatrix}$

$^c$52. $\begin{bmatrix} 3 & 1 \\ 2 & 1 \end{bmatrix} \begin{bmatrix} 3 & 2 \\ 4 & -1 \end{bmatrix}$

53. $\begin{bmatrix} 1 & 0 \\ 0 & 1 \end{bmatrix} \begin{bmatrix} 3 & -1 & 5 \\ 2 & 4 & -2 \end{bmatrix}$

54. $\begin{bmatrix} 2 & -1 & 5 \\ 2 & 4 & -2 \end{bmatrix} \begin{bmatrix} 1 & 0 \\ 0 & 1 \end{bmatrix}$

55. $\begin{bmatrix} 1 & -1 & -2 \\ -1 & 2 & 3 \end{bmatrix} \begin{bmatrix} 1 & -1 \\ 2 & 3 \\ -1 & -2 \end{bmatrix}$

56. $\begin{bmatrix} 1 & -1 \\ 2 & 3 \\ -1 & -2 \end{bmatrix} \begin{bmatrix} 1 & -1 & -2 \\ -1 & 2 & 3 \end{bmatrix}$

$^c$57. $\begin{bmatrix} -1 & 1 & 2 \\ 2 & -2 & 1 \end{bmatrix} \begin{bmatrix} 3 & 4 & 0 & -2 \\ 1 & -2 & 2 & -1 \\ 1 & -1 & 3 & 2 \end{bmatrix}$

$^c$58. $\begin{bmatrix} 0 & -8 & 8 & 5 \\ 5 & 11 & -1 & 0 \end{bmatrix} \begin{bmatrix} 2 & 3 \\ 1 & 2 \\ -1 & 1 \\ -2 & 1 \end{bmatrix}$

$^c$59. $\begin{bmatrix} 3 & 4 & 0 & -2 \\ 1 & -2 & 2 & -1 \\ 1 & -1 & 3 & 2 \end{bmatrix} \begin{bmatrix} 2 & 3 \\ 1 & 2 \\ -1 & 1 \\ -2 & 1 \end{bmatrix}$

$$^c60. \begin{bmatrix} -1 & 1 & 2 \\ 2 & -2 & 1 \end{bmatrix} \begin{bmatrix} 14 & 15 \\ 0 & 0 \\ -6 & 6 \end{bmatrix} \qquad 61. \begin{bmatrix} 2 & 1 & -1 & 3 \end{bmatrix} \begin{bmatrix} 3 \\ -1 \\ 2 \\ -1 \end{bmatrix}$$

$$^c62. \begin{bmatrix} 3 \\ -1 \\ 2 \\ -1 \end{bmatrix} \begin{bmatrix} 2 & 1 & -1 & 3 \end{bmatrix}$$

In Exercises 63 through 77 multiply the pairs of matrices in the order given.

$$63. \begin{bmatrix} 1 & 1 & 2 \\ 3 & 2 & 3 \\ 2 & 1 & 2 \end{bmatrix} \begin{bmatrix} 1 & -1 & 0 \\ -3 & 0 & 2 \\ 1 & 1 & -1 \end{bmatrix}$$

$$64. \begin{bmatrix} 1 & 1 & 2 \\ 3 & 2 & 3 \\ 2 & 1 & 2 \end{bmatrix} \begin{bmatrix} 0 & 0 & 1 \\ -3 & 2 & -3 \\ 2 & -1 & 1 \end{bmatrix}$$

$$65. \begin{bmatrix} 1 & 1 & 2 \\ 3 & 2 & 3 \\ 2 & 1 & 2 \end{bmatrix} \begin{bmatrix} -1 & 0 & 1 \\ 0 & -2 & -3 \\ 1 & 1 & 1 \end{bmatrix}$$

$$66. \begin{bmatrix} 1 & 1 & 2 \\ 3 & 2 & 3 \\ 2 & 1 & 2 \end{bmatrix} \begin{bmatrix} -1 & 0 & 1 \\ 0 & 2 & -3 \\ 1 & -1 & 1 \end{bmatrix}$$

$$67. \begin{bmatrix} -8 & 3 & 1 \\ -2 & 1 & 0 \\ 13 & -5 & -1 \end{bmatrix} \begin{bmatrix} 9 & 7 & 8 \\ 21 & 16 & 17 \\ 11 & 9 & 16 \end{bmatrix}$$

$$^c68. \begin{bmatrix} 1 & 2 & 1 \\ 2 & 5 & 2 \\ 3 & 1 & 2 \end{bmatrix} \begin{bmatrix} -6 & 0 & -18 \\ -1 & 0 & -5 \\ 10 & 1 & 31 \end{bmatrix}$$

$$69. \begin{bmatrix} 1 & 1 & 2 \\ 3 & 2 & 3 \\ 2 & 1 & 2 \end{bmatrix} \begin{bmatrix} -1 & 1 & 0 \\ 3 & -2 & -7 \\ 0 & 1 & 5 \end{bmatrix}$$

$$^c70. \begin{bmatrix} -1 & 0 & 1 \\ 0 & 2 & -3 \\ 1 & -1 & 1 \end{bmatrix} \begin{bmatrix} 7 & 7 & 10 \\ 15 & 13 & 20 \\ 9 & 8 & 13 \end{bmatrix}$$

$$71. \begin{bmatrix} 1 & -2 & 1 \\ 2 & -4 & 2 \\ -1 & 2 & -1 \end{bmatrix} \begin{bmatrix} 3 & 2 & -2 \\ 2 & 1 & -3 \\ 1 & 0 & -4 \end{bmatrix}$$

$$72. \begin{bmatrix} -1 & 0 & 1 \\ 0 & 2 & -3 \\ 1 & -1 & 1 \end{bmatrix} \begin{bmatrix} 4 & 4 & 4 \\ 8 & 8 & 8 \\ 5 & 5 & 5 \end{bmatrix}$$

$$73. \begin{bmatrix} 4 & 4 & 4 \\ 8 & 8 & 8 \\ 5 & 5 & 5 \end{bmatrix} \begin{bmatrix} -1 & 0 & 1 \\ 0 & 2 & -3 \\ 1 & -1 & 1 \end{bmatrix}$$

74. $\begin{bmatrix} 15 & 17 & 10 \\ 25 & 37 & 46 \\ 15 & 34 & 96 \end{bmatrix} \begin{bmatrix} 0 & 0 & 0 \\ 0 & 0 & 0 \\ 0 & 0 & 0 \end{bmatrix}$

75. $\begin{bmatrix} 0 & 0 & 0 \\ 0 & 0 & 0 \\ 0 & 0 & 0 \end{bmatrix} \begin{bmatrix} 138 & 74 & -28 \\ 96 & 27 & 43 \\ 25 & 38 & 49 \end{bmatrix}$

76. $\begin{bmatrix} 1 & 0 & 0 \\ 0 & 1 & 0 \\ 0 & 0 & 1 \end{bmatrix} \begin{bmatrix} 71 & 89 & 43 \\ 27 & 96 & 185 \\ 34 & 86 & 57 \end{bmatrix}$

c77. $\begin{bmatrix} 32 & 41 & 76 \\ 194 & 38 & 49 \\ 25 & 86 & 97 \end{bmatrix} \begin{bmatrix} 1 & 0 & 0 \\ 0 & 1 & 0 \\ 0 & 0 & 1 \end{bmatrix}$

*78. What are the missing numbers in the following calculation?

$$\begin{bmatrix} 1 & -1 & 2 \\ 3 & 1 & 4 \\ 2 & & 1 \end{bmatrix} \begin{bmatrix} 1 & 2 & 3 \\ 4 & & 2 \\ & 3 & 6 \end{bmatrix} = \begin{bmatrix} -1 & & \\ & 19 & \\ & & 12 \end{bmatrix}$$

79. Write down the $6 \times 6$ identity matrix.

80. (a) How many ones are in the $100 \times 100$ identity matrix?
    (b) How many zeros are in the $100 \times 100$ identity matrix?

81. What do you get if you multiply an identity matrix by itself?

PHE wished to use its model company, PHEM, to help in its consideration of price structures. Here are two price structures, b and c, now under consideration.

|  | b | c |
|---|---|---|
| Hamburger | $.50 | $.45 |
| Cheeseburger | .60 | .65 |
| Fries | .45 | .50 |
| Shake | .50 | .45 |

82. Let $B = \begin{bmatrix} .50 \\ .60 \\ .45 \\ .50 \end{bmatrix}$. Using the symbolism of Exercise 29 write the product that gives the total proceeds from each store in July, using the price structure b. Carry out the multiplication.

83. Let $C = \begin{bmatrix} .45 \\ .65 \\ .50 \\ .45 \end{bmatrix}$. Write the operation, using one of the four matrices of Exercise 29, that gives the total proceeds from each store in the third quarter, using price structure c.

84. "Now what?" said the head of the computer room. "I've stored the data in the machine and labeled them matrix A. All I know is that the size of A is $50 \times 75$. I've not only lost all other record of it but now this computer is broken and will perform only matrix multiplication. The boss wants to know the $(20, 15)$ entry of A and he is

coming personally in two minutes. There isn't time to fix the machine. What can I do?

(a) Describe a matrix whose product with matrix A is matrix A.

(b) Describe a matrix whose product with matrix A is $R_{20}$ of matrix A.

(c) Describe a matrix whose product with matrix A is $C_{15}$ of matrix A.

(d) How can I obtain just the $(20, 15)$ entry of matrix A by using matrix multiplications?

85. Another application of matrix multiplication at AC is the following. One summer the managers decided to start selling their goods at three different department stores. Each contract was negotiated separately, the result being that each store paid a different price for each item purchased. Table 2 resulted.

**Table 24**
**Price Paid by**
**Stores (in dollars)**

| Store | Item | | | | |
|---|---|---|---|---|---|
| | | | | Two-person tents | Four-person tents |
| | Light bags | Heavy bags | Jackets | | |
| Hartford, CT | 100 | 120 | 80 | 100 | 250 |
| Providence, RI | 120 | 150 | 90 | 80 | 200 |
| Barre, VT | 150 | 200 | 100 | 90 | 200 |

Each store placed the same order with each factory, as shown in Table 25.

**Table 25**
**Items Purchased by**
**Each Store from**
**AC Factories**

| Item | Factory | | |
|---|---|---|---|
| | Danbury | Springfield | Rutland |
| Light sleeping bags | 50 | 50 | 50 |
| Heavy sleeping bags | 30 | 40 | 30 |
| Down jackets | 60 | 80 | 60 |
| Two-person tents | 40 | 50 | 0 |
| Four-person tents | 0 | 40 | 30 |

Use matrix multiplication to determine the total amount each store paid each factory, and write the result as a table.

**Section 2.7**
**Summary**

In Chapter 5 we will study linear models in which the variables are related by an inequality such as
$a_1x_1 + \ldots + a_nx_n \le b$ or
$a_1x_1 + \ldots + a_nx_n \ge b$.

There are many practical situations in which a linear model is relevant. For example, this is the case whenever variables $x_1, \ldots, x_n$ are related by an equation of the form

$$a_1x_1 + \ldots + a_nx_n = b$$

where not all numbers $a_i$ are zero. If we view such equations as conditions that must be satisfied by the variables $x_1, \ldots, x_n$, then a system of linear equations is a concise presentation of the fact that a given collection of variables must satisfy a number of conditions simultaneously. Gauss-Jordan reduction is the simplest way to solve a system of linear equations. While it is merely a systematic matrix formulation of the substitution technique presented in Section 2.1, it is much more efficient for large systems than random substitution. The shortcuts presented in Section 4 of this chapter represent just a few of the ways in which one can take advantage of the arrangement of numbers in a particular problem.

In Section 2.1 we used geometry to represent two-variable equations as lines in the plane. In Section 5 of this chapter we extended our discussion to the three-variable case of planes in space.

Matrices were introduced in Section 2.2 as an aid in Gauss-Jordan reduction. In Section 2.6 matrices were studied as mathematical objects derived from tables of numbers. We saw that matrices are like ordinary numbers in that they can be added and subtracted (if they are the same size) and multiplied (if the first matrix has as many columns as the second matrix has rows). But, for most matrices A and B, AB is not equal to BA. Matrices will be applied to many problems throughout this text.

Matrix division will be discussed in Chapter 6, Section 2.

---
**TERMS**

---

Coordinates of a point in the plane, page 56
Ordered pair, page 56
Linear equation, page 57
Graphing a line, page 57
System of equations, page 60
Matrix of a system of equations, page 65
Coordinates of a point in space, page 103
Coefficient matrix, page 119
Requirement matrix, page 119
Identity matrix, page 127

---

COMPUTATIONAL TECHNIQUES

---

To graph the equation $ax_1 + bx_2 = c$ use the flow chart on page 60.

To find all solutions, if any, of a system of equations: use the three row operations to clear columns as described in the flow chart on page 80. Shortcuts may help.

To multiply a matrix by a number, multiply each entry by that number.

To add or subtract two matrices, add or subtract the corresponding entries. (The matrices must be the same size.)

5. To multiply one matrix by another:
   (a) first learn how to multiply a row by a column (flow chart, page 115);
   (b) then learn how to multiply a matrix by a column (flow chart, page 117);
   (c) then use the flow chart on page 122. (See also the two paragraphs on page 123.)

**Review Exercises**   Reread Chapter 2, then do the following exercises without looking back. Answers to all these exercises are in Appendix C.

1. One day last month Bill suggested that we could make some extra money by doing odd jobs around our housing development. Everybody knew that Bill was lazy but, since he agreed to put up the money for the necessary equipment, I agreed to talk to Jane and Fred, the twins, about joining our company. During our short business meeting we decided to offer three services:

   (i) We would mow lawns. In the development each lawn is exactly the same size. I can do a lawn in an afternoon; Jane can do 2; Bill is allergic to grass; and Fred, being Jane's twin, can also do 2.

   (ii) We would trim hedges. In the development each yard has the same number of hedges. I can trim 2 sets of hedges the same day I mow the lawns. Jane can do 3 in addition to her mowing. Bill reluctantly agrees to do 1. Fred does the same as Jane.

   (iii) We would wash windows. Each house in our development is the same. I decided that even with the mowing and trimming I could handle 3 window-washing jobs after supper. Much to our surprise, lazy Bill said he would do 2 window-washing jobs a day. Jane will not wash windows so Fred will not either.

   (a) The first week's orders are in: mow 13 lawns; trim 29 sets of hedges; wash 33 sets of windows. While Jane and Fred do not care how many days they work, neither will work for a fractional part of a day. What are the possible work schedules?

   (b) In the second week we are asked to mow 18 lawns, trim 36 sets of hedges, and wash 30 sets of windows. Fred catches a cold but agrees to work exactly half as much as Jane. What are the possible work schedules?

   (c) In the third week, the orders are for 19 mowings, 34 trimmings, and 21 washings. Our employers, not understanding matrix algebra, began to think that Jane was lazier than Bill, who insists that he must wash both sides of each window to do the job properly. For this reason, Jane demands to work at least 1 day more than Bill. Fred will not work for a fractional part of a day. What are the possible work schedules?

(d) In the fourth week a black sedan with plainclothes detectives begins following Bill around. Our orders fall off and we decide to work fractional parts of days if we must; that is, all of us except Jane. The orders are for 8 mowings, 17 trimmings, and 17 washings. What are the work schedules now?

The fifth week finds Bill in jail on grand larceny charges and all our equipment impounded. We quit.

2. Plot the following five points:
   (a) $\left(0, 3\frac{1}{2}\right)$    (b) $(4, 0)$    (c) $\left(2\frac{1}{2}, -3\right)$
   (d) $(-1, -3)$    (e) $\left(2\frac{1}{2}, 3\right)$

3. Graph the following lines.
   (a) $3x_1 + 2x_2 = 6$
   (b) $2\frac{1}{2}x_1 = 3$
   (c) $5x_2 = -7$
   (d) $-2x_1 - 4x_2 = 9$
   (e) $3x_1 - 4x_2 = 0$

4. Solve the following systems of equations.

   (a) $\begin{bmatrix} 2x_1 + x_2 = 7 \\ x_1 + x_2 = 5 \end{bmatrix}$

   (b) $\begin{bmatrix} 2x_1 + x_2 = 7 \\ 4x_1 + 2x_2 = 8 \end{bmatrix}$

   (c) $\begin{bmatrix} 2x_1 + x_2 = 7 \\ 4x_1 + 2x_2 = 14 \end{bmatrix}$

   (d) $\begin{bmatrix} \frac{1}{2}x_1 - \frac{1}{3}x_2 = 3 \\ \frac{2}{5}x_1 + \frac{3}{8}x_2 = 4 \end{bmatrix}$

   (e) $\begin{bmatrix} 2x_1 + x_2 + 2x_3 = 5 \\ 2x_1 + 2x_2 + 2x_3 = 10 \\ x_1 + 2x_2 + x_3 = 4 \end{bmatrix}$

   (f) $\begin{bmatrix} 2x_1 + 2x_2 + x_3 = 5 \\ 2x_1 + 2x_2 + 2x_3 = 6 \\ x_1 + x_2 + 2x_3 = 4 \end{bmatrix}$

   (g) $\begin{bmatrix} 3x_1 + 3x_2 + 2x_3 = 5 \\ x_1 + 2x_2 + x_3 = 1 \\ 4x_1 + 3x_2 + 4x_3 = 7 \end{bmatrix}$

   (h) $\begin{bmatrix} 2x_1 + 2x_2 + x_3 = 1 \\ 2x_1 + 3x_2 + 2x_3 = 5 \\ x_1 + x_2 + x_3 = 2 \end{bmatrix}$

   (i) $\begin{bmatrix} 10x_1 + 8x_2 + 4x_3 + 3x_4 = 27 \\ 7x_1 + 4x_2 + 3x_3 + 3x_4 = 19 \\ 4x_1 + 4x_2 + 2x_3 = 12 \end{bmatrix}$

   (j) $\begin{bmatrix} 7x_2 + x_3 - 6x_4 = 4 \\ x_1 - x_3 + x_4 = 2 \\ -x_1 - 5x_2 + 4x_4 = 5 \\ -3x_2 + 2x_4 = 7 \end{bmatrix}$

5. Calculate each of the following or, when appropriate, write "not defined."
   (a) $\begin{bmatrix} -\frac{2}{3} & \frac{3}{4} & -1 \end{bmatrix} - \begin{bmatrix} \frac{4}{3} & -\frac{5}{6} & -\frac{4}{5} \end{bmatrix}$
   (b) $\begin{bmatrix} 1 & 2 & 3 & 4 \\ 5 & 6 & 7 & 8 \end{bmatrix} + \begin{bmatrix} 9 & 1 & 0 \\ 3 & 2 & 1 \end{bmatrix}$

(c) $\frac{2}{3}\begin{bmatrix} -3 & 2 \\ 6 & -\frac{1}{4} \end{bmatrix}$     (d) $\frac{5}{6}\begin{bmatrix} -\frac{1}{2} \\ \frac{3}{2} \end{bmatrix} - \frac{6}{5}\begin{bmatrix} \frac{2}{3} \\ -\frac{4}{9} \end{bmatrix}$

(e) $10\begin{bmatrix} 0.1 & -0.2 & 0.3 \\ -0.1 & 0.5 & -0.6 \\ 0.7 & -0.8 & 0.9 \end{bmatrix}$

(f) $\begin{bmatrix} 1 & 2 \\ 3 & 4 \end{bmatrix}\begin{bmatrix} 5 & 6 \\ 7 & 8 \end{bmatrix} - \begin{bmatrix} 1 & 2 \\ 3 & 4 \end{bmatrix}\begin{bmatrix} 5 & 6 \\ 7 & 8 \end{bmatrix}$

(g) $\begin{bmatrix} 1 & 2 \\ 3 & 4 \end{bmatrix}\begin{bmatrix} 5 & 6 \\ 7 & 8 \end{bmatrix} - \begin{bmatrix} 5 & 6 \\ 7 & 8 \end{bmatrix}\begin{bmatrix} 1 & 2 \\ 3 & 4 \end{bmatrix}$

(h) $\begin{bmatrix} 1 & 2 \\ 3 & 4 \end{bmatrix}\begin{bmatrix} 5 & 6 \\ 7 & 8 \end{bmatrix} - \begin{bmatrix} 1 & 2 \\ 3 & 4 \end{bmatrix}\begin{bmatrix} 4 & 6 \\ 7 & 7 \end{bmatrix}$

(i) $\begin{bmatrix} 1 & 2 & 3 \\ 4 & 5 & 6 \end{bmatrix}\begin{bmatrix} 7 & 8 & 9 \\ 10 & 11 & 12 \end{bmatrix}$

(j) $\begin{bmatrix} 3 & 0 & -1 & 2 \\ 2 & -1 & 0 & -3 \\ 4 & -2 & 3 & -1 \\ -1 & 3 & -2 & 1 \end{bmatrix}\begin{bmatrix} 0 & -1 \\ -3 & 3 \\ 4 & 0 \\ 2 & -4 \end{bmatrix}$

## Supplementary Exercises

The notation $x_1^2$, read "$x_1$ squared," means $x_1 \cdot x_1$. See Appendix A, Section 2a, if needed.

1. Graph the points $(2, -\frac{3}{2}), (-\frac{3}{2}, 2), (-2, \frac{3}{2}), (-\frac{3}{2}, -2)$.
*2. Indicate all points with coordinates $(x_1, x_2)$ such that $x_1$ and $x_2$ are integers, $-3 < x_1 < 4$, $-2 < x_2 < 10$, and $x_1^2 < x_2$.

In Exercises 3 through 12 graph the line with the given equation.

3. $x_1 + x_2 = 1q$       4. $x_1 + 4x_2 = 8$       5. $-4x_1 + x_2 = 12$
6. $x_1 + 3x_2 = 0$       7. $\frac{1}{2}x_1 - \frac{2}{3}x_2 = \frac{3}{4}$       8. $-\frac{7}{12}x_1 + \frac{12}{7}x_2 = 1$
9. $-\frac{7}{12}x_1 + \frac{12}{7}x_2 = 0$       10. $x_1 + x_2 + 2 = 0$
11. $3x_1 + 4 = 5x_2 + 6$       12. $x_1 = x_2$

In Exercises 13 through 17 find the point of intersection of the given pairs of lines:

13. $2x_1 - 3x_2 = -5, x_1 + x_2 = 5$       14. $6x_1 + 2x_2 = 3, 3x_1 + x_2 = 8$
15. $6x_1 + 2x_2 = 3, 4x_1 - 2x_2 = 5$       16. $5x_1 = 4, 6x_2 = 5$
17. $-9x_1 + 12x_2 = 27, 3x_1 - 4x_2 = -9$

In Exercises 18 through 53 solve the given system of equations

18. $\begin{bmatrix} 2x_1 + x_2 = 7 \\ x_1 + x_2 = 5 \end{bmatrix}$       19. $\begin{bmatrix} x_1 + x_2 = 10 \\ x_1 - x_2 = 4 \end{bmatrix}$

20. $\begin{bmatrix} 5x_1 + 7x_2 = -2 \\ 3x_1 + 4x_2 = -1 \end{bmatrix}$       21. $\begin{bmatrix} 2x_1 + 2x_2 = 10 \\ x_1 - 3x_2 = -15 \end{bmatrix}$

22. $\begin{bmatrix} 3x_1 - x_2 = 2 \\ 2x_1 + x_2 = 3 \end{bmatrix}$       23. $\begin{bmatrix} 2x_1 + x_2 + x_3 = 3 \\ x_1 - x_2 + 3x_3 = 8 \\ 2x_1 + x_2 - x_3 = -1 \end{bmatrix}$

24. $\begin{bmatrix} -x_1+2x_2-2x_3= & 10 \\ x_1- x_2+ x_3= -5 \\ 2x_1+2x_2+ x_3= & 4 \end{bmatrix}$    25. $\begin{bmatrix} 3x_1+ x_2+x_3=6 \\ x_1+2x_2+x_3=6 \\ x_1+ x_2+x_3=4 \end{bmatrix}$

26. $\begin{bmatrix} 2x_1 & + x_3=3 \\ x_1 & +2x_3=0 \\ 2x_1+x_2+ x_3=8 \end{bmatrix}$    27. $\begin{bmatrix} x_1+ x_2+2x_3=3 \\ -x_1- x_2+3x_3=2 \\ x_1+2x_2+3x_3=7 \end{bmatrix}$

28. $\begin{bmatrix} 2x_1+3x_2+2x_3=5 \\ 3x_1+2x_2+2x_3=5 \\ 5x_1+4x_2+4x_3=9 \end{bmatrix}$    29. $\begin{bmatrix} x_1-3x_2+ x_3= -1 \\ x_1-4x_2+2x_3= 0 \\ 2x_1+ x_2-5x_3= -9 \end{bmatrix}$

30. $\begin{bmatrix} 2x_1+ x_2+2x_3= 5 \\ 2x_1+2x_2+2x_3=10 \\ x_1+2x_2+ x_3= 4 \end{bmatrix}$    31. $\begin{bmatrix} 2x_1+2x_2+ x_3=5 \\ 2x_1+2x_2+2x_3=6 \\ x_1+ x_2+2x_3=4 \end{bmatrix}$

32. $\begin{bmatrix} 3x_1+3x_2+2x_3=5 \\ x_1+2x_2+ x_3=1 \\ 4x_1+3x_2+4x_3=7 \end{bmatrix}$    33. $\begin{bmatrix} 2x_1+2x_2+ x_3=1 \\ 2x_1+3x_2+2x_3=5 \\ x_1+ x_2+ x_3=2 \end{bmatrix}$

34. $\begin{bmatrix} 3x_1+ x_2-2x_3= -1 \\ 3x_1+2x_2+3x_3= 13 \\ 2x_1+ x_2+2x_3= 9 \end{bmatrix}$    35. $\begin{bmatrix} 2x_1+2x_2- x_3= 4 \\ 5x_1+4x_2+5x_3=24 \\ 3x_1+2x_2+3x_3=14 \end{bmatrix}$

36. $\begin{bmatrix} 5x_1+2x_2+ x_3=1 \\ 5x_1+4x_2+5x_3=5 \\ 3x_1+3x_2+4x_3=4 \end{bmatrix}$    37. $\begin{bmatrix} 3x_1+2x_2+4x_3=3 \\ 3x_1+2x_2+ x_3=2 \\ 2x_1+2x_2+2x_3=7 \end{bmatrix}$

38. $\begin{bmatrix} 3x_1+2x_2+3x_3=1 \\ 2x_1+3x_2+2x_3=2 \\ 3x_1+3x_2+2x_3=1 \end{bmatrix}$    39. $\begin{bmatrix} 2x_1+3x_2=13 \\ x_1+2x_2= 8 \\ 3x_1+ x_2= 9 \end{bmatrix}$

40. $\begin{bmatrix} 2x_1+ x_2+ x_3= 8 \\ x_1+2x_2+ x_3= 7 \\ 3x_1+ x_2+2x_3=13 \\ 2x_1+2x_2+ x_3=11 \end{bmatrix}$    41. $\begin{bmatrix} x_1 +x_3 = -1 \\ x_2+x_3+x_4= 2 \\ x_1+x_2+x_3 = 1 \\ x_1+x_2+x_3+x_4= 2 \end{bmatrix}$

42. $\begin{bmatrix} x_1+2x_2- x_3- x_4-x_5= 2 \\ x_2+2x_3- x_4 = 4 \\ x_3+2x_4-x_5= 6 \\ x_1+ x_2 +x_5= 8 \\ 3x_2 +x_4 =10 \end{bmatrix}$

43. $\begin{bmatrix} x_1-4x_2-2x_3+6x_4= 4 \\ 3x_1+2x_2+3x_3 =15 \\ x_1+2x_2+2x_3-2x_4= 5 \end{bmatrix}$

44. $\begin{bmatrix} 6x_1 + x_2 + 3x_3 + 2x_4 = 13 \\ 4x_1 + x_2 + 2x_3 + 2x_4 = 10 \end{bmatrix}$

45. $\begin{bmatrix} 4x_1 + 6x_2 + 2x_3 + 12x_4 = 35 \\ 2x_1 + 5x_2 + 2x_3 + 10x_4 = 28 \\ 4x_1 + 7x_2 + 2x_3 + 4x_4 = 39 \end{bmatrix}$

46. $\begin{bmatrix} 3x_1 + 2x_2 + 4x_3 = 4 \\ x_1 + 3x_2 + 2x_3 = 9 \end{bmatrix}$

47. $\begin{bmatrix} 2x_1 + 3x_2 = 5 \\ 2x_1 + 2x_2 = 4 \\ 4x_1 + x_2 = 6 \end{bmatrix}$

48. $\begin{bmatrix} 2x_1 + 3x_2 + x_3 = 7 \\ 4x_1 + 6x_2 + 3x_3 = 17 \end{bmatrix}$

49. $\begin{bmatrix} 3x_1 - x_2 + x_3 + 9x_4 = 2 \\ 4x_1 + x_2 - 2x_3 - 3x_4 = -11 \\ x_1 + x_2 - 2x_3 - 6x_4 = -7 \\ x_1 - x_2 + 3x_4 = -2 \end{bmatrix}$

50. $\begin{bmatrix} 2x_1 + 4x_2 + 3x_4 = 7 \\ 6x_1 + 4x_2 + 3x_3 + 5x_4 = 15 \\ 4x_1 + 4x_2 + 4x_4 = 10 \end{bmatrix}$

51. $\begin{bmatrix} 10x_1 + 8x_2 + 4x_3 + 3x_4 = 27 \\ 7x_1 + 4x_2 + 3x_3 + 3x_4 = 19 \\ 4x_1 + 4x_2 + 2x_3 = 12 \end{bmatrix}$

52. $\begin{bmatrix} 3x_1 + 2x_2 + x_3 = 1 \\ 2x_1 + x_2 + x_3 = 2 \\ x_1 + x_2 + 2x_3 = 3 \\ 2x_1 + x_2 + 2x_3 = 4 \end{bmatrix}$

53. $\begin{bmatrix} 2x_1 + 2x_2 + x_3 + 3x_4 = 4 \\ 2x_1 + 2x_2 + 2x_3 + x_4 = 2 \\ 5x_1 + 4x_2 + 4x_3 + 5x_4 = 3 \\ 3x_1 + 3x_2 + 3x_3 + 2x_4 = 1 \end{bmatrix}$

C54. The staff numerologist at AC has decided to adjust the relative numbers of employees. For some mystical reason, he arbitrarily decides they should have 5 times as many junior executives as senior executives and 50 times as many workers as junior executives. The budget department allows $107,000 for weekly salaries, and the contract stipulates salaries at $200 a week for workers, $500 a week for junior executives, and $1,000 a week for senior executives. Determine the size of the new staff.

55. I just joined the faculty and I want my grade distribution to fit in with everyone else's. In my class of 32 students, I decide that only 5 should get As or Bs (just as on Professor Smith's roster); I decide to give as many Cs as As and Fs combined (for balance). I decide to give 6 more Ds than Bs (to prove I'm tough). Finally, I decide to give 6 more Fs than As. What is my grade distribution?

56. Radio station WJBJ has four kinds of programming: advertising, public service announcements, music, and news. They are on the air 24 hours a day. They must net at least $73,400 a day over expenses, which are $150 an hour to produce the music and $1,600 an hour for the news. The only way to meet these expenses is through selling advertising at a rate of $10,000 an hour. The station manager decides to spend $\frac{5}{8}$ of the day on news and music and $\frac{1}{3}$ of the day on advertising. How much time will be spent on each of the four areas?

57. Sometimes Anne-Marie wishes she did not work for the CACN (Commission for Arms Control for Neutralia); it's so complicated. Each country in the FNC (Four Nation Conference) has both

new-style and old-style regiments. In Blantyria each change of a regiment from old to new results in an increase of 9 tanks and 1 helicopter and a decrease of 4 missiles and 6 planes. Each such change in Iwalam results in an increase of 5 missiles and 2 helicopters and a decrease of 2 tanks and 3 planes. Each such change in Neofrom results in an increase of 3 tanks and 4 helicopters and a decrease of 7 missiles and 1 plane. Each such change in Concordia results in an increase of 6 missiles and 7 planes and a decrease of 1 tank and 5 helicopters. She can also order changes from new-regiment armament back to old, resulting in the opposite changes. The CACN requires a total FNC armament change comprising a reduction of 71 tanks and 34 helicopters with offsetting increases of 79 missiles and 61 planes. What orders should Anne-Marie give?

58. Two exotic spices, lucrish and bargie, are made from different parts (leaf and root, respectively) of the same plant. Two species of this plant can be grown commercially. Each acre planted with *Aecus fistula* produces 178 kilograms of lucrish and 432 of bargie. Each acre planted with *Aecus seirens* produces 976 kilos of lucrish and 815 of bargie. We must produce exactly 1,033,590 kilograms of lucrish and 1,142,769 of bargie. How many acres will we need?

59. And it was foretold that in the Third Age the princess would be visited by 4 heroes at different times. On each visit Galadriel would bring 8 rings, 4 anklets, 4 coronets, 1 crystal sphere, and 9 roses; Aragorn would bring 3 rings, 7 anklets, 5 coronets, 7 crystal spheres, and 5 roses; Frodo would bring 7 rings, 9 anklets, 4 coronets, 2 crystal spheres, and 4 roses; Meriadoc would bring 9 rings, 2 anklets, 9 coronets, 2 crystal spheres, and 5 roses; and Gimli would bring 6 rings, one anklet, 6 coronets, 1 crystal sphere, and half a dozen roses. And so it happened, and at the end of this age the princess had 163 rings, 82 anklets, 157 coronets, 54 crystal spheres, and 125 roses. Which hero did not visit the princess?

60. Eddie, Alfred, and Frank play first, second, and third base, respectively, for the PHE Burgerchamps. In practice they sometimes hit a few grounders to each other. Whenever he bats, Alfred hits 12 grounders to first and 16 to third; Eddie hits 19 to second and 15 to third; and Frank hits 2 to first and 7 to second. Eddie and Albert always bat in the same practice sessions. By the end of the season, each player had received the same number of grounders from the other two. How many sessions were there?

61. We are ready to print our histories of Maine, Utah, and Iowa. Each history consists of Volume I: Text, printed on high-grade paper; Volume II: Plates, printed on coated paper; and Volume III: Notes, printed on medium-grade paper. The numbers of pages in the volumes are: Maine: I—764, II—621, III—981; Utah: I—237, II—537, III—127; Iowa: I—359, II—472, III—754. We have enough high-grade stock for 567,060 pages, enough coated stock for 769,218 pages, and enough medium-grade stock for 681,650 pages. Please use it all up.

*62. We remarked in Section 2.2 that the operation of switching two rows was not as fundamental to Gauss-Jordan reduction as the operations of adding a multiple of a row to another row and multiplying a row by a nonzero number. Show, for example, how to change the matrix

$$\begin{bmatrix} 0 & 1 & 2 \\ 3 & 1 & 0 \\ 1 & 2 & 3 \end{bmatrix} \text{ to the matrix } \begin{bmatrix} 1 & 2 & 3 \\ 3 & 1 & 0 \\ 0 & 1 & 2 \end{bmatrix} \text{ by using only these last two}$$

types of row operations.

63. Here is a way to find an equation for the line through two points. We illustrate by finding an equation for the line through $(2, -3)$ and $(-3, 4)$:

(1) Write the system of equations $x_1 a + x_2 b - c = 0$ for the given points $(x_1, x_2)$.

$$\begin{bmatrix} 2a - 3b - c = 0 \\ -3a + 4b - c = 0 \end{bmatrix}$$

(2) Solve (here the variables are a, b, and c):

$$\begin{bmatrix} 2 & -3 & -1 & 0 \\ -3 & 4 & -1 & 0 \end{bmatrix} \begin{bmatrix} 1 & -\frac{3}{2} & -\frac{1}{2} & 0 \\ 0 & -\frac{1}{2} & -\frac{5}{2} & 0 \end{bmatrix} \begin{bmatrix} 1 & 0 & 7 & 0 \\ 0 & 1 & 5 & 0 \end{bmatrix}.$$

Answer: $(-7c, -5c, c)$ where c is free.

(3) Choose a specific solution where a, b, and c are not all zero: $a = 7, b = 5, c = -1$.

(4) An equation for the line is $ax_1 + bx_2 = c$: $7x_1 + 5x_2 = -1$.

(5) Check: $7 \cdot 2 + 5 \cdot (-3) = -1 \checkmark$; $7 \cdot (-3) + 5 \cdot 4 = -1 \checkmark$.

Use this procedure to find equations for the lines determined by the following pairs of points:

(a) $(1, 2), (3, 4)$      (d) $(0, 0), (9, 12)$

(b) $(-7, 6), (5, 10)$      (e) $(4, 0), (19, 0)$

(c) $\left(\frac{7}{3}, -\frac{7}{4}\right), \left(-5, \frac{15}{4}\right)$      (f) $(0, 6), (-4, 0)$

64. Find two $2 \times 2$ matrices, none of whose entries is zero, whose product is a matrix all of whose entries are zero.

65. If A is a $7 \times 4$ matrix, B is a matrix, and AB is a square matrix, what is the size of B?

66. What number x makes the equation

$$\begin{bmatrix} 4 & 3 \\ -2 & 1 \end{bmatrix} - x \begin{bmatrix} 9 & -3 \\ 6 & -18 \end{bmatrix} = \begin{bmatrix} -2 & 5 \\ -6 & 13 \end{bmatrix} \text{ true?}$$

67. Verify that the matrix $\begin{bmatrix} 2 & 3 & -1 \\ 4 & 1 & 6 \\ 0 & 2 & 5 \end{bmatrix}$ is a square root of the matrix

$$\begin{bmatrix} 16 & 7 & 11 \\ 12 & 25 & 32 \\ 8 & 12 & 37 \end{bmatrix}.$$

68. Find $2 \times 2$ matrices [ ] such that:

(a) $\begin{bmatrix} & \\ & \end{bmatrix}\begin{bmatrix} 1 & 2 \\ 3 & 4 \end{bmatrix} = \begin{bmatrix} 3 & 6 \\ 3 & 4 \end{bmatrix}$  (b) $\begin{bmatrix} & \\ & \end{bmatrix}\begin{bmatrix} 1 & 2 \\ 3 & 4 \end{bmatrix} = \begin{bmatrix} 1 & 2 \\ -9 & -12 \end{bmatrix}$

(c) $\begin{bmatrix} 1 & 2 \\ 3 & 4 \end{bmatrix}\begin{bmatrix} & \\ & \end{bmatrix} = \begin{bmatrix} 1 & 1 \\ 3 & 2 \end{bmatrix}$  (d) $\begin{bmatrix} 1 & 2 \\ 3 & 4 \end{bmatrix}\begin{bmatrix} & \\ & \end{bmatrix} = \begin{bmatrix} \frac{1}{3} & -\frac{1}{2} \\ 1 & -2 \end{bmatrix}$

(e) $\begin{bmatrix} & \\ & \end{bmatrix}\begin{bmatrix} 1 & 2 \\ 3 & 4 \end{bmatrix} = \begin{bmatrix} 7 & 14 \\ \frac{3}{4} & 1 \end{bmatrix}$

69. If $\begin{bmatrix} 4x & 3 \\ 2 & -1 \end{bmatrix}\begin{bmatrix} 2 & -3 \\ 6x & 5 \end{bmatrix} = \begin{bmatrix} 13 & 9 \\ 1 & -11 \end{bmatrix}$, find x.

70. If $\begin{bmatrix} 3x+27 & 4 \\ 5x & y \end{bmatrix} = \begin{bmatrix} 2x-y & 4 \\ 10 & y \end{bmatrix}$, find x and y.

71. (a) What happens to a $3 \times 4$ matrix if the matrix $\begin{bmatrix} 7 & 0 & 0 \\ 0 & 7 & 0 \\ 0 & 0 & 7 \end{bmatrix}$ is multiplied by it?

(b) What happens to a $3 \times 4$ matrix if it is multiplied by the matrix $\begin{bmatrix} 7 & 0 & 0 & 0 \\ 0 & 7 & 0 & 0 \\ 0 & 0 & 7 & 0 \\ 0 & 0 & 0 & 7 \end{bmatrix}$?

(c) What happens to a $3 \times 4$ matrix if the matrix $\begin{bmatrix} 7 & 0 & 0 \\ 0 & 1 & 0 \\ 0 & 0 & 1 \end{bmatrix}$ is multiplied by it?

(d) What happens to a $3 \times 4$ matrix if it is multiplied by the matrix $\begin{bmatrix} 7 & 0 & 0 & 0 \\ 0 & 1 & 0 & 0 \\ 0 & 0 & 1 & 0 \\ 0 & 0 & 0 & 1 \end{bmatrix}$?

*(e) What happens to a $3 \times 4$ matrix if $\begin{bmatrix} 0 & 1 & 0 \\ 1 & 0 & 0 \\ 0 & 0 & 1 \end{bmatrix}$ is multiplied by it?

*(f) What happens to a $3 \times 4$ matrix if it is multiplied by $\begin{bmatrix} 0 & 0 & 0 & 2 \\ 1 & 0 & 0 & 0 \\ 0 & 1 & 0 & 0 \\ 0 & 0 & 1 & 0 \end{bmatrix}$?

72. A major league baseball team has 25 members and plays a schedule of 162 games. What size matrix is required to record the number of hits by each player in each game?

See Exercise 72.  *73. Let M be the matrix that gives the number of hits by each player in each game in a given season.

(a) Find a matrix B such that MB gives the total hits for the season by each team member.

(b) Find a matrix A such that AM gives the total number of hits by the team in each game.

74. The Happy Nite Motel Corporation operates a chain of 12 motels. Each motel has 30 rooms and each room can hold from 1 to 4 people. The rate matrix A is a $12 \times 30$ matrix giving the nightly charge per person for each room in each motel. The occupancy matrix for June 15 is a $30 \times 12$ matrix B giving the number of persons in each room of each motel on the night of June 15.
    (a) What information is contained at address $(5,5)$ of AB?
    $^{c}$(b) What information is contained at address $(5,4)$ of AB?

75. "I'm doomed," said PHE's chief of data processing to his friend. "I was given what I thought was the full November production matrix N and a chart of 9 possible price structures for all our food items. I was asked to find the November proceeds from each store, assuming each different structure. So I assembled the price structures, column by column, into a $35 \times 9$ matrix M and multiplied to get NM, which contains all the answers. Now," he groaned, "I find out that the November production matrix had left out several days, so that each entry in N should be 25% larger. Not only that," he sighed, "the board has decided that all of the possible price structures were too high and that each price must be reduced by 20%. I have this sheaf of papers containing the old product NM, but now I have to recalculate everything, and the board expects the full results in 10 minutes. What shall I tell them?"

*76. Solve the system
$$\left[ \begin{array}{c} \left[ \begin{array}{cc} 2 & -1 \\ 0 & 1 \end{array} \right] X_1 + \left[ \begin{array}{cc} -1 & 2 \\ 3 & 1 \end{array} \right] X_2 = \left[ \begin{array}{cc} 3 & 2 \\ 7 & 0 \end{array} \right] \\ \left[ \begin{array}{cc} 0 & 1 \\ 3 & 2 \end{array} \right] X_1 + \left[ \begin{array}{cc} 2 & -3 \\ 1 & 1 \end{array} \right] X_2 = \left[ \begin{array}{cc} -2 & 1 \\ 10 & 11 \end{array} \right] \end{array} \right],$$
where the variables $X_1$ and $X_2$ are both $2 \times 2$ matrices.

A matrix of this form is a **partitioned matrix**; that is, a matrix broken up into smaller matrices. In this case we have a $5 \times 4$ matrix partitioned into four **submatrices**. Partitioned matrices occur in more theoretical treatments of this subject and are necessary from a practical standpoint when presenting a computer with a matrix which is in itself too large to be handled as a single entity.

77. After a particularly rough day at the office, Janet was so tired of looking at matrices that she left the following problem on her boss's desk:
    Multiply the following matrix by $-3$.
$$\left[ \begin{array}{c} \left[ \begin{array}{c} -6 \\ \frac{1}{2} \\ 0 \end{array} \right] \left[ \begin{array}{ccc} 2 & 3 & -4 \\ \frac{1}{2} & 0 & 2 \\ 5 & -7 & 18 \end{array} \right] \\ \left[ \begin{array}{c} -3 \\ 2 \end{array} \right] \left[ \begin{array}{ccc} -1 & 0 & \frac{7}{8} \\ -\frac{3}{4} & \frac{5}{8} & -19 \end{array} \right] \end{array} \right]$$
    Work this problem.

78. Add the following pair of partitioned matrices.
$$\left[ \begin{array}{c} \left[ \begin{array}{cc} 2 & 3 \\ -4 & 1 \end{array} \right] \left[ \begin{array}{ccc} -2 & 1 & 4 \\ 8 & 2 & -1 \end{array} \right] \\ \left[ \begin{array}{cc} 3 & 0 \\ -2 & 1 \\ 5 & 3 \end{array} \right] \left[ \begin{array}{ccc} 3 & -2 & -1 \\ 4 & 0 & 5 \\ 2 & -1 & 3 \end{array} \right] \end{array} \right], \left[ \begin{array}{c} \left[ \begin{array}{cc} -1 & 4 \\ 5 & 2 \end{array} \right] \left[ \begin{array}{ccc} 3 & -1 & 2 \\ 8 & -2 & 7 \end{array} \right] \\ \left[ \begin{array}{cc} 0 & -1 \\ 4 & 3 \\ 2 & 5 \end{array} \right] \left[ \begin{array}{ccc} 0 & -1 & -4 \\ 3 & 2 & -5 \\ 2 & -1 & 4 \end{array} \right] \end{array} \right]$$

Suppose we have to multiply two 100 $\times 100$ matrices on a computer which can handle only matrices of size $25 \times 25$ or smaller. If we partition each $100 \times 100$ matrix into four $25 \times 25$ matrices A, B, C, D, and E, F, G, H we have

$$\begin{bmatrix} A & \vdots & B \\ \hdashline C & \vdots & D \end{bmatrix} \cdot \begin{bmatrix} E & \vdots & F \\ \hdashline G & \vdots & H \end{bmatrix} =$$

$$\begin{bmatrix} AE+BG & \vdots & AF+BH \\ \hdashline CE+DG & \vdots & CF+DH \end{bmatrix}$$

To compute each block of this matrix, the machine has only to multiply and add $25 \times 25$ matrices.

79. Partitioned matrices can be multiplied like regular matrices. For example, to obtain the $(1, 1)$ entry in the product

$$\begin{bmatrix} \begin{bmatrix} 1 & 0 & -1 \\ 2 & 1 & 2 \end{bmatrix} & \begin{bmatrix} 0 & 0 \\ 0 & 0 \end{bmatrix} \\ \begin{bmatrix} 0 & 0 & 0 \\ 0 & 0 & 0 \\ 0 & 0 & 0 \end{bmatrix} & \begin{bmatrix} 1 & 0 \\ 0 & 0 \\ 0 & 1 \end{bmatrix} \\ \begin{bmatrix} 1 & 0 & 0 \\ 0 & 1 & 0 \\ 0 & 0 & 1 \end{bmatrix} & \begin{bmatrix} 1 & 1 \\ 1 & 0 \\ 2 & 1 \end{bmatrix} \end{bmatrix} \begin{bmatrix} \begin{bmatrix} 1 & 0 & 0 \\ 0 & 1 & 0 \\ 0 & 0 & 1 \end{bmatrix} & \begin{bmatrix} 1 \\ 2 \\ -1 \end{bmatrix} \\ \begin{bmatrix} 0 & 0 & 1 \\ 0 & 2 & 1 \end{bmatrix} & \begin{bmatrix} 1 \\ 3 \end{bmatrix} \end{bmatrix}$$

multiply $R_1$ of the first matrix by $C_1$ of the second matrix:

$$\begin{bmatrix} \begin{bmatrix} 1 & 0 & -1 \\ 2 & 1 & 2 \end{bmatrix} \begin{bmatrix} 0 & 0 \\ 0 & 0 \end{bmatrix} \end{bmatrix} \begin{bmatrix} \begin{bmatrix} 1 & 0 & 0 \\ 0 & 1 & 0 \\ 0 & 0 & 1 \end{bmatrix} \\ \begin{bmatrix} 0 & 0 & 1 \\ 0 & 2 & 1 \end{bmatrix} \end{bmatrix} = \begin{bmatrix} 1 & 0 & -1 \\ 2 & 1 & 2 \end{bmatrix} \begin{bmatrix} 1 & 0 & 0 \\ 0 & 1 & 0 \\ 0 & 0 & 1 \end{bmatrix} +$$

$$\begin{bmatrix} 0 & 0 \\ 0 & 0 \end{bmatrix} \begin{bmatrix} 0 & 0 & 1 \\ 0 & 2 & 1 \end{bmatrix} = \begin{bmatrix} 1 & 0 & -1 \\ 2 & 1 & 2 \end{bmatrix} + \begin{bmatrix} 0 & 0 & 0 \\ 0 & 0 & 0 \end{bmatrix} = \begin{bmatrix} 1 & 0 & -1 \\ 2 & 1 & 2 \end{bmatrix}$$

(a) Finish this computation and write the product as a $3 \times 2$ partitioned matrix.

(b) Erase all the brackets and multiply the resulting $8 \times 5$ matrix and $5 \times 4$ matrix. Compare the results.

80. Multiply the $2 \times 3$ matrix
$$\begin{bmatrix} \begin{bmatrix} 2 \\ 1 \\ 3 \end{bmatrix} & \begin{bmatrix} 0 & 0 & 0 \\ 0 & 0 & 0 \\ 0 & 0 & 0 \end{bmatrix} & \begin{bmatrix} 1 & 0 \\ 0 & 1 \\ 0 & 0 \end{bmatrix} \\ \begin{bmatrix} -1 \\ 3 \\ 4 \\ 2 \end{bmatrix} & \begin{bmatrix} 1 & 0 & 0 \\ 0 & 1 & 0 \\ 0 & 0 & 0 \\ 0 & 0 & 0 \end{bmatrix} & \begin{bmatrix} -2 & 0 \\ 3 & 1 \\ 2 & 0 \\ 5 & 1 \end{bmatrix} \end{bmatrix}$$

by the $3 \times 2$ matrix
$$\begin{bmatrix} \begin{bmatrix} 1 & -1 & 4 \end{bmatrix} & \begin{bmatrix} 6 & 2 & 1 \end{bmatrix} \\ \begin{bmatrix} -1 & 2 & 3 \\ 0 & 1 & 4 \\ 2 & -1 & -4 \end{bmatrix} & \begin{bmatrix} 0 & -1 & 2 \\ 8 & 3 & 2 \\ 5 & 1 & 4 \end{bmatrix} \\ \begin{bmatrix} 2 & 3 & 2 \\ -1 & 4 & 1 \end{bmatrix} & \begin{bmatrix} 0 & 0 & 0 \\ 2 & 0 & 0 \end{bmatrix} \end{bmatrix}$$

Problems 81 through 88 are examples of essentially every type of system of four equations in four variables. Solve them.

81. $$\begin{bmatrix} x_1 - x_2 + x_3 + 2x_4 = 9 \\ 2x_1 + x_2 - x_3 + x_4 = 0 \\ x_1 + 2x_2 + x_3 - x_4 = 3 \\ 3x_1 - x_2 + 3x_3 + x_4 = 20 \end{bmatrix}$$

$$c82. \quad \begin{bmatrix} x_1 + x_2 + x_3 - 4x_4 = & 1 \\ x_1 - x_2 + x_3 \quad\quad = & 1 \\ x_2 + x_3 - 3x_4 = & -1 \\ 2x_1 - x_2 + 2x_3 - 2x_4 = & 2 \end{bmatrix}$$

$$83. \quad \begin{bmatrix} x_1 - 2x_2 + 4x_3 + 5x_4 = & 5 \\ -x_1 + x_2 - x_3 - 3x_4 = & -3 \\ 2x_1 + x_2 - 7x_3 \quad\quad = & 0 \\ 3x_1 - 2x_2 \quad\quad + 7x_4 = & 7 \end{bmatrix}$$

$$c84. \quad \begin{bmatrix} 2x_1 - 4x_2 - 2x_3 + 2x_4 = & 6 \\ x_1 - 2x_2 - x_3 + x_4 = & 3 \\ -x_1 + 2x_2 + x_3 - x_4 = & -3 \\ 3x_1 - 6x_2 - 3x_3 + 3x_4 = & 9 \end{bmatrix}$$

$$85. \quad \begin{bmatrix} x_1 + 2x_2 - x_3 + 4x_4 = & 3 \\ 2x_1 - x_2 + x_3 - 3x_4 = & 7 \\ x_1 + 2x_2 + 3x_3 - 4x_4 = & 11 \\ 3x_1 - x_2 - x_3 + x_4 = & 6 \end{bmatrix}$$

$$c86. \quad \begin{bmatrix} 3x_1 - x_2 + 2x_3 - x_4 = 7 \\ 2x_1 - 2x_2 + x_3 - 2x_4 = 2 \\ x_1 - x_2 + x_3 - x_4 = 3 \\ x_1 - 3x_2 + 2x_3 - 3x_4 = 5 \end{bmatrix}$$

$$87. \quad \begin{bmatrix} x_1 + 2x_2 - x_3 - 2x_4 = 3 \\ 2x_1 - x_2 - 3x_3 + x_4 = 0 \\ x_1 + x_2 - 2x_3 - x_4 = 1 \\ 2x_1 - x_2 + x_3 + x_4 = 4 \end{bmatrix}$$

$$c88. \quad \begin{bmatrix} x_1 + x_2 - x_3 + x_4 = 7 \\ 3x_1 + 2x_2 + x_3 - x_4 = 2 \\ x_1 - 2x_2 + x_3 + 2x_4 = 6 \\ 5x_1 + x_2 + x_3 + 2x_4 = 5 \end{bmatrix}$$

89. How many matrices of each of the following sizes can be made using the numbers $1, 2, 3, 4, 5, 6, 7$, with no number used more than once?
(a) $1 \times 7$ (b) $7 \times 1$ (c) $2 \times 3$ (d) $3 \times 3$

90. Janet is conjecturing about the production matrix M of Pocono Productions (PP), a small competitor of AC. She knows M has at least 12 rows and 8 columns and at most 19 rows and 15 columns. How many possible sizes might M be?

91. The probabilities of getting $1, 2, 3, 4, 5, 6$ in a toss of a balanced die are, respectively, the $(1, 1)$, $(1, 2)$, $(1, 3)$, $(1, 4)$, $(1, 5)$, and $(1, 6)$ entries of a $1 \times 6$ matrix P. Write P for each of the following dice.
(a) The faces are numbered $1, 2, 3, 4, 5, 6$.
(b) The faces are numbered $1, 6, 2, 4, 3, 5$.

   (c) The faces are numbered 7, 8, 9, 10, 11, 12.

   (d) The faces are numbered 5, 6, 7, 8, 9, 10.

   (e) Two faces are numbered 2, two others are numbered 4, and the rest are numbered 6.

   (f) The numbers 1, 2, 3, 4, 5, 6 are written on every face.

   (g) The numbers 1 and 2 are on the same face, and the other faces are numbered 3, 4, 5, 6, 7.

   (h) One face is numbered 1 and 2, another is numbered 2 and 3, and the rest are numbered 5.

92. Take an actual die and roll it 5 times, recording your results in a row matrix R. Now roll it 5 more times and record your results in a column matrix C.

   (a) What are the sizes of R and C?

   (b) How many different row matrices could be obtained in this way?

   (c) Calculate RC = M. What size is M?

   (d) Calculate CR = T. What size is T?

   (e) What is the probability that M = T?

   *(f) How many different matrices like M could be obtained in this way?

   *(g) Can you determine how many different matrices like T could be obtained in this way?

93. I follow a daily exercise program in which the idea is to exercise 6 mornings a week. Either I swim or I jog or I bicycle. But I hate jogging, so I make certain that I swim more than I jog, and I bicycle exactly one day more than I jog. What are my possible exercise schedules?

94. I have three factories. Factory A makes 300 toy cars and 20 beach balls per hour. Factory B makes 700 toy cars and 70 beach balls per hour. Factory C makes 200 toy cars and 30 beach balls per hour. I have orders for 2,500 toy cars and 300 beach balls. What are the limits on the number of hours I can operate factory C and fill my orders exactly; that is, what are the smallest and the largest number of hours I can operate the factory? (Note: a factory cannot be operated for less than zero hours.)

95. Consider the four points (1, 0), (2, 0), (0, 1), and (0, 2).

   (a) How many different lines can be drawn through pairs of these points?

See Exercise 63 above.

   (b) Write the equations of each of the lines of part (a).

   *(c) How many different lines can be drawn through n points, no three of which lie on a line, if each line contains two of the points?

96. (a) Write a $3 \times 5$ matrix in which the entries at addresses $(i, j)$ and $(j, i)$ are equal for all possible pairs $(i, j)$.

   (b) Write a $3 \times 5$ matrix in which the entries at addresses $(i, j)$ and $(j, i)$ are equal for exactly three pairs $(i, j)$ with $i \neq j$.

# Chapter 3
# Multistage
# Processes

Appalachian Creations is one of the few corporations now actively recruiting. Prospective employees express interest in the firm at a campus interview, by speaking to a store manager, or by submitting a written application. AC uses a three-step process as shown in the following chart.

All candidates who have not had a campus interview are interviewed by the personnel department before they are interviewed at the main office. The numbers in the chart indicate the percent expected to move from one stage to the next.

AC HIRING CHART

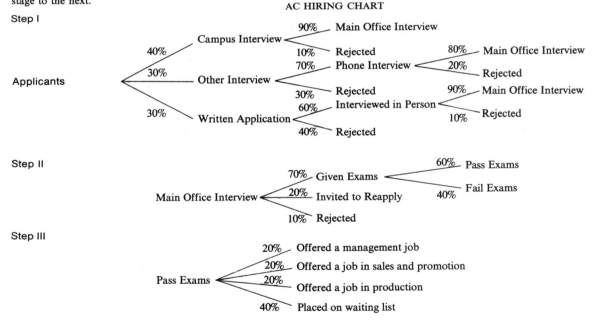

Step I

Step II

Step III

**Section 3.1**
**Tree Diagrams**

The chart used to summarize and to illustrate AC's multistage hiring process is called a **tree diagram**. In general we use the term **multistage process** in reference to any experiment that can be

In Section 2 of Chapter 1 we defined an **experiment** to be any action that results in outcomes. This is purposely vague. While we do not want to exclude scientific experiments, our main concern here is with experiments such as decision-making in business.

thought of as being performed in several steps. Besides AC's hiring procedure, other examples include most manufacturing processes and many of our more complicated actions in everyday life: getting through college, selecting a mate, and so on. A tree diagram is often a convenient way to illustrate a multistage process. It helps us to organize our thoughts and stresses the interrelationships between the various parts of the experiment, as in AC's three-step hiring chart. However, before we get into such complicated examples, we describe some rather simple, purely mathematical multistage processes.

**Problem 1**

A hat contains 3 coins and 2 dice. An object is taken from the hat. If it is a coin, it is flipped and the result is recorded; if a die is chosen, it is tossed and the result is recorded. Use a tree diagram to describe this experiment.

**Solution**

The possible results of the first action are: coin (C), die (D). This is diagramed as follows:

$$\begin{matrix} & C \\ < & \\ & D \end{matrix}$$

If C occurs the possible results are: heads (H), tails (T). This is diagramed:

$$C < \begin{matrix} H \\ T \end{matrix}$$

Note that the possible results of an action may depend on what has happened before.

If D occurs the possible outcomes are 1, 2, 3, 4, 5, 6. This is diagramed:

$$D < \begin{matrix} 1 \\ 2 \\ 3 \\ 4 \\ 5 \\ 6 \end{matrix}$$

Putting these diagrams together we have the tree diagram for the experiment:

Note the resemblance (however vague) to a tree.

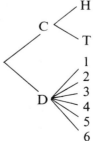

Problem 2

Two coins are flipped and the number of heads is recorded. Use a tree diagram to describe the experiment.

Solution

Even if the coins are flipped together we may think of them as being flipped one at a time. The H and T in stage 1 refer to one coin; both Hs and Ts in stage 2 refer to the other coin.

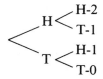

Problem 3

I put 15¢ change in a hat. You choose a coin and flip it. If it comes up heads you win the value of the coin multiplied by the number of coins left in the hat; if tails, you win 7¢. Describe the experiment with a tree diagram.

Solution

A tree diagram is a complete picture of a multistage process. Thus, in this example each different way of winning 7¢ must be recorded separately.

We describe the possible results of the first stage, in which I contribute 15¢ by ordered triples with the first entry the number of pennies (p), the second the number of nickles (n), the third the number of dimes (d).

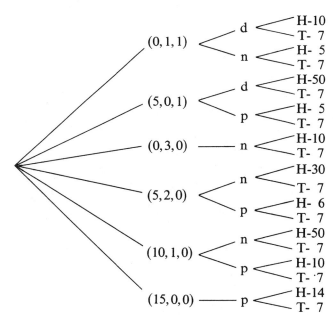

How can we be sure we have listed all possible ways to contribute 15¢? We can describe this process by a tree diagram with four stages:

(1) contribute any allowed number of dimes,
(2) contribute any allowed number of nickels,
(3) contribute enough pennies to reach 15¢,

(4) record the result with an ordered triple, as in the first part of the problem.

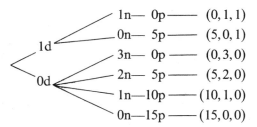

Problem 4 · Janet's basketball team is to play a series of games against Mary's team, with the first team that wins a total of 2 games being declared the winner of the series. Describe this situation with a tree diagram.

Solution · Each action has two possible results: M denotes "Mary's team wins"; J denotes "Janet's team wins."

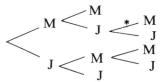

*Here we see an example of a multistage process in which the number of stages required to complete the experiment depends on what happens.*

Now in order to apply probability theory to a multistage process we must know the probabilities of being on each branch of the tree diagram of that process. In general these probabilities depend on the results of previous stages and are therefore conditional probabilities, as defined in Chapter 1, Section 5. For example, the probability of being on branch * of the diagram above is not merely the probability of Mary's team winning a game; it is the probability that Mary's team wins the third game, given that Janet's team won the second game and Mary's won the first. In general, things can get very complicated. In order to obtain a useful mathematical model we must make some simplifying assumptions about the process being studied. We shall do this, in various ways, in this chapter and in Chapter 4, Section 4.

*In the case of the AC hiring chart the probabilities are the percent figures written on the branches of the trees given at the beginning of this chapter.*

Exercises · Draw tree diagrams for each of the following experiments.
1. A coin is flipped three times.
2. Three coins are flipped.
3. Two dice are tossed.
4. A die is tossed twice.

First team with 4 wins takes the series.

Put an * next to this problem if you plan not to consult a map.

Only the heavy lines, not the sides of the corridors, are considered as walls.

The points are called 15, 30, 40, and game. A tie is called deuce; no points is called love. A point won after deuce is called advantage. Fortunately, most of this is irrelevant for working this problem.

5. A die is tossed. If it comes up less than 5, a coin is flipped. If it comes up 5 or 6, the die is tossed again.

6. There is a series of games between teams A and B. The first team to win either 2 games in a row or a total of 4 games wins the series.

7. Darlene, Edward, and Frank have a series of shooting matches, each with 1 winner. The first to win 2 matches wins the series.

8. The Mets and Yankees play a World Series.

9. Marilyn is willing to go out with Jack, Bill, or Tom, whoever calls first. But after the second date with the same man, she will move away and forget all three of them.

10. An urn contains 6 red balls and 1 black ball. You keep drawing out balls until you get the black one.

11. All the hymns in Pastor Greife's church have 3, 4, or 8 verses, and there are lots of each type. The Pastor always chooses at least 2 hymns with different numbers of verses, and he knows the congregation will not sing more than 14 verses in one service.

12. PHE wants to build, one at a time, a total of 3 stores somewhere in Maine, New Hampshire, Vermont, Massachusetts, Connecticut, or Rhode Island. They do not want 2 stores in the same state, and when they build a store in a state they will not build the next store in a state that borders it.

13. Use a tree diagram to describe this maze. Use the symbols L (left), R (right), and S (straight). When a wall or the * is encountered the experiment is over.

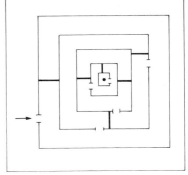

14. My apartment has 3 windows. Each window has an upper pane and a lower pane. If I raise the lower pane on a window it would make no sense to lower the upper pane, since that would close the window again. I want to open 2 panes.

*15. In tennis, each player scores points. The first player to score 4 points is the winner of the game unless the other player has 3 points. In this case the game continues until one player scores 2 points in a row. Describe the relevant tree diagram.

**Section 3.2**
**Bayes' Theorem**

The principle of sorting, which was so useful in counting, can be extended to probability. This is usually accomplished by breaking the sample space into a collection of events such that each possible outcome is in one and only one of the events. Such a collection is called a partition of the sample space. In this section we will use three examples to illustrate this approach.

Example 1

The Dice Game. In the table on page 33 we have listed the 36 possible outcomes of the throw of a red and a green die. It is natural to break up this sample space as follows:

$$\{(1,1)\}, \{(1,2),(2,1)\}, \{(1,3),(2,2),(3,1)\},$$

$$\{(1,4),(2,3),(3,2),(4,1)\}, \{(1,5),(2,4),(3,3),(4,2),(5,1)\},$$

$$\{(1,6),(2,5),(3,4),(4,3),(5,2),(6,1)\},$$

$$\{(2,6),(3,5),(4,4),(5,3),(6,2)\},$$

$$\{(3,6),(4,5),(5,4),(6,3)\},$$

$$\{(4,6),(5,5),(6,4)\}, \{(5,6),(6,5)\}, \{(6,6)\}$$

Here we have grouped together all outcomes with the same total number of spots. If we label these subsets $A_2, A_3, \ldots, A_{12}$ (where the subscript denotes the total number of spots showing), we have

This is a little unusual. In most situations we will denote the elements of a partition by sets $A_1, \ldots, A_n$, where the subscripts begin at 1.

$$A_2 = \{(1,1)\}$$
$$A_3 = \{(1,2),(2,1)\}$$
$$A_4 = \{(1,3),(2,2),(3,1)\}$$
$$A_5 = \{(1,4),(2,3),(3,2),(4,1)\}$$

and so on.

**Partitions**

This kind of sorting of a sample space is called a partition. In the language of sets, a **partition** of a set S is a collection of sets $A_1, A_2, \ldots, A_n$ such that each element of S is in one and only one of the sets $A_i$, where i is one of the numbers from one to n. We will also suppose that each of the sets $A_i$ is a subset of S. This definition has two important consequences:

(1) since every element of S is in one of the sets $A_i$ and since the $A_i$'s contain only elements of S, it follows that the union of the $A_i$'s must equal S:

The union of a collection of sets is the set of all elements that are in at least one of the sets in the collection.

$$A_1 \cup A_2 \cup \ldots \cup A_n = S \qquad \qquad 1$$

(2) since every element of S is in *only* one of the sets $A_i$, each pair of them must be disjoint:

If $i=j$, then $A_i \cap A_j = A_i \cap A_i = A_i$.

$$\text{if } i \neq j, \text{ then } A_i \cap A_j = \varnothing \qquad \qquad 2$$

In statement (2) i and j may be any two (different) numbers from 1 to n. Thus, (2) is really $C_2^n = n(n-1)/2$ separate statements.

Example 2

Tent Sales at Appalachian Creations. In this example we consider only two-person tents sold during the last fiscal year. The experiment involves the recording of the date and place of sale of a tent. The sample space for this experiment is a complete list of places and dates of sale. Two possible outcomes are: Lou's Sporting Goods, Montpelier, VT, March 5; and The Happy Hiker, St. Helena, CA, June 13. There are two partitions of this sample space which AC uses in its surveys. In the partition by states, the first outcome above belongs to Vermont and the second belongs to California. In the partition by months, the first outcome belongs to March and the second to June.

In the 1930s AC used a simpler partition of two-person tent sales: $A_1 = $ Massachusetts, $A_2 = $ rest of New England, $A_3 = $ rest of country. Equation **1** then becomes $A_1 \cup A_2 \cup A_3 = S$; that is, every tent was sold in Massachusetts, in the rest of New England, or in the rest of the country. Since $C_2^3 = 3$, Equation **2** becomes the three separate equations $A_1 \cap A_2 = \varnothing$, $A_1 \cap A_3 = \varnothing$, and $A_2 \cap A_3 = \varnothing$. These are true since, from 1930 on, no single tent was sold in more than one place. For example, the first of these equations says that no single tent was sold both in Massachusetts and in the rest of New England.

On October 29, 1929, Thomas Black, the founder of AC, sold his first tent to a hitchhiker he carried from New York through Massachusetts and into Vermont. He recorded the place of sale as "various."

Example 3

Alan's Neighborhood. Many ethnic groups are represented in the section of the city where Alan lives. A few years ago the census bureau came into Alan's neighborhood and performed (many times) the experiment "select an individual at random." The sample space for this experiment is the set of all persons who might be selected. However, this time the census bureau was interested only in the ethnic background of the individual selected, so naturally they partitioned the sample space into five events: Greek, Black, Chinese, Polish, Other. If we let $G = $ Greek, $B = $ Black, $C = $ Chinese, $P = $ Polish, and $O = $ Other, we have the following version of equation **1**:

$$G \cup B \cup C \cup P \cup O = S$$

and equation **2**:

$$G \cap B = \varnothing, \; G \cap C = \varnothing, \; G \cap P = \varnothing, \; G \cap O = \varnothing, \; B \cap C = \varnothing,$$
$$B \cap P = \varnothing, \; B \cap O = \varnothing, \; C \cap P = \varnothing, \; C \cap O = \varnothing, \; P \cap O = \varnothing.$$

Of course, the choice of this particular partition was determined by the nature of Alan's neighborhood: 14% Greek, 18% Black, 10% Chinese, and 14% Polish.

$C_2^5 = 10$, so there are 10 equations.

There are other interesting events in the sample space of Example 3. The principal of the local elementary school is interested in the event $E = $ "a person (in Alan's neighborhood) between the ages of 5 and 12." Notice that the census bureau's partition also partitions this event:

$$G \cap E, \; B \cap E, \; C \cap E, \; P \cap E, \; O \cap E$$

For example, $G \cap E$ is simply the set of all individuals in Alan's neighborhood who have a Greek background and who are between the ages of 5 and 12. Although this is obviously a partition of the set E, we will now verify this fact. Each child in E has some ethnic background, therefore he or she is necessarily in one of the sets $G \cap E$, $B \cap E$, $C \cap E$, $P \cap E$, or $O \cap E$. Hence we have

$$(G \cap E) \cup (B \cap E) \cup (C \cap E) \cup (P \cap E) \cup (O \cap E) = E$$

This is the fault of the census bureau. Don't blame us. If a child insists on having two (or more) ethnic backgrounds, he or she is put into the "other" category.

Since no child has two ethnic backgrounds, no two sets in the partition have an element in common:

$$(G \cap E) \cap (B \cap E) = \varnothing, \text{ etc.}$$

(There are 10 cases to verify to be sure equation **2** in the definition of a partition is satisfied.)

For another example, the local health club partitions Alan's neighborhood as follows:

| Classification | Age Group |
|---|---|
| I = Infant | 0–2 |
| T = Tot | 3–4 |
| E = Elementary School Child | 5–12 |
| Y = Young Adult | 13–24 |
| A = Adult | 25–65 |
| M = Mature | over 65 |

This partition will yield a partition of any event in the sample space. For example, the event "Greek" is partitioned:

$$I \cap G, \; T \cap G, \; E \cap G, \; Y \cap G, \; A \cap G, \; M \cap G.$$

Here again $I \cap G$ represents the set of infants with Greek background, and so on.

In general we have the following result from set theory.

> If $A_1, A_2, \ldots, A_n$ is a partition of a set S and B is any subset of S, then $A_1 \cap B, A_2 \cap B, \ldots, A_n \cap B$ is a partition of B.

**3**

Problem 1    Which of the following collections of sets are partitions of $S = \{1, 2, 3, 4\}$?

(a)  $\{1,3\}, \{2,4\}$     (e)  $\{1,3\}, \{2,3,4\}$

(b)  $\{1\}, \{2\}, \{3\}, \{4\}$     (f)  $\{1,4\}, \{2\}$

(c)  $\{1,2,4\}, \{3\}$     (g)  $\{1,5\}, \{2,3,4\}$

(d)  $\{1,2,3,4\}$     (h)  $\{1,3\}, \varnothing, \{2,4\}$

Certainly collections (a), (b), and (c) are partitions of S. Note that the sets in a partition do not all have to be the same size. Collection (d) is also a partition, but it isn't of much use, since it doesn't really split up S at all. Collection (e) is not a partition of S, because the element 3 of S is in more than one of the sets. Collection (f) is not a partition of S, since 3 is in S but it is in none of the sets listed. Collection (g) is not a partition of S, because the set $\{1,5\}$ is not a subset of S. Collection (h) is a partition of S which is practically the same as the partition (a).

Some authors require that the sets in a partition be nonempty, thus ruling out (h). In probability, however, it is more convenient and natural to allow the empty set to be in a partition. Note that the empty set is disjoint from any set: $A \cap \varnothing = \varnothing$ since no set has elements that are also in the empty set.

If $A_1, A_2, \ldots, A_n$ is a partition of S, and B is a subset of S, the collection of sets $A_1 \cap B, A_2 \cap B, \ldots, A_n \cap B$ is called the partition of B *obtained from* the partition $A_1, A_2, \ldots, A_n$.

Problem 2

Find the partitions of $B = \{2,3,4\}$ obtained from the partitions of Problem 1.

Solution

This problem makes sense since B is a subset of $S = \{1,2,3,4\}$.

$$(a) \quad \begin{aligned} A_1 \cap B &= \{1,3\} \cap \{2,3,4\} = \{3\} \\ A_2 \cap B &= \{2,4\} \cap \{2,3,4\} = \{2,4\} \end{aligned}$$

Thus, the partition is $\{3\}, \{2,4\}$.

$$(b) \quad \begin{aligned} A_1 \cap B &= \{1\} \cap \{2,3,4\} = \varnothing \\ A_2 \cap B &= \{2\} \cap \{2,3,4\} = \{2\} \\ A_3 \cap B &= \{3\} \cap \{2,3,4\} = \{3\} \\ A_4 \cap B &= \{4\} \cap \{2,3,4\} = \{4\} \end{aligned}$$

In this case the partition is $\varnothing$, $\{2\}$, $\{3\}$, $\{4\}$.

$$(c) \quad \begin{aligned} A_1 \cap B &= \{1,2,4\} \cap \{2,3,4\} = \{2,4\} \\ A_2 \cap B &= \{3\} \cap \{2,3,4\} = \{3\} \end{aligned}$$

The collections $\{3\}, \{2,4\}$ and $\{2,4\}, \{3\}$ are the same since the order in which the sets appear is immaterial.

The partition is $\{2,4\}, \{3\}$. This is the same as the partition obtained from (a), even though (a) and (c) are different partitions of S.

Now how does Janet Witherspoon use all these ideas to help in finding the probability of an event B? Suppose $A_1, A_2, \ldots, A_n$ is a partition of S. Since $A_1 \cap B, A_2 \cap B, \ldots, A_n \cap B$ is a partition of B, we can use it to compute P(B). We know that

$$B = (A_1 \cap B) \cup (A_2 \cap B) \cup \ldots \cup (A_n \cap B)$$

and that each two distinct sets in this union are disjoint. Thus,

$$P(B) = P(A_1 \cap B) + P(A_2 \cap B) + \cdots + P(A_n \cap B).$$

Since we have previously verified such an equation for only two sets, some explanation is in order. To compute P(B) we simply add all the probabilities P(x) for each x in B. Now each x in B is in exactly one of the sets $A_i \cap B$. If we then add all the P(x) with x in $A_i \cap B$, we will get $P(A_i \cap B)$. Finally, if we add all the $P(A_i \cap B)$, we will have added together all the P(x) for all x in any one of the $A_i \cap B$; that is, for all x in B. The equation which we obtained is the one that Janet actually uses.

As complicated as the right-hand side of equation **4** may appear, it is often the easiest way to compute the probability of an event from given information.

> If $A_1, A_2, \ldots, A_n$ is a partition of the sample space of an experiment with the probability distribution P, and if B is any event in the experiment, then
>
> $$P(B) = P(A_1 \cap B) + P(A_2 \cap B) + \cdots + P(A_n \cap B)$$

**4**

**Problem 3**  An experiment has five outcomes: a, b, c, d, e with probabilities given by Table 1.

**Table 1**

| Outcome | Probability |
|---------|-------------|
| a | $\frac{1}{4}$ |
| b | $\frac{8}{35}$ |
| c | $\frac{1}{5}$ |
| d | $\frac{1}{28}$ |
| e | $\frac{2}{7}$ |

Verify equation **4** for the partition $\{c, d\}, \{a, e\}, \{b\}$, and for the event $\{b, c, d\}$,

**Solution**  Let $A_1 = \{c, d\}$, $A_2 = \{a, e\}$, $A_3 = \{b\}$, and $B = \{b, c, d\}$. Then

$$A_1 \cap B = \{c, d\} \cap \{b, c, d\} = \{c, d\}$$
$$A_2 \cap B = \{a, e\} \cap \{b, c, d\} = \varnothing$$
$$A_3 \cap B = \{b\} \cap \{b, c, d\} = \{b\}$$

We first calculate the right-hand side of equation **4**: $P(A_1 \cap B) = P(c, d) = P(c) + P(d) = \frac{1}{5} + \frac{1}{28} = \frac{33}{140}$; $P(A_2 \cap B) = P(\varnothing) = 0$; $P(A_3 \cap B) = P(b) = \frac{8}{35}$. The sum of these fractions is $\frac{33}{140} + 0 + \frac{8}{35} = \frac{65}{140} = \frac{13}{28}$. In this case we know the event B explicitly and can compute $P(B) = P(b, c, d) = P(b) + P(c) + P(d) = \frac{8}{35} + \frac{1}{5} + \frac{1}{28} = \frac{65}{140} = \frac{13}{28}$. $\checkmark$

In result **4** suppose we take B to be S, the whole sample space.

Every element of $A_1$ is an element of S; hence $A_1 \cap S = A_1$.

Then $A_1 \cap B = A_1 \cap S = A_1$, since $A_1$ is a subset of S. Also $A_2 \cap B =$

$A_2 \cap S = A_2$ and so on. Result **4** tells us that

$$P(S) = P(A_1 \cap S) + P(A_2 \cap S) + \cdots + P(A_n \cap S)$$
$$= P(A_1) + P(A_2) + \cdots + P(A_n)$$

But by Rule 3, page 18, $P(S) = 1$. Thus, for any partition $A_1, \ldots, A_n$ we have

$$P(A_1) + P(A_2) + \cdots + P(A_n) = 1 \qquad\qquad\mathbf{5}$$

We can use this equation as a partial check that a collection of sets $A_1, A_2, \ldots, A_n$ is a partition of S. If equation **5** is *not* satisfied, then we may be certain that $A_1, A_2, \ldots, A_n$ is not a partition of S. Unfortunately, even if equation **5** is satisfied we cannot be sure we have a partition.

Result **5** can easily be derived directly: $1 = P(S) =$ the sum of all $P(x)$ where x is in $S =$ (the sum of all $P(x)$ where x is in $A_1$) + (the sum of all $P(x)$ where x is in $A_2$) + $\cdots$ + (the sum of all $P(x)$ where x is in $A_n$) = $P(A_1)$ + $P(A_2) + \cdots + P(A_n)$.

**Problem 4**

It is claimed that events $A_1$, $A_2$, and $A_3$ are a partition of a given experiment. You believe that $P(A_1) = \frac{2}{3}$, $P(A_2) = \frac{1}{5}$, and $P(A_3) = \frac{1}{15}$. What can you conclude?

**Solution**

$$P(A_1) + P(A_2) + P(A_3) = \tfrac{2}{3} + \tfrac{1}{5} + \tfrac{1}{15} = \tfrac{14}{15} \neq 1.$$

You can conclude that either the claim is wrong or one or more of your beliefs is wrong.

**Problem 5**

A balanced die is thrown. Let $A_1$ be the event "an odd number comes up" and let $A_2$ be the event "a number greater than 3 comes up."
(a) Is equation **5** satisfied?
(b) What can you conclude from your answer to (a)?
(c) Is $A_1$, $A_2$, a partition of the sample space of the experiment?

**Solution**

(a) $A_1 = \{1, 3, 5\}$ and $A_2 = \{4, 5, 6\}$. Equation **5** is satisfied since $P(A_1) + P(A_2) = \frac{1}{2} + \frac{1}{2} = 1$.
(b) Nothing.
(c) $A_1$, $A_2$ is not a partition since 5 is in both $A_1$ and $A_2$. (Also, the possible outcome, 2, is in neither $A_1$ nor $A_2$.)

In order to apply result **4** to a practical problem, Janet has to select a partition $A_1, A_2, \ldots, A_n$ of S that makes it easy (or at least possible) for her to compute $P(A_1 \cap B), P(A_2 \cap B), \ldots, P(A_n \cap B)$. She succeeded in doing this when, during her second year, she was asked to reconstruct the proportion of tents sold the previous year that were winter-weight, two-person tents. Her boss had used the word "reconstruct" because this important piece of information was once known but was now mysteriously missing from the files.

Janet found that the monthly sales records were intact, however, and she proceeded as follows. The sample space S is the full record of two-person tent sales of Example 2, p. 155. Let B be the event "winter-weight." The "proportion of winter-weight tents sold" is just another way to express P(B). Let $M_1$ be the event "January," $M_2$ = "February,"..., $M_{12}$ = "December." Then $M_1, M_2, ..., M_{12}$ is the partition of S by months as described above. Each monthly report gave the proportion of winter-weight tents sold that month. In the notation of conditional probability (Chapter 1, Section 5) this gave Janet the numbers $P(B|M_1)$, $P(B|M_2), ..., P(B|M_{12})$. From the year sales summary she found the proportion of tents sold each month, that is, $P(M_1)$, $P(M_2), ..., P(M_{12})$. Applying equation **4** of Section 1.5 she found $P(M_1 \cap B) = P(B|M_1)P(M_1)$, $P(M_2 \cap B) = P(B|M_2)P(M_2)$, and so on.

> This sales summary percentage combined all monthly sales into one percentage figure, so the winter-weight tents could not be distinguished.

Janet had thus calculated $P(M_1 \cap B), ..., P(M_{12} \cap B)$. These are simply the proportions of winter-weight tents sold each month. To compute the proportion sold in the entire year she simply added the monthly figures. Thus, the year figure P(B) is given by equation **4**:

$$P(B) = P(M_1 \cap B) + P(M_2 \cap B) + \cdots + P(M_{12} \cap B).$$

When later that week the original report was found where it had slipped behind the file cabinet, Janet's career received a boost: the original number agreed with her calculation of P(B).

**Problem 6**   Last Tuesday Alan woke up in the middle of the night with a headache. He stumbled into the bathroom and blindly took two pills from a bottle in the medicine chest. He felt funny when he awoke in the morning. When he looked in the medicine chest, he was shocked to see that his wife's prescription was right next to the aspirin bottle. He had chosen one of the bottles at random. Taking his wife's pills might have serious consequences. He called the doctor immediately and described his symptoms. The doctor said that, if Alan had taken aspirin, there was a 10% chance he would have those symptoms anyway. If he had taken his wife's medication, there was an 80% chance that he would have the symptoms he described. What Alan wants to know is the probability that he took the aspirin.

**Solution**   We will let A = "took aspirin," B = "took wife's medication," Y = "has symptoms," N = "doesn't have symptoms." We know that Alan has the symptoms; what we want to know is the probability that he took aspirin given that he has the symptoms:

P(A|Y). What data do we have? First, Alan feels that there is an equal chance he took aspirin or the other medication, so we let $P(A) = \frac{1}{2}$ and $P(B) = \frac{1}{2}$. The doctor said that there was a 10% chance he would have the symptoms given that he took aspirin; so $P(Y|A) = \frac{10}{100}$. Similarly, $P(Y|B) = \frac{80}{100}$. What information do we need to compute P(A|Y)? From the definition we have

$$P(A|Y) = P(A \cap Y)/P(Y).$$

If we recall equation **4** of Section 1.5 we can compute $P(A \cap Y) = P(Y|A)P(A) = \frac{10}{100} \cdot \frac{1}{2} = \frac{5}{100} = \frac{1}{20}$. But what about P(Y), the probability that Alan has symptoms?

The problem we have before us is called a problem in inverse probabilities. We have data of the form P(Y|A) and we are asked to determine the inverse (in the English sense of "opposite") probability, P(A|Y). This is the most common and most important sort of problem in conditional probability. The general method, which we illustrate below, will easily solve any problem of this type that is small enough to do by hand. For computer users and formula addicts we will also provide a formula, "Bayes' formula," named after the man who invented this technique.

We will outline the general method in large type and illustrate it in small type as we go along.

Step 1    View the problem as a two stage experiment.

        (a) Alan takes medicine.
        (b) Alan gets symptoms.

Step 2    Draw a tree diagram which lists the possible outcomes at each stage of the experiment.

In our case we have:

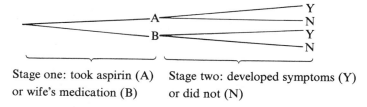

Stage one: took aspirin (A)   Stage two: developed symptoms (Y)
or wife's medication (B)      or did not (N)

Step 3    Assign probabilities to each branch of this diagram as follows:
(1) To each branch in stage 1 assign the probability of the event at the end of the branch;

(2) To each branch in stage 2 assign the conditional probability of the event at the right given the event at the left.

In symbols:

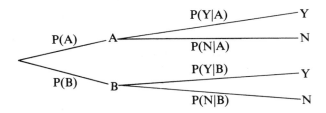

In numbers:

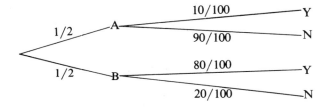

The number assigned to each branch is simply the probability that Alan will be going along it. For example, we have assigned $\frac{1}{2}$ to the branch to B, since that is the probability that Alan will be at B after the first stage. We assign $\frac{20}{100}$ to the branch from B to N since that is the probability that Alan will go from B to N, i.e., take his wife's medication, yet show no symptoms.

Step 4    Multiply the probabilities along consecutive branches and list the results at the right.

In symbols:

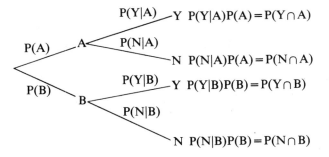

In numbers:

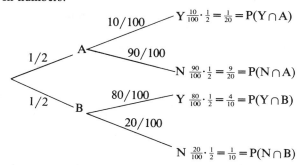

The equations on the right are simply applications of equations **3** and **4**, Section 1.5, to this case. Now there are exactly two ways that Alan could get symptoms:

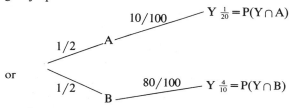

or

In words: Alan could take aspirin and develop symptoms or take his wife's pills and develop symptoms. These are the only ways he could have developed symptoms, and the two ways are mutually exclusive.

Thus, $P(Y) = \frac{1}{20} + \frac{4}{10} = \frac{1}{20} + \frac{8}{20} = \frac{9}{20}$. If this is not obvious to you, note that A, B is a partition of the sample space, so that $Y \cap A$, $Y \cap B$ is a partition of the event Y. Then equation **4** of Section 1.5 yields $P(Y) = P(Y \cap A) + P(Y \cap B) = \frac{9}{20}$. In general:

**Step 5**   Locate all occurrences in the tree diagram of the "given" event (that is, the event to the right of the | symbol) in the conditional probability you wish to find. Add the numbers next to these occurrences to obtain the probability of the "given" event.

In the present case

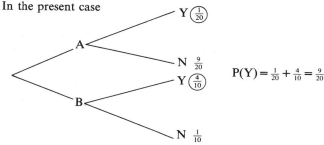

As a check, the numbers at ends of the tree diagram must total one, since they are the probabilities of a partition of the sample space: $\frac{1}{20} + \frac{9}{20} + \frac{4}{10} + \frac{1}{10} = 1 \checkmark$.

$P(Y) = \frac{1}{20} + \frac{4}{10} = \frac{9}{20}$

Symbolically: $P(Y) = P(A \cap Y) + P(B \cap Y)$.

Step 6 Locate the number next to the branch in the tree diagram that connects the two events in the conditional probability you wish to find. This number is the probability that both events occur. Divide this number by the probability of the "given" event found in Step Five to obtain the answer.

In the present case:

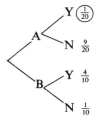

ANSWER $\frac{1}{20} \div \frac{9}{20} = \frac{1}{20} \cdot \frac{20}{9} = \frac{1}{9}$.

Symbolically: $P(A|Y) = P(A \cap Y)/P(Y)$.

He was treated and released in time for lunch.

So the probability was only $\frac{1}{9}$ that Alan took aspirin. Therefore he rushed to the hospital.

Remark 1 In our solution we used only the branches to Y in the tree diagram. The branches to N did not have to be drawn, although without them we would not have had a check. In the next problem we will save time by not drawing the entire tree in Step Two.

Remark 2 Some individuals prefer to work these problems numerically. Here is how that is done. *Pretend* that 200 Alans had headaches and blindly took medicine. Then the number in each state can be calculated as follows:

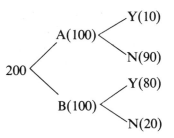

Thus, $10 + 80 = 90$ of the 200 Alans will have symptoms and of these only the first 10 will have taken aspirin. So 10 out of 90 Alans with symptoms will have taken aspirin. Hence the desired probability is $\frac{10}{90} = \frac{1}{9}$, as before.

Problem 7

Solution

The information in Table 2 is sent to national headquarters in the form of a $4 \times 12$ *preference matrix*. The seven extra columns relate to ethnic groups not in this district and are filled with zeros. Some columns do not total 100% because, there are, in fact, five other political parties represented in Alan's district.

Consider again the situation of Problem 3 of Section 1.5, p. 40. A voter, selected at random, supports the Republican candidate. What is the probability that he is of Greek extraction?

If we again let G = "of Greek extraction" and R = "supports Republican candidate," we are asked to find P(G|R). By Equation **1** of Section 1.5

$$P(G|R) = P(G \cap R)/P(R)$$

We know $P(G \cap R)$. It is simply $P(R|G)P(G) = .056$, which we calculated in Problem 3 of Section 1.5. However, we do not know P(R). All we have are the results of surveys as presented in Tables 2 and 3:

Table 2
Current Voter
Preferences (percent)
by Ethnic Background

|  | Greek | Black | Chinese | Polish | Other |
|---|---|---|---|---|---|
| Republican | 40 | 20 | 60 | 20 | 40 |
| Democrat | 40 | 60 | 20 | 70 | 50 |
| Socialist | 5 | 10 | 0 | 10 | 5 |
| Undecided | 15 | 5 | 10 | 0 | 5 |

Table 3
Census Bureau's
Estimates of Ethnic
Background of Voters

| | |
|---|---|
| Greek | 14% |
| Black | 18% |
| Chinese | 10% |
| Polish | 14% |
| Other | 44% |

Recognizing this as a problem in inverse probabilities we draw a tree diagram to help us picture the situation. We also notice that for the moment we only care about Republicans.

Thus, P(Republican) = .356 and we have our answer:

$$P(G|R) = \tfrac{.056}{.356} = .157.$$

We can just as easily compute any of the following inverse

probabilities. Notice the pattern:

$P(\text{Greek}|\text{Republican})$ $= .056/(.056+.036+.060+.028+.176)$
$= .056/.356 = .157.$

$P(\text{Black}|\text{Republican})$ $= .036/(.056+.036+.060+.028+.176)$
$= .036/.356 = .101.$

$P(\text{Chinese}|\text{Republican})$ $= .060/(.056+.036+.060+.028+.176)$
$= .060/.356 = .169.$

$P(\text{Polish}|\text{Republican})$ $= .028/(.056+.036+.060+.028+.176)$
$= .028/.356 = .079.$

$P(\text{Other}|\text{Republican})$ $= .064/(.056+.036+.060+.028+.176)$
$= .064/.356 = .180.$

Suppose the problem had said: "A voter is picked at random and he is found to be a Socialist. What is the probability he is black?" We are now concerned with the Socialist branches. Using Tables 2 and 3 again we construct the following tree:

| | | | | |
|---|---|---|---|---|
| .05 | Greek | .05 | Socialist | $(.14)(.05) = 0.007$ |
| .18 | Black | .10 | Socialist | $(.18)(.10) = 0.018$ |
| .10 | Chinese | .00 | Socialist | $(.10)(.00) = 0.000$ |
| .14 | Polish | .10 | Socialist | $(.14)(.10) = 0.014$ |
| .44 | Other | .05 | Socialist | $(.44)(.05) = 0.002$ |
| | | | Total | 0.061 |

Thus, $P(\text{Black}|\text{Socialist}) = \frac{.018}{.061} = .295.$

The Reverend Thomas Bayes (d. 1761) was an obscure English clergyman whose two papers on probability marked the beginning of statistics; that is, he was the first to apply probability to make inferences about a population from information contained in a random sample. His papers (published posthumously in 1763–1764) went unnoticed until a more famous mathematician, Pierre Simon Laplace (1749–1827) reformulated his results.

Bayes' formula is the general formula that results when you apply the above procedure to an arbitrary pair of events A and B. It is hardly worth stating and certainly not worth memorizing. The arithmetic is exactly the same whether you use the tree diagram or the formula. The difficulty with the formula is that it is often hard to decide which events to assign to which letters in the formula whereas this is always clear with a tree diagram.

Let the events $A_1, A_2, \ldots, A_n$ be a partition of an experiment and let B be an event in the experiment. Suppose that each of $A_1, A_2, \ldots, A_n$ has positive probability. Then by equation **4**, $P(B) = P(B \cap A_1) + P(B \cap A_2) + \cdots + P(B \cap A_n)$, and so

$$P(B) = P(B|A_1)P(A_1) + P(B|A_2)P(A_2) + \cdots + P(B|A_n)P(A_n) \quad \textbf{6}$$

Equation **6** is known as the **partition equation**. Now suppose B also has positive probability. Let $A_i$ be any one of the events $A_1, A_2, \ldots, A_n$. Then $P(A_i|B) = P(A_i \cap B)/P(B) = P(B|A_i)P(A_i)/P(B)$; so by the partition equation

$$P(A_i|B) = \frac{P(B|A_i)P(A_i)}{P(B|A_1)P(A_1) + P(B|A_2)P(A_2) + \cdots + P(B|A_n)P(A_n)} \quad \textbf{7}$$

Equation **7** is Bayes' formula. In Problem 7 we had $n = 5$, $A_1 =$ Greek, $A_2 =$ Black, $A_3 =$ Chinese, $A_4 =$ Polish, $A_5 =$ Other, and $B =$ Republican.

**Exercises 3.2**   In Exercises 1 through 6 decide which of the collections are partitions of the record of AC's last year's sales in the USA of four-person tents. Explain why you reject certain collections.

1. First, second, third, and fourth quarters.
2. Sales on or before May 31; sales on or after June 1.
3. Boston area, Massachusetts, rest of U.S.
4. Sales in months containing the letter r; sales in June, July, or August.
5. Original 13 colonies, Louisiana Purchase, Texas, California, Alaska, Hawaii.
6. States admitted to the union before 1913; states admitted after 1950.

7. Write out all the set equations necessary to express the fact that $A_1$, $A_2$, $A_3$, $A_4$ are a partition of S.

In Exercises 8 through 12 tell whether or not the collection is a partition of $S = \{p, q, r, s, t\}$.

8. $\{r, t\}, \{s, p\}, \{q\}$
9. $S, \varnothing$
10. $\{r, t, p\}, \{q, s, p\}$
11. $\{q, t\}, \{s, p\}, \{r\}$
12. $\{p\}, \varnothing, \{t, s\}, \{q\}, \{r\}$

See tabulation in problem 9, p. 33.

13. Let S be the sample space for dice. For $n = 1, 2, 3, 4, 5, 6$, let $A_n$ be the set of all possible outcomes that have probability $\frac{n}{36}$. Write out $A_1, A_2, A_3, A_4, A_5, A_6$ and show that they are a partition of S.

In Exercises 14 through 17, find the partition of B obtained from the partition of Exercise 13 and check the validity of equation **4**.

14. $B = \{2, 4, 8\}$
15. $B =$ odd number.
16. $B =$ more than nine.
17. $B =$ multiple of five.

18. PHE sales records for last week indicate that 62% of the customers bought burgers (of one kind or another), 19% bought fishfeasts, and 19% bought foot-long hot dogs. Do these types of purchases provide a partition of last week's customers?

19. The chances of meeting an Arab-American Socialist in Alan's voting district are slim—3 in 2,000, although 35% of the local Arabs are Socialists. What is the probability that a voter chosen at random is an Arab-American?

20. In my neighborhood only 0.1% of the dogs are rabid and bite people. However, one-half of the rabid dogs bite. What is the probability that a random dog in my neighborhood is rabid?

21. My orchestra is 75% string players, 20% wind players, and 5% percussion players. Ten percent of the string players, 40% of the wind players, and 80% of the percussion players are absolutely first rate. What are the chances that a member of the orchestra chosen at random as the union representative will be an absolutely first-rate player?

22. An appliance factory produces irons, toasters, hair dryers, rotisserie broilers, waffle irons, electric skillets, and crock pots. Some of these appliances are returned for repair within the one year warranty period. See the tabulation below.

|  | Iron | Toaster | Hair dryer | Rotisserie broiler | Waffle iron | Electric skillet | Crock pot |
|---|---|---|---|---|---|---|---|
| Percent of total | 30 | 25 | 20 | 5 | 3 | 8 | 9 |
| Percent returned | 1 | 2 | 2 | 18 | 8 | 5 | 9 |

   (a) What percent of the units made are returned?
   (b) What percent of the units returned are irons? toasters? crock pots?

*23. Nineteen species of ants have been subjected to radiation, which in the fourth generation has produced mutations. Call the species $A, B, C, \ldots, S$. In the fourth generation there are the same number of ants of species A, E, I, and O, and twice as many in each of the other species. Eighteen percent in each of species A through H are fourth generation mutants, and 7% in each of the other species are mutants. If a fourth generation ant is mutant, what are the chances that it belongs to species A, C, I, or Q?

24. I roll a balanced die. If the result is even, I flip a balanced coin. If the result is odd, I flip two balanced coins. When I completed the experiment yesterday I had exactly 1 head come up. What is the probability that I had rolled a 3?

*25. I roll a balanced die. If it comes up even, I roll it again; if it comes up odd, I roll a pair of balanced dice. If a total of 6 spots come up, what is the probability that the first die came up 4?

26. I may have a disease believed present in only 1% of the population. Rather than send me to the hospital for an extensive examination, my doctor administers a simple and inexpensive test. While the results are negative (that is, do not indicate that I have the disease), he warns me that 10% of persons with the disease test negatively. Also, only 80% of persons without the disease test negatively. Given these data, what are the odds that I have the disease?

27. When Joe gets in the car he buckles his seatbelt only one-third of the time. Of people injured in accidents, 90% do not have seatbelts. What are the chances that Joe will be injured in an accident?

### Section 3.3
### Markov Chains

Each candy bar has a coupon worth 10 points which is good toward many valuable prizes.

In the employees' lunchroom at Appalachian Creations are two candy machines. One is provided by the Workmen's Association (WA); the other by the Worker's Brotherhood (WB). Each of these organizations has its own candy bar wrapper redemption program. Incidentally, each candy wrapper has a biographical sketch of a famous athlete or scientist. Alan, who buys exactly one candy bar each lunchtime, is trying to collect all the athlete wrappers from both machines. If he gets an athlete bar, he tries the same machine again the next day. If he gets a scientist bar, he switches machines (and throws out the wrapper but keeps the coupon). After several months Alan noticed that only about 40% of his coupons were WA coupons.

He wondered about this. In fact, one week he happened to be there while the servicemen were refilling the machines. Both men realized that the athlete bars were more popular. In the WA machine, $\frac{2}{3}$ of the bars were athlete bars, and in the WB machine $\frac{3}{4}$ were athlete bars. Since there was a greater probability of getting an athlete bar from the WB machine, it seemed reasonable to Alan that he should have more WB coupons. "But $\frac{3}{4} = 75\%$ and I have less than 60% WB coupons. Maybe I'll ask my math teacher about this."

That night Alan did ask about his problem. His professor said: "That is a problem in Markov chains. The theory of Markov chains predicts that you can expect to have about 57% WB coupons. Unfortunately, we won't have time to talk about Markov chains this semester."

We will also solve Alan's problem, although he won't ever know the solution unless he happens to read this book.

Fortunately for us, a Markov chain problem also came up at the management level at AC, so we can discuss them from a business point of view.

In late August of last year, the president of AC sent Janet a confidential memo:

> Janet, I just don't know about our new vice-president in charge of advertising. Our only real competition comes from Adirondack Knapsacks (AK) and Pocono Productions (PP). Our sales of freeze-dried foods have been good, but an independent survey organization shook us up a little bit when they sent us Table 4.

Table 4
Fractions of
Consumers Who Switched
Brands (June–July)

We read from Table 4, for example, that $\frac{2}{3}$ of AC's June customers remained with them in July, while $\frac{1}{6}$ switched to AK and $\frac{1}{6}$ switched to PP.

| From/To | AC | AK | PP |
|---|---|---|---|
| AC | $\frac{2}{3}$ | $\frac{1}{6}$ | $\frac{1}{6}$ |
| AK | $\frac{1}{4}$ | $\frac{1}{2}$ | $\frac{1}{4}$ |
| PP | $\frac{1}{8}$ | $\frac{7}{8}$ | 0 |

In July, our new advertising VP tried to convince consumers not to buy AK foods. This approach had some success; however, purchasers of PP foods were turned off by this approach, and, in the ensuing backlash, they bought only AK foods in August. (See Table 5.)

Table 5
Fractions of
Consumers Who Switched
Brands (July–August)

| From/To | AC | AK | PP |
|---|---|---|---|
| AC | $\frac{2}{3}$ | 0 | $\frac{1}{3}$ |
| AK | $\frac{1}{2}$ | 0 | $\frac{1}{2}$ |
| PP | 0 | 1 | 0 |

We will answer these questions in the next section.

Does our new VP have good judgment? What would have been the long-range effect of the first buying trend? Is the long-range effect of the new trend any better for us? Has she steered us in a better direction?

Janet replied, "Of course, you can't expect any consumer trend to last very long. However, it is possible to decide which buying trend we would rather see persist."

The mathematical model for situations such as those encountered by Alan and Janet is called a **Markov chain**, after the mathematician A. A. Markov, who invented the concept in 1907.

The examples above illustrate the two fundamental properties of a Markov chain:

(1) A Markov chain involves certain *states* (or positions) of individuals or things. Each individual or thing under consideration is always in one of these states.

(2) From time to time a transition occurs; that is, certain percentages of the individuals in each state move or change to another state. These *transition percentages* persist—that is, the percentage that moves from one given state to another given state is the same each time transition occurs.

In Alan's case he was in one of two states: at the WA machine or at the WB machine. In AC's problem, each customer was in exactly one of three states: a consumer of AC, or of AK, or of PP foods.

In Alan's case he bought a candy bar each day. In the AC example brand-switching was checked each month. In applications to science the time interval of a Markov chain can range anywhere from much less than a second to more than a thousand years.

A square matrix each of whose entries is between 0 and 1 in which the entries in each row sum to 1 is sometimes called a Markov matrix.

The usefulness of Markov chains in business situations is limited by the assumption that the transition percentages persist. Nevertheless, we have already pointed out that they can at least give an idea of where things are headed. The model has found many more applications in the natural sciences, where the assumptions of persistence are often quite realistic.

Our two assumptions have the following consequences: If a matrix is made from the table of transition percentages (e.g., Tables 4 and 5), then this matrix will be square and each of its rows will sum to 1 (or 100%). It will be square because we are concerned with the transition percentage for moving from any state into any state. Each row sums to 1 (or 100%), because all the individuals in any given state move from that state into some state. We are now ready to begin solving problems involving Markov chains.

In the next section we will complete the solution of the problems posed above. Our concern for the rest of this section will be with the short-range effects of Markov chains.

**Problem 1**   Rather than be forced to resign, an unusually sneaky government employee decides to look busy. Since the two warehouses he supervises stock only obsolete equipment, he is never bothered by requisitions. He received his last shipment for storage 17 years ago. When he began his deception, the warehouses contained a total of 14,400 items. Each week he labels $\frac{1}{3}$ of the stock in warehouse A "For Shipment" and $\frac{1}{4}$ of the stock in warehouse B "For Shipment." He then ships the indicated items to the other warehouse. Supposing the material to be evenly divided when he begins this project, what will be the distribution after one week, two weeks, and three weeks?

**Solution**   One way to solve this problem is by use of a tree diagram (Figure 1). The fractions on each arrow indicate what part of the contents of the warehouse at the tail of the arrow is shipped to the warehouse at the head of the arrow. The letter O at the bottom

Figure 1

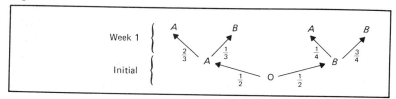

refers to the "outside": when the material arrived, one half was sent to each warehouse. Since the problem stipulates that we have 14,400 items altogether, it is possible to compute the numbers involved in each transfer. These numbers have been included in Figure 2.

**Figure 2**

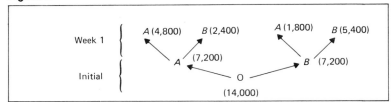

By adding the numbers at the top of the tree in Figure 2, we see that after one week there are $4,800 + 1,800 = 6,600$ items in warehouse A and $2,400 + 5,400 = 7,800$ items in warehouse B. We can determine the distribution of goods after two weeks by simply extending the tree, as shown in Figure 3. Warehouse A now contains $3,200 + 600 + 1,200 + 1,350 = 6,350$ items, and warehouse B contains the other 8,050 items.

**Figure 3**

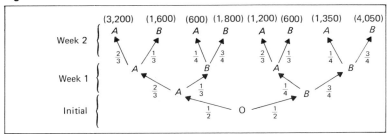

If we are interested only in the fraction of items in each warehouse at the end of two weeks we could simply divide: $\frac{6,350}{14,400} = \frac{127}{288}$ in warehouse A and $\frac{8,050}{14,400} = \frac{161}{288}$ in warehouse B. However, there is a more direct way to obtain these fractions. For each letter at the top of the tree, multiply the fractions on each branch leading down from that letter to O. Figure 4 shows the result. The sum of the fractions at the As is $\frac{2}{9} + \frac{1}{24} + \frac{1}{12} + \frac{3}{32} = \frac{127}{288}$, and the sum of the fractions at the Bs is $\frac{1}{9} + \frac{1}{8} + \frac{1}{24} + \frac{9}{32} = \frac{161}{288}$. To obtain the actual number of items, we simply multiply:

For A: $\frac{127}{288} \times 14,400 = 6,350$

For B: $\frac{161}{288} \times 14,400 = 8,058$

Figure 4

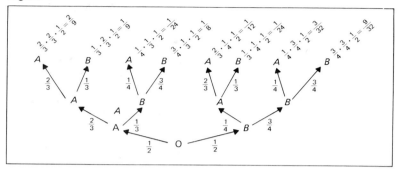

These computations were not too bad, but to extend the tree for a third week involves 16 more branches. If we were interested in four or five weeks, these techniques would be very tedious. Fortunately, it is possible to use matrices to condense and simplify our work. We first write the transition-fraction table (Table 6) as a matrix:

Table 6
Transition Fractions

| From/To | Room A | Room B |
|---------|--------|--------|
| Room A | $\frac{2}{3}$ | $\frac{1}{3}$ |
| Room B | $\frac{1}{4}$ | $\frac{3}{4}$ |

TRANSITION MATRIX

$$\begin{bmatrix} \frac{2}{3} & \frac{1}{3} \\ \frac{1}{4} & \frac{3}{4} \end{bmatrix}$$

Next, we write the initial-state table (Table 7) as a row matrix:

Table 7
Initial-state

| | Room | |
|--------|-------|-------|
| | A | B |
| Amount | 7,200 | 7,200 |

INITIAL-STATE MATRIX

$$\begin{bmatrix} 7,200 & 7,200 \end{bmatrix}$$

We now multiply the initial-state matrix by the transition matrix.

$$\begin{bmatrix} 7,200 & 7,200 \end{bmatrix}\begin{bmatrix} \frac{3}{2} & \frac{1}{3} \\ \frac{1}{4} & \frac{3}{4} \end{bmatrix}$$

$$= \begin{bmatrix} \frac{2}{3} \times 7,200 + \frac{1}{4} \times 7,200 & \frac{1}{3} \times 7,200 + \frac{3}{4} \times 7,200 \end{bmatrix}$$

$$= \begin{bmatrix} 4,800 + 1,800 & 2,400 + 5,400 \end{bmatrix}$$

$$= \begin{bmatrix} 6,600 & 7,800 \end{bmatrix}$$

The answer is the same as that obtained above. Even the arithmetic is identical. We call the row matrix so obtained a **distribution matrix**, since it indicates the distribution of items, in this case at the end of the first week. Here is the general rule:

> To obtain the distribution matrix for a certain period, multiply the distribution matrix for the previous period by the transition matrix.

Thus, to obtain the distribution figures for the second week we multiply the Week 1 distribution matrix by the transition matrix:

$$[6{,}600 \quad 7{,}800] \begin{bmatrix} \frac{2}{3} & \frac{1}{3} \\ \frac{1}{4} & \frac{3}{4} \end{bmatrix} = [6{,}350 \quad 8{,}050]$$

Our answer matches that found above: at the end of the second week, there are 6,350 items in warehouse A and 8,050 items in warehouse B. It is now relatively simple to compute the distribution for the third week:

$$[6{,}350 \quad 8{,}050] \begin{bmatrix} \frac{2}{3} & \frac{1}{3} \\ \frac{1}{4} & \frac{3}{4} \end{bmatrix} = [6{,}245\tfrac{5}{6} \quad 8{,}154\tfrac{1}{6}] \qquad \mathbf{1}$$

Fortunately, some of the items in the warehouse are liquid and can be divided to meet the conditions of this answer: $6{,}246\tfrac{5}{6}$ items in room A and $8{,}154\tfrac{1}{6}$ items in room B.

Suppose we were asked to compute the distribution of items in the sixth week. We could perform 3 more multiplications of the various distribution matrices. However, there is a slightly more direct way to obtain this answer. We first reconsider our procedure for obtaining the third week's distribution. For this we multiplied:

$$[6{,}350 \quad 8{,}050] \begin{bmatrix} \frac{2}{3} & \frac{1}{3} \\ \frac{1}{4} & \frac{3}{4} \end{bmatrix}$$

But [6,350  8,050] was itself obtained by a multiplication. Substituting, we obtain

$$[6{,}350 \quad 8{,}050] \begin{bmatrix} \frac{2}{3} & \frac{1}{3} \\ \frac{1}{4} & \frac{3}{4} \end{bmatrix} = \left( [6{,}600 \quad 7{,}800] \begin{bmatrix} \frac{2}{3} & \frac{1}{3} \\ \frac{1}{4} & \frac{3}{4} \end{bmatrix} \right) \begin{bmatrix} \frac{2}{3} & \frac{1}{3} \\ \frac{1}{4} & \frac{3}{4} \end{bmatrix}$$

Finally, [6,600  7,800] was obtained through a multiplication. If we substitute again, we obtain

$$[6{,}350 \quad 8{,}050]\begin{bmatrix} \frac{2}{3} & \frac{1}{3} \\ \frac{1}{4} & \frac{3}{4} \end{bmatrix}$$

$$= \left(\left([7{,}200 \quad 7{,}200]\begin{bmatrix} \frac{2}{3} & \frac{1}{3} \\ \frac{1}{4} & \frac{3}{4} \end{bmatrix}\right)\begin{bmatrix} \frac{2}{3} & \frac{1}{3} \\ \frac{1}{4} & \frac{3}{4} \end{bmatrix}\right)\begin{bmatrix} \frac{2}{3} & \frac{1}{3} \\ \frac{1}{4} & \frac{3}{4} \end{bmatrix}$$

Now whenever matrices are multiplied it can be shown that the manner in which we insert parentheses is irrelevant. We can just as correctly write

$$[6{,}350 \quad 8{,}050]\begin{bmatrix} \frac{2}{3} & \frac{1}{3} \\ \frac{1}{4} & \frac{3}{4} \end{bmatrix}$$

$$= [7{,}200 \quad 7{,}200]\left(\begin{bmatrix} \frac{2}{3} & \frac{1}{3} \\ \frac{1}{4} & \frac{3}{4} \end{bmatrix}\begin{bmatrix} \frac{2}{3} & \frac{1}{3} \\ \frac{1}{4} & \frac{3}{4} \end{bmatrix}\begin{bmatrix} \frac{2}{3} & \frac{1}{3} \\ \frac{1}{4} & \frac{3}{4} \end{bmatrix}\right)$$

Let us agree to call the product in parentheses the *third power* of the matrix, and write

$$\begin{bmatrix} \frac{2}{3} & \frac{1}{3} \\ \frac{1}{4} & \frac{3}{4} \end{bmatrix}\begin{bmatrix} \frac{2}{3} & \frac{1}{3} \\ \frac{1}{4} & \frac{3}{4} \end{bmatrix}\begin{bmatrix} \frac{2}{3} & \frac{1}{3} \\ \frac{1}{4} & \frac{3}{4} \end{bmatrix} = \begin{bmatrix} \frac{2}{3} & \frac{1}{3} \\ \frac{1}{4} & \frac{3}{4} \end{bmatrix}^3$$

just as we would for numbers. Then the third week's distribution is simply the product

$$[7{,}200 \quad 7{,}200]\begin{bmatrix} \frac{2}{3} & \frac{1}{3} \\ \frac{1}{4} & \frac{3}{4} \end{bmatrix}^3 = [7{,}200 \quad 7{,}200]\begin{bmatrix} \frac{203}{432} & \frac{229}{432} \\ \frac{229}{576} & \frac{347}{576} \end{bmatrix}$$

In other words, to obtain the distribution matrix for the third week we multiply the initial-state matrix by the third power of the transition matrix. Now if we want to know the distribution matrix for the sixth week, we need only multiply the initial-state matrix by the sixth power of the transition matrix:

$$[7{,}200 \quad 7{,}200]\begin{bmatrix} \frac{2}{3} & \frac{1}{3} \\ \frac{1}{4} & \frac{3}{4} \end{bmatrix}^6$$

To find the sixth power of our matrix, we multiply the third power by itself: that is,

$$\begin{bmatrix} \frac{2}{3} & \frac{1}{3} \\ \frac{1}{4} & \frac{3}{4} \end{bmatrix}^6$$

$$= \left( \begin{bmatrix} \frac{2}{3} & \frac{1}{3} \\ \frac{1}{4} & \frac{3}{4} \end{bmatrix} \begin{bmatrix} \frac{2}{3} & \frac{1}{3} \\ \frac{1}{4} & \frac{3}{4} \end{bmatrix} \begin{bmatrix} \frac{2}{3} & \frac{1}{3} \\ \frac{1}{4} & \frac{3}{4} \end{bmatrix} \right) \left( \begin{bmatrix} \frac{2}{3} & \frac{1}{3} \\ \frac{1}{4} & \frac{3}{4} \end{bmatrix} \begin{bmatrix} \frac{2}{3} & \frac{1}{3} \\ \frac{1}{4} & \frac{3}{4} \end{bmatrix} \begin{bmatrix} \frac{2}{3} & \frac{1}{3} \\ \frac{1}{4} & \frac{3}{4} \end{bmatrix} \right)$$

$$= \begin{bmatrix} \frac{2}{3} & \frac{1}{2} \\ \frac{1}{4} & \frac{3}{4} \end{bmatrix}^3 \begin{bmatrix} \frac{2}{3} & \frac{1}{2} \\ \frac{1}{4} & \frac{3}{4} \end{bmatrix}^3$$

$$= \begin{bmatrix} \frac{203}{432} & \frac{229}{432} \\ \frac{229}{576} & \frac{347}{576} \end{bmatrix} \begin{bmatrix} \frac{203}{432} & \frac{229}{432} \\ \frac{229}{576} & \frac{347}{576} \end{bmatrix} = \begin{bmatrix} \frac{812}{1,728} & \frac{916}{1,728} \\ \frac{687}{1,728} & \frac{1,041}{1,728} \end{bmatrix} \begin{bmatrix} \frac{812}{1,728} & \frac{916}{1,728} \\ \frac{687}{1,728} & \frac{1,041}{1,728} \end{bmatrix}$$

$$= \frac{1}{1,728} \cdot \frac{1}{1,728} \begin{bmatrix} 812 & 916 \\ 687 & 1,041 \end{bmatrix} \begin{bmatrix} 812 & 916 \\ 687 & 1,041 \end{bmatrix}$$

$$= \frac{1}{2,985,984} \begin{bmatrix} 1,288,636 & 1,697,348 \\ 1,273,011 & 1,712,973 \end{bmatrix}$$

The final answer is then

$$\begin{bmatrix} 7,200 & 7,200 \end{bmatrix} \left( \frac{1}{2,985,984} \begin{bmatrix} 1,288,636 & 1,697,348 \\ 1,273,011 & 1,712,973 \end{bmatrix} \right)$$

$$= \frac{1}{2,985,984} \begin{bmatrix} 7,200 & 7,200 \end{bmatrix} \begin{bmatrix} 1,288,636 & 1,697,348 \\ 1,273,011 & 1,712,973 \end{bmatrix}$$

$$= \frac{7,200}{2,985,984} \begin{bmatrix} 1 & 1 \end{bmatrix} \begin{bmatrix} 1,288,636 & 1,697,348 \\ 1,273,011 & 1,712,973 \end{bmatrix}$$

$$= \frac{25}{10,368} \begin{bmatrix} 2,561,647 & 3,410,321 \end{bmatrix}$$

$$= \begin{bmatrix} 6,176 \frac{8,407}{10,368} & 8,223 \frac{1,961}{10,368} \end{bmatrix}$$

Notice that the distribution has not changed much since the third week (shown in equation **1**). In the next section we will learn that making more and more shifts moves the distribution closer and closer to the theoretical long-range distribution

$$\begin{bmatrix} 6,171 \frac{3}{7} & 8,228 \frac{4}{7} \end{bmatrix}$$

Note that $\frac{3}{7}$ of 14,400 is $6,171 \frac{3}{7}$ and $\frac{4}{7}$ of 14,400 is $8,228 \frac{4}{7}$.

that is, $\frac{3}{7}$ of the material will be in warehouse A and $\frac{4}{7}$ will be in warehouse B.

We could just as easily have worked this problem under the assumption that the stock was initially divided in some other proportion. Suppose for example that $\frac{1}{3}$ of the stock was initially in warehouse A and $\frac{2}{3}$ in warehouse B. In this case, the initial-state matrix would be

$$[4{,}800 \quad 9{,}600]$$

We would use this matrix in place of the matrix [7,200  7,200].

We will also discover a rather remarkable fact in the next section: for most Markov chains the long-range distribution does not depend upon the initial distribution. Thus, no matter what percentage of goods is in each warehouse initially (even if 100% is in one warehouse) the long-range result will be the same: $\frac{3}{7}$ in warehouse A and $\frac{4}{7}$ in warehouse B.

**Problem 2**  Mr. Olney has taught his second-grade class a sand-passing game to help them learn about fractions. The game is for 3 players, whom we will refer to as A, B, and C. Each of the players sits before a large box of sand with a measuring scoop. Every 5 minutes Mr. Olney rings his bell. When he does, each player transfers a certain fraction of his or her sand to each of the other two players. Player A gives $\frac{1}{6}$ of his sand to player B, $\frac{1}{6}$ of his sand to player C, and keeps the other $\frac{2}{3}$ for himself. Player B gives $\frac{1}{4}$ of his sand to A, $\frac{1}{4}$ to C and keeps $\frac{1}{2}$ for himself. Player C gives $\frac{1}{8}$ of her sand to A and $\frac{7}{8}$ to B. She keeps none for herself. The passing of the sand constitutes one round. The game consists of three 5-minute rounds. Before the start of the game, Mr. Olney pours unequal amounts of sand into the 3 boxes. The object of the game is to figure out where to sit so as to have the most sand at the end of 3 rounds. Suppose that for the first 4 games Mr. Olney distributes the sand and the players sit as shown in Table 8. Who will win each of the games?

**Table 8**
**Fractional Distribution of Sand**

| Game/Player | A | B | C |
|---|---|---|---|
| 1 | $\frac{1}{3}$ | $\frac{1}{3}$ | $\frac{1}{3}$ |
| 2 | $\frac{1}{2}$ | 0 | $\frac{1}{2}$ |
| 3 | $\frac{3}{4}$ | 0 | $\frac{1}{4}$ |
| 4 | 0 | 0 | 1 |

**Solution**  The transition matrix for the game is

$$\begin{bmatrix} \frac{2}{3} & \frac{1}{6} & \frac{1}{6} \\ \frac{1}{4} & \frac{1}{2} & \frac{1}{4} \\ \frac{1}{8} & \frac{7}{8} & 0 \end{bmatrix}$$

Since the game lasts for 3 rounds, we are interested in the third power of this matrix:

$$
\begin{bmatrix} \frac{2}{3} & \frac{1}{6} & \frac{1}{6} \\ \frac{1}{4} & \frac{1}{2} & \frac{1}{4} \\ \frac{1}{8} & \frac{7}{8} & 0 \end{bmatrix}^3 = \begin{bmatrix} \frac{2}{3} & \frac{1}{6} & \frac{1}{6} \\ \frac{1}{4} & \frac{1}{2} & \frac{1}{4} \\ \frac{1}{8} & \frac{7}{8} & 0 \end{bmatrix} \begin{bmatrix} \frac{2}{3} & \frac{1}{6} & \frac{1}{6} \\ \frac{1}{4} & \frac{1}{2} & \frac{1}{4} \\ \frac{1}{8} & \frac{7}{8} & 0 \end{bmatrix} \begin{bmatrix} \frac{2}{3} & \frac{1}{6} & \frac{1}{6} \\ \frac{1}{4} & \frac{1}{2} & \frac{1}{4} \\ \frac{1}{8} & \frac{7}{8} & 0 \end{bmatrix}
$$

$$
= \begin{bmatrix} \frac{73}{144} & \frac{49}{144} & \frac{22}{144} \\ \frac{31}{96} & \frac{49}{96} & \frac{16}{96} \\ \frac{29}{96} & \frac{44}{96} & \frac{23}{96} \end{bmatrix} \begin{bmatrix} \frac{2}{3} & \frac{1}{6} & \frac{1}{6} \\ \frac{1}{4} & \frac{1}{2} & \frac{1}{4} \\ \frac{1}{8} & \frac{7}{8} & 0 \end{bmatrix}
$$

$$
= \frac{1}{16} \begin{bmatrix} \frac{73}{9} & \frac{49}{9} & \frac{22}{9} \\ \frac{31}{6} & \frac{49}{6} & \frac{16}{6} \\ \frac{29}{6} & \frac{44}{6} & \frac{23}{6} \end{bmatrix} \begin{bmatrix} \frac{2}{3} & \frac{1}{6} & \frac{1}{6} \\ \frac{1}{4} & \frac{1}{2} & \frac{1}{4} \\ \frac{1}{8} & \frac{7}{8} & 0 \end{bmatrix}
$$

$$
= \frac{1}{16} \begin{bmatrix} \frac{1,528}{216} & \frac{1,342}{216} & \frac{586}{216} \\ \frac{838}{144} & \frac{1,048}{144} & \frac{418}{144} \\ \frac{797}{144} & \frac{1,127}{144} & \frac{380}{144} \end{bmatrix}
$$

$$
= \frac{1}{16 \cdot 72 \cdot 6} \begin{bmatrix} 3,056 & 2,684 & 1,172 \\ 2,514 & 3,144 & 1,254 \\ 2,391 & 3,381 & 1,140 \end{bmatrix}
$$

In this problem we are not actually given the quantity of sand involved. Instead, we use the fractions in the four distribution matrices:

$$\begin{bmatrix} \frac{1}{3} & \frac{1}{3} & \frac{1}{3} \end{bmatrix} \qquad\qquad 2$$

$$\begin{bmatrix} \frac{1}{2} & 0 & \frac{1}{2} \end{bmatrix} \qquad\qquad 3$$

$$\begin{bmatrix} \frac{3}{4} & 0 & \frac{1}{4} \end{bmatrix} \qquad\qquad 4$$

$$\begin{bmatrix} 0 & 0 & 1 \end{bmatrix} \qquad\qquad 5$$

We multiply each of these distribution matrices by the third power of the transition matrix:

FOR MATRIX **2**:

$$\begin{bmatrix} \frac{1}{3} & \frac{1}{3} & \frac{1}{3} \end{bmatrix} \frac{1}{16\cdot72\cdot6} \begin{bmatrix} 3{,}056 & 2{,}684 & 1{,}172 \\ 2{,}514 & 3{,}144 & 1{,}254 \\ 2{,}391 & 3{,}381 & 1{,}140 \end{bmatrix}$$

$$= \frac{1}{3} \cdot \frac{1}{16\cdot72\cdot6} \begin{bmatrix} 1 & 1 & 1 \end{bmatrix} \begin{bmatrix} 3{,}056 & 2{,}684 & 1{,}172 \\ 2{,}514 & 3{,}144 & 1{,}254 \\ 2{,}391 & 3{,}381 & 1{,}140 \end{bmatrix}$$

$$= \frac{1}{3} \cdot \frac{1}{16\cdot72\cdot6} \begin{bmatrix} 7{,}961 & 9{,}209 & 3{,}566 \end{bmatrix}$$

Without multiplying out the denominator of the fraction, we see that after three transitions B is ahead, A is in second place, and C is last.

FOR MATRIX **3**:

$$\begin{bmatrix} \frac{1}{2} & 0 & \frac{1}{2} \end{bmatrix} \frac{1}{16\cdot72\cdot6} \begin{bmatrix} 3{,}056 & 2{,}684 & 1{,}172 \\ 2{,}514 & 3{,}144 & 1{,}254 \\ 2{,}391 & 3{,}381 & 1{,}140 \end{bmatrix}$$

$$= \frac{1}{2} \cdot \frac{1}{16\cdot72\cdot6} \begin{bmatrix} 1 & 0 & 1 \end{bmatrix} \begin{bmatrix} 3{,}056 & 2{,}684 & 1{,}172 \\ 2{,}541 & 3{,}144 & 1{,}254 \\ 2{,}391 & 3{,}381 & 1{,}140 \end{bmatrix}$$

$$= \frac{1}{16\cdot72\cdot6} \begin{bmatrix} 5{,}447 & 6{,}065 & 2{,}312 \end{bmatrix}$$

The order of finish is the same here as in the previous case.

FOR MATRIX **4**:

$$\begin{bmatrix} \frac{3}{4} & 0 & \frac{1}{4} \end{bmatrix} \frac{1}{16\cdot72\cdot6} \begin{bmatrix} 3{,}056 & 2{,}684 & 1{,}172 \\ 2{,}541 & 3{,}144 & 1{,}254 \\ 2{,}391 & 3{,}381 & 1{,}140 \end{bmatrix}$$

$$= \frac{1}{4} \cdot \frac{1}{16\cdot72\cdot6} \begin{bmatrix} 3 & 0 & 1 \end{bmatrix} \begin{bmatrix} 3{,}056 & 2{,}684 & 1{,}172 \\ 2{,}541 & 3{,}144 & 1{,}254 \\ 2{,}391 & 3{,}381 & 1{,}140 \end{bmatrix}$$

$$= \frac{1}{4} \cdot \frac{1}{16\cdot72\cdot6} \begin{bmatrix} 11{,}559 & 11{,}443 & 4{,}656 \end{bmatrix}$$

In this case A wins, B finishes second, and C is last.

FOR MATRIX **5**:

$$\begin{bmatrix} 0 & 0 & 1 \end{bmatrix} \frac{1}{16\cdot72\cdot6} \begin{bmatrix} 3{,}056 & 2{,}684 & 1{,}172 \\ 2{,}541 & 3{,}144 & 1{,}254 \\ 2{,}391 & 3{,}381 & 1{,}140 \end{bmatrix}$$

$$= \frac{1}{16\cdot72\cdot6} \begin{bmatrix} 2{,}391 & 3{,}381 & 1{,}140 \end{bmatrix}$$

This results in the same order of finish as with matrices **2** and **3**.

This is the usual practice. However, in many business applications it is easier to interpret the fractions as percentages.

One can also interpret the fractions in a Markov matrix as probabilities. In the first example in this section we discussed Alan's candy bar buying habits. Knowing the percentage of each type of candy bar in each machine, we can write the matrix of transition probabilities (Table 9):

Table 9
Transition Probabilities

| From/To | WA | WB |
|---------|-----|-----|
| WA | $\frac{2}{3}$ | $\frac{1}{3}$ |
| WB | $\frac{1}{4}$ | $\frac{3}{4}$ |

If we assume that Alan buys his first candy bar from a machine chosen at random, the initial distribution is

$$\left[ \begin{matrix} \frac{1}{2} & \frac{1}{2} \end{matrix} \right]$$

You may have noticed that we actually discussed these data at length in Problem 1. There it was mentioned that the long-range distribution was

$$\left[ \begin{matrix} \frac{3}{7} & \frac{4}{7} \end{matrix} \right]$$

Since $\frac{4}{7} \doteq 57\%$, we have an explanation of why Alan has about 57% WB coupons.

We remarked early in this section that, in order to be classified as a Markov chain, a process must have a persistent transition matrix. While this hypothesis is essential in the analysis of long-range effects, we can also handle situations in which the transition matrix varies, provided we are only interested in short-term results.

Problem 3

I am the TV manager for Channel 2 in a small Midwestern town. Our only competition is Channel 7. I decide to survey the Tuesday night viewing habits of everyone who owns a set. Here are the results:

(1) At the start of the evening, $\frac{3}{8}$ of the potential viewers watch our 6:00–7:00 news and $\frac{4}{8}$ watch Channel 7's news.

(2) At 7:00, $\frac{6}{8}$ of our viewers stay with us and $\frac{1}{8}$ change channels. Of Channel 7's viewers, $\frac{3}{4}$ stay with them and the rest switch their sets off. Of the people who were not watching, $\frac{3}{4}$ switch on our national news and $\frac{1}{4}$ switch on Channel 7's.

(3) At 7:30, $\frac{3}{4}$ of our viewers remain faithful and the rest switch to Channel 7; $\frac{1}{4}$ of their viewers remain faithful and $\frac{1}{2}$ switch to us; anyone with his or her set off keeps it off.

What fraction of viewers will be watching our 7:30 show?

Solution  This process has three states: a viewer either watches Channel 2, watches Channel 7, or has his set off. The initial-state matrix is

$$\begin{bmatrix} \frac{3}{8} & \frac{4}{8} & \frac{1}{8} \end{bmatrix}$$

The first transition matrix is:

$$\begin{bmatrix} \frac{6}{8} & \frac{1}{8} & \frac{1}{8} \\ 0 & \frac{3}{4} & \frac{1}{4} \\ \frac{3}{4} & \frac{1}{4} & 0 \end{bmatrix}$$

The second transition matrix is:

$$\begin{bmatrix} \frac{3}{4} & \frac{1}{4} & 0 \\ \frac{1}{2} & \frac{1}{4} & \frac{1}{4} \\ 0 & 0 & 1 \end{bmatrix}$$

To answer the question, we simply multiply:

$$\begin{bmatrix} \frac{3}{8} & \frac{4}{8} & \frac{1}{8} \end{bmatrix} \begin{bmatrix} \frac{6}{8} & \frac{1}{8} & \frac{1}{8} \\ 0 & \frac{3}{4} & \frac{1}{4} \\ \frac{3}{4} & \frac{1}{4} & 0 \end{bmatrix} \begin{bmatrix} \frac{3}{4} & \frac{1}{4} & 0 \\ \frac{1}{2} & \frac{1}{4} & \frac{1}{4} \\ 0 & 0 & 1 \end{bmatrix}$$

$$= \left(\tfrac{1}{8}\right)\left(\tfrac{1}{8}\right)\left(\tfrac{1}{4}\right)\begin{bmatrix} 3 & 4 & 1 \end{bmatrix}\begin{bmatrix} 6 & 1 & 1 \\ 0 & 6 & 2 \\ 6 & 2 & 0 \end{bmatrix}\begin{bmatrix} 3 & 1 & 0 \\ 2 & 1 & 1 \\ 0 & 0 & 4 \end{bmatrix}$$

$$= \tfrac{1}{256}\begin{bmatrix} 3 & 4 & 1 \end{bmatrix}\begin{bmatrix} 20 & 7 & 5 \\ 12 & 6 & 14 \\ 22 & 8 & 2 \end{bmatrix}$$

$$= \tfrac{1}{256}\begin{bmatrix} 130 & 53 & 73 \end{bmatrix}$$

We see that $\frac{130}{256}$ or about 51% of the viewers will be watching our show; $\frac{53}{256}$ or about 21% of the viewers will be watching Channel 7's show; and $\frac{73}{256}$ or about 29% of the viewers will have their sets off.

> The general procedure is this: to determine a subsequent distribution, multiply the initial state matrix by the appropriate product of transition matrices.

As we saw in Section 3.1 tree diagrams can handle even more complicated situations, such as a game where a player drops out after losing three times in a row. In this case the number of states does not remain constant.

In the next two sections we will apply the techniques developed there to determine the long-range distribution of Markov chains. In particular, we will answer the question which the president of AC asked Janet.

$^C$1. Each week a dispatcher sends a rather large group of traveling salespeople to 2 towns: town A and town B. Where a salesperson is sent is determined by where he or she went in the previous week. Half the people who went to town A are sent back there and the rest are sent to town B. Everyone who went to town B is sent back to town B. Suppose the dispatcher begins by sending $\frac{1}{3}$ of all his salespeople to town A and $\frac{2}{3}$ to town B. What is the situation after six weeks?

2. In Exercise 1, what do you think will be the long-range effect of the dispatcher's policy?

3. A product is purchased by 128,000 consumers. Initially $\frac{1}{4}$ of them buy it from us and $\frac{3}{4}$ buy it from them. Each month we get $\frac{1}{2}$ of their customers and they get $\frac{1}{4}$ of ours. How many customers will we have after three months?

4. A charitable organization accepts donations from a special group of potential contributors in the amount of $2 or $5. Of those who did not contribute this month, $\frac{3}{4}$ will contribute $5 next month and the rest will contribute $2. Of those who contributed $2 this month, $\frac{1}{2}$ will contribute $5 next month and the rest will contribute nothing. Everyone who contributed $5 last month will contribute nothing this month. Assuming this trend continues, how much money can the charity expect to receive in the third month if its 768,000 potential contributors are initially evenly divided among the 3 possible states?

5. Market research predicts the following monthly brand-switching trends by consumers (Tables 10, 11, and 12). If $\frac{2}{5}$ of the consumers bought Brand X in June, what fraction (according to these transition matrices) will buy Brand X in September?

**Table 10**
**June–July**

| From/To | Brand X | Brand Z |
|---------|---------|---------|
| Brand X | $\frac{1}{2}$ | $\frac{1}{2}$ |
| Brand Z | $\frac{1}{4}$ | $\frac{3}{4}$ |

**Table 11**
**July–August**

| From/To | Brand X | Brand Z |
|---------|---------|---------|
| Brand X | 1 | 0 |
| Brand Z | $\frac{1}{3}$ | $\frac{2}{3}$ |

**Table 12**
**August–September**

| From/To | Brand X | Brand Z |
|---------|---------|---------|
| Brand X | $\frac{3}{4}$ | $\frac{1}{4}$ |
| Brand Z | 0 | 1 |

<sup>C</sup>6. In its continuing competition with MacDougal's, Petaluma Hamburger Emporium is planning 4 consecutive weeks of discount sales of certain products. There are 2 different discount plans: (1) half-price beverages, and (2) free fries with any $1.50 purchase. It is believed that one week of plan 1 will result in PHE's retaining $\frac{2}{3}$ of its customers and McD's getting $\frac{1}{3}$ while McD retains $\frac{3}{4}$ of its customers and PHE gets $\frac{1}{4}$. One week of plan 2 is expected to result in PHE's retaining $\frac{1}{2}$ of its customers and McD's getting $\frac{1}{2}$ while McD retains $\frac{1}{4}$ of its customers and PHE gets $\frac{3}{4}$. Just before the four-week sale, PHE has twice as many customers as McD. What will the distribution be at the end of the sale under each of the following schemes of operation?

(a) first week, plan 1; second, plan 2; third, 1; fourth, 2.
(b) first, 2; second, 1; third, 2; fourth, 1.
(c) first and second, 1; third and fourth, 2.

Comment on these results.

7. American Aluminum Tubing (AAT) is trying to convince AC to purchase a machine that automatically assembles backpack frames. The particular model that they are selling is a highly complex device, which tends to break down. If it makes it through an entire week without breaking down, the probability is $\frac{3}{4}$ that it will make it through the next week without breaking down. If it does break down one week, it will be skillfully repaired and its chances of breaking down again the next week are reduced to $\frac{1}{8}$. If the probability is $\frac{1}{3}$ that the machine will break down in the first week after installation, what is the probability that it will be broken down three weeks after installation?

### Section 3.4
### Regular and
### Absorbing Markov Chains

In this section we apply Gauss-Jordan reduction to the problem of determining the long-range effects of two commonly occurring types of Markov chains: the regular chain and the absorbing chain. These are most easily defined in terms of their transition matrices. A chain is **regular** if some power of its transition matrix has no zero entries. For example, the transition matrix

$$\begin{bmatrix} \frac{1}{2} & \frac{1}{2} & 0 \\ 0 & \frac{1}{2} & \frac{1}{2} \\ \frac{1}{2} & 0 & \frac{1}{2} \end{bmatrix}$$

yields a regular chain, since its second power,

$$\begin{bmatrix} \frac{1}{2} & \frac{1}{2} & 0 \\ 0 & \frac{1}{2} & \frac{1}{2} \\ \frac{1}{2} & 0 & \frac{1}{2} \end{bmatrix} \begin{bmatrix} \frac{1}{2} & \frac{1}{2} & 0 \\ 0 & \frac{1}{2} & \frac{1}{2} \\ \frac{1}{2} & 0 & \frac{1}{2} \end{bmatrix} = \begin{bmatrix} \frac{1}{4} & \frac{1}{2} & \frac{1}{4} \\ \frac{1}{4} & \frac{1}{4} & \frac{1}{2} \\ \frac{1}{2} & \frac{1}{4} & \frac{1}{4} \end{bmatrix}$$

has no zero entries. The transition matrix

$$\begin{bmatrix} \frac{1}{4} & \frac{3}{4} \\ \frac{1}{2} & \frac{1}{2} \end{bmatrix}$$

also provides a regular chain, since its first power, namely itself, has no zero entries.

A state in a Markov chain is an **absorbing state** if its row in the transition matrix has a 1 on the main diagonal. For example, the first, third, and fourth states in the following transition matrix are absorbing states.

$$\begin{bmatrix} 1 & 0 & 0 & 0 \\ \frac{1}{4} & \frac{1}{2} & 0 & \frac{1}{4} \\ 0 & 0 & 1 & 0 \\ 0 & 0 & 0 & 1 \end{bmatrix} \qquad \mathbf{1}$$

In an absorbing state, the 1 on the main diagonal indicates that at each transition everything in the absorbing state stays there. Once an item enters an absorbing state, it can never leave. A Markov chain is called an **absorbing chain** if some of the material in each state will eventually end up in an absorbing state. In the matrix

$$\begin{bmatrix} 0 & \frac{1}{2} & \frac{1}{2} \\ 0 & 1 & 0 \\ \frac{1}{2} & 0 & \frac{1}{2} \end{bmatrix} \qquad \mathbf{2}$$

state 2 is an absorbing state. At each transition, $\frac{1}{2}$ of the material in state 1 moves into the absorbing state. While nothing moves directly from state 3 into state 2, in one transition $\frac{1}{2}$ of the material in state 3 moves into state 1, and from there $\frac{1}{2}$ of it moves into the absorbing state 2 on the next transition. Thus, this matrix defines an absorbing chain.

One way to determine whether or not a matrix yields an absorbing chain is by making a tree diagram, as follows.

(1) List all the states. In the Markov chain with transition matrix **2** we have three:

$$1$$
$$2$$
$$3$$

(2) For each state listed, draw an arrow for each nonzero entry in its row. At the end of the arrow, place the number of the

**Figure 5**

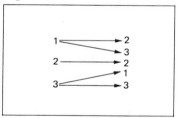

**Figure 6**

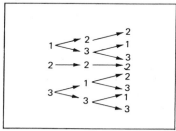

**Figure 7**

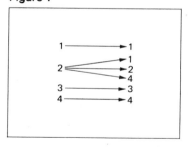

column of the nonzero entry. In our case, the first row has nonzero entries in columns 2 and 3; the second row has a nonzero entry only in the second column; the third row has nonzero entries in columns 1 and 3. We extend the tree (Figure 5).

(3) Repeat step 2 with the new list of states. Our case is shown in Figure 6. Continue until it is clear that either (a) there is a sequence of branches leading from each state on the left to an absorbing state, or (b) for some state on the left there will never be a sequence of branches leading to an absorbing state.

In Figure 7, we carry out this procedure for the Markov chain with transition matrix **1**. In one step we move from each state into some absorbing state.

As a final example, consider the matrix

$$
\begin{bmatrix}
\frac{1}{2} & \frac{1}{4} & 0 & \frac{1}{4} & 0 \\
\frac{1}{2} & \frac{1}{4} & 0 & \frac{1}{8} & \frac{1}{8} \\
0 & 0 & 1 & 0 & 0 \\
0 & 0 & 0 & \frac{7}{8} & \frac{1}{8} \\
0 & 1 & 0 & 0 & 0
\end{bmatrix}
$$

While state 3 is an absorbing state, the fact that its column is cleared indicates that nothing can ever move into this state from another state. Since this is the only absorbing state, this matrix does not define an absorbing chain. We leave to the reader the task of drawing the appropriate tree diagram.

**Regular Markov Chains**

Our first problem involves a regular Markov chain:

**Problem 1**

At a party I offer peanuts and cashews in 2 huge bowls at opposite ends of my apartment. The bowl at the north end contains a mixture of $\frac{1}{4}$ peanuts and $\frac{3}{4}$ cashews. The bowl at the south end has a mixture of $\frac{1}{2}$ peanuts and $\frac{1}{2}$ cashews. My friend Luis loves peanuts but hates cashews. If he takes a nut from a bowl and it turns out to be a peanut, he selects another nut from the same bowl. Otherwise, he moves across the room to the other bowl. Luis eats nuts at the rate of 1 per minute. My party lasts for 4 hours. Where will he most likely be at the end of the party?

**Solution**

Since the bowls are huge, Luis will not significantly change the proportion of nuts by removing a few.

We label the bowls N and S. If Luis is at bowl N, then $\frac{1}{4}$ of the time he will get a peanut and remain there. Otherwise, he will move to bowl S. At bowl S he will get a peanut about $\frac{1}{2}$ of the time. Otherwise he will move to bowl N. Table 13 is the transition table for this problem.

Table 13
Transition Table

| From/To | N | S |
|---|---|---|
| N | $\frac{1}{4}$ | $\frac{3}{4}$ |
| S | $\frac{1}{2}$ | $\frac{1}{2}$ |

The associated matrix is

$$\begin{bmatrix} \frac{1}{4} & \frac{3}{4} \\ \frac{1}{2} & \frac{1}{2} \end{bmatrix}$$

The problem not only asks us to find the 240th power of this matrix but has even neglected to supply us with an initial state matrix—that is, it has not mentioned how likely it is that Louis would begin at bowl N.

We could make a valiant attempt to compute

$$\begin{bmatrix} \frac{1}{4} & \frac{3}{4} \\ \frac{1}{2} & \frac{1}{2} \end{bmatrix}^{240}$$

$$\begin{bmatrix} \frac{1}{4} & \frac{3}{4} \\ \frac{1}{2} & \frac{1}{2} \end{bmatrix}\begin{bmatrix} \frac{1}{4} & \frac{3}{4} \\ \frac{1}{2} & \frac{1}{2} \end{bmatrix} = \begin{bmatrix} \frac{7}{16} & \frac{9}{16} \\ \frac{3}{8} & \frac{5}{8} \end{bmatrix} \quad \text{(the 2nd power)}$$

$$\begin{bmatrix} \frac{7}{16} & \frac{9}{16} \\ \frac{3}{8} & \frac{5}{8} \end{bmatrix}\begin{bmatrix} \frac{7}{16} & \frac{9}{16} \\ \frac{3}{8} & \frac{5}{8} \end{bmatrix} = \begin{bmatrix} \frac{103}{256} & \frac{153}{256} \\ \frac{51}{128} & \frac{77}{128} \end{bmatrix} \quad \text{(the 4th power)}$$

$$\begin{bmatrix} \frac{103}{256} & \frac{153}{256} \\ \frac{51}{128} & \frac{77}{128} \end{bmatrix}\begin{bmatrix} \frac{103}{256} & \frac{153}{256} \\ \frac{51}{128} & \frac{77}{128} \end{bmatrix} = \begin{bmatrix} \frac{26,215}{65,536} & \frac{39,321}{65,536} \\ \frac{13,107}{32,768} & \frac{19,661}{32,768} \end{bmatrix} \quad \text{(the 8th power)}$$

Maybe looking at decimals instead of fractions would simplify matters. We compute

$$\begin{bmatrix} \frac{7}{16} & \frac{9}{16} \\ \frac{3}{8} & \frac{5}{8} \end{bmatrix} \doteq \begin{bmatrix} .44 & .56 \\ .38 & .62 \end{bmatrix} \quad \text{(the 2nd power)}$$

$$\begin{bmatrix} \frac{103}{256} & \frac{153}{256} \\ \frac{51}{128} & \frac{77}{128} \end{bmatrix} \doteq \begin{bmatrix} .402 & .598 \\ .398 & .602 \end{bmatrix} \quad \text{(the 4th power)}$$

$$\begin{bmatrix} \frac{26,215}{65,536} & \frac{39,321}{65,536} \\ \frac{13,107}{32,768} & \frac{19,661}{32,768} \end{bmatrix} \doteq \begin{bmatrix} .400009 & .599991 \\ .399994 & .600006 \end{bmatrix} \quad \text{(the 8th power)}$$

As we raise the transition matrix to higher and higher powers, we seem to be getting closer and closer to the matrix

$$\begin{bmatrix} .4 & .6 \\ .4 & .6 \end{bmatrix} = \begin{bmatrix} \frac{2}{5} & \frac{3}{5} \\ \frac{2}{5} & \frac{3}{5} \end{bmatrix}$$

In fact, we get so close to the "limit" matrix that for all practical purposes we can assume

$$\begin{bmatrix} \frac{1}{4} & \frac{3}{4} \\ \frac{1}{2} & \frac{1}{2} \end{bmatrix}^{240} = \begin{bmatrix} \frac{2}{5} & \frac{3}{5} \\ \frac{2}{5} & \frac{3}{5} \end{bmatrix}$$

For a regular matrix, that is, a transition matrix of a regular Markov chain (p. 183), it turns out to be fairly easy to compute the limit without doing any matrix multiplications at all. We will return to this in a moment. Right now there is that other problem, the lack of an initial-state matrix. Let us try some particular examples. Suppose that at $\frac{1}{3}$ of my parties Luis begins his nut-eating at the north end. The initial-state matrix is then

$$\begin{bmatrix} \frac{1}{3} & \frac{2}{3} \end{bmatrix}$$

and the final distribution matrix is

$$\begin{bmatrix} \frac{1}{3} & \frac{2}{3} \end{bmatrix} \begin{bmatrix} \frac{2}{5} & \frac{3}{5} \\ \frac{2}{5} & \frac{3}{5} \end{bmatrix} = \begin{bmatrix} \frac{2}{5} & \frac{3}{5} \end{bmatrix}$$

Thus, he would be expected to end up at the south end at $\frac{3}{5}$ of my parties. Suppose we assume that initially he always goes to the north end. In this case the initial state matrix is

$$\begin{bmatrix} 1 & 0 \end{bmatrix}$$

and the final distribution is

$$\begin{bmatrix} 1 & 0 \end{bmatrix} \begin{bmatrix} \frac{2}{5} & \frac{3}{5} \\ \frac{2}{5} & \frac{3}{5} \end{bmatrix} = \begin{bmatrix} \frac{2}{5} & \frac{3}{5} \end{bmatrix}$$

which is the same as before. Here are a few other cases:

$$\begin{bmatrix} \frac{1}{8} & \frac{7}{8} \end{bmatrix} \begin{bmatrix} \frac{2}{5} & \frac{3}{5} \\ \frac{2}{5} & \frac{3}{5} \end{bmatrix} = \begin{bmatrix} \frac{2}{5} & \frac{3}{5} \end{bmatrix}$$

$$\begin{bmatrix} .0713 & .9287 \end{bmatrix} \begin{bmatrix} \frac{2}{5} & \frac{3}{5} \\ \frac{2}{5} & \frac{3}{5} \end{bmatrix} = \begin{bmatrix} \frac{2}{5} & \frac{3}{5} \end{bmatrix}$$

$$\begin{bmatrix} 0 & 1 \end{bmatrix} \begin{bmatrix} \frac{2}{5} & \frac{3}{5} \\ \frac{2}{5} & \frac{3}{5} \end{bmatrix} = \begin{bmatrix} \frac{2}{5} & \frac{3}{5} \end{bmatrix}$$

In fact, the final distribution will be the same, no matter what the initial-state matrix is. The limit matrix will always have identical rows and the final distribution will be the same as each of these rows. This property of Markov chains is called **washing out**. In a regular Markov chain, the effect of the initial condition eventually disappears.

We now turn to the question of computing the final distribution associated with a regular Markov chain. The flow chart for this procedure is given on the next page. We will illustrate its use in Problem 4. This flow chart actually applies to a larger class of Markov chains than just the regular chains, as we shall see in the next section.

In describing how to calculate the long-range distribution of a regular Markov chain, it will be convenient to introduce a new matrix operation: transposing. Given a matrix one finds its **transpose** by switching its rows and colomns, as in the following examples.

**Problem 2**  Find the transpose of the matrix

$$\begin{bmatrix} 2 & 1 \\ 3 & 4 \\ 5 & 7 \end{bmatrix}$$

**Solution**  The matrix has three rows: 2  1; 3  4; and 5  7. We form a new matrix, which has these rows as columns:

The original matrix has two columns: $\begin{matrix} 2 & 1 \\ 3 & 4 \\ 5 & 7 \end{matrix}$. We could also have formed the transposed matrix by writing these columns as rows, obtaining the same answer as before.

$$\begin{bmatrix} 2 & 3 & 5 \\ 1 & 4 & 7 \end{bmatrix}$$

Thus, the first row becomes the first column, and so forth. This new matrix is the transpose of the original matrix.

**Problem 3**  What is the transpose of the following matrix?

$$\begin{bmatrix} \frac{2}{3} & \frac{1}{6} & \frac{1}{6} \\ \frac{1}{4} & \frac{1}{2} & \frac{1}{4} \\ \frac{1}{8} & \frac{7}{8} & 0 \end{bmatrix}$$

**Answer**

$$\begin{bmatrix} \frac{2}{3} & \frac{1}{4} & \frac{1}{8} \\ \frac{1}{6} & \frac{1}{2} & \frac{7}{8} \\ \frac{1}{6} & \frac{1}{4} & 0 \end{bmatrix}$$

### To Determine Final Distribution
### of a Regular Markov Chain

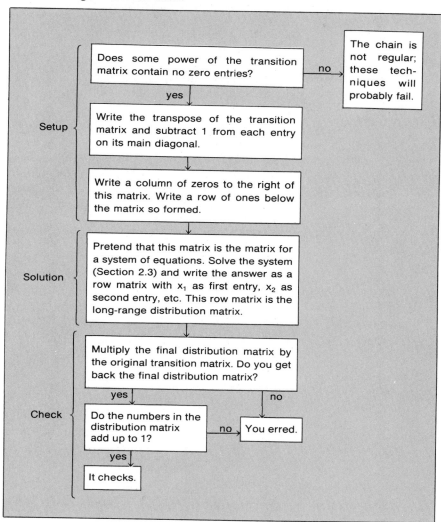

**Setup**

Does some power of the transition matrix contain no zero entries? — no → The chain is not regular; these techniques will probably fail.

yes ↓

Write the transpose of the transition matrix and subtract 1 from each entry on its main diagonal.

↓

Write a column of zeros to the right of this matrix. Write a row of ones below the matrix so formed.

**Solution**

Pretend that this matrix is the matrix for a system of equations. Solve the system (Section 2.3) and write the answer as a row matrix with $x_1$ as first entry, $x_2$ as second entry, etc. This row matrix is the long-range distribution matrix.

**Check**

Multiply the final distribution matrix by the original transition matrix. Do you get back the final distribution matrix?

yes ↓          no →

Do the numbers in the distribution matrix add up to 1? — no → You erred.

yes ↓

It checks.

**Problem 4**  What will be the long-range effect of the brand-switching trend described in Table 4, page 169?

**Solution**  The transition matrix from the table is

$$
\begin{bmatrix}
\frac{2}{3} & \frac{1}{6} & \frac{1}{6} \\
\frac{1}{4} & \frac{1}{2} & \frac{1}{4} \\
\frac{1}{8} & \frac{7}{8} & 0
\end{bmatrix}
$$

This is a regular transition matrix, since the product

$$
\begin{bmatrix}
\frac{2}{3} & \frac{1}{6} & \frac{1}{6} \\
\frac{1}{4} & \frac{1}{2} & \frac{1}{4} \\
\frac{1}{8} & \frac{7}{8} & 0
\end{bmatrix}
\begin{bmatrix}
\frac{2}{3} & \frac{1}{6} & \frac{1}{6} \\
\frac{1}{4} & \frac{1}{2} & \frac{1}{4} \\
\frac{1}{8} & \frac{7}{8} & 0
\end{bmatrix}
=
\begin{bmatrix}
\frac{73}{144} & \frac{49}{144} & \frac{22}{144} \\
\frac{31}{96} & \frac{49}{96} & \frac{16}{96} \\
\frac{29}{96} & \frac{44}{96} & \frac{23}{96}
\end{bmatrix}
$$

is a matrix with no zero entries. Following the instructions of the flow chart, we write the transpose of the transition matrix,

$$
\begin{bmatrix}
\frac{2}{3} & \frac{1}{4} & \frac{1}{8} \\
\frac{1}{6} & \frac{1}{2} & \frac{7}{8} \\
\frac{1}{6} & \frac{1}{4} & 0
\end{bmatrix}
$$

subtract 1 from each entry on its main diagonal,

$$
\begin{bmatrix}
-\frac{1}{3} & \frac{1}{4} & \frac{1}{8} \\
\frac{1}{6} & -\frac{1}{2} & \frac{7}{8} \\
\frac{1}{6} & \frac{1}{4} & -1
\end{bmatrix}
$$

add a column of 0s to the right

$$
\begin{bmatrix}
-\frac{1}{3} & \frac{1}{4} & \frac{1}{8} & 0 \\
\frac{1}{6} & -\frac{1}{2} & \frac{7}{8} & 0 \\
\frac{1}{6} & \frac{1}{4} & -1 & 0
\end{bmatrix}
$$

and, finally, insert a row of 1s beneath.

$$
\begin{bmatrix}
-\frac{1}{3} & \frac{1}{4} & \frac{1}{8} & 0 \\
\frac{1}{6} & -\frac{1}{2} & \frac{7}{8} & 0 \\
\frac{1}{6} & \frac{1}{4} & -1 & 0 \\
1 & 1 & 1 & 1
\end{bmatrix}
$$

Treating this as a system of 4 equations in 3 unknowns, we solve by Gauss-Jordan reduction:

$$
\begin{bmatrix}
1 & -\frac{3}{4} & -\frac{3}{8} & 0 \\
0 & -\frac{3}{8} & \frac{15}{16} & 0 \\
0 & \frac{3}{8} & -\frac{15}{16} & 0 \\
0 & \frac{7}{4} & \frac{11}{8} & 1
\end{bmatrix}
\begin{bmatrix}
1 & 0 & -\frac{9}{4} & 0 \\
0 & 1 & -\frac{5}{2} & 0 \\
0 & 0 & \frac{23}{4} & 1 \\
0 & 0 & 0 & 0
\end{bmatrix}
\begin{bmatrix}
1 & 0 & 0 & \frac{9}{23} \\
0 & 1 & 0 & \frac{10}{23} \\
0 & 0 & 1 & \frac{4}{23} \\
0 & 0 & 0 & 0
\end{bmatrix}
$$

The answer is $x_1 = \frac{9}{23}$, $x_2 = \frac{10}{23}$, $x_3 = \frac{4}{23}$. Thus, the long-range distribution will be

$$\left[\begin{array}{ccc} \frac{9}{23} & \frac{10}{23} & \frac{4}{23} \end{array}\right]$$

Applying this to the original problem, we see that, if consumer trends continue, AC eventually will control $\frac{9}{23}$ or about 39% of the market, AK will control $\frac{10}{23}$ or about 44%, and PP will control $\frac{4}{23}$ or about 17%.

We check this answer by computing

$$\left[\begin{array}{ccc} \frac{9}{23} & \frac{10}{23} & \frac{4}{23} \end{array}\right] \left[\begin{array}{ccc} \frac{2}{3} & \frac{1}{6} & \frac{1}{6} \\ \frac{1}{4} & \frac{1}{2} & \frac{1}{4} \\ \frac{1}{8} & \frac{7}{8} & 0 \end{array}\right] = \left[\begin{array}{ccc} \frac{9}{23} & \frac{10}{23} & \frac{4}{23} \end{array}\right]$$

Analyzing this checking procedure should remove some of the mystery from the flow chart. All that the procedure involves is solving the matrix equation

In fact it is easier for some students to set up and solve this system than it is for them to remember the steps in the flow chart.

$$\left[\begin{array}{ccc} x_1 & x_2 & x_3 \end{array}\right] \left[\begin{array}{ccc} \frac{2}{3} & \frac{1}{6} & \frac{1}{6} \\ \frac{1}{4} & \frac{1}{2} & \frac{1}{4} \\ \frac{1}{8} & \frac{7}{8} & 0 \end{array}\right] = \left[\begin{array}{ccc} x_1 & x_2 & x_3 \end{array}\right]$$

with the side condition that $x_1 + x_2 + x_3 = 1$.

Our answer also tells us that, as we raise the matrix

$$\left[\begin{array}{ccc} \frac{2}{3} & \frac{1}{6} & \frac{1}{6} \\ \frac{1}{4} & \frac{1}{2} & \frac{1}{4} \\ \frac{1}{8} & \frac{7}{8} & 0 \end{array}\right]$$

to successively higher powers, we move closer and closer to the limit matrix

$$\left[\begin{array}{ccc} \frac{9}{23} & \frac{10}{23} & \frac{4}{23} \\ \frac{9}{23} & \frac{10}{23} & \frac{4}{23} \\ \frac{9}{23} & \frac{10}{23} & \frac{4}{23} \end{array}\right]$$

all of whose rows are the same as the final distribution matrix.

**Problem 5**   What will be the long-range effect of the brand-switching trend described in Table 5?

**Solution**   The transition matrix for this problem is given by

$$\left[\begin{array}{ccc} \frac{2}{3} & 0 & \frac{1}{3} \\ \frac{1}{2} & 0 & \frac{1}{2} \\ 0 & 1 & 0 \end{array}\right]$$

This transition matrix is regular since, as you may check, its third power has no zero entries. The system to be solved is

$$
\begin{bmatrix}
-\frac{1}{3} & \frac{1}{2} & 0 & 0 \\
0 & -1 & 1 & 0 \\
\frac{1}{3} & \frac{1}{2} & -1 & 0 \\
1 & 1 & 1 & 1
\end{bmatrix}
$$

and the final distribution matrix is

$$
\begin{bmatrix} \frac{3}{7} & \frac{2}{7} & \frac{2}{7} \end{bmatrix}
$$

See Appendix A, Section 8.

Now AC will control $\frac{3}{7}$ or about 43% of the market and the other two companies will share the rest evenly. Since $\frac{9}{23} < \frac{3}{7}$, the sales VP did indeed move the company in a better direction.

**Absorbing Markov Chains**

We now turn our attention to absorbing chains.

**Problem 6**

In 1960, when AC and AK were the only major Eastern sporting goods companies, a newcomer, Sporting and Recreation of Boston (SARB), caused quite a stir. Market research indicated that, while hardly anyone had heard of SARB, practically everyone who bought their products was so impressed that he or she never again bought anything from AC or AK. From the brand-switching (transition) table for May–June 1960 (Table 14) we see that $\frac{1}{2}$ of AC's customers remained loyal, $\frac{1}{4}$ went to AK, and $\frac{1}{4}$ went to SARB. All of AK's customers went to AC and, as we have said, all of SARB's customers stayed with that company.

**Table 14**
**Fractions of Consumers Who Switch Brands (May–June 1960)**

| From/To | AC | AK | SARB |
|---------|-----|-----|------|
| AC | $\frac{1}{2}$ | $\frac{1}{4}$ | $\frac{1}{4}$ |
| AK | 1 | 0 | 0 |
| SARB | 0 | 0 | 1 |

In May, the customers were divided thus: $\frac{1}{2}$ bought from AC, $\frac{3}{8}$ from AK, and $\frac{1}{8}$ from SARB. Assuming that this buying trend persists, what will be the distribution of consumers after 16 months? What will happen in the long run?

**Solution**

From the table, we immediately obtain the transition matrix

$$
\begin{bmatrix}
\frac{1}{2} & \frac{1}{4} & \frac{1}{4} \\
1 & 0 & 0 \\
0 & 0 & 1
\end{bmatrix}
$$

Since the problem asks us to determine the situation in 16 months, we raise this matrix to the 16th power, as follows:

$$
\begin{bmatrix} \frac{1}{2} & \frac{1}{4} & \frac{1}{4} \\ 1 & 0 & 0 \\ 0 & 0 & 1 \end{bmatrix}
\begin{bmatrix} \frac{1}{2} & \frac{1}{4} & \frac{1}{4} \\ 1 & 0 & 0 \\ 0 & 0 & 1 \end{bmatrix}
=
\begin{bmatrix} \frac{1}{2} & \frac{1}{8} & \frac{3}{8} \\ \frac{1}{2} & \frac{1}{4} & \frac{1}{4} \\ 0 & 0 & 1 \end{bmatrix}
\text{(the 2nd power)}
$$

$$
\begin{bmatrix} \frac{1}{2} & \frac{1}{8} & \frac{3}{8} \\ \frac{1}{2} & \frac{1}{4} & \frac{1}{4} \\ 0 & 0 & 1 \end{bmatrix}
\begin{bmatrix} \frac{1}{2} & \frac{1}{8} & \frac{3}{8} \\ \frac{1}{2} & \frac{1}{4} & \frac{1}{4} \\ 0 & 0 & 1 \end{bmatrix}
=
\begin{bmatrix} \frac{10}{32} & \frac{3}{32} & \frac{19}{32} \\ \frac{3}{8} & \frac{1}{8} & \frac{1}{2} \\ 0 & 0 & 1 \end{bmatrix}
\text{(the 4th power)}
$$

$$
\begin{bmatrix} \frac{10}{32} & \frac{3}{32} & \frac{19}{32} \\ \frac{3}{8} & \frac{1}{8} & \frac{1}{2} \\ 0 & 0 & 1 \end{bmatrix}
\begin{bmatrix} \frac{10}{32} & \frac{3}{32} & \frac{19}{32} \\ \frac{3}{8} & \frac{1}{8} & \frac{1}{2} \\ 0 & 0 & 1 \end{bmatrix}
=
\begin{bmatrix} \frac{68}{512} & \frac{21}{512} & \frac{423}{512} \\ \frac{42}{256} & \frac{13}{512} & \frac{201}{256} \\ 0 & 0 & 1 \end{bmatrix}
\text{(the 8th power)}
$$

$$
\begin{bmatrix} \frac{68}{512} & \frac{21}{512} & \frac{423}{512} \\ \frac{42}{256} & \frac{13}{256} & \frac{201}{256} \\ 0 & 0 & 1 \end{bmatrix}
\begin{bmatrix} \frac{68}{512} & \frac{21}{512} & \frac{423}{512} \\ \frac{42}{256} & \frac{13}{256} & \frac{201}{256} \\ 0 & 0 & 1 \end{bmatrix}
$$

$$
=
\begin{bmatrix} \frac{6,388}{262,144} & \frac{1,974}{262,144} & \frac{253,782}{262,144} \\ \frac{7,896}{262,144} & \frac{2,440}{262,144} & \frac{251,808}{262,144} \\ 0 & 0 & 1 \end{bmatrix}
\text{(the 16th power)}
$$

If we replace the fractions in the last matrix by decimal approximations we obtain the matrix

$$
\begin{bmatrix} 0.0244 & 0.0075 & 0.9681 \\ 0.0301 & 0.0093 & 0.9606 \\ 0.0000 & 0.0000 & 1.0000 \end{bmatrix}
$$

Note that, after 16 months, 96.81% of AC's customers and 96.06% of AK's customers have switched to SARB. The distribution we are looking for is obtained by multiplying the initial state matrix

$$
\begin{bmatrix} \frac{1}{2} & \frac{3}{8} & \frac{1}{8} \end{bmatrix}
$$

by the transition matrix:

$$
\begin{bmatrix} \frac{1}{2} & \frac{3}{8} & \frac{1}{8} \end{bmatrix}
\begin{bmatrix} 0.0244 & 0.0075 & 0.9681 \\ 0.0301 & 0.0093 & 0.9606 \\ 0.0000 & 0.0000 & 1.0000 \end{bmatrix}
$$

$$
= \begin{bmatrix} .0235 & .0073 & .9692 \end{bmatrix} \doteq \begin{bmatrix} 2.3\% & 0.7\% & 96.92\% \end{bmatrix}
$$

Thus, after 16 months, approximately 2.3% of the backpackers will be buying AC products, 0.7% will be buying AK products, and approximately 96.92% will be buying SARB products, SARB will

Fortunately for the other companies, SARB began to have management problems, and a little price war forced them to merge with AC before things got out of hand.

have essentially cornered the market, and AC and AK will both be forced out of business. In the long run the distribution will be

$$\begin{bmatrix} 0 & 0 & 100\% \end{bmatrix}$$

Another point to be made here is that the transition matrices gave AC an idea of how much time they had to act. For instance, in just two months the distribution of consumers would be

$$\begin{bmatrix} \frac{1}{2} & \frac{3}{8} & \frac{1}{8} \end{bmatrix} \begin{bmatrix} \frac{1}{2} & \frac{1}{8} & \frac{3}{8} \\ \frac{1}{2} & \frac{1}{4} & \frac{1}{4} \\ 0 & 0 & 1 \end{bmatrix} = \begin{bmatrix} \frac{14}{32} & \frac{5}{32} & \frac{13}{32} \end{bmatrix}$$

which indicates that SARB would already dominate much of the market.

In the previous problem the state represented by SARB was an absorbing state. While not many individuals switched to SARB at any one transition (only $\frac{1}{4}$ of AC's customers), once at SARB, they all stayed; that is, they were absorbed. Thus, SARB would slowly drain off all the business. Actually, there are two kinds of absorbing states. One, like SARB's, has disastrous consequences for the competition. But the other is not so bad.

**Problem 7**

In August 1967, the management of AC nearly panicked when they heard that another company, Elite Klimbing Gear (EKG), had achieved 100% consumer loyalty. However, a short investigation disclosed that EKG's equipment was for show and never intended for the rigors of the mountains. The consumers all understood this. None of AC's customers bought EKG's equipment, although $\frac{1}{2}$ did switch to AK. AK's customers reacted in the same way. What will happen as time goes on?

**Solution**

The transition table is Table 15.

**Table 15
Fractions of Consumer
Who Switch Brands
(August–September 1967)**

| From/To | AC | AK | EKG |
|---------|-----|-----|-----|
| AC | $\frac{1}{2}$ | $\frac{1}{2}$ | 0 |
| AK | $\frac{1}{2}$ | $\frac{1}{2}$ | 0 |
| EKG | 0 | 0 | 1 |

The transition matrix is

$$\begin{bmatrix} \frac{1}{2} & \frac{1}{2} & 0 \\ \frac{1}{2} & \frac{1}{2} & 0 \\ 0 & 0 & 1 \end{bmatrix}$$

Squaring this matrix yields

$$\begin{bmatrix} \frac{1}{2} & \frac{1}{2} & 0 \\ \frac{1}{2} & \frac{1}{2} & 0 \\ 0 & 0 & 1 \end{bmatrix} \begin{bmatrix} \frac{1}{2} & \frac{1}{2} & 0 \\ \frac{1}{2} & \frac{1}{2} & 0 \\ 0 & 0 & 1 \end{bmatrix} \begin{bmatrix} \frac{1}{2} & \frac{1}{2} & 0 \\ \frac{1}{2} & \frac{1}{2} & 0 \\ 0 & 0 & 1 \end{bmatrix}$$

Any power of this matrix will therefore just equal the original matrix. Thus, after the first month, no further change will occur. Let the letter a denote the number of customers AC has in the beginning, b the number with AK, and c the number with EKG. We compute:

$$\begin{bmatrix} a & b & c \end{bmatrix} \begin{bmatrix} \frac{1}{2} & \frac{1}{2} & 0 \\ \frac{1}{2} & \frac{1}{2} & 0 \\ 0 & 0 & 1 \end{bmatrix} = \begin{bmatrix} \frac{1}{2}(a+b) & \frac{1}{2}(a+b) & c \end{bmatrix}$$

Thus, after one month, and from then on, AC and AK will have the same number of customers while EKG will have only its original number of customers.

While this problem is similar to the previous one in that no one leaves the state EKG, it differs in that no one ever enters this state from another state. Note that the 1 on the main diagonal indicates that everyone in that state returns to it and that whether or not its column is cleared indicates whether or not it can be entered from another state.

For absorbing chains, there are two cases to be considered. If there is only one absorbing state, the initial conditions wash out and eventually all of the distribution ends up being absorbed into that state. If there is more than one absorbing state, then, while everything is absorbed into one of these states, nonabsorbing states will send a certain fraction to each absorbing state. For example, in the absorbing transition matrix

$$\begin{bmatrix} 1 & 0 & 0 & 0 \\ 0 & 1 & 0 & 0 \\ 0 & \frac{1}{2} & \frac{1}{4} & \frac{1}{4} \\ 0 & 0 & 0 & 1 \end{bmatrix}$$

**3**

everything in states 1, 2, or 4 stays there and some of the distribution initially in state 3 ends up being absorbed by one of these states. Since state 1 is isolated, nothing that did not start there will end up there. The only problem is to determine how states 2 and 4 share in the final distribution.

Before giving a flow chart specifying how to do this, we compute a few powers of matrix 3.

$$\begin{bmatrix} 1 & 0 & 0 & 0 \\ 0 & 1 & 0 & 0 \\ 0 & \frac{1}{2} & \frac{1}{4} & \frac{1}{4} \\ 0 & 0 & 0 & 1 \end{bmatrix}^2 = \begin{bmatrix} 1 & 0 & 0 & 0 \\ 0 & 1 & 0 & 0 \\ 0 & \frac{5}{8} & \frac{1}{16} & \frac{5}{16} \\ 0 & 0 & 0 & 1 \end{bmatrix} = \frac{1}{16}\begin{bmatrix} 16 & 0 & 0 & 0 \\ 0 & 16 & 0 & 0 \\ 0 & 10 & 1 & 5 \\ 0 & 0 & 0 & 16 \end{bmatrix}$$

(the 2nd power);

$$\left(\frac{1}{16}\begin{bmatrix} 16 & 0 & 0 & 0 \\ 0 & 16 & 0 & 0 \\ 0 & 10 & 1 & 5 \\ 0 & 0 & 0 & 16 \end{bmatrix}\right)^2 = \frac{1}{256}\begin{bmatrix} 256 & 0 & 1 & 0 \\ 0 & 256 & 0 & 0 \\ 0 & 170 & 1 & 85 \\ 0 & 0 & 0 & 256 \end{bmatrix}$$

$$\doteq \begin{bmatrix} 1 & 0 & 0 & 0 \\ 0 & 1 & 0 & 0 \\ 0 & 0.664 & 0.004 & 0.332 \\ 0 & 0 & 0 & 1 \end{bmatrix}$$

Thus it seems that the limit matrix will be

$$\begin{bmatrix} 1 & 0 & 0 & 0 \\ 0 & 1 & 0 & 0 \\ 0 & \frac{2}{3} & 0 & \frac{1}{3} \\ 0 & 0 & 0 & 1 \end{bmatrix}$$

We will show that this is so in Problem 8.

Each row of this limit matrix gives the (fractional) long-range distribution of the items originally in the state specified by the row. For example, from row 3 we see that none of the items originally in state 3 will end up on state 1 or 3; $\frac{2}{3}$ of them will end up in state 2; and $\frac{1}{3}$ of them will end up in state 4.

Each column of the limit matrix gives the portion of the items initially in the various states that end up in the state specified by the column. For example, from column 2 we see that all of the items initially in state 2 end up in state 2; and $\frac{2}{3}$ of the items initially in state 3 end up in state 2.

The following flow chart shows how to obtain the limit matrix without computing high powers of the transition matrix or guessing from decimal approximations.

**Problem 8** Given the Markov chain with transition matrix

$$\begin{bmatrix} 1 & 0 & 0 & 0 \\ 0 & 1 & 0 & 0 \\ 0 & \frac{1}{2} & \frac{1}{4} & \frac{1}{4} \\ 0 & 0 & 0 & 1 \end{bmatrix}$$

what is the limit matrix?

**To Determine the Limit Matrix
for a Given Absorbing
Transition Matrix**

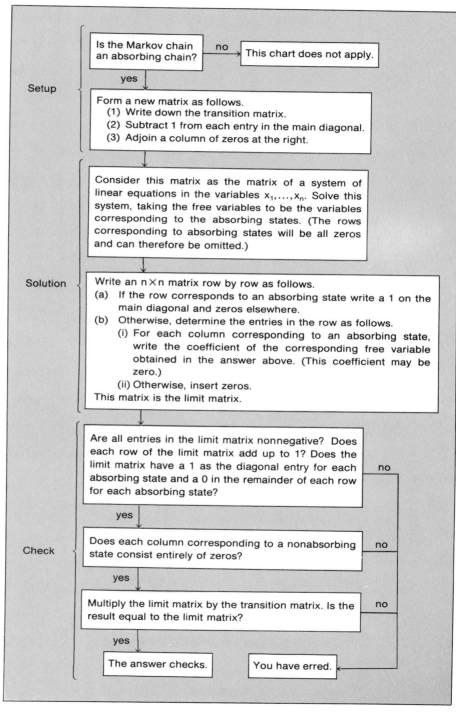

Solution

Note that each row corresponding to
an absorbing state in the system to be
solved consists entirely of zeros.

There are three absorbing states: states 1, 2, and 4. The flow chart instructs us first to write down the transition matrix, and then to subtract 1 from each of its diagonal entries:

$$\begin{bmatrix} 0 & 0 & 0 & 0 \\ 0 & 0 & 0 & 0 \\ 0 & \frac{1}{2} & -\frac{3}{4} & \frac{1}{4} \\ 0 & 0 & 0 & 0 \end{bmatrix}$$

We adjoin a column of zeros and solve the resulting system, taking the free variables to be those corresponding to the absorbing states:

$$\begin{bmatrix} 0 & 0 & 0 & 0 & 0 \\ 0 & 0 & 0 & 0 & 0 \\ 0 & \frac{1}{2} & -\frac{3}{4} & \frac{1}{4} & 0 \\ 0 & 0 & 0 & 0 & 0 \end{bmatrix} \begin{bmatrix} 0 & 0 & 0 & 0 & 0 \\ 0 & 0 & 0 & 0 & 0 \\ 0 & -\frac{2}{3} & 1 & -\frac{1}{3} & 0 \\ 0 & 0 & 0 & 0 & 0 \end{bmatrix}$$

The solution is:

$$x_1 \text{ is free}$$
$$x_2 \text{ is free}$$
$$x_3 = \tfrac{2}{3}x_2 + \tfrac{1}{3}x_4$$
$$x_4 \text{ is free}$$

The limit matrix is then:

$$\begin{bmatrix} 1 & 0 & 0 & 0 \\ 0 & 1 & 0 & 0 \\ 0 & \frac{2}{3} & 0 & \frac{1}{3} \\ 0 & 0 & 0 & 1 \end{bmatrix}$$

as predicted.

It is now easy to compute the long-range distribution for a given initial distribution and given absorbing Markov chain.

Check:

$$\begin{bmatrix} 1 & 0 & 0 & 0 \\ 0 & 1 & 0 & 0 \\ 0 & \frac{1}{2} & \frac{1}{4} & \frac{1}{4} \\ 0 & 0 & 0 & 1 \end{bmatrix} \begin{bmatrix} 1 & 0 & 0 & 0 \\ 0 & 1 & 0 & 0 \\ 0 & \frac{2}{3} & 0 & \frac{1}{3} \\ 0 & 0 & 0 & 1 \end{bmatrix}$$

$$= \begin{bmatrix} 1 & 0 & 0 & 0 \\ 0 & 1 & 0 & 0 \\ 0 & \frac{2}{3} & 0 & \frac{1}{3} \\ 0 & 0 & 0 & 1 \end{bmatrix} \checkmark$$

Problem 9

Given the initial distribution

$$\begin{bmatrix} \frac{1}{8} & \frac{1}{2} & \frac{1}{4} & \frac{1}{8} \end{bmatrix}$$

what will be the long-range distribution of the Markov chain with transition matrix

$$\begin{bmatrix} 1 & 0 & 0 & 0 \\ 0 & 1 & 0 & 0 \\ 0 & \frac{1}{2} & \frac{1}{4} & \frac{1}{4} \\ 0 & 0 & 0 & 1 \end{bmatrix}$$

**To Determine the
Long-Range Distribution
for a Given Initial
Distribution and Given
Absorbing Markov Chain**

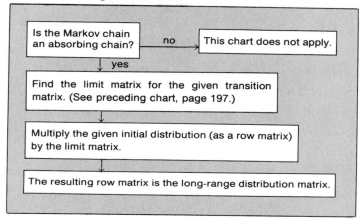

Solution    According to the flow chart, we need merely multiply the initial distribution by the limit matrix:

$$\begin{bmatrix} \frac{1}{8} & \frac{1}{2} & \frac{1}{4} & \frac{1}{8} \end{bmatrix} \begin{bmatrix} 1 & 0 & 0 & 0 \\ 0 & 1 & 0 & 0 \\ 0 & \frac{2}{3} & 0 & \frac{1}{3} \\ 0 & 0 & 0 & 1 \end{bmatrix} = \begin{bmatrix} \frac{1}{8} & \frac{2}{3} & 0 & \frac{5}{24} \end{bmatrix}$$

**Exercises 3.4**    1.  Compute the fourth powers of the matrices

$$\begin{bmatrix} \frac{2}{3} & 0 & \frac{1}{3} \\ \frac{1}{2} & 0 & \frac{1}{2} \\ 0 & 1 & 0 \end{bmatrix}$$

and

$$\begin{bmatrix} 1 & 0 & 0 & 0 \\ 0 & 1 & 0 & 0 \\ 0 & \frac{1}{2} & \frac{1}{4} & \frac{1}{4} \\ 0 & 0 & 0 & 1 \end{bmatrix}$$

Compare your answers with the results predicted in the text. (To compare, change all the entries to decimals.)

$^{c}$2.  Compute the long-range distribution associated with the transition matrix

$$\begin{bmatrix} \frac{1}{3} & \frac{1}{3} & \frac{1}{3} \\ \frac{1}{4} & \frac{1}{2} & \frac{1}{4} \\ 0 & 1 & 0 \end{bmatrix}$$

3. Compute the limit matrix for the following transition matrix:

$$\begin{bmatrix} 1 & 0 & 0 & 0 & 0 \\ \frac{1}{4} & 0 & \frac{1}{2} & \frac{1}{4} & 0 \\ 0 & 0 & 1 & 0 & 0 \\ 0 & 0 & 0 & 1 & 0 \\ 0 & \frac{1}{3} & \frac{1}{3} & 0 & \frac{1}{3} \end{bmatrix}$$

What will be the long-range effect of this transition matrix on the initial distribution $[\frac{1}{10} \quad \frac{1}{5} \quad \frac{3}{10} \quad \frac{3}{10} \quad \frac{1}{10}]$?

See Exercise 7, page 183. C4. International Interstate Tubing (IIT) is also trying to convince AC to purchase a machine that automatically assembles pack frames. Its breakdown rate is given in Table 16.

Table 16
IIT Breakdown Probabilities

| From/To | Not broken | Broken |
|---|---|---|
| Not broken | $\frac{5}{8}$ | $\frac{3}{8}$ |
| Broken | $\frac{9}{10}$ | $\frac{1}{10}$ |

Compute the long-range distributions for this machine and the AAT machine and decide which machine AC should buy.

5. What is the long-range distribution for the transition matrix

$$\begin{bmatrix} 0 & \frac{3}{4} & 0 & \frac{1}{4} \\ 0 & 0 & 1 & 0 \\ \frac{1}{2} & \frac{1}{2} & 0 & 0 \\ 0 & 0 & 0 & 1 \end{bmatrix}$$

6. What is the long-range distribution for the transition matrix

$$\begin{bmatrix} \frac{1}{3} & \frac{1}{3} & \frac{1}{3} \\ \frac{1}{2} & \frac{1}{2} & 0 \\ 0 & \frac{1}{2} & \frac{1}{2} \end{bmatrix}$$

7. Compute the limit matrix for the following transition matrix.

$$\begin{bmatrix} \frac{1}{4} & 0 & \frac{1}{2} & 0 & 0 & \frac{1}{4} \\ 0 & 1 & 0 & 0 & 0 & 0 \\ \frac{1}{2} & \frac{1}{4} & 0 & \frac{1}{4} & 0 & 0 \\ 0 & 0 & 0 & 1 & 0 & 0 \\ 0 & 0 & 0 & 0 & 1 & 0 \\ 0 & 0 & 0 & \frac{1}{2} & \frac{1}{2} & 0 \end{bmatrix}$$

What will be the long-range effect of this transition matrix on the initial distribution matrix $[\frac{1}{12} \quad \frac{2}{12} \quad \frac{3}{12} \quad \frac{4}{12} \quad \frac{1}{12} \quad \frac{1}{12}]$?

8. Compute the first five powers of the transition matrix

$$\begin{bmatrix} 0 & 1 & 0 & 0 \\ 0 & 0 & 1 & 0 \\ 0 & 0 & 0 & 1 \\ 1 & 0 & 0 & 0 \end{bmatrix}$$

What can you conclude about the long-range effect of such a transition matrix?

9. What is the long-range effect of the transition matrix

$$\begin{bmatrix} \frac{7}{8} & \frac{1}{8} & 0 \\ 0 & \frac{15}{16} & \frac{1}{16} \\ \frac{7}{8} & 0 & \frac{1}{8} \end{bmatrix}$$

on any given initial-distribution matrix?

10. What is the long-range distribution for the Markov chain

$$\begin{bmatrix} \frac{1}{8} & \frac{3}{4} & \frac{1}{8} \\ \frac{7}{8} & 0 & \frac{1}{8} \\ 1 & 0 & 0 \end{bmatrix}$$

11. Compute the limit matrix for the following transition matrix.

$$\begin{bmatrix} 0 & 0 & 1 & 0 & 0 \\ 0 & 1 & 0 & 0 & 0 \\ \frac{1}{4} & 0 & \frac{1}{2} & 0 & \frac{1}{4} \\ 0 & 0 & 0 & 1 & 0 \\ \frac{1}{4} & \frac{1}{2} & 0 & \frac{1}{4} & 0 \end{bmatrix}$$

What will be the long-range effect of this transition matrix on the initial distribution [81  27  18  15  12]?

*12. What is the long-range effect of the transition matrix

$$\begin{bmatrix} 1 & 0 & 0 & 0 \\ 0 & \frac{1}{3} & \frac{1}{3} & \frac{1}{3} \\ 0 & \frac{1}{4} & \frac{1}{2} & \frac{1}{4} \\ 0 & 0 & 1 & 0 \end{bmatrix}$$

on the initial distribution $[\frac{1}{4} \quad \frac{1}{8} \quad \frac{1}{2} \quad \frac{1}{8}]$?

13. The three PHE stores in Little Rock are keeping track of their customers. Every week, $\frac{1}{2}$ of the customers in store 1 switch to store 2 and $\frac{1}{3}$ to store 3; $\frac{5}{6}$ of the customers in store 2 switch to store 1; $\frac{1}{5}$ of the customers in store 3 switch to store 1 and $\frac{3}{5}$ to store 2. The total pool of customers stays the same: 1,200 kids, 50 parents, and 1 retired dentist. In the long run, how many customers will each store have?

14. My taxi company is in competition with another taxi company in a small town with a population of 5,574. An independent survey reveals that most residents do not use a taxi 2 days in a row. In fact, 95% of the persons who use my taxi on one day will not use a taxi the next day and 92% of the competitor's customers will not use a taxi the next day. Furthermore, 10% of the people who did not use a taxi on a given day select me on the next day and 12% select him. Of course, a few people do use a taxi on 2 consecutive days. However, I lose 20% of my customers to him and get 25% of his customers. Yesterday I happened to have had 800 customers and he had 300

customers. How many customers will we each have 90 days from today?

C15. The Erehwon Valley is completely isolated from the rest of the world. In fact, no one outside the valley has ever heard of it. The major activities in the valley involve the production of food, clothing, and shelter, so there are only three occupations: farmer, clothier, and carpenter. The average yearly expenditure for each sector of the economy is given in Table 17.

Table 17
Yearly Expenditures
(as percent of income)

|  | Food | Clothing | Shelter |
|---|---|---|---|
| Farmer | 50 | 20 | 30 |
| Clothier | 40 | 40 | 20 |
| Carpenter | 50 | 30 | 20 |

In the long run, what will be the distribution of wealth if these trends persist?

## Section 3.5
## Periodic and
## Ergodic Markov Chains

By a finite Markov chain we mean one that has only a finite number of states.

In this section we complete our study of Markov chains by showing how to calculate the long-range distribution of any finite Markov chain that has one. Such chains are called **ergodic**. Since regular chains have long-range distributions, they are ergodic. However, not all ergodic chains are regular. It is actually rather easy to handle the general case by combining the techniques of the previous section. We begin by discussing another important type of Markov chain—the *periodic* chain. It can be shown that every finite Markov chain is ergodic, is periodic, or is a combination of both types.

### Periodic Chains

All the people in Amnestia, Mississippi, (pop. 3,284) are fanatical consumers with incredibly bad memories. Their characters are flawed only by a childish dissatisfaction with their purchases once they get them home. The merchants, who are all from out of town, are completely unscrupulous. They realize that Amnestians will buy *anything* but then try to return it the next week. Thus, they have a set policy of not allowing returns without a receipt—which the customers, in their excitement, always forget. The only noninstinctive things the townspeople can remember are: (i) where they live; (ii) where they shopped last week; and (iii) how much they hated it. Each one shops at the next store down the "block" when he returns to town. There are five stores: Alpha's, Beta's, Gramma's, Delta's, and Epsilon's. Now, Epsilon's is a very small store and its manager has to make special preparations whenever more then 800 people show up on a given Saturday. While it is easy for him to figure out when this will happen without using Markov chains, he could use them to solve this problem as follows.

The stores are open only on Saturdays.

The merchants have, rather cleverly, arranged their shops around a circle.

As you can see from this matrix, the stores are arranged around the circle in the order A D B G E.

The transition matrix is

$$
\begin{array}{c c}
 & \begin{array}{c c c c c} A & B & G & D & E \end{array} \\
\begin{array}{c} A \\ B \\ G \\ D \\ E \end{array} &
\begin{bmatrix}
0 & 0 & 0 & 1 & 0 \\
0 & 0 & 1 & 0 & 0 \\
0 & 0 & 0 & 0 & 1 \\
0 & 1 & 0 & 0 & 0 \\
1 & 0 & 0 & 0 & 0
\end{bmatrix}
\end{array}
$$

The initial state matrix for the first Saturday this year is

$$[729 \quad 383 \quad 829 \quad 705 \quad 638]$$

Here is a calculation which yields the distributions for each subsequent Saturday.

(1) First Saturday:   [729  383  829  705  638]

$$
[729 \quad 383 \quad 829 \quad 705 \quad 638]
\begin{bmatrix}
0 & 0 & 0 & 1 & 0 \\
0 & 0 & 1 & 0 & 0 \\
0 & 0 & 0 & 0 & 1 \\
0 & 1 & 0 & 0 & 0 \\
1 & 0 & 0 & 0 & 0
\end{bmatrix}
$$

$$= [638 \quad 705 \quad 383 \quad 729 \quad 829]$$

(2) Second Saturday:   [638  705  383  729  829]

$$
[638 \quad 705 \quad 383 \quad 729 \quad 829]
\begin{bmatrix}
0 & 0 & 0 & 1 & 0 \\
0 & 0 & 1 & 0 & 0 \\
0 & 0 & 0 & 0 & 1 \\
0 & 1 & 0 & 0 & 0 \\
1 & 0 & 0 & 0 & 0
\end{bmatrix}
$$

$$= [829 \quad 729 \quad 705 \quad 638 \quad 383]$$

(3) Third Saturday:   [829  729  705  638  383]

$$
[829 \quad 729 \quad 705 \quad 638 \quad 383]
\begin{bmatrix}
0 & 0 & 0 & 1 & 0 \\
0 & 0 & 1 & 0 & 0 \\
0 & 0 & 0 & 0 & 1 \\
0 & 1 & 0 & 0 & 0 \\
1 & 0 & 0 & 0 & 0
\end{bmatrix}
$$

$$= [383 \quad 638 \quad 729 \quad 829 \quad 705]$$

(4) Fourth Saturday:   [383  638  729  829  705]

$$
[383 \quad 638 \quad 729 \quad 829 \quad 705]
\begin{bmatrix}
0 & 0 & 0 & 1 & 0 \\
0 & 0 & 1 & 0 & 0 \\
0 & 0 & 0 & 0 & 1 \\
0 & 1 & 0 & 0 & 0 \\
1 & 0 & 0 & 0 & 0
\end{bmatrix}
$$

$$= [705 \quad 829 \quad 638 \quad 383 \quad 729]$$

(5) Fifth Saturday:     [705  829  638  383  729]

$$[705 \quad 829 \quad 638 \quad 383 \quad 729] \begin{bmatrix} 0 & 0 & 0 & 1 & 0 \\ 0 & 0 & 1 & 0 & 0 \\ 0 & 0 & 0 & 0 & 1 \\ 0 & 1 & 0 & 0 & 0 \\ 1 & 0 & 0 & 0 & 0 \end{bmatrix}$$

$$= [729 \quad 383 \quad 829 \quad 705 \quad 638]$$

(6) Sixth Saturday:     [729  383  829  705  638]

Of course, the sixth Saturday is the same as the first—after six weeks everyone has gone once around the "circle" and is back where he or she started. We see that Epsilon's has 829 customers on the second Saturday, seventh Saturday, twelfth Saturday, and so on.

In mathematics the term **periodic** means repeating.

This is a very simple example of a *periodic* Markov chain. We can represent it with a diagram

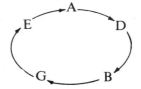

which shows how the material (customers) flows through the five states (stores).

One day the manager of Epsilon's noticed that on the first, sixth, eleventh, and equivalent Saturdays he and his neighbors had a larger total of customers than on other weekends. His accountant verified this by completing the following table.

| Week | E | A | G | TOTAL |
|------|------|------|------|-------|
| 1 | 638 | 729 | 829 | 2,196 |
| 2 | 829 | 638 | 383 | 1,850 |
| 3 | 383 | 829 | 705 | 1,917 |
| 4 | 705 | 383 | 729 | 1,817 |
| 5 | 729 | 705 | 638 | 2,072 |

In an effort to improve his business he invested in some building materials and just after the eleventh Saturday he built two walls and two new sidewalks.

The customers are now forced to proceed directly from A to G
and from D to B. The new transition matrix is:

$$
\begin{array}{c}
\ \\
A \\
B \\
G \\
D \\
E
\end{array}
\begin{array}{c}
\begin{array}{ccccc} A & B & G & D & E \end{array} \\
\begin{bmatrix}
0 & 0 & 1 & 0 & 0 \\
0 & 0 & 0 & 1 & 0 \\
0 & 0 & 0 & 0 & 1 \\
0 & 1 & 0 & 0 & 0 \\
1 & 0 & 0 & 0 & 0
\end{bmatrix}
\end{array}
$$

You should compute each week's distribution by examining the diagram
and then compare your answers with
our results here.

While the diagram above is sufficient for most purposes, we
will once again verify that the mathematics does model reality.

(1) Week just prior to the change:   [729   383   829   705   638]

$$
\begin{bmatrix} 729 & 383 & 829 & 705 & 638 \end{bmatrix}
\begin{bmatrix}
0 & 0 & 1 & 0 & 0 \\
0 & 0 & 0 & 1 & 0 \\
0 & 0 & 0 & 0 & 1 \\
0 & 1 & 0 & 0 & 0 \\
1 & 0 & 0 & 0 & 0
\end{bmatrix}
$$

$$
= \begin{bmatrix} 638 & 705 & 729 & 383 & 829 \end{bmatrix}
$$

(2) Second week:   [638   705   729   383   829]

$$
\begin{bmatrix} 638 & 705 & 729 & 383 & 829 \end{bmatrix}
\begin{bmatrix}
0 & 0 & 1 & 0 & 0 \\
0 & 0 & 0 & 1 & 0 \\
0 & 0 & 0 & 0 & 1 \\
0 & 1 & 0 & 0 & 0 \\
1 & 0 & 0 & 0 & 0
\end{bmatrix}
$$

Notice that B and D are now back as
they were initially.

$$
= \begin{bmatrix} 829 & 383 & 638 & 705 & 729 \end{bmatrix}
$$

(3) Third week:   [829   383   638   705   729]

$$
\begin{bmatrix} 829 & 383 & 638 & 705 & 729 \end{bmatrix}
\begin{bmatrix}
0 & 0 & 1 & 0 & 0 \\
0 & 0 & 0 & 1 & 0 \\
0 & 0 & 0 & 0 & 1 \\
0 & 1 & 0 & 0 & 0 \\
1 & 0 & 0 & 0 & 0
\end{bmatrix}
$$

$$
= \begin{bmatrix} 729 & 705 & 829 & 383 & 638 \end{bmatrix}
$$

Now A, G, and E are back as they
were initially, but B and D are not.

(4) Fourth week:   [729   705   829   383   638]

$$[729 \quad 705 \quad 829 \quad 383 \quad 638] \begin{bmatrix} 0 & 0 & 1 & 0 & 0 \\ 0 & 0 & 0 & 1 & 0 \\ 0 & 0 & 0 & 0 & 1 \\ 0 & 1 & 0 & 0 & 0 \\ 1 & 0 & 0 & 0 & 0 \end{bmatrix}$$

$$= [638 \quad 383 \quad 729 \quad 705 \quad 829]$$

Again, B and D are back as they were initially.

(5) Fifth week:   [638   383   729   705   829]

$$[638 \quad 383 \quad 729 \quad 705 \quad 829] \begin{bmatrix} 0 & 0 & 1 & 0 & 0 \\ 0 & 0 & 0 & 1 & 0 \\ 0 & 0 & 0 & 0 & 1 \\ 0 & 1 & 0 & 0 & 0 \\ 1 & 0 & 0 & 0 & 0 \end{bmatrix}$$

$$= [829 \quad 705 \quad 638 \quad 383 \quad 729]$$

(6) Sixth week:   [829   705   638   383   729]

$$[829 \quad 705 \quad 638 \quad 383 \quad 729] \begin{bmatrix} 0 & 0 & 1 & 0 & 0 \\ 0 & 0 & 0 & 1 & 0 \\ 0 & 0 & 0 & 0 & 1 \\ 0 & 1 & 0 & 0 & 0 \\ 1 & 0 & 0 & 0 & 0 \end{bmatrix}$$

$$= [729 \quad 383 \quad 829 \quad 705 \quad 638]$$

(7) Seventh week:   [729   383   829   705   638]

Now all the states are back as they were initially. It takes 6 transitions to get *both* cycles in phase.

Problem 1   Draw a diagram and explain what happens under the following transition matrix.

|   | A | B | C | D | E | F | G | H |
|---|---|---|---|---|---|---|---|---|
| A | 0 | 0 | 1 | 0 | 0 | 0 | 0 | 0 |
| B | 0 | 0 | 0 | 1 | 0 | 0 | 0 | 0 |
| C | 0 | 0 | 0 | 0 | 1 | 0 | 0 | 0 |
| D | 0 | 0 | 0 | 0 | 0 | 1 | 0 | 0 |
| E | 1 | 0 | 0 | 0 | 0 | 0 | 0 | 0 |
| F | 0 | 0 | 0 | 0 | 0 | 0 | 0 | 1 |
| G | 0 | 0 | 0 | 0 | 0 | 0 | 1 | 0 |
| H | 0 | 1 | 0 | 0 | 0 | 0 | 0 | 0 |

Solution

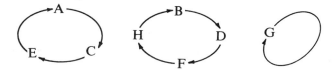

(1) G is an isolated absorbing state.
(2) A, E, and C form a *cycle,* which repeats every 3 transitions.
(3) B, D, H, F form a cycle, which repeats every 4 transitions.
(4) Since 12 is evenly divisible by 3 and 4, the entire chain repeats every 12 transitions; since 12 is the smallest number evenly divisible by 3 and 4, the chain does not repeat more often.

It is also possible to have a periodic transition matrix that does not consist entirely of zeros and ones.

**Problem 2**   Draw a diagram to help explain what happens under the following transition matrix.

$$
\begin{array}{c c c c c c}
 & A & B & C & D & E \\
A & \begin{bmatrix} 0 \\ 0 \\ 0 \\ 0 \\ 1 \end{bmatrix} & \begin{matrix} \frac{1}{3} \\ 0 \\ 0 \\ 0 \\ 0 \end{matrix} & \begin{matrix} \frac{1}{3} \\ 0 \\ 0 \\ 0 \\ 0 \end{matrix} & \begin{matrix} \frac{1}{3} \\ 0 \\ 0 \\ 0 \\ 0 \end{matrix} & \begin{matrix} 0 \\ 1 \\ 1 \\ 1 \\ 0 \end{bmatrix} \\
\end{array}
$$

Answer

$$ A \longrightarrow \boxed{\begin{matrix} B \\ C \\ D \end{matrix}} \longrightarrow E $$

**Closed Sets of States**   In Problem 1 we partitioned the collection of states as follows.

$$\{A, C, E\}, \{B, D, F, H\}, \{G\}$$

Problem 3 will help to clarify this definition.

(i) For this particular problem, each set in the partition represents a **closed set of states**. For a collection of states to be a closed set of states it must be possible to get from any state in the set to any state in the set (including back to the same state) after one or more transitions. Furthermore, there must be no other states that can be reached from states in the closed set.

Problem 3 Determine the closed sets of states for the following Markov chain.

|   | A | B | C | D | E | F | G | H | I | J | K | L |
|---|---|---|---|---|---|---|---|---|---|---|---|---|
| A | 0 | 0 | 0 | 0 | 0 | 0 | 0 | 1 | 0 | 0 | 0 | 0 |
| B | 0 | $\frac{1}{3}$ | 0 | 0 | $\frac{2}{3}$ | 0 | 0 | 0 | 0 | 0 | 0 | 0 |
| C | 0 | 0 | $\frac{1}{2}$ | 0 | 0 | 0 | 0 | 0 | 0 | $\frac{1}{2}$ | 0 | 0 |
| D | 0 | 0 | 0 | 0 | 0 | 0 | 0 | 0 | 1 | 0 | 0 | 0 |
| E | 0 | $\frac{1}{4}$ | 0 | 0 | 0 | 0 | $\frac{3}{4}$ | 0 | 0 | 0 | 0 | 0 |
| F | $\frac{1}{6}$ | $\frac{1}{6}$ | $\frac{1}{6}$ | 0 | $\frac{1}{6}$ | 0 | 0 | 0 | 0 | 0 | $\frac{1}{6}$ | $\frac{1}{6}$ |
| G | 0 | 0 | 0 | 0 | 1 | 0 | 0 | 0 | 0 | 0 | 0 | 0 |
| H | 0 | 0 | 0 | 1 | 0 | 0 | 0 | 0 | 0 | 0 | 0 | 0 |
| I | 1 | 0 | 0 | 0 | 0 | 0 | 0 | 0 | 0 | 0 | 0 | 0 |
| J | 0 | 0 | $\frac{1}{3}$ | 0 | 0 | 0 | 0 | 0 | 0 | 0 | $\frac{2}{3}$ | 0 |
| K | 0 | $\frac{1}{8}$ | 0 | 0 | 0 | $\frac{3}{8}$ | 0 | 0 | $\frac{1}{8}$ | $\frac{1}{4}$ | 0 | $\frac{1}{8}$ |
| L | 0 | 0 | 0 | 0 | 0 | 0 | 0 | 0 | 0 | 0 | 0 | 1 |

Solution (i) Consider state A. It is possible to get from state A to state H and to no other state. A and H will be in the same closed set if we can also get from H to A. We check this with a tree diagram as in the last section.

We see that, not only is it possible to get from H to A, but it is also possible to get between any two states in the set {A, D, H, I}. Our diagram also tells us that it is impossible to get from any state in this set to a state not in this set. Thus, this is a closed set of states.

(ii) Consider state B. We can go from state B into state B or state E. Can we also go from E to B?

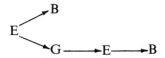

Again, our tree diagram tells us more: we can get between any two states in the set {B, E, G}. Our tree diagram also tells us that it is impossible to get from any state in this set to a state not in this set. Thus, {B, E, G} is also a closed set of states.

(iii) Consider state C. We can go from C to C or J. The tree diagram is:

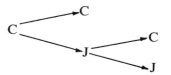

Thus {C, J} is a closed set of states.

We have already taken care of states D and E in parts (i) and (ii).

(iv) Consider state F. We can get to states A, B, C, E, K, and L from F. From parts (i), (ii), and (iii) we know that we cannot get to state F from any of states A, B, C, or E. We see that we can get from state K into state F. Since L is absorbing, we cannot get from L to anywhere. Now is {F, K} a closed set of states? No. Although you can get between any two states in this set you can also get to states not in this set. It follows that F does not belong to a closed set of states. Such a state is said to be **transient**.

(v) Consider state K. Since we can get from K to B but not vice versa, K is also transient.

(vi) State L is absorbing. However, one can get from state L to state L and to no other states. Thus {L} is a closed set of states.

Why?

In any finite Markov chain, the closed *sets* of states behave like absorbing states toward the transient states. Since you cannot ever leave a closed set of states, and since everything in a transient state can get into some closed set of states, everything will eventually end up in one of the closed sets of states. These observations are the basis for the flow chart on page 210.

Problem 4

Calculate the long-range distribution of material in each closed set of states for the transition matrix in Problem 3, given the initial distribution.

$$[\; 12 \quad 10 \quad 18 \quad 6 \quad 3 \quad 45 \quad 4 \quad 20 \quad 32 \quad 16 \quad 15 \quad 8 \;]$$

Solution

There are 4 closed sets of states:

$$C_1 = \{A, D, H, I\}$$
$$C_2 = \{B, E, G\}$$
$$C_3 = \{C, J\}$$
$$C_4 = \{L\}$$

**To Determine the Limit Matrix
and the Final Distribution for a
Finite Markov Chain in Terms of
Closed Sets of States**

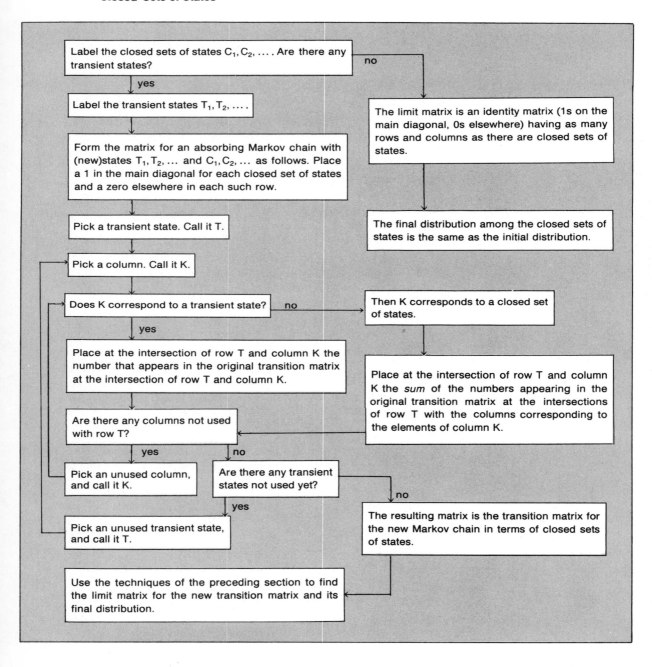

and two transient states:

$$T_1 = F$$
$$T_2 = K$$

Initially,

$$C_1 \text{ has } 12+6+20+32 = 70,$$
$$C_2 \text{ has } 10+3+4 = 17,$$
$$C_3 \text{ has } 18+16 = 34,$$
$$C_4 \text{ has } 8,$$
$$T_1 \text{ has } 45,$$
$$\text{and} \quad T_2 \text{ has } 15.$$

So the initial distribution matrix for the new chain will be

$$\begin{bmatrix} 70 & 17 & 34 & 8 & 45 & 15 \end{bmatrix}$$

Since the chain itself is absorbing, the new transition matrix reads, in part:

$$
\begin{array}{c}
\\ C_1 \\ C_2 \\ C_3 \\ C_4 \\ T_1 \\ T_2
\end{array}
\begin{array}{cccccc}
C_1 & C_2 & C_3 & C_4 & T_1 & T_2 \\
\left[\begin{array}{cccccc}
1 & 0 & 0 & 0 & 0 & 0 \\
0 & 1 & 0 & 0 & 0 & 0 \\
0 & 0 & 1 & 0 & 0 & 0 \\
0 & 0 & 0 & 1 & 0 & 0 \\
 & & & & & \\
 & & & & &
\end{array}\right]
\end{array}
$$

From the original matrix we see that $T_1$ sends

$$\tfrac{1}{6} + 0 + 0 + 0 = \tfrac{1}{6} \text{ to } C_1$$
$$\tfrac{1}{6} + \tfrac{1}{6} + 0 \quad = \tfrac{1}{3} \text{ to } C_2$$
$$\tfrac{1}{6} + 0 \quad\quad = \tfrac{1}{6} \text{ to } C_3$$
$$\tfrac{1}{6} \quad\quad\quad = \tfrac{1}{6} \text{ to } C_4$$
$$\tfrac{1}{6} \quad\quad\quad = \tfrac{1}{6} \text{ to } T_2$$

and $T_2$ sends

$$0 + 0 + 0 + \tfrac{1}{8} = \tfrac{1}{8} \text{ to } C_1$$
$$\tfrac{1}{8} + 0 + 0 \quad = \tfrac{1}{8} \text{ to } C_2$$
$$0 + \tfrac{1}{4} \quad\quad = \tfrac{1}{4} \text{ to } C_3$$
$$\tfrac{1}{8} \quad\quad\quad = \tfrac{1}{8} \text{ to } C_4$$
$$\tfrac{3}{8} \quad\quad\quad = \tfrac{3}{8} \text{ to } T_1$$

Thus, we complete the transition matrix

$$
\begin{array}{c}
\\
C_1 \\
C_2 \\
C_3 \\
C_4 \\
T_1 \\
T_2
\end{array}
\begin{array}{c}
\begin{array}{cccccc}
C_1 & C_2 & C_3 & C_4 & T_1 & T_2
\end{array} \\
\left[
\begin{array}{cccccc}
1 & 0 & 0 & 0 & 0 & 0 \\
0 & 1 & 0 & 0 & 0 & 0 \\
0 & 0 & 1 & 0 & 0 & 0 \\
0 & 0 & 0 & 1 & 0 & 0 \\
\frac{1}{6} & \frac{1}{3} & \frac{1}{6} & \frac{1}{6} & 0 & \frac{1}{6} \\
\frac{1}{8} & \frac{1}{8} & \frac{1}{4} & \frac{1}{8} & \frac{3}{8} & 0
\end{array}
\right]
\end{array}
$$

We now apply the technique of the previous section, which in this case involves solving the system

$$
\left[
\begin{array}{cccccc}
\frac{1}{6} & \frac{1}{3} & \frac{1}{6} & \frac{1}{6} & -1 & \frac{1}{6} \\
\frac{1}{8} & \frac{1}{8} & \frac{1}{4} & \frac{1}{8} & \frac{3}{8} & -1
\end{array}
\right]
$$

The result is

$$
x_5 = \tfrac{1}{5}x_1 + \tfrac{17}{45}x_2 + \tfrac{2}{9}x_3 + \tfrac{1}{5}x_4
$$

$$
x_6 = \tfrac{1}{5}x_1 + \tfrac{4}{15}x_2 + \tfrac{1}{3}x_3 + \tfrac{1}{5}x_4
$$

and the limit matrix is

We have omitted rows that consist entirely of zeroes.

$$
\left[
\begin{array}{cccccc}
1 & 0 & 0 & 0 & 0 & 0 \\
0 & 1 & 0 & 0 & 0 & 0 \\
0 & 0 & 1 & 0 & 0 & 0 \\
0 & 0 & 0 & 1 & 0 & 0 \\
\frac{1}{5} & \frac{17}{45} & \frac{2}{9} & \frac{1}{5} & 0 & 0 \\
\frac{1}{5} & \frac{4}{15} & \frac{1}{3} & \frac{1}{5} & 0 & 0
\end{array}
\right]
$$

We multiply

$$
\begin{bmatrix} 70 & 17 & 34 & 8 & 45 & 15 \end{bmatrix}
\left[
\begin{array}{cccccc}
1 & 0 & 0 & 0 & 0 & 0 \\
0 & 1 & 0 & 0 & 0 & 0 \\
0 & 0 & 1 & 0 & 0 & 0 \\
0 & 0 & 0 & 1 & 0 & 0 \\
\frac{1}{5} & \frac{17}{45} & \frac{2}{9} & \frac{1}{5} & 0 & 0 \\
\frac{1}{5} & \frac{4}{15} & \frac{1}{3} & \frac{1}{5} & 0 & 0
\end{array}
\right]
$$

Note that we are not saying, for example, how many each of A, D, H, and I gets in the long run. Collectively, they get 82. In fact, material keeps cycling around among A, D, H, and I, and the amount in each of these states never settles down.

$$
= \begin{bmatrix} 82 & 38 & 49 & 20 & 0 & 0 \end{bmatrix}
$$

to obtain the final distribution. We see that, of the 189 objects present initially, 82 will, in the long run, be distributed among states A, D, H, and I; 38 among B, E, and G; 49 between C and J; and 20 at L.

**Irreducible Chains**

Of course, you must also be able to get from a state back to itself. Note that if a chain has an absorbing state, that is, a 1 on the main diagonal, it cannot be irreducible.

A Markov chain is **irreducible** if all its states are in the same closed set of states; that is, it is irreducible if one can get from any state to any state in some number of transitions. The following can be shown.

Every irreducible finite Markov chain is either regular or periodic.

Theoretically, it is possible to tell if a chain is regular by raising its transition matrix to powers. But if you have already found that the chain is irreducible, there is an easier method, which we present in the following flow chart.

**To Determine Whether an Irreducible Markov Chain Is Regular or Periodic**

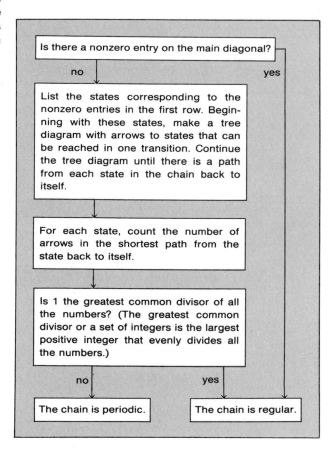

Problem 5    Determine whether the following irreducible chain is regular or periodic

$$
\begin{array}{c c}
 & \begin{array}{c c c c c} A & B & C & D & E \end{array} \\
\begin{array}{c} A \\ B \\ C \\ D \\ E \end{array} &
\left[\begin{array}{c c c c c}
0 & \frac{1}{3} & \frac{1}{3} & \frac{1}{3} & 0 \\
1 & 0 & 0 & 0 & 0 \\
0 & 0 & 0 & 0 & 1 \\
0 & 0 & 0 & 0 & 1 \\
1 & 0 & 0 & 0 & 0
\end{array}\right]
\end{array}
$$

Solution    Here is the tree diagram required by the flow chart.

$$
B \to A \overset{\nearrow B \to A}{\underset{\searrow D \to E}{\to C \to E}}
$$

We do not actually need to complete the fourth stage to obtain the required information.

$$
C \to E \to A \to C \overset{\nearrow B}{\underset{\searrow D}{\to E}}
$$

$$
D \to E \to A \overset{\nearrow B}{\underset{\searrow D}{\to C}}
$$

Here are the shortest paths:

| From | Path | Length |
|------|------|--------|
| A | A→B→A | 2 |
| B | B→A→B | 2 |
| C | C→E→A→C | 3 |
| D | D→E→A→D | 3 |
| E | E→A→C→E | 3 |

Since 1 is the largest integer that evenly divides 2 and 3, the chain is regular. In fact, the sixth power of the transition matrix is

$$
\frac{1}{27}
\begin{bmatrix}
13 & 4 & 4 & 4 & 2 \\
12 & 1 & 1 & 1 & 12 \\
3 & 6 & 6 & 6 & 6 \\
3 & 6 & 6 & 6 & 6 \\
12 & 1 & 1 & 1 & 12
\end{bmatrix}
$$

Problem 6    Determine whether the following irreducible chain is regular or periodic.

$$
\begin{array}{c c c c c c}
 & A & B & C & D & E \\
\begin{array}{c} A \\ B \\ C \\ D \\ E \end{array} &
\left[\begin{array}{c c c c c}
0 & \frac{1}{2} & 0 & 0 & \frac{1}{2} \\
0 & 0 & 1 & 0 & 0 \\
0 & 0 & 0 & 1 & 0 \\
1 & 0 & 0 & 0 & 0 \\
1 & 0 & 0 & 0 & 0
\end{array}\right]
\end{array}
$$

**Solution** Here is the tree diagram required by the flow chart.

$$
B{\rightarrow}C{\rightarrow}D{\rightarrow}A
\begin{array}{l} \nearrow B{\rightarrow}C{\rightarrow}D \\ \searrow E \end{array}
$$

$$
E{\rightarrow}A
\begin{array}{l} \nearrow B \\ \searrow E{\rightarrow}A \end{array}
$$

Here are the shortest paths.

| From | Path | Length |
|------|------|--------|
| A | A→E→A | 2 |
| B | B→C→D→A→B | 4 |
| C | C→D→A→B→C | 4 |
| D | D→A→B→C→D | 4 |
| E | E→A→E | 2 |

Since 2 divides evenly into 2 and 4, the chain is periodic.

**Ergodic Chains**

If a matrix has an absorbing state, this state by itself forms a closed set of states with the regular transition matrix [1].

Given a finite Markov chain it is now an easy matter to determine whether or not it is ergodic. First, list the closed set of states. Each of these sets forms a Markov chain of its own. If each of the closed sets of states forms a regular Markov chain, the original chain is an **ergodic chain**. Otherwise, one or more of the closed sets of states forms a periodic Markov chain, and the given chain is not ergodic.

**Problem 7** Determine the long range effect on the initial distribution

| A | B | C | D | E | F | G | H |
|------|------|------|------|------|------|------|------|
| 20,020 | 16,328 | 20,391 | 42,389 | 21,386 | 45,034 | 14,219 | 60,060 |

| I | J | K | L | M | N | O | P |
|------|------|------|------|------|------|------|------|
| 18,654 | 11,285 | 13,274 | 21,390 | 10,010 | 20,914 | 39,268 | 17,334 |

of the transition matrix

|   | A | B | C | D | E | F | G | H | I | J | K | L | M | N | O | P |
|---|---|---|---|---|---|---|---|---|---|---|---|---|---|---|---|---|
| A | 0 | $\frac{1}{4}$ | $\frac{1}{8}$ | 0 | $\frac{1}{8}$ | 0 | 0 | $\frac{3}{8}$ | 0 | 0 | $\frac{1}{8}$ | 0 | 0 | 0 | 0 | 0 |
| B | 0 | 0 | 0 | 0 | 0 | 0 | $\frac{1}{3}$ | 0 | 0 | $\frac{1}{3}$ | 0 | 0 | 0 | $\frac{1}{3}$ | 0 | 0 |
| C | 0 | 0 | 0 | 0 | 0 | 0 | 0 | 0 | 0 | 0 | $\frac{1}{3}$ | $\frac{2}{3}$ | 0 | 0 | 0 | 0 |
| D | 0 | 0 | 0 | $\frac{1}{5}$ | 0 | $\frac{4}{5}$ | 0 | 0 | 0 | 0 | 0 | 0 | 0 | 0 | 0 | 0 |
| E | 0 | 0 | 0 | 0 | $\frac{1}{2}$ | 0 | 0 | 0 | $\frac{1}{2}$ | 0 | 0 | 0 | 0 | 0 | 0 | 0 |
| F | 0 | 0 | 0 | $\frac{3}{5}$ | 0 | $\frac{2}{5}$ | 0 | 0 | 0 | 0 | 0 | 0 | 0 | 0 | 0 | 0 |
| G | 0 | 1 | 0 | 0 | 0 | 0 | 0 | 0 | 0 | 0 | 0 | 0 | 0 | 0 | 0 | 0 |
| H | $\frac{1}{9}$ | $\frac{2}{9}$ | 0 | 0 | $\frac{1}{9}$ | 0 | 0 | 0 | 0 | 0 | $\frac{2}{9}$ | 0 | $\frac{1}{9}$ | $\frac{1}{9}$ | 0 | $\frac{1}{9}$ |
| I | 0 | 0 | 0 | 0 | $\frac{1}{2}$ | 0 | 0 | 0 | $\frac{1}{2}$ | 0 | 0 | 0 | 0 | 0 | 0 | 0 |
| J | 0 | 0 | 0 | 0 | 0 | 0 | 0 | 0 | 0 | 0 | 0 | 0 | 0 | 0 | 0 | 1 |
| K | 0 | 0 | $\frac{1}{4}$ | 0 | 0 | 0 | 0 | 0 | 0 | 0 | $\frac{1}{2}$ | $\frac{1}{4}$ | 0 | 0 | 0 | 0 |
| L | 0 | 0 | $\frac{1}{3}$ | 0 | 0 | 0 | 0 | 0 | 0 | 0 | $\frac{2}{3}$ | 0 | 0 | 0 | 0 | 0 |
| M | $\frac{1}{4}$ | 0 | 0 | 0 | $\frac{1}{4}$ | 0 | 0 | 0 | 0 | $\frac{1}{4}$ | 0 | 0 | 0 | 0 | 0 | $\frac{1}{4}$ |
| N | 0 | 0 | 0 | 0 | 0 | 0 | 0 | 0 | 0 | 0 | 0 | 0 | 0 | 0 | 0 | 1 |
| O | 0 | 0 | 0 | 0 | 0 | 0 | 0 | 0 | 0 | 0 | 0 | 0 | 0 | 0 | 1 | 0 |
| P | 0 | 1 | 0 | 0 | 0 | 0 | 0 | 0 | 0 | 0 | 0 | 0 | 0 | 0 | 0 | 0 |

**Solution**

**Step 1**  Determine the closed sets of states and the transient states.

(i) Here is a tree diagram for state A:

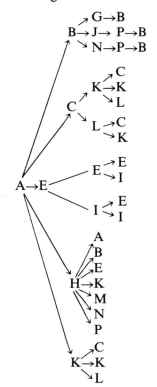

By carefully examining this tree diagram you should be able to locate the following closed sets of states:

$$\{B,G,J,N, P\},\{C,K,L\},\{E,I\}$$

and the following transient states:

$$A,H.$$

(ii) Here is a diagram for the next state, that we have not yet discussed.

Thus, $\{D,F\}$ is a closed set.

(iii) Next we consider state M. Since it is possible to get from M to the closed set $\{E,I\}$, and since M is not in this closed set, M is transient.

(iv) O is obviously an absorbing state, so $\{O\}$ is a closed set.

Step 2    Write the transition matrices for each of the closed sets, and determine their share in the initial distribution.

|       | B | G | J | N | P |  |
|-------|---|---|---|---|---|---|
| B | 0 | $\frac{1}{3}$ | $\frac{1}{3}$ | $\frac{1}{3}$ | 0 | 16,328 |
| G | 1 | 0 | 0 | 0 | 0 | 14,219 |
| $C_1$: J | 0 | 0 | 0 | 0 | 1 | 11,285 |
| N | 0 | 0 | 0 | 0 | 1 | 20,914 |
| P | 1 | 0 | 0 | 0 | 0 | 17,334 |

Total 80,080

|       | C | K | L |  |
|-------|---|---|---|---|
| C | 0 | $\frac{1}{3}$ | $\frac{2}{3}$ | 20,391 |
| $C_2$: K | $\frac{1}{4}$ | $\frac{1}{2}$ | $\frac{1}{4}$ | 13,274 |
| L | $\frac{1}{3}$ | $\frac{2}{3}$ | 0 | 21,390 |

Total 55,055

|       | E | I |  |
|-------|---|---|---|
| $C_3$: E | $\frac{1}{2}$ | $\frac{1}{2}$ | 21,386 |
| I | $\frac{1}{2}$ | $\frac{1}{2}$ | 18,654 |

Total 40,040

|       | D | F |  |
|-------|---|---|---|
| $C_4$: D | $\frac{1}{5}$ | $\frac{4}{5}$ | 42,389 |
| F | $\frac{3}{5}$ | $\frac{2}{5}$ | 45,034 |

Total 87,423

|       | O |  |
|-------|---|---|
| $C_5$: O | [1] | 39,268 |

Total 39,268

In Problem 5 we determined that $C_1$ was regular. The other closed sets are obviously regular. Hence the chain is ergodic.

Step 3 Compute the long-range distributions for each of the closed sets using the technique of Section 3.4. Here are the results.

$$C_1: \quad \begin{bmatrix} \frac{3}{8} & \frac{1}{8} & \frac{1}{8} & \frac{1}{8} & \frac{1}{4} \end{bmatrix}$$

$$C_2: \quad \begin{bmatrix} \frac{12}{55} & \frac{28}{55} & \frac{15}{55} \end{bmatrix}$$

$$C_3: \quad \begin{bmatrix} \frac{1}{2} & \frac{1}{2} \end{bmatrix}$$

$$C_4: \quad \begin{bmatrix} \frac{3}{7} & \frac{4}{7} \end{bmatrix}$$

$$C_5: \quad \begin{bmatrix} 1 \end{bmatrix}$$

Step 4 Label the transient states $T_1 = A$, $T_2 = H$, and $T_3 = M$ and proceed as in Problem 4.

|       | $C_1$ | $C_2$ | $C_3$ | $C_4$ | $C_5$ | $T_1$ | $T_2$ | $T_3$ |
|-------|-------|-------|-------|-------|-------|-------|-------|-------|
| $C_1$ | 1 | 0 | 0 | 0 | 0 | 0 | 0 | 0 |
| $C_2$ | 0 | 1 | 0 | 0 | 0 | 0 | 0 | 0 |
| $C_3$ | 0 | 0 | 1 | 0 | 0 | 0 | 0 | 0 |
| $C_4$ | 0 | 0 | 0 | 1 | 0 | 0 | 0 | 0 |
| $C_5$ | 0 | 0 | 0 | 0 | 1 | 0 | 0 | 0 |
| $T_1$ | $\frac{1}{4}$ | $\frac{1}{4}$ | $\frac{1}{8}$ | 0 | 0 | 0 | $\frac{3}{8}$ | 0 |
| $T_2$ | $\frac{4}{9}$ | $\frac{2}{9}$ | $\frac{1}{9}$ | 0 | 0 | $\frac{1}{9}$ | 0 | $\frac{1}{9}$ |
| $T_3$ | $\frac{1}{2}$ | 0 | $\frac{1}{4}$ | 0 | 0 | $\frac{1}{4}$ | 0 | 0 |

We see that $C_4$ and $C_5$ are isolated absorbing states, so we remove them and consider the smaller matrix:

|       | $C_1$ | $C_2$ | $C_3$ | $T_1$ | $T_2$ | $T_3$ |
|-------|-------|-------|-------|-------|-------|-------|
| $C_1$ | 1 | 0 | 0 | 0 | 0 | 0 |
| $C_2$ | 0 | 1 | 0 | 0 | 0 | 0 |
| $C_3$ | 0 | 0 | 1 | 0 | 0 | 0 |
| $T_1$ | $\frac{1}{4}$ | $\frac{1}{4}$ | $\frac{1}{8}$ | 0 | $\frac{3}{8}$ | 0 |
| $T_2$ | $\frac{4}{9}$ | $\frac{2}{9}$ | $\frac{1}{9}$ | $\frac{1}{9}$ | 0 | $\frac{1}{9}$ |
| $T_3$ | $\frac{1}{2}$ | 0 | $\frac{1}{4}$ | $\frac{1}{4}$ | 0 | 0 |

Using the technique of the previous section we obtain the following limit matrix

$$
\begin{bmatrix}
1 & 0 & 0 & 0 & 0 & 0 \\
0 & 1 & 0 & 0 & 0 & 0 \\
0 & 0 & 1 & 0 & 0 & 0 \\
\frac{42}{91} & \frac{32}{91} & \frac{17}{91} & 0 & 0 & 0 \\
\frac{154}{273} & \frac{74}{273} & \frac{45}{273} & 0 & 0 & 0 \\
\frac{56}{91} & \frac{8}{91} & \frac{27}{91} & 0 & 0 & 0
\end{bmatrix}
$$

We compute

$$
\begin{bmatrix} 80{,}080 & 55{,}055 & 40{,}040 & 20{,}020 & 60{,}060 & 10{,}010 \end{bmatrix}
\begin{bmatrix}
1 & 0 & 0 & 0 & 0 & 0 \\
0 & 1 & 0 & 0 & 0 & 0 \\
0 & 0 & 1 & 0 & 0 & 0 \\
\frac{42}{91} & \frac{32}{91} & \frac{17}{91} & 0 & 0 & 0 \\
\frac{154}{273} & \frac{74}{273} & \frac{45}{273} & 0 & 0 & 0 \\
\frac{56}{91} & \frac{8}{91} & \frac{27}{91} & 0 & 0 & 0
\end{bmatrix}
$$

$$
= \begin{bmatrix} 129{,}360 & 79{,}255 & 56{,}650 & 0 & 0 \end{bmatrix}
$$

Therefore, the long-range distribution among closed sets of states is

$C_1$   129,360
$C_2$    79,255
$C_3$    56,650
$C_4$    87,423   (present initially)
$C_5$    39,268   (present initially)

**Step 5**   Distribute the quantities obtained in step 4 according to the fractions obtained in step 3.

State:          Final distribution.

$$
C_1 \begin{cases}
B \\
G \\
J \\
N \\
P
\end{cases}
\begin{array}{l}
48{,}510 = \tfrac{3}{8} \cdot 129{,}360 \\
16{,}170 = \tfrac{1}{8} \cdot 129{,}360 \\
16{,}170 = \tfrac{1}{8} \cdot 129{,}360 \\
16{,}170 = \tfrac{1}{8} \cdot 129{,}360 \\
32{,}340 = \tfrac{1}{4} \cdot 129{,}360
\end{array}
$$

$$C_2 \begin{cases} C & 17{,}292 = \frac{12}{55} \cdot 79{,}255 \\ K & 40{,}348 = \frac{28}{55} \cdot 79{,}255 \\ L & 21{,}615 = \frac{15}{55} \cdot 79{,}255 \end{cases}$$

$$C_3 \begin{cases} E & 28{,}325 = \frac{1}{2} \cdot 56{,}650 \\ I & 28{,}325 = \frac{1}{2} \cdot 56{,}650 \end{cases}$$

$$C_4 \begin{cases} D & 37{,}467 = \frac{3}{7} \cdot 87{,}423 \\ F & 49{,}956 = \frac{4}{7} \cdot 87{,}423 \end{cases}$$

$$C_5 \quad O \qquad 39{,}268$$

Alphabetically, we have finally

| State | Long-range quantity |
|-------|---------------------|
| A | 0 |
| B | 48,510 |
| C | 17,292 |
| D | 37,467 |
| E | 28,325 |
| F | 49,956 |
| G | 16,170 |
| H | 0 |
| I | 28,325 |
| J | 16,170 |
| K | 40,348 |
| L | 21,615 |
| M | 0 |
| N | 16,170 |
| O | 39,268 |
| P | 32,340 |

There are no fractions in this table because the authors arranged the numbers in the problem so that the answer would not involve fractions.

The long-range pattern for *periodic* closed sets is more difficult to determine. We will not discuss that problem in this text.

Exercises 3.5   The matrices in Exercises 1 through 6 are transition matrices for periodic Markov chains. Draw a tree diagram which indicates the flow of material governed by the chain.

1. $\begin{bmatrix} 0 & 1 & 0 \\ 0 & 0 & 1 \\ 1 & 0 & 0 \end{bmatrix}$

2. $\begin{bmatrix} 0 & 0 & 1 & 0 \\ 0 & 0 & 0 & 1 \\ 1 & 0 & 0 & 0 \\ 0 & 1 & 0 & 0 \end{bmatrix}$

3. $\begin{bmatrix} 0 & 1 & 0 & 0 & 0 \\ 0 & 0 & 0 & 1 & 0 \\ 0 & 0 & 0 & 0 & 1 \\ 1 & 0 & 0 & 0 & 0 \\ 0 & 0 & 1 & 0 & 0 \end{bmatrix}$

4. $\begin{bmatrix} 0 & 1 & 0 & 0 & 0 & 0 \\ 0 & 0 & 0 & 1 & 0 & 0 \\ 0 & 0 & 0 & 0 & 1 & 0 \\ 1 & 0 & 0 & 0 & 0 & 0 \\ 0 & 0 & 0 & 0 & 0 & 1 \\ 0 & 0 & 1 & 0 & 0 & 0 \end{bmatrix}$

5. $\begin{bmatrix} 0 & 1 & 0 & 0 & 0 \\ 0 & 0 & \frac{1}{2} & \frac{1}{4} & \frac{1}{4} \\ 1 & 0 & 0 & 0 & 0 \\ 1 & 0 & 0 & 0 & 0 \\ 1 & 0 & 0 & 0 & 0 \end{bmatrix}$

*6. $\begin{bmatrix} 0 & 0 & 1 & 0 & 0 & 0 & 0 \\ 0 & 0 & 0 & 0 & 0 & \frac{1}{2} & \frac{1}{2} \\ 0 & \frac{1}{3} & 0 & \frac{1}{3} & \frac{1}{3} & 0 & 0 \\ 0 & 0 & 0 & 0 & 0 & \frac{3}{4} & \frac{1}{4} \\ 0 & 0 & 0 & 0 & 0 & \frac{1}{3} & \frac{2}{3} \\ 1 & 0 & 0 & 0 & 0 & 0 & 0 \\ 1 & 0 & 0 & 0 & 0 & 0 & 0 \end{bmatrix}$

In Exercises 7 through 9 write the Markov matrix which describes the situation illustrated by the tree diagram.

7.

8.

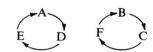

9.

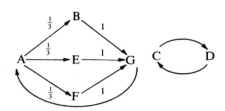

In Exercises 10 through 13 determine whether or not the given matrix is the transition matrix for a regular or periodic chain.

10.
$$\begin{bmatrix} 0 & \frac{1}{2} & \frac{1}{2} & 0 & 0 \\ 0 & 0 & 0 & \frac{1}{3} & \frac{2}{3} \\ 0 & 0 & 0 & 0 & 1 \\ 1 & 0 & 0 & 0 & 0 \\ 1 & 0 & 0 & 0 & 0 \end{bmatrix}$$

11.
$$\begin{bmatrix} 0 & \frac{1}{3} & 0 & 0 & \frac{1}{3} & 0 & \frac{1}{3} \\ 0 & 0 & \frac{1}{4} & \frac{1}{2} & 0 & \frac{1}{4} & 0 \\ 1 & 0 & 0 & 0 & 0 & 0 & 0 \\ 1 & 0 & 0 & 0 & 0 & 0 & 0 \\ 0 & 0 & 1 & 0 & 0 & 0 & 0 \\ \frac{1}{2} & \frac{1}{2} & 0 & 0 & 0 & 0 & 0 \\ 0 & 0 & 1 & 0 & 0 & 0 & 0 \end{bmatrix}$$

12.
$$\begin{bmatrix} 0 & 0 & 0 & 0 & 0 & 1 & 0 \\ 1 & 0 & 0 & 0 & 0 & 0 & 0 \\ 0 & \frac{1}{3} & 0 & \frac{1}{3} & 0 & 0 & \frac{1}{3} \\ 1 & 0 & 0 & 0 & 0 & 0 & 0 \\ 0 & \frac{1}{3} & 0 & \frac{1}{3} & 0 & 0 & \frac{1}{3} \\ \frac{1}{3} & 0 & \frac{1}{3} & 0 & \frac{1}{3} & 0 & 0 \\ 1 & 0 & 0 & 0 & 0 & 0 & 0 \end{bmatrix}$$

13.
$$\begin{bmatrix} 0 & \frac{1}{3} & 0 & 0 & \frac{1}{3} & 0 & \frac{1}{3} \\ 0 & 0 & \frac{1}{4} & \frac{1}{2} & 0 & \frac{1}{4} & 0 \\ 1 & 0 & 0 & 0 & 0 & 0 & 0 \\ 1 & 0 & 0 & 0 & 0 & 0 & 0 \\ 0 & 0 & 1 & 0 & 0 & 0 & 0 \\ 1 & 0 & 0 & 0 & 0 & 0 & 0 \\ 0 & 0 & 1 & 0 & 0 & 0 & 0 \end{bmatrix}$$

14. Find all closed sets of states for the following transition matrix.

|   | A | B | C | D | E | F | G | H | I | J | K | L |
|---|---|---|---|---|---|---|---|---|---|---|---|---|
| A | $\frac{1}{6}$ | $\frac{1}{3}$ | $\frac{1}{3}$ | 0 | 0 | 0 | 0 | 0 | 0 | 0 | 0 | $\frac{1}{6}$ |
| B | 0 | 0 | 0 | 0 | 1 | 0 | 0 | 0 | 0 | 0 | 0 | 0 |
| C | 0 | 0 | $\frac{1}{8}$ | 0 | 0 | 0 | $\frac{1}{8}$ | 0 | 0 | 0 | $\frac{3}{4}$ | 0 |
| D | 0 | 0 | 0 | 1 | 0 | 0 | 0 | 0 | 0 | 0 | 0 | 0 |
| E | 0 | 0 | 0 | 0 | 0 | 0 | 0 | 1 | 0 | 0 | 0 | 0 |
| F | 0 | 0 | 0 | $\frac{2}{3}$ | 0 | $\frac{1}{6}$ | 0 | 0 | $\frac{1}{6}$ | 0 | 0 | 0 |
| G | 0 | 0 | $\frac{1}{2}$ | 0 | 0 | 0 | $\frac{1}{4}$ | 0 | 0 | 0 | $\frac{1}{4}$ | 0 |
| H | 0 | 0 | 0 | 0 | 0 | 0 | 0 | 0 | 0 | 1 | 0 | 0 |
| I | 0 | 0 | 0 | 0 | 0 | $\frac{1}{3}$ | 0 | 0 | $\frac{2}{3}$ | 0 | 0 | 0 |
| J | 0 | 1 | 0 | 0 | 0 | 0 | 0 | 0 | 0 | 0 | 0 | 0 |
| K | 0 | 0 | $\frac{3}{4}$ | 0 | 0 | 0 | $\frac{1}{4}$ | 0 | 0 | 0 | 0 | 0 |
| L | $\frac{1}{8}$ | $\frac{1}{8}$ | $\frac{1}{8}$ | $\frac{1}{8}$ | 0 | 0 | 0 | $\frac{3}{8}$ | 0 | 0 | 0 | $\frac{1}{8}$ |

15. Determine the long-range effect of the transition matrix

$$
\begin{bmatrix}
\frac{1}{4} & \frac{3}{4} & 0 & 0 & 0 & 0 & 0 \\
\frac{1}{2} & \frac{1}{2} & 0 & 0 & 0 & 0 & 0 \\
0 & 0 & \frac{2}{3} & \frac{1}{6} & \frac{1}{6} & 0 & 0 \\
0 & 0 & \frac{1}{4} & \frac{1}{2} & \frac{1}{4} & 0 & 0 \\
0 & 0 & \frac{1}{8} & \frac{7}{8} & 0 & 0 & 0 \\
0 & 0 & \frac{1}{4} & \frac{1}{12} & \frac{1}{6} & \frac{1}{4} & \frac{1}{4} \\
0 & 0 & 0 & 0 & 0 & 0 & 1
\end{bmatrix}
$$

on the initial distribution [285  60  300  600  480  690  345].

16. What is the effect of the transition matrix

$$
\begin{bmatrix}
0 & \frac{1}{3} & 0 & \frac{1}{3} & 0 & \frac{1}{3} & 0 & 0 \\
0 & 0 & \frac{1}{5} & 0 & \frac{3}{5} & 0 & 0 & \frac{1}{5} \\
0 & 0 & \frac{1}{4} & 0 & 0 & \frac{3}{4} & 0 & 0 \\
0 & \frac{1}{2} & 0 & 0 & 0 & 0 & \frac{1}{2} & 0 \\
\frac{1}{8} & 0 & \frac{3}{4} & 0 & 0 & 0 & 0 & \frac{1}{8} \\
0 & 0 & \frac{1}{2} & 0 & 0 & \frac{1}{2} & 0 & 0 \\
1 & 0 & 0 & 0 & 0 & 0 & 0 & 0 \\
0 & 0 & 0 & 1 & 0 & 0 & 0 & 0
\end{bmatrix}
$$

on the initial distribution

[217  322  151  282  397  242  389  245]?

17. What is the effect of the transition matrix

|   | A | B | C | D | E | F | G | H | I | J | K | L |
|---|---|---|---|---|---|---|---|---|---|---|---|---|
| A | $\frac{1}{4}$ | 0 | 0 | 0 | 0 | 0 | 0 | 0 | $\frac{1}{2}$ | $\frac{1}{4}$ | 0 | 0 |
| B | 0 | $\frac{7}{8}$ | 0 | $\frac{1}{8}$ | 0 | 0 | 0 | 0 | 0 | 0 | 0 | 0 |
| C | 0 | 0 | $\frac{1}{2}$ | 0 | 0 | $\frac{1}{4}$ | 0 | $\frac{1}{4}$ | 0 | 0 | 0 | 0 |
| D | 0 | 0 | 0 | $\frac{15}{16}$ | 0 | 0 | 0 | 0 | 0 | 0 | $\frac{1}{16}$ | 0 |
| E | 0 | 0 | 0 | 0 | $\frac{1}{6}$ | 0 | $\frac{5}{6}$ | 0 | 0 | 0 | 0 | 0 |
| F | 0 | 0 | 1 | 0 | 0 | 0 | 0 | 0 | 0 | 0 | 0 | 0 |
| G | 0 | 0 | 0 | 0 | $\frac{1}{2}$ | 0 | $\frac{1}{6}$ | 0 | 0 | 0 | 0 | $\frac{1}{3}$ |
| H | 0 | 0 | $\frac{1}{3}$ | 0 | 0 | $\frac{1}{3}$ | 0 | $\frac{1}{3}$ | 0 | 0 | 0 | 0 |
| I | $\frac{1}{2}$ | $\frac{1}{12}$ | $\frac{1}{12}$ | $\frac{1}{12}$ | 0 | $\frac{1}{12}$ | 0 | $\frac{1}{12}$ | 0 | 0 | $\frac{1}{12}$ | 0 |
| J | 0 | 0 | $\frac{1}{4}$ | 0 | 0 | 0 | $\frac{1}{4}$ | $\frac{1}{4}$ | 0 | 0 | 0 | $\frac{1}{4}$ |
| K | 0 | $\frac{7}{8}$ | 0 | 0 | 0 | 0 | 0 | 0 | 0 | 0 | $\frac{1}{8}$ | 0 |
| L | 0 | 0 | 0 | 0 | $\frac{3}{5}$ | 0 | $\frac{1}{5}$ | 0 | 0 | 0 | $\frac{1}{5}$ | 0 |

on the initial distribution given in the following tabulation:

| | |
|---|---|
| A: | 171,248 |
| B: | 200,000 |
| C: | 360,992 |
| D: | 140,000 |
| E: | 170,000 |
| F: | 304,000 |
| G: | 0 |
| H: | 20,000 |
| I: | 513,744 |
| J: | 171,248 |
| K: | 2,496 |
| L: | 1,248 |

*18. I operate one of two Guzzler Gas stations in Amnestia, Mississippi. There are two Phillerup stations and one Big Bill station. Our customers change their loyalties each week according to the following diagram:

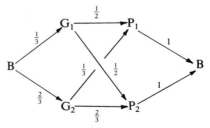

where both B's denote the same Big Bill's; $G_1$ denotes my station; $G_2$ denotes the other Guzzler; $P_1$ and $P_2$ denote the Phillerup stations. Last week we had the following numbers of customers:

$$\begin{array}{ll} B & 261 \\ G_1 & 0 \\ G_2 & 0 \\ P_1 & 434 \\ P_2 & 682 \end{array}$$

I am getting tired of having no customers every third week. I devise two sure-fire schemes to change all this.

*Scheme 1* will cause all my customers who usually go to $P_1$ to go back to B each week.

*Scheme 2* will cause half my customers who usually go to $P_2$ to go back to B.

I will implement one of these schemes this week. Which one is better?

**Section 3.6**
**Summary**

Many experiments can usefully be considered multistage processes and be illustrated by *tree diagrams*. The events reached by the first set of branches in a tree diagram form a *partition* of the sample space. If $A_1, A_2, \ldots, A_n$ are a partition of a sample space and if B is an event in the sample space, then $A_1 \cap B, A_2 \cap B, \ldots, A_n \cap B$ is a partition of B, and

$$P(B) = P(A_1 \cap B) + P(A_2 \cap B) + \cdots + P(A_n \cap B). \qquad \mathbf{1}$$

Combining equation **1** with our results on conditional probability, we obtain *Bayes' formula*,

It is easier to use a tree diagram than this formula to solve a problem.

$$P(A_i \mid B) = \frac{P(B \mid A_i)P(A_i)}{P(B \mid A_1)P(A_1) + P(B \mid A_2)P(A_2) + \cdots P(B \mid A_n)P(A_n)}, \qquad \mathbf{2}$$

where we must assume $P(B), P(A_1), P(A_2), \ldots,$ and $P(A_n)$ are not zero.

A special type of multistage process is the *Markov chain*, which involves the transition of material among various states. If a given Markov chain is *regular* or *ergodic*, then every initial distribution approaches the same long-range distribution. For *absorbing* Markov chains the long-range distribution of material among absorbing states depends upon the initial distribution. For *periodic* Markov chains the material cycles around and does not approach a long-range distribution.

TERMS

Partition, page 154
Bayes' formula, page 166
Markov chain, page 170
Distribution matrix, page 174
Regular Markov chain, page 183
Absorbing state, page 184
Absorbing Markov chain, page 184
Periodic Markov chain, pages 201–204
Closed set of states, page 207
Irreducible Markov chain, page 213
Ergodic Markov chain, page 215

COMPUTATIONAL TECHNIQUES

Flow chart to determine the final
    distribution of a regular Markov chain, page 189
Flow chart to determine the limit matrix
    for a given absorbing transition matrix, page 197
Flow chart to determine the long-range
    distribution for a given initial distribution
    and given absorbing Markov chain, page 199
Flow chart to determine the limit matrix
    and distribution for a Markov chain
    in terms of closed sets of states, page 210
Flow chart to determine whether an irreducible
    Markov chain is regular or periodic, page 213

**Review Exercises**     Reread the chapter; then do these exercises without looking back. Answers to all these exercises are in Appendix C.

1. A PHE warehouse in Miami, Florida, has four rooms containing cases of concentrated orange juice. Room A contains 1,000 cases, B, 1,100 cases, C, 900 cases, and D, 1,400 cases. Each case has 2 layers of canned concentrate, 12 cans per layer. The wholesaler thinks that the PHE inspector will choose a can from the top layer four times as often as from the bottom, so he has distributed low-quality juice as follows: in room A, 6 low-quality cans in each bottom layer, 2 in each top; in B, 5 in the bottom, 1 in the top; in C, 4 per case at random; in half of D, 7 in the bottom, none in the top. All the remaining cans are high quality. Here are three different assumptions about the inspector:

   (a) The wholesaler was right. The inspector chooses the room, case, and can in the layer at random.

   (b) The inspector chooses everything at random.

(c) The inspector chooses A, B, C equally often, but D half the time, and everything else at random.

What are the chances that the inspector finds a low quality can in one inspection

(a) under assumption (a)?

(b) under assumption (b)?

(c) under assumption (c)?

2. Suppose the sample space S consists of the numbers from 1 to 10. Which of the following are partitions of S?

   (a) 1, multiples of 2, multiples of 3, multiples of 5.

   (b) Numbers less than 6, even numbers greater than 6, multiples of 3 or 7.

   (c) 1 and every third number after it, 2 and every third number after it, multiples of 3.

3. "I am very sorry, Mr. Gregory. You did not pass our aptitude test so you will not get the job. However, an independent survey indicates that only 30% of our applicants are qualified. In fact, we have found that only $\frac{1}{100}$ of those who really are qualified fail the exam." Alan left the office, but he was really upset with himself. His friend, the shop steward, had told him that even if you weren't qualified there was a 90% chance you would pass the test anyway. What is the probability that Alan really is qualified for the job?

4. We have two machines. The old machine produces 25% of our output. The new machine produces the rest. The inspectors inspect each machine's output. They have a greater respect for the old machine and tend to be less careful with its production. Of the items that pass, $\frac{1}{3}$ of the old machine's production is defective and $\frac{1}{10}$ of the new machine's production is defective. All the items are finally mixed together. I got a defective item. What is the probability the new machine made it?

5. Right now Shoddy Mfg. and Shiny Imports each have 1,000 customers. Each month $\frac{4}{5}$ of Shoddy's customers switch to Shiny and $\frac{1}{10}$ of Shiny's switch to Shoddy. Shoddy must have at least 225 customers to survive. How long do they have?

6. Compute the limit matrix for the transition matrix

$$\begin{bmatrix} \frac{1}{2} & 0 & \frac{1}{2} \\ 0 & \frac{1}{3} & \frac{2}{3} \\ \frac{1}{4} & \frac{1}{2} & \frac{1}{4} \end{bmatrix}.$$

What is the long-range effect of this transition matrix on the initial distribution $[\frac{1}{8} \quad \frac{3}{8} \quad \frac{1}{2}]$?

7. (a) What is an absorbing state of a Markov chain?

   (b) True or False? Every Markov chain that has one or more absorbing states is an absorbing Markov chain.

8. Compute the limit matrix for the transition matrix

$$\begin{bmatrix} 1 & 0 & 0 & 0 \\ 0 & 1 & 0 & 0 \\ 0 & \frac{1}{2} & \frac{3}{8} & \frac{1}{8} \\ 0 & 0 & 0 & 1 \end{bmatrix}$$

What is the long-range effect of this transition matrix on the initial distribution $[\frac{1}{6} \quad \frac{1}{3} \quad \frac{1}{3} \quad \frac{1}{6}]$?

9. What is the distribution of the Markov chain with transition matrix

$$\begin{bmatrix} 0 & 1 & 0 & 0 & 0 \\ 1 & 0 & 0 & 0 & 0 \\ 0 & 0 & 0 & 1 & 0 \\ 0 & 0 & 0 & 0 & 1 \\ 0 & 0 & 1 & 0 & 0 \end{bmatrix}$$

and the initial distribution $[\frac{1}{10} \quad \frac{3}{7} \quad \frac{5}{14} \quad \frac{2}{35} \quad \frac{3}{70}]$ after 723 transitions?

10. Find the long-range effect of the Markov chain with transition matrix

$$\begin{bmatrix} \frac{1}{4} & \frac{1}{4} & \frac{1}{2} & 0 & 0 \\ 0 & \frac{1}{2} & 0 & \frac{1}{2} & 0 \\ 0 & 0 & \frac{3}{4} & 0 & \frac{1}{4} \\ 0 & \frac{2}{3} & 0 & \frac{1}{3} & 0 \\ 0 & 0 & \frac{1}{3} & 0 & \frac{2}{3} \end{bmatrix}$$

upon the distribution $[\frac{1}{5} \quad \frac{1}{5} \quad \frac{1}{5} \quad \frac{1}{5} \quad \frac{1}{5}]$.

## Supplementary Exercises

1. Write out *all* partitions of the sample space {red, white, blue}.
2. "While only one person in 1,000 has this particular disease, I'm worried that you might have it, since you do have all the symptoms." The doctor continued, "If you didn't have the disease, there is only a $\frac{1}{100}$ chance you would have all the symptoms, and, if you had the disease, there is only a $\frac{1}{1,000}$ chance you wouldn't have *all* the symptoms." What is the probability that I have the disease?
3. My city likes to audit income tax returns. If you are audited one year, the probability is $\frac{3}{4}$ that you will be audited again the next year. If you are not audited one year, the probability is $\frac{3}{4}$ that you will not be audited again the next year. I was not audited last year. What is the probability that I will be audited within three years?
4. When my cub scout troop visits the penny arcade, initially $\frac{1}{3}$ use the movie viewers, $\frac{1}{3}$ try the fortune teller, $\frac{1}{6}$ use the sand loader, and $\frac{1}{6}$ try the strength tester. I notice that once they start on the movie viewers or sand loader they stay there the rest of the day. While nobody ever tries the fortune teller twice in a row, they are equally likely to try any of the other three amusements after having their fortune told. Finally, having tried the strength tester, they are

As a matter of proper dress, the teams wear ascots.

equally likely to try any of the four amusements next. I have 66 cub scouts in my troop. Approximately how many can I expect to find at each amusement at the end of the day?

5. Teams A and B play a series of games with no ties. A has a 75% chance of winning the first game and a 50% chance of winning each later game, except if B wins 2 in a row A will be sure to win the next game after that, if it is played. The first team to win a total of 3 games wins the series.

   (a) What are the chances B will win?

   (b) What are the chances of a five-game series?

   (c) What are the chances A will win the series in 4 games?

6. Teams A, B, and C engage in a series of three-way contests. A has a 50% chance of winning each contest. If B wins a contest, it has a 50% chance of winning the next contest. If C wins a contest, it has a 40% chance of winning the next contest. The first team to win two contests wins the series. What are the chances that C will win the series?

7. Find what will be the final distribution of the initial distribution [63 84 87 48 71] in the Markov chain with the following transition matrix?

$$\begin{bmatrix} 1 & 0 & 0 & 0 & 0 \\ \frac{1}{3} & \frac{1}{6} & 0 & \frac{1}{6} & \frac{1}{3} \\ 0 & 0 & 1 & 0 & 0 \\ \frac{1}{5} & \frac{2}{5} & 0 & \frac{1}{5} & \frac{1}{5} \\ 0 & 0 & 0 & 0 & 1 \end{bmatrix}$$

8. The Secretary of State says that there is a $\frac{2}{3}$ chance he will sign a secret agreement with the Liechtensteiners. While the Liechtensteiners will not discuss the agreement, high-level sources indicate that, if the agreement is signed, there is a $\frac{3}{4}$ chance they will secretly send troops into Switzerland. If the agreement isn't signed, there is only a $\frac{1}{3}$ chance troops will be sent into Switzerland. The Swiss, on the other hand, say that, if Liechtenstein does send in troops, there is a 90% chance that Vaduz will be shelled. Otherwise, there is only a 20% chance. Vaduz has not been shelled. What is the probability a secret agreement was signed?

9. Given the Markov chain with transition matrix

$$\begin{bmatrix} \frac{3}{4} & \frac{1}{8} & 0 & \frac{1}{8} & 0 & 0 & 0 & 0 \\ 0 & 0 & 0 & \frac{2}{3} & 0 & \frac{1}{3} & 0 & 0 \\ 0 & 0 & 1 & 0 & 0 & 0 & 0 & 0 \\ 0 & 0 & 0 & \frac{1}{4} & \frac{1}{2} & \frac{1}{4} & 0 & 0 \\ 0 & \frac{1}{5} & \frac{1}{5} & \frac{2}{5} & \frac{1}{5} & 0 & 0 & 0 \\ 0 & 0 & 0 & 0 & 0 & 0 & 1 & 0 \\ 0 & \frac{2}{7} & 0 & 0 & 0 & \frac{4}{7} & 0 & \frac{1}{7} \\ 0 & 0 & \frac{1}{9} & \frac{2}{9} & \frac{1}{3} & 0 & 0 & \frac{1}{3} \end{bmatrix}$$

(a) Which states are absorbing states?

(b) Is this an absorbing chain?

10. At the beginning, we had 10,944 customers and they had 11,520. During each of the first 3 weeks, $\frac{1}{2}$ of our customers switched to them and $\frac{1}{4}$ of theirs switched to us. During each of the next 2 weeks, $\frac{1}{3}$ of our customers switched to them and $\frac{2}{3}$ of theirs switched to us. At the end of the fifth week, how many customers do we have and how many do they have?

11. "Our campaign is fantastic," said the ad-agency director to the president of company A. "Look at the percentage of switches in one month between your company and companies B and C."

Percentage of Switches

| From/To | A | B | C |
|---|---|---|---|
| A | 87.5 | 12.5 | 0 |
| B | 0 | $33\frac{1}{3}$ | $66\frac{2}{3}$ |
| C | 25 | 50 | 25 |

"Why, if this continues for a few years you'll wipe out your competition." What will in fact happen?

12. What fraction of a given distribution will finally enter each state of the Markov chain with the following transition matrix?

$$\begin{bmatrix} \frac{2}{5} & \frac{1}{5} & \frac{1}{5} & \frac{1}{5} & 0 \\ \frac{1}{4} & \frac{1}{4} & \frac{1}{4} & \frac{1}{4} & 0 \\ \frac{1}{6} & \frac{1}{6} & \frac{1}{3} & \frac{1}{3} & 0 \\ 0 & 0 & 0 & 1 & 0 \\ 0 & 0 & 0 & 0 & 1 \end{bmatrix}$$

*13. Slam Corp. has 7 machines that make tennis balls. The balls are made in 3 colors, red, yellow, and white. Two-thirds of the balls made are white, although two-thirds of the balls made by machine 7 are red. The total production of red and yellow balls is the same. Machines 1 through 6 each make 15% of the balls. I have a red ball. What is the probability that it was made by machine 7?

*14. I think I left a package under my seat on the bus I take to work. A co-worker often rides the bus but I don't want to bother him unless it is fairly likely he rode the same bus I did. My bus goes around a short circuit that takes about a half-hour. Since he wasn't on the 7:30 bus with me and since I saw him at work at 9:00, I presume he took either the 8:00 or the 8:30 bus. If he gets up on time (and he does so $\frac{1}{6}$ of the mornings), he can catch the 8:00 bus. If he sleeps a little bit late (which he does $\frac{2}{3}$ of the time), then he can still catch the 8:30 bus. Otherwise, he drives his car. If he catches the 8:00 bus and it is raining, he almost always remembers (with probability $\frac{9}{10}$) his umbrella. If he catches the 8:30 bus, and it is raining, he is in such a hurry he almost always (with probability $\frac{9}{10}$) forgets his umbrella. If he drives, he always forgets his umbrella. If he drives, he shows up at the last minute but he can still find a parking space in the close lot $\frac{3}{10}$ of the time. If it is raining and he walks from the bus stop or the far parking lot without an umbrella, he always gets his newspaper soaked and throws it out as he enters the building. It was pouring down rain this morning and he is sitting at his desk reading his newspaper. Should I ask him about my package?

Teams A and K play a series of games, with the first team to win 4 games being declared the winner. Here are 3 different assumptions.
(a) Suppose A is twice as likely as K to win each game.
(b) Suppose the chances of A's winning the first game are 0.6, but after that the teams have equal chances of winning each game.
(c) Suppose any team that wins 2 in a row is sure to win the next game (if it is played) but sure to lose the game after that. Also suppose K's chances of winning the first game are 0.7 and of winning the second game are 0.6.

15. What is the probability that K will win the series in 4 games
    (a) under assumption (a)?
    (b) under assumption (b)?
    (c) under assumption (c)?
16. What is the probability that A will win the series in 6 games
    (a) under assumption (a)?
    (b) under assumption (b)?
    (c) under assumption (c)?
*17. What is the probability that K will lose the series
    (a) under assumption (a)?
    (b) under assumption (b)?
    (c) under assumption (c)?
18. What is the probability that the series will run 7 games
    (a) under assumption (a)?
    (b) under assumption (b)?
    (c) under assumption (c)?

# Chapter 4
# Random
# Variables
# and
# Probability
# Distributions

Such numbers are often broken with dashes to improve readability. However, a number such as 351-0762-19 is just 351076219 to a computer.

Nowadays it seems that everything and everybody has a number. Alan has a social security number, a driver's license number, a phone number, a payroll number, a student number, and various charge account numbers. He even has a few numbers he does not know about. For example, to save space in its files, a clerk in the AC personnel department assigns a number to each employee according to the rule: single$=0$; married$=1$; separated (legally or otherwise)$=2$. Alan also has a few numbers that only he and his wife can recall offhand: his height in inches, his weight in pounds, his shirt size, his body temperature (whenever it's over 100°), and so on.

In this chapter we will describe a few ways in which probability can be applied to problems in the real world. Applied probability is called **statistics**. As might be expected, all our statistical techniques will deal only with numbers. However, in Chapter 1 our abstract discussions of probability did not always lead directly to numbers. For example, the experiment "select an individual at random" does not have numerical outcomes, although as we have seen there are many possible numbers one might assign to each outcome. We begin by discussing such assignments of numbers.

**Section 4.1**
**Random Variables**

Last week Janet Witherspoon and Bill Crimmins, the new head of campstove production, got into a heated argument over stove quality.

"Bill, I know *you* think it's the best stove in the world, but our advertising people need some statistics," Janet continued

232

matter-of-factly. "We need to know such things as: How long does it take to boil water? How long will it burn on one tank of fuel? What's the lowest outdoor temperature at which it will operate? How long will it last?"

"How are we going to find all that out?" Bill responded testily. "Each stove is a little bit different. If we check them all, we'll be selling used stoves and I'll quit."

"We'll only need to check a small sample."

"But then how can you be sure about each stove we sell?"

"We can't be absolutely sure, but if we pick the right size sample we can be 95% sure or even 99% sure that the sample accurately reflects the population," Janet said confidently. "For example, we'll perform the experiment 'select a campstove at random.' We'll do this a few times. To each outcome we will assign a number. In our first test we'll assign the number of seconds it takes to boil water. After we collect these data, we can perform some statistical tests. However, the first step is collecting data, and this is nothing more than determining the number (of seconds) to assign to each possible outcome, that is, each campstove."

In this section we will take this first step. Here are a few examples to keep in mind:

**Example 1**

If it happens that the outcomes of an experiment are numbers, then we will often associate these numbers with themselves.

Toss a die. Assign to each outcome the number that comes up. For example, to the outcome 3 assign the number 3.

**Example 2**

Select an individual at random. To each individual assign his or her height to the nearest inch.

**Example 3**

Gamble. Assign to each possible outcome the amount you will win if that outcome occurs. A loss of $2 will be viewed as a win of −$2.

**Example 4**

Select an employee at AC at random. Assign the number 0 if the employee is single, 1 if married, and 2 if separated.

**Example 5**

For the purposes of this test AC begins with the water at 5°C.

Select an AC campstove at random. Assign to each outcome the number of seconds it takes to boil one liter of water.

Statisticians call the assignment of numbers to the outcomes of experiments random variables. Although we could think of better names for this concept we will follow tradition and use this term.

> A **random variable** on an experiment with sample space
> S is a rule that assigns a number to each element of S.

We will denote random variables by the letter X. In Example 4 above, S is the set of all AC employees and X is the rule "if the employee is single, assign 0; if married, assign 1; if separated, assign 2." In this case the rule X can be given by a tabulation:

| | |
|---|---|
| single | 0 |
| married | 1 |
| separated | 2 |

**Problem 1**

My friend, Flippa, flips a nickel and a dime. I win each coin that comes up heads. I must pay him a quarter for each coin that comes up tails. Describe the random variable that gives my winnings.

**Solution**

We can describe the four possible outcomes by ordered pairs: $(H, H), (H, T), (T, H), (T, T)$ where the first entry gives the result of the nickel toss and the second gives the result of the dime toss. The required random variable is described by the following tabulation.

Notice that we can describe the random variable without knowing the probability of the outcomes.

| Outcome | Assigned number | Comment |
|---|---|---|
| (H, H) | 15 | I win both coins: (5 + 10) |
| (H, T) | −20 | I win the nickel but lose a quarter (5 − 25) |
| (T, H) | −15 | I win the dime but lose a quarter (10 − 25) |
| (T, T) | −50 | I lose two quarters (−25 + (−25)) |

**Problem 2**

Anthropometry is the study of human measurement.

The anthropometry department at Local College decides to determine the average height of students at LC. They select 10 students at random. Describe the relevant random variable.

**Solution**

The relevant random variable assigns height in inches to each possible outcome—i.e., to each student at LC. The anthropometrists will use the partial tabulation below to infer things about the entire distribution.

| Student | Outcome |
|---|---|
| Ralph Williams | 75 |
| Lucinda Green | 66 |
| Kenneth Knight | 72 |
| Lena Schlenker | 70 |
| Edwin Talbot | 66 |
| Dolores Haze | 61 |
| Emil Rosato | 74 |
| Louise Windmuller | 61 |
| Ted Falter | 69 |

Problem 3 After paying 50¢ at a booth at the county fair, Alan spins a wheel of fortune numbered 1 to 13. If the wheel stops at a multiple of 3, they pay him $1.00; if it stops at a multiple of 5, they pay him $2.00; otherwise, he gets nothing. Describe the random variable that gives his net winnings.

Answer

| Outcome | Net winnings (in cents) |
|---------|-------------------------|
| 1 | −50 |
| 2 | −50 |
| 3 | 50 |
| 4 | −50 |
| 5 | 150 |
| 6 | 50 |
| 7 | −50 |
| 8 | −50 |
| 9 | 50 |
| 10 | 150 |
| 11 | −50 |
| 12 | 50 |
| 13 | −50 |

A random variable on an experiment can be used to describe events. If $X$ is a random variable on a sample space $S$ of an experiment, then a statement about the values of $X$ will completely describe an event. For instance, in the campstove example (Example 5), where $X$ was the assignment of boiling times to stoves, the statement $X = 400$ describes all stoves that boil water in exactly 400 seconds. The statement $X \geq 420$ refers to the event consisting of all outcomes (stoves) that require 420 seconds or more to boil water. In the marital-status example (Example 4) the statement $X = 0$ refers to the set of single AC employees.

Problem 4 In the wheel-of-fortune example of the previous problem, describe the following events:
(a) $X = 50$
(b) $X = 150$
(c) $X = 0$
(d) $-20 \leq X \leq 70$
(e) $-60 \leq X$

Solution (a) From the tabulation presented in the solution of the previous problem we see that $X = 50$ for the outcomes 3, 6, 9, and 12. Thus, $X = 50$ is the event $\{3, 6, 9, 12\}$.
(b) Similarly, $X$ associates the value 150 to outcomes 5 and 10. Thus, $X = 150$ is the event $\{5, 10\}$.
(c) For this experiment $X$ is never 0, so $X = 0$ is the impossible event $\varnothing$.

(d) For this experiment, the only value of X between $-20$ and 70 is 50. It follows that this event is the same as the event $X = 50$ given in part (a). So $-20 \leq X \leq 70$ is also a description of the event $\{3, 6, 9, 12\}$.

(e) Every value assigned by X is greater than $-60$ so for this experiment we see that this event is certain to occur: $(-60 \leq X) = \{1, 2, 3, 4, 5, 6, 7, 8, 9, 10, 11, 12, 13\} = S$, the sample space.

**Problem 5** For the experiment of Problem 2 about heights of students, use words to describe the following events

(a) $X = 61$

(b) $60 \leq X \leq 72$

(c) $X \leq 120$

(d) $X \leq 12$

**Solution**
(a) $X = 61$ is simply the event "61 inches (5′1″) tall." Two of the individuals in our table are in this event. It is likely that there are many other students at Local College who are also 61 inches tall and who therefore are also in this event.

(b) This is the event "between five and six feet tall." The planning department at LC would like to know the probability of this event since they call this event "of normal height." If a high percentage of students are not in this event, then they need to revise their thinking about such things as the design of the booths in the cafeteria.

(c) $X \leq 120$ is the certain event, S.

(d) $X \leq 12$ is the impossible event, $\varnothing$.

If we happen to know the probability distribution for an experiment, we can compute the probability of events expressed in terms of random variables.

**Problem 6** Toss a balanced die and let X be the random variable that gives the numerical outcome (see Example 1). Compute the following probabilities:

(a) $P(X = 2)$

(b) $P(3 \leq X \leq 5)$

(c) $P(X \leq 7)$

(d) $P(X > 7)$

**Solution**
(a) The event $X = 2$ consists of the single outcome, 2. Thus $P(X = 2) = P(2) = \frac{1}{6}$.

(b) $P(3 \leq X \leq 5) = P(3, 4, 5) = \frac{1}{2}$

(c) $P(X \leq 7) = P(1, 2, 3, 4, 5, 6) = 1$

(d) $P(X > 7) = P(\varnothing) = 0$

Problem 7 When Professor Vanmeter of the LC anthropometry department was describing the statistical techniques he would use to determine the average height of students at LC, someone pointed out that Student Health Services weighed and measured everyone upon admission. At the next lecture, Vanmeter sheepishly admitted that the complete figures were available (Table 1):

Table 1

At LC they measure height to the nearest inch. By partitioning heights into intervals between selected half-inch values, we will eliminate the problem of deciding in which interval a particular height belongs.

| Height | Number of students | % |
|---|---|---|
| under $57\frac{1}{2}$ | 15 | .2 |
| $57\frac{1}{2}$–$60\frac{1}{2}$ | 563 | 6.8 |
| $60\frac{1}{2}$–$63\frac{1}{2}$ | 1,318 | 16.0 |
| $63\frac{1}{2}$–$66\frac{1}{2}$ | 2,070 | 25.1 |
| $66\frac{1}{2}$–$69\frac{1}{2}$ | 2,859 | 34.7 |
| $69\frac{1}{2}$–$72\frac{1}{2}$ | 1,146 | 13.9 |
| $72\frac{1}{2}$–$75\frac{1}{2}$ | 270 | 3.3 |
| $75\frac{1}{2}$–$78\frac{1}{2}$ | 5 | .1 |
| over $78\frac{1}{2}$ | 2 | .0 |
| Total | 8,248 | |

The percentages are rounded to the first decimal place. The last percentage is 0.0 since $2/8248 \doteq .02\%$.

Consider the experiment "select a student at LC at random." Let X be the random variable that assigns height to students. What are the following probabilities?

(a) $P(63\frac{1}{2} \leq X \leq 66\frac{1}{2})$

(b) $P(X \leq 72\frac{1}{2})$

(c) $P(69\frac{1}{2} \leq X)$

(d) $P(X = 68)$

Solution

(a) The table tells us that 25.1% of the students at LC are between $63\frac{1}{2}$ and $66\frac{1}{2}$ inches tall. Accordingly, $P(63\frac{1}{2} \leq X \leq 66\frac{1}{2}) = .251$.

(b) It is easier to calculate the probability of the complementary event $X > 72\frac{1}{2}$. From the table, $P(X > 72\frac{1}{2}) = .033 + .001 + .000 = .034$. Thus, $P(X \leq 72\frac{1}{2}) = 1 - P(X > 72\frac{1}{2}) = 1 - .034 = .966$.

See equation 3, Section 1.3, p. 24.

(c) $P(69\frac{1}{2} \leq X) = .139 + .033 + .001 + .000 = .173$.

(d) This information is not available from the table. We could say that since 3 heights (67″, 68″, 69″) occur in the interval $66\frac{1}{2} \leq X \leq 69\frac{1}{2}$ persons of height 68″ should make up $\frac{1}{3}$ of the 2,859. Actually, we do not know so we had best not say anything.

Problem 8 Eight percent of the workers at AC are separated. Let X be the marital-status random variable of Example 4. Find $P(X < 2)$.

Answer $P(X < 2) = 1 - P(X \geq 2) = 1 - P(\text{separated}) = 1 - 0.08 = 0.92$.

It is possible to graph the probabilities assigned by random variables. Such graphs, important for several reasons, enable us to see how probabilities are distributed to the various outcomes. The graph provides a convenient summary of the random variable X. The best method for us is called the **histogram** or bar graph.

Consider the experiment of Problem 7: Select a student at Local College at random. Probabilities assigned to the height random variable are given in the last column of Table 1. We will use this table as our first illustration of the general procedure outlined below.

**Step 1**

In all our examples, we will assume that we have done both.

Pick points on the 1-axis that do not correspond to values assigned by the random variable. The histogram will have a better appearance if the selected points are evenly spaced.

We are assuming that all heights under $57\frac{1}{2}$ are over $54\frac{1}{2}$ and that all heights over $78\frac{1}{2}$ are under $81\frac{1}{2}$, thus continuing the equal spacing. Even if not true, the data at the extreme ends of Table 1 are so few that this assumption will not affect the appearance of the histogram.

In our case we will choose the points $54\frac{1}{2}$, $57\frac{1}{2}$, $60\frac{1}{2}$, $63\frac{1}{2}$, $66\frac{1}{2}$, $69\frac{1}{2}$, $72\frac{1}{2}$, $75\frac{1}{2}$, $78\frac{1}{2}$, $81\frac{1}{2}$. Since all heights have been measured to the nearest inch there will be no problem deciding where to put each value assigned by X.

**Step 2**

For each pair a, b of consecutive points chosen in step 1, draw a bar of height $P(a \le X \le b)$ above the 1-axis between a and b.

In our case, we would place a bar of height $P(63\frac{1}{2} \le X \le 66\frac{1}{2}) = 0.251$ above the 1-axis between $63\frac{1}{2}$ and $66\frac{1}{2}$. The complete graph appears below.

The first and last bars in this graph are too short to be seen. If we changed the vertical scale to make these end bars visible, the center bars would be too tall to fit on the paper.

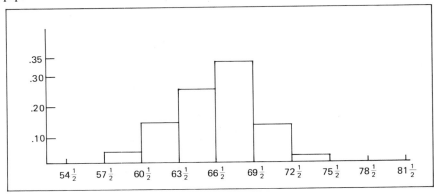

Here are a few remarks.

Remark 1   The 2-axis is used only to indicate the heights of the bar. We could insert this reference line anywhere near the graph.

Remark 2   We could also use a histogram to represent the second column in Table 1:

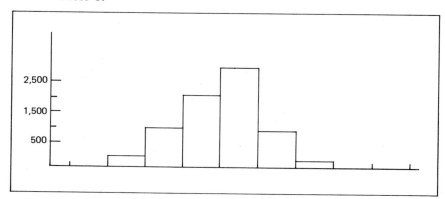

This is exactly the same graph.

Remark 3   The relative scales used on the axes may be important. For example, when the administration at LC was eager to hire the 7'2" ace basketball coach, John L. Dunker, and the 5'1" Dean of Students, Ralph R. Mild, they were very careful how they presented these height data:

For the prospective coach

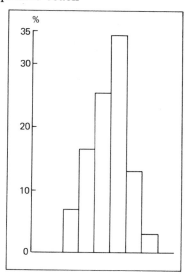

For the prospective dean

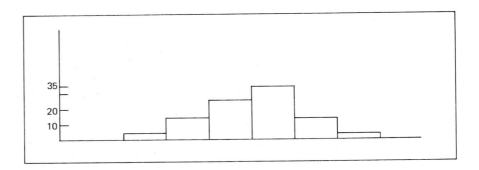

In the amusing book, *How to Lie with Statistics*, (New York: Norton, 1954), Darrel Huff describes many other ways in which facts are often presented to gain a special advantage.

Problem 9   Two balanced dice are tossed. Let X be the number of spots that come up. Draw a histogram for X.

Solution   In this case it is reasonable to represent the probability of each value of X with a bar. The following tabulation is reproduced from Chapter 1, page 33.

A list of the probabilities of all the values of a random variable X is called the **probability distribution** of X.

| Outcome | Probability |
|---------|-------------|
| 2 | $\frac{1}{36}$ |
| 3 | $\frac{2}{36}$ |
| 4 | $\frac{3}{36}$ |
| 5 | $\frac{4}{36}$ |
| 6 | $\frac{5}{36}$ |
| 7 | $\frac{6}{36}$ |
| 8 | $\frac{5}{36}$ |
| 9 | $\frac{4}{36}$ |
| 10 | $\frac{3}{36}$ |
| 11 | $\frac{2}{36}$ |
| 12 | $\frac{1}{36}$ |

For this histogram we use the points $1\frac{1}{2}$, $2\frac{1}{2}$, and so on, as the dividing points for the bars:

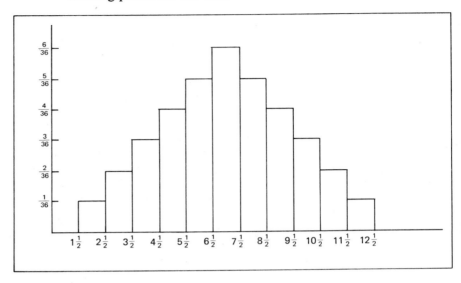

In this case each histogram bar has a width of one unit. Whenever this happens the area of the bar and its height are given by the same number. Thus, for example, the area of the bar centered over the outcome 4 is $1 \times \frac{3}{36} = \frac{3}{36} = P(X=4)$. For such histograms, area can be used to represent probabilities. For example, the probability of getting a 5, 6, 7, 8, or 9 is simply the area of the shaded region in the following graph.

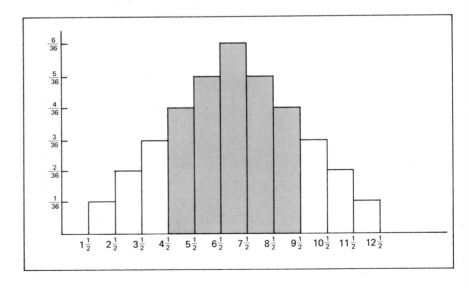

We may apply this technique only to histograms in which each bar has the same width.

Areas can also be used to represent probabilities in histograms in which the bars do not have width one. This is done by adjusting the heights of the bars, as in the following problem.

**Problem 10**

(See Example 5.) AC has tested 100 stoves, with the results shown in Table 2. Present these data in a histogram in which areas represent probabilities. Shade the area that represents the probability of a boiling time of more than 402 seconds.

Table 2
Boiling Times to
Nearest Second for
One Quart of Water,
Covered, at 5°C

| Time | Number of stoves | Probability |
|---|---|---|
| 367.5–372.5 | 2 | .02 |
| 372.5–377.5 | 8 | .08 |
| 377.5–382.5 | 11 | .11 |
| 382.5–387.5 | 16 | .16 |
| 387.5–392.5 | 20 | .20 |
| 392.5–397.5 | 17 | .17 |
| 397.5–402.5 | 13 | .13 |
| 402.5–407.5 | 7 | .07 |
| 407.5–412.5 | 3 | .03 |
| 412.5–417.5 | 2 | .02 |
| 417.5–422.5 | 1 | .01 |

**Solution**

Each time interval is 5 seconds wide, so each bar in the histogram is of width 5. In order for the area of the bar to equal the probability it represents, we must divide its height by 5. For example, the second probability listed in the table must be shown as a bar of height $\frac{.08}{5} = .016$, so that its area is width $\times$ height $= 5 \times .016 = .08$.

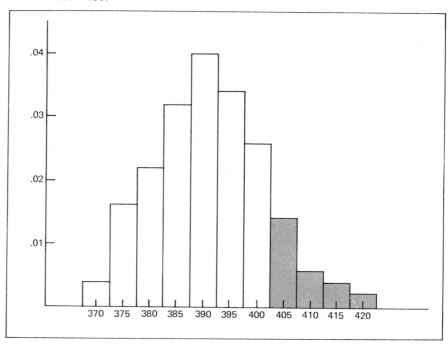

**Joint Events**

Often several different random variables are defined on the same experiment. Consider the set of all completed employee information forms in the AC data processing center. These forms make up the sample space of the experiment, "apply for work at AC." The numerical encoding of the information on those forms involves several random variables. We have already considered the "marital status" random variable. Another is the "age bracket" random variable:

At present, AC does not hire anyone who is under 18 or over 65 years of age.

| Age (in years) | Code |
|---|---|
| $17\frac{1}{2}$–$25\frac{1}{2}$ | 1 |
| $25\frac{1}{2}$–$40\frac{1}{2}$ | 2 |
| $40\frac{1}{2}$–$60\frac{1}{2}$ | 3 |
| $60\frac{1}{2}$–$65\frac{1}{2}$ | 4 |

Still another is the "formal education" random variable:

| Formal education | Code |
|---|---|
| No high school diploma | 10 |
| High school diploma only | 20 |
| Associate degree, but no other degrees | 30 |
| Bachelor's degree, but no graduate degrees | 40 |
| Graduate degree | 50 |

AC uses seven other random variables on this experiment, but we will not consider them now.

When several random variables are defined on the same sample space S, we will denote them by $X_1, X_2$, and so on.

**Problem 11**

See section 1.2, p. 13, for a review of union and intersection.

For the AC employee-information experiment, let $X_1$ be the "marital status" random variable, $X_2$ be the "age bracket" random variable, and $X_3$ be the "formal education" random variable. Describe, in words, each of the following events.
(a) $X_1 = 1$
(b) $X_1 = 1$ and $X_2 = 2$
(c) $X_1 = 1 \cap X_2 = 2 \cap X_3 = 20$
(d) $(X_1 = 0 \cap X_2 = 4) \cup (X_2 = 3 \cap X_3 = 50)$

**Answer**

(a) The employee is married.
(b) The employee is married and between 26 and 40 years old.
(c) The employee is married, between 26 and 40 years old, and has only a high school diploma.
(d) Either the employee is single and over 60 or the employee is between 41 and 60 and has a graduate degree.

An event such as "$X_1 = 1$ and $X_2 = 2$", described by the values of two or more random variables of the same experiment, is sometimes called a **joint event**. The probability of a joint event of $X_1$ and $X_2$ is a **joint probability**. Complete information about the joint probabilities of the two random variables $X_1$ and $X_2$ on the same sample space may be displayed in matrix form. Consider, for example, the random variables $X_1$ (marital status) and $X_2$ (age bracket) at AC. After much compiling and counting, the personnel office has determined that

For example, $P(X_1 = 0 \cap X_2 = 1)$ is simply the percentage of AC employees who are single and between the ages of 18 and 25.

$$P(X_1 = 0 \cap X_2 = 1) = 0.24, \qquad P(X_1 = 1 \cap X_2 = 3) = 0.00,$$
$$P(X_1 = 0 \cap X_2 = 2) = 0.22, \qquad P(X_1 = 1 \cap X_2 = 4) = 0.02,$$
$$P(X_1 = 0 \cap X_2 = 3) = 0.10, \qquad P(X_1 = 2 \cap X_2 = 1) = 0.04,$$
$$P(X_1 = 0 \cap X_2 = 4) = 0.06, \qquad P(X_1 = 2 \cap X_2 = 2) = 0.03,$$
$$P(X_1 = 1 \cap X_2 = 1) = 0.18, \qquad P(X_1 = 2 \cap X_2 = 3) = 0.01,$$
$$P(X_1 = 1 \cap X_2 = 2) = 0.10, \qquad P(X_1 = 2 \cap X_2 = 4) = 0.00.$$

This information may be tabulated as follows.

|       |      | $X_2$ |      |      |
|-------|------|------|------|------|
| $X_1$ | 1    | 2    | 3    | 4    |
| 0     | .24  | .22  | .10  | .06  |
| 1     | .18  | .10  | .00  | .02  |
| 2     | .04  | .03  | .01  | .00  |

If we always head rows with values assigned by $X_1$ in increasing order and head columns with values assigned by $X_2$ in increasing order, then we may safely omit the headings and obtain the **matrix of joint probabilities** for $X_1$ and $X_2$:

$$\begin{bmatrix} .24 & .22 & .10 & .06 \\ .18 & .10 & .00 & .02 \\ .04 & .03 & .01 & .00 \end{bmatrix} \qquad \mathbf{1}$$

From this matrix it is easy to compute the value of $P(X_1 = a)$ and of $P(X_2 = b)$ for each value of a and b. Consider, for example, $P(X_1 = 0)$. Since the events $X_2 = 1$, $X_2 = 2$, $X_2 = 3$, and $X_2 = 4$, are a partition of the sample space, we have, by result **4** of Section 3.2, $P(X_1 = 0) = P(X_1 = 0 \cap X_2 = 1) + P(X_1 = 0 \cap X_2 = 2) + P(X_1 = 0 \cap X_2 = 3) + P(X_1 = 0 \cap X_2 = 4) = 0.24 + 0.22 + 0.10 + 0.06 = 0.62$. Note that we have merely added the entries in row 1 of matrix **1**. Similarly, for example, to obtain $P(X_2 = 2)$ we add the entries in column 2: $P(X_2 = 2) = P(X_1 = 0 \cap X_2 = 2) + P(X_1 = 1 \cap X_2 = 2) + P(X_1 = 2 \cap X_2 = 2) = 0.22 + 0.10 + 0.03 = 0.35$. In the same

Since $X_1 = 0, X_1 = 1, X_1 = 2$ is a partition, we must have $P(X_1 = 0) + P(X_1 = 1) + P(X_1 = 2) = 0.62 + 0.30 + 0.08 = 1.00$. Similarly, $0.46 + 0.35 + 0.11 + 0.08 = 1.00$. We see from each of these results that in order for a matrix to be a matrix of joint probabilities all its entries must be non-negative and they must sum to one. Conversely, any matrix which satisfies these two conditions could be the matrix of joint probabilities for some experiment and some two random variables.

way we obtain:

$$
\begin{bmatrix}
.24 & .22 & .10 & .06 \\
.18 & .10 & .00 & .02 \\
.04 & .03 & .01 & .00
\end{bmatrix}
\begin{matrix}
0.62 = P(X_1 = 0) \\
0.30 = P(X_1 = 1) \\
0.08 = P(X_1 = 2)
\end{matrix}
\qquad \textbf{2}
$$

$$0.46 = P(X_2 = 1) \quad 0.35 = P(X_2 = 2) \quad 0.11 = P(X_2 = 3) \quad 0.08 = P(X_2 = 4)$$

Two random variables $X_1$ and $X_2$ on the sample space are said to be **independent** if, for every number a assigned by $X_1$ and every number b assigned by $X_2$, the events $X_1 = a$ and $X_2 = b$ are independent. By results **11** and **12** of Section 1.5, if the events $X_1 = a$ and $X_2 = b$ are independent, then

$$P(X_1 = a \cap X_2 = b) = P(X_1 = a)P(X_2 = b) \qquad \textbf{3}$$

Conversely if equation **3** holds, then the events are independent. This together with the previous discussion suggests the following flow chart to check independence.

**To Check Two Random Variables, Defined on the Same Sample Space, for Independence**

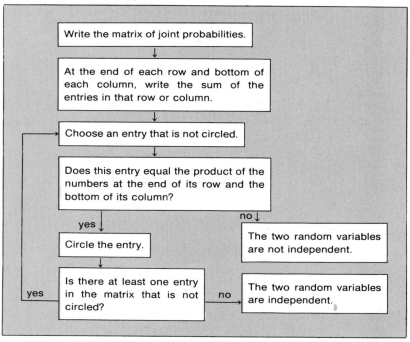

**Problem 12**

**Solution**

Are the AC personnel random variables $X_1$ and $X_2$ independent? We have already written the matrix (matrix **1**) and summed its rows and columns (matrix **2**). Checking the $(1, 1)$ entry: $(0.62)(0.46) \neq 0.24$. Hence, without looking further, we declare that $X_1$ and $X_2$ are not independent.

**Problem 13**

Suppose $X_1$ and $X_2$, random variables on the same sample space, are independent. Suppose $X_1$ assigns the numbers 9, 14, and 17; $X_2$ assigns the numbers $-8$, $-3$, 0, and 41. We are given that $P(X_1 = 9) = \frac{2}{3}$, $P(X_1 = 14) = \frac{1}{12}$, $P(X_1 = 14 \cap X_2 = -3) = \frac{1}{48}$, $P(X_1 = 9 \cap X_2 = 0) = \frac{2}{9}$, and $P(X_1 = 17 \cap X_2 = 41) = \frac{1}{24}$. Write the matrix of joint probabilities.

**Solution**

$P(X_1 = 17) = 1 - P(X_1 = 9) - P(X_1 = 14) = 1 - \frac{2}{3} - \frac{1}{12} = \frac{1}{4}$. Since $X_1$ and $X_2$ are independent, we have $P(X_1 = 14 \cap X_2 = -3) = P(X_1 = 14)P(X_2 = -3) = (\frac{1}{12})P(X_2 = -3) = \frac{1}{48}$, so $P(X_2 = -3) = \frac{1}{48} \div \frac{1}{12} = \frac{1}{4}$. Then $P(X_1 = 9 \cap X_2 = 0) = (\frac{2}{3})P(X_2 = 0) = \frac{2}{9}$, so $P(X_2 = 0) = \frac{1}{3}$. Next, $P(X_1 = 17 \cap X_2 = 41) = (\frac{1}{4})P(X_2 = 41) = \frac{1}{24}$, so $P(X_2 = 41) = \frac{1}{6}$. Then $P(X_2 = -8) = 1 - \frac{1}{4} - \frac{1}{3} - \frac{1}{6} = \frac{1}{4}$. We may now multiply row sums by column sums to fill in the matrix:

$$
\begin{bmatrix}
\frac{1}{6} & \frac{1}{6} & \frac{2}{9} & \frac{1}{9} \\
\frac{1}{48} & \frac{1}{48} & \frac{1}{36} & \frac{1}{72} \\
\frac{1}{16} & \frac{1}{16} & \frac{1}{12} & \frac{1}{24}
\end{bmatrix}
\begin{matrix}
\frac{2}{3} \\
\frac{1}{12} \\
\frac{1}{4}
\end{matrix}
$$
$$
\begin{matrix}
\frac{1}{4} & \frac{1}{4} & \frac{1}{3} & \frac{1}{6}
\end{matrix}
$$

**Problem 14**

Two balanced dice, one red and one green, are tossed. Suppose $X_1$ assigns to each outcome twice the number that comes up on the red die. Suppose $X_2$ assigns to each outcome three times the number that comes up on the green die. Are $X_1$ and $X_2$ independent?

**First Solution**

The first solution really isn't a solution in the technical sense. The real world contains many examples of pairs of random variables which "ought" to be independent or which are "almost" independent yet which are not independent in the strict sense of the definition. The decision as to whether the mathematical theory of independent random variables is relevant in these cases is left up to the judgment of the user. Of course, as we see in the second solution, the particular random variables we are considering here actually are independent.

Yes, since $X_1$ is governed only by the red die, $X_2$ is governed only by the green die, and the two dice are certainly independent.

Second Solution   The matrix is a $6 \times 6$ matrix with each entry $\frac{1}{36}$. The row and column sums are each $\frac{1}{36} + \frac{1}{36} + \frac{1}{36} + \frac{1}{36} + \frac{1}{36} + \frac{1}{36} = \frac{1}{6}$, and we have $(\frac{1}{6})(\frac{1}{6}) = \frac{1}{36}$ each time. Therefore, $X_1$ and $X_2$ are independent.

Problem 15   A rack contains a set of pool balls numbered from 1 to 15. Ed closes his eyes and chooses a ball at random, then replaces it. If the number of the ball is 5 or less, he wins \$5; otherwise he wins \$10. Stan closes his eyes and chooses a ball at random, then replaces it. If the number of the ball he chooses is either less than 4 or greater than 9, he wins \$5; otherwise, he wins \$10. Let $X_1$ be Ed's random variable and $X_2$ be Stan's random variable. Are $X_1$ and $X_2$ independent?

Solution   $P(X_1 = 5 \cap X_2 = 5) = P(1, 2, 3) = \frac{3}{15} = \frac{1}{5}$. Similarly we obtain the other entries of the joint probability matrix

$$\begin{bmatrix} \frac{1}{5} & \frac{2}{15} \\ \frac{2}{5} & \frac{4}{15} \end{bmatrix} \begin{matrix} \frac{1}{3} \\ \frac{2}{3} \end{matrix}$$
$$\begin{matrix} \frac{3}{5} & \frac{2}{5} \end{matrix}$$

We have also written the row and column sums. Then: $\frac{1}{3} \cdot \frac{3}{5} = (\frac{1}{5})$, $\frac{1}{3} \cdot \frac{2}{5} = (\frac{2}{15})$, $\frac{2}{3} \cdot \frac{3}{5} = (\frac{2}{5})$, and $\frac{2}{3} \cdot \frac{2}{5} = (\frac{4}{15})$. Hence, $X_1$ and $X_2$ are independent.

Exercises 4.1   In Exercises 1 through 4 tell which assignments are a random variable and which are not, and why.

1. The clerk in the AC employment office guesses the ethnic background of each applicant.
2. The clerk in the AC employment office guesses the ethnic background of each applicant and records his guess using a number for each ethnic type he needs.
3. The clerk in the AC employment office, in order to look mysterious, wrote down a long number every time an applicant came in last week.
4. The clerk in the AC employment office, in order to help each applicant who came in last week feel important, wrote the number 1 on top of her application form as he handed it to her.

In Exercises 5 through 8 make a table for the random variable described. In each exercise the experiment is: flip a coin and toss a die.

5. Win a dollar for heads; lose a dollar for tails.
6. Win a dollar for even; lose a dollar for odd.
7. Win a dollar for heads; lose a dollar for tails; win a dollar for even; lose a dollar for odd.

$^C$8. Win a dollar for heads, 2 dollars for tails, and a dollar for each spot that comes up, *except* lose 5 dollars for 3 and 10 dollars for 6.

9. Let X be the random variable of Exercise 8. Suppose the coin and die are balanced. Find:
   (a) $P(X=2)$
   (b) $P(X=3)$
   (c) $P(X<0)$
   (d) $P(X\neq0)$
   (e) $P(X=9)$

10. Repeat Exercise 9 supposing the coin has 2 tails.

11. Repeat Exercise 9 supposing the coin is normal, the die is balanced, but the $\vdots$ on the die has faded to $\cdot$

12. The tabulation shows the percentage of orders at a typical PHE store that are of various amounts.

| Amount (in cents) | Percent |
|---|---|
| less than $25\frac{1}{2}$ | 5 |
| $25\frac{1}{2}$ to $75\frac{1}{2}$ | 10 |
| $75\frac{1}{2}$ to $150\frac{1}{2}$ | 30 |
| $150\frac{1}{2}$ to $200\frac{1}{2}$ | 40 |
| $200\frac{1}{2}$ to $300\frac{1}{2}$ | 10 |
| $300\frac{1}{2}$ to $500\frac{1}{2}$ | 3 |
| over $500\frac{1}{2}$ | 2 |

Let X be the random variable that gives the amount of purchase by a customer in a typical PHE store. Find:

(a) $P(X \leq 2.00)$
(b) $P(.25 \leq X \leq 3.00)$

In Exercises 13 and 14, draw a histogram of the random variable.

13.

| a | $-2$ | $-1$ | 0 | 1 | 2 | 3 | 4 |
|---|---|---|---|---|---|---|---|
| $P(X=a)$ | .10 | .15 | .05 | .20 | .10 | .25 | .15 |

14.

| a | $-4$ | $-3$ | $-2$ | $-1$ | 0 | 1 | 2 |
|---|---|---|---|---|---|---|---|
| $P(X=a)$ | .010 | .580 | .030 | .360 | .001 | .009 | .010 |

In Exercises 15 and 16 part (a), present the data in histograms in which areas represent probabilities. In part (b) shade the areas that represent the given probabilities.

15. (a)

| Range | Probability |
|---|---|
| $-8 - -1$ | .15 |
| $-1 - 6$ | .10 |
| $6 - 13$ | .10 |
| $13 - 20$ | .40 |
| $20 - 27$ | .05 |
| $27 - 34$ | .10 |
| $34 - 41$ | .00 |
| $41 - 48$ | .10 |

(b) P(not between 6 and 27)

16. (a)

| Range | Probability |
|-------|-------------|
| 5 – 10 | .20 |
| 10 – 15 | .12 |
| 15 – 20 | .18 |
| 20 – 25 | .04 |
| 25 – 30 | .06 |
| 30 – 35 | .20 |
| 35 – 40 | .05 |
| 40 – 45 | .15 |

(b) P(between 10 and 30, or at least 35)

17. Balanced dice, one white and one black, are tossed. Payoff $X_1$ (in dollars) is 4 times what the white die comes up, minus what the black die comes up. Payoff $X_2$ (in pesos) is 4 times what the black die comes up minus what the white die comes up.
    (a) Guess whether or not $X_1$ and $X_2$ are independent.
    (b) Apply the flow chart on p. 245. Was your guess correct?

18. Let $X_1$ be the payoff for the balanced wheel of fortune of Problem 3, p. 235. Let $X_2$ be the payoff: win $5 for a power of 2, lose $10 for a multiple of 3, break even otherwise. Are $X_1$ and $X_2$ independent?

**Section 4.2
Expectation**

Expectation is the word used in probability for the familiar notation of average or mean. In this section we will show how to calculate expectations.

Sitting on the loading dock of the AC warehouse waiting for the next delivery truck, Alan idly tosses a balanced die and imagines he is a famous gambler like his ancestor, Arlo. "Every time it comes up less than 4, I win $50," he thinks. "Every time it comes up 4 or 5, I win $100. But whenever it comes up 6, I lose $300."

A coworker remarks, "Better cut that out, Alan—you'll lose your shirt." Alan wonders how he really would do in the long run. He begins to keep track on a carton on the dock:

Losing $300 is the same as "winning" minus $300.

| Outcome | Number | Winnings | |
|---------|--------|----------|---|
| 1, 2 or 3 | 308 | 308× 50= | $15,400 |
| 4 or 5 | 186 | 186×100= | $18,600 |
| 6 | 106 | 106×(−300)= | −$31,800 |
| Total | 600 | | $2,200 |

"There must be an easier way. Let's see, if I toss the die 6,000 times I can expect a 1, 2, or 3 about $\frac{1}{2}$ the time. So I can expect to win $50 about 3,000 times, for a total of $150,000. I would get a 4 or 5 about 2,000 times and win $200,000. On the other hand, I can expect about 1,000 tosses to come up 6; that will cost me $300,000. In total I'll come out ahead by

$$150,000 + 200,000 - 300,000 = \$50,000.$$

Of course that's only after I toss the die 6,000 times. On the average I'll win $50,000/6,000 = \$8\frac{1}{3}$ per toss."

A more careful mathematical description involves a few variables. Let n denote the number of times Alan tosses the die. We can tabulate the data as before.

| Outcome | Number | Winnings |
|---------|--------|----------|
| 1, 2 or 3 | a | + 50a |
| 4 or 5 | b | +100b |
| 6 | c | −300c |
| Total | n | 50a + 100b − 300c |

The average winnings tell us how much we can expect to win each time the game is played:

$$\frac{1}{n}(50a + 100b - 300c) = 50\frac{a}{n} + 100\frac{b}{n} - 300\frac{c}{n}$$

When we say that $\frac{a}{n}$ gets closer and closer to $\frac{1}{2}$ as the number n gets bigger, we do not mean to imply that $\frac{a}{n}$ ever reaches $\frac{1}{2}$, nor do we mean that even if $\frac{a}{n}$ does reach $\frac{1}{2}$ it will stay there. What we mean is that if you try any number other than $\frac{1}{2}$, say 0.499, then, after you have tossed the die enough times (we don't know how many), $\frac{a}{n}$ will be closer to $\frac{1}{2}$ than it is to 0.499 and from then on $\frac{a}{n}$ will stay closer to $\frac{1}{2}$ than to 0.499. (This is but one of several apparently reasonable views of the "meaning" of probability.)

What can we say about the fractions $\frac{a}{n}$, $\frac{b}{n}$ and $\frac{c}{n}$? The more times Alan tosses the die (that is, the bigger n is), the closer we should expect these fractions to get to $\frac{1}{2}$, $\frac{1}{3}$, and $\frac{1}{6}$; that is, we expect

$$\frac{a}{n} = P(1, 2, \text{ or } 3) = \frac{1}{2}$$

$$\frac{b}{n} = P(4 \text{ or } 5) = \frac{1}{3}$$

$$\frac{c}{n} = P(6) = \frac{1}{6}$$

Alan can expect to win about

$$50P(1,2,3) + 100P(4 \text{ or } 5) - 300P(6) = 50\frac{1}{2} + 100\frac{1}{3} - 300\frac{1}{6} = \$8\frac{1}{3}$$

each time he plays the game.

We see from Section 4.1 that all this talk about winnings in a game of chance is really just a description of a random variable. We are led then to the following definition.

> Let X be a random variable and let $x_1, x_2, \ldots, x_n$ be the numbers assigned by X. The **expectation of** X, denoted E(X), is the number
>
> $$E(X) = x_1 P(X = x_1) + x_2 P(X = x_2) + \ldots + x_n P(X = x_n)$$

**1**

**Problem 1**

The worn die (p. 21):

| 1 | 2 | 3 | 4 | 5 | 6 |
|------|------|------|------|------|------|
| .161 | .170 | .165 | .163 | .173 | .168 |

Suppose Alan had been tossing the worn die he had inherited from Arlo. What would be his expected winnings per toss?

Solution    Let X be the amount won on a toss. Then $E(X) = 50P(X = 50) + 100P(X = 100) + (-300) \cdot P(X = -300) = 50(.161 + .170 + .165) + 100(.163 + .173) - 300(.168) = 8.00$ dollars per toss.

Problem 2    A survey of the number of children in the families in Alan's home town yielded the following tabulation.

| Number of children in family | Number of families |
|---|---|
| 0 | 142 |
| 1 | 218 |
| 2 | 376 |
| 3 | 150 |
| 4 | 72 |
| 5 | 12 |
| 6 | 9 |
| more than 6 | 0 |
| Total | 979 |

How many children are in the "average" family?

Solution    We may interpret these data as follows. The experiment is to choose a family at random. The random variable X assigns to the family chosen the number of children in it. Then the number of children in the average family is $E(X) = 0P(X = 0) + 1P(X = 1) + 2P(X = 2) + 3P(X = 3) + 4P(X = 4) + 5P(X = 5) + 6P(X = 6) = 0(\frac{142}{979}) + 1(\frac{218}{979}) + 2(\frac{376}{979}) + 3(\frac{150}{979}) + 4(\frac{72}{979}) + 5(\frac{12}{979}) + 6(\frac{6}{979}) = \frac{164}{89} \doteq 1.84$ children.

When the exact values of the random variable are not known, it is necessary to approximate the expectation, as in the following problem.

Problem 3    The head basketball coach at Local College called the anthropometry department and asked: "What is the average height of students at LC?" The chairman of the department agreed to find out, but shortly after he hung up the phone he remembered that all he had was Table 3 below. What should he do?

Solution    In this problem we do not know the exact values of the height random variable. For example, we know that 1,318 individuals are between $60\frac{1}{2}$ and $63\frac{1}{2}$ inches tall, but we do not know exactly how many are of each of the heights 61, 62, and 63 inches. In problems involving grouped data, the standard procedure is to suppose that the values of the random variable are evenly distributed throughout the group. In this case, we will suppose that 62″ will serve to represent this group. The result will be that we will have only an approximation to the expectation. However, if there are a lot of data and the group limits are reasonably narrow, then it will usually be a fairly good approximation (Table 3).

Table 3

We are assuming that we can include everyone under $57\frac{1}{2}$ inches in height in the first group and everyone over $78\frac{1}{2}$ inches in height in the last group without significantly affecting our answers.

| Group | Representative | Number | Percent |
|---|---|---|---|
| $54\frac{1}{2}$–$57\frac{1}{2}$ | 56 | 15 | .2 |
| $57\frac{1}{2}$–$60\frac{1}{2}$ | 59 | 563 | 6.8 |
| $60\frac{1}{2}$–$63\frac{1}{2}$ | 62 | 1,318 | 16.0 |
| $63\frac{1}{2}$–$66\frac{1}{2}$ | 65 | 2,070 | 25.1 |
| $66\frac{1}{2}$–$69\frac{1}{2}$ | 68 | 2,859 | 34.6 |
| $69\frac{1}{2}$–$72\frac{1}{2}$ | 71 | 1,146 | 13.9 |
| $72\frac{1}{2}$–$75\frac{1}{2}$ | 74 | 270 | 3.3 |
| $75\frac{1}{2}$–$78\frac{1}{2}$ | 77 | 5 | .1 |
| $78\frac{1}{2}$–$81\frac{1}{2}$ | 80 | 2 | .0 |

Total 8,248

We now use the second and fourth columns to compute the average: $.002 \times 56 + .068 \times 59 + .160 \times 62 + .251 \times 65 + .347 \times 68 + .139 \times 71 + .033 \times 74 + .001 \times 77 + 0 \times 80 \doteq 66.3$ inches.

Alternately we could say, for example, that *all* 15 individuals in the group $54\frac{1}{2}$ to $57\frac{1}{2}$ are $56''$ tall, and so on and use the second and third columns:

$15 \times 56 + 563 \times 59 + 1318 \times 62 + 2070 \times 65 + 2859 \times 68 + 1146 \times 71 + 270 \times 74 + 5 \times 77 + 2 \times 80 = 546,626$.

Since there are 8,248 individuals, we must divide to obtain the average: $546,626 / 8,248 \doteq 66.3$ inches, as before.

**Useful Properties of Expectation**

Another day on the loading dock Alan recklessly decided to triple the stakes, so that if the die came up less than 4 he won $150, if 4 or 5 he won $300, and if 6 he lost $900. Now his expected winnings per game are $150P(X = 150) + 300P(X = 300) - 900P(X = -900) = 150P(1, 2, 3) + 300P(4, 5) - 900P(6) = 150(\frac{1}{2}) + 300(\frac{1}{3}) - 900(\frac{1}{6}) = \$25$. The new expectation is triple the old expectation(p. 250): $3(8\frac{1}{3}) = 25$. It should come as no surprise that this result holds in general. If X is a random variable that assigns the values $x_1, x_2, \ldots, x_n$ and if c is a constant, then cX is the random variable that assigns the values $cx_1, cx_2, \ldots, cx_n$, respectively. Then $E(cX) = cx_1 P(cX = cx_1) + cx_2 P(cX = cx_2) + \ldots + cx_n P(cX = cx_n) = cxP(X = x_1) + cxP(X = x_2) + \ldots + cxP(X = x_n) = c[x_1 P(X = x_1) + x_2 P(X = x_2) + \ldots + x_n P(X = x_n)] = cE(X)$. Thus:

> If X is a random variable and c is a constant, then
> $$E(cX) = cE(X).$$

**2**

Problem 4

Elaborate calculations have shown that the value of the average wholesale order from AC is $840. If all prices are raised 9%, and if this does not affect order size, what will be the value of the average order?

Solution

Of course the answer is obvious, but we wish to put it in a probability-theoretic context.

The experiment is to choose a wholesale order at random; X is the value of the order. After the price increase, the random variable is 1.09X. Then the value of an average order will be $E(1.09X) = 1.09E(X) = 1.09 \cdot 840 = \$915.60$.

Two random variables X and Y on the same experiment can be combined in many ways: addition, subtraction, multiplication, and so on. Consider the throw of two balanced dice. Here are two random variables and their sum.

| Outcome | 2 | 3 | 4 | 5 | 6 | 7 | 8 | 9 | 10 | 11 | 12 |
|---|---|---|---|---|---|---|---|---|---|---|---|
| Probability | $\frac{1}{36}$ | $\frac{2}{36}$ | $\frac{3}{36}$ | $\frac{4}{36}$ | $\frac{5}{36}$ | $\frac{6}{36}$ | $\frac{5}{36}$ | $\frac{4}{36}$ | $\frac{3}{36}$ | $\frac{2}{36}$ | $\frac{1}{36}$ |
| X | 2 | 2 | 2 | 3 | 3 | 3 | 4 | 4 | 4 | 5 | 5 |
| Y | 2 | 2 | 3 | 3 | 4 | 4 | 3 | 3 | 5 | 2 | 6 |
| X+Y | 4 | 4 | 5 | 6 | 7 | 7 | 7 | 7 | 9 | 7 | 11 |

We have

$$E(X) = 2\left(\tfrac{1}{36} + \tfrac{2}{36} + \tfrac{3}{36}\right) + 3\left(\tfrac{4}{36} + \tfrac{5}{36} + \tfrac{6}{36}\right) +$$
$$4\left(\tfrac{5}{36} + \tfrac{4}{36} + \tfrac{3}{36}\right) + 5\left(\tfrac{2}{36} + \tfrac{1}{36}\right) = \tfrac{120}{36} = \tfrac{10}{3};$$
$$E(Y) = 2\left(\tfrac{1}{36} + \tfrac{2}{36} + \tfrac{2}{36}\right) + 3\left(\tfrac{3}{36} + \tfrac{4}{36} + \tfrac{5}{36} + \tfrac{4}{36}\right) +$$
$$4\left(\tfrac{5}{36} + \tfrac{6}{36}\right) + 5\left(\tfrac{3}{36}\right) + 6\left(\tfrac{1}{36}\right) = \tfrac{123}{36}, \text{ and}$$
$$E(X+Y) = 4\left(\tfrac{1}{36} + \tfrac{2}{36}\right) + 5\left(\tfrac{3}{36}\right) + 6\left(\tfrac{4}{36}\right) +$$
$$7\left(\tfrac{5}{36} + \tfrac{6}{36} + \tfrac{5}{36} + \tfrac{4}{36} + \tfrac{2}{36}\right) + 9\left(\tfrac{3}{36}\right) + 11\left(\tfrac{1}{36}\right) = \tfrac{243}{36}$$

from which we see that $E(X+Y) = E(X) + E(Y)$. It can be shown that this and the corresponding result for subtraction hold in general.

> If X and Y are random variables on the same experiment, then
>
> $$E(X+Y) = E(X) + E(Y)$$   3
> $$E(X-Y) = E(X) - E(Y)$$   4

Problem 5

Let X and Y be random variables on the same experiment, with $E(X) = 12$ and $E(Y) = -9$. Find $E(-2X + 3Y)$.

Solution    Using equations **3** and **2**, $E(-2X+3Y)=E(-2X)+E(3Y)=$
$-2E(X)+3E(Y)=(-2)(12)+3(-9)=-51.$

Problem 6    Let $X_1, X_2, X_3, X_4$ be random variables on the same experiment,
with $E(X_1)=E(X_2)=10$, $E(X_3)=-8$, and $E(X_4)=100$. Find
$E(6X_1-(\frac{1}{5})X_2+(\frac{3}{4})X_3-0.02X_4)$.

Solution    By equations **2**, **3**, and **4**, $E(6X_1-(\frac{1}{5})X_2+(\frac{3}{4})X_3-0.02X_4)=$
$6E(X_1)-(\frac{1}{5})E(X_2)+(\frac{3}{4})E(X_3)-0.02E(X_4)=60-2-6-2=50.$

If X and Y are random variables on the same experiment, we
say that X is less than or equal to Y, written $X \le Y$, if for each
possible outcome of the experiment the number assigned by X is
less than or equal to the number assigned by Y.

Problem 7    A ball is drawn from an urn containing 1 red, 1 white, and 1 blue
ball. Which of the following random variables is less than or equal
to which?

| Outcome: | Red | White | Blue |
|---|---|---|---|
| $X_1$ | −2 | 4 | 7 |
| $X_2$ | −1 | 5 | 5 |
| $X_3$ | −3 | 4 | 6 |

Solution    $X_3 \le X_1$, because $-3 \le -2$, $4 \le 4$, and $6 \le 7$. Since $X_2$ assigns a
larger value to red than $X_1$ or $X_3$ but $X_2$ assigns a smaller value to
blue than $X_1$ or $X_3$, there are no other relations of this type
between these random variables, except of course $X_1 \le X_1$, $X_2 \le$
$X_2$, $X_3 \le X_3$.

We say $X_1$ and $X_2$ are *not comparable*.
Also, $X_2$ and $X_3$ are not comparable.

Suppose X and Y are random variables on the same experi-
ment and $X \le Y$. Let $a_1, a_2, \ldots, a_n$ be all the possible outcomes of
the experiment, let $x_1, x_2, \ldots, x_n$, respectively, be the values assigned
to these outcomes by X, and let $y_1, y_2, \ldots, y_n$, respectively, be the
values assigned by Y. By definition of the relation $X \le Y$ we have
$x_1 \le y_1$, $x_2 \le y_2$, $\ldots$, $x_n \le y_n$. Then $x_1P(a_1) \le y_1P(a_1)$, $x_2P(a_2) \le$
$y_2P(a_2), \ldots, x_nP(a_n) \le y_nP(a_n)$. Then $x_1P(a_1)+x_2P(a_2)+\ldots+x_nP(a_n)$
$\le y_1P(a_1)+y_2P(a_2)+\ldots+y_nP(a_n)$; that is, $E(X) \le E(Y)$. In
summary:

See Appendix A, Section 8, for the
rules for dealing with inequalities.

> If X and Y are random variables on the same
> experiment and $X \le Y$ then
> $$E(X) \le E(Y)$$

  **5**

In general there is no very useful result about the expectation
of the product of two random variables. However, if the random

Independence of random variables was discussed in Section 1 of this chapter.

variables are independent, then the following very pleasant result can be shown.

> If the random variables X and Y, defined on the same experiment, are independent, then
>
> $$E(XY) = E(X)E(Y)$$

**6**

**Problem 8**

In Problem 15 of Section 4.1 it was shown that the random variables X and Y on the billiard-ball experiment, defined by the tabulations

| x | P(X=x) | y | P(Y=y) |
|---|--------|---|--------|
| 5 | $\frac{1}{3}$ | 5 | $\frac{3}{5}$ |
| 10 | $\frac{2}{3}$ | 10 | $\frac{2}{5}$ |

**Solution**

were independent. Verify equation **6** for X and Y.

The values of xy are 25, 50, and 100. $P(XY = 25) = P(X = 5 \cap Y = 5) = (\frac{1}{3})(\frac{3}{5}) = \frac{1}{5}$, $P(XY = 50) = P((X = 5 \cap Y = 10) \cup (X = 10 \cap Y = 5)) = (\frac{1}{3})(\frac{2}{5}) + (\frac{2}{3})(\frac{3}{5}) = \frac{8}{15}$, and $P(XY = 100) = P(X = 10 \cap Y = 10) = (\frac{2}{3})(\frac{2}{5}) = \frac{4}{15}$. Then $E(XY) = 25(\frac{1}{5}) + 50(\frac{8}{15}) + 100(\frac{4}{15}) = \frac{175}{3}$, and $E(X)E(Y) = (5(\frac{1}{3}) + 10(\frac{2}{3}))(5(\frac{3}{5}) + 10(\frac{2}{5})) = (\frac{25}{3})(7) = \frac{175}{3}$ $\checkmark$.

**One final remark**

If a random variable assigns the same number to every possible outcome, then the expected value is obviously just that number. If, say, the random variable X assigns the number c to every possible outcome of an experiment, then the event X = c is certain, and therefore $E(X) = cP(X = c) = c \cdot 1 = c$. We may summarize this simply by stating that, if c is a constant, then

$$E(c) = c$$

**7**

**Exercises 4.2**

In Exercises 1 through 4 find E(X).

1.

| x | 1 | 2 | 3 | 4 | 5 |
|---|---|---|---|---|---|
| P(X=x) | $\frac{1}{4}$ | $\frac{1}{8}$ | $\frac{1}{4}$ | $\frac{1}{8}$ | $\frac{1}{4}$ |

2.

| x | -3 | $-\frac{1}{2}$ | 0 | 1 | $\frac{3}{2}$ |
|---|----|----|---|---|----|
| P(X=x) | $\frac{1}{3}$ | $\frac{1}{9}$ | $\frac{1}{9}$ | $\frac{1}{3}$ | $\frac{1}{9}$ |

3.

| x | 1 | $-\frac{1}{2}$ | $\frac{1}{3}$ | $-\frac{1}{4}$ | $\frac{1}{5}$ | $-\frac{1}{6}$ | $\frac{1}{7}$ |
|---|---|----|----|----|----|----|----|
| P(X=x) | $\frac{1}{10}$ | $\frac{1}{5}$ | $\frac{1}{10}$ | $\frac{1}{5}$ | $\frac{1}{10}$ | $\frac{1}{10}$ | $\frac{1}{5}$ |

4.

| x | $-\frac{3}{4}$ | $-\frac{7}{8}$ | $\frac{9}{8}$ | $-\frac{16}{15}$ | $\frac{17}{13}$ |
|---|---|---|---|---|---|
| P(X=x) | $\frac{1}{9}$ | $\frac{5}{252}$ | $\frac{2}{7}$ | $\frac{1}{3}$ | $\frac{1}{4}$ |

In Exercises 5 through 8 two balanced dice are tossed. Find the expected winnings per game, on the average.

5. 7 or 11, win 100; otherwise, lose 20.
6. At least 9, win 40; otherwise, lose 30.
7. A multiple of 3, win 300; a multiple of 5, lose 400; otherwise, win 100.

*See Appendix A, Section 2a, for powers, if needed.*

8. A power of 2, lose 4,000; a power of 3, win 5,000; a multiple of 5 or 6, win 8,000; otherwise, break even.
9. Sales at the largest PHE store in Memphis, Tennessee, on July 4 were as shown below. What was the expected typical sale?

*In the $5.00 or over class, the average sale was $6.00*

| Amount | $0.01 – $0.49 | 0.50 – 1.24 | 1.25 – 1.99 | 2.00 – 2.49 | 2.50 – 3.49 | 3.50 – 4.49 | 5.00 or over |
|---|---|---|---|---|---|---|---|
| Number of sales | 42 | 120 | 480 | 300 | 630 | 120 | 210 |

10. A group of hikers, sponsored by AC, started down Mt. Katahdin along the Appalachian Trail on July 4. In the first 24 hours they covered distances as follows.

| Miles | 0– 4.9 | 5– 9.9 | 10– 14.9 | 15– 19.9 | 20– 24.9 | 25– 29.9 | 30– 34.9 | 35 or over |
|---|---|---|---|---|---|---|---|---|
| Number of hikers | 4 | 7 | 9 | 22 | 6 | 6 | 2 | 1 |

What is the expected distance (in miles) covered by a hiker?

*1 kilometer $\doteq$ 0.62 mile.*

11. The data given in exercise 10 are mislabeled. The distances given are in kilometers. Explain how to use equation **2** to obtain the correct answer to the exercise.
12. My expected average loss in a certain game was $12.00 per play, but I felt lucky so I planned to try it. But then the stakes were raised by 250%. Now what is my expected average loss per game?

*Absolute value is discussed in Appendix A, Section 9.*

To each toss of two balanced dice, the random variable $X_1$ assigns the sum of the numbers that come up; $X_2$ assigns the absolute value of the difference of the numbers; $X_3$ assigns the product of the numbers; and $X_4$ assigns the average of the numbers. Exercises 13 through 21 apply to this situation.

13. Find $E(X_1)$, $E(X_2)$, $E(X_3)$, and $E(X_4)$.
14. Find $E(X_1 + X_2)$.
15. Find $E(X_3 - X_4)$.
16. Find $E(2X_1 - 3X_2 + X_3 - \frac{1}{2}X_4)$.
17. Does $E(X_1 X_2)$ equal $E(X_1)E(X_2)$?
18. Does $E(X_3/X_4) = E(X_3)/E(X_4)$?
19. Which of $X_1, X_2, X_3, X_4$ is $\leq$ which?

We are using "small" and "large" in
the sense of the number line. For example, $-7$ is smaller than $-2$.

*20. Let X be the random variable. Let min X ("minimum of X") be the
smallest number assigned by X and max X ("maximum of X") be
the largest number assigned by X. Prove that we always have
min $X \le E(X) \le$ max X.

21. Recall that AC employees are coded 0 if they are single, 1 if
married, and 2 if separated. Now 32% of the employees are single,
60% are married, and 8% are separated. What is the "expected
marital status" of an AC employee? What does your answer signify?

### Section 4.3
### Mean and
### Standard Deviation

Alan was unhappy with his score of 5,
but he had to agree with his teacher's
remark that he was lucky to have
come out that well, considering how
little homework he had done.

The accent in "arithmetic" in the
term "arithmetic average" is on the
third syllable: arith*me*tic average.

Alan's teacher at Local College gives a 10-point quiz each week.
Twenty-one students took the first quiz, and their scores were:
$2, 3, 4, 5, 6, 6, 6, 7, 7, 7, 7, 8, 8, 8, 8, 9, 9, 9, 10, 10$. The sum of these
scores is 147. Since there are 21 scores, the "average" score is
$\frac{147}{21} = 7$. This sort of average, obtained by adding the scores and
dividing by the number of students, is called the **arithmetic average**
or **mean** score. The second test also had a mean of 7, but the
distribution of scores was somewhat different: $3, 4, 4, 5, 6, 6,$
$7, 7, 7, 7, 7, 7, 7, 8, 8, 8, 8, 9, 9, 10, 10$. (Again there are 21 scores total-
ing 147.) Obviously there are many different ways that 21 grades
can have a mean score of 7. On the third quiz, for example, the
instructor made the mistake of asking a very easy question worth 7
points and a very hard question worth 3 points. The grade distribution was: $7, 7, 7, 7, 7, 7, 7, 7, 7, 7, 7, 7, 7, 7, 7, 7, 7, 7, 7, 7, 7$. Again, the
mean was 7.

Consider the experiment of picking a student in Alan's class
at random. Let $X_1$ be the student's score on quiz 1, $X_2$ her score on
quiz 2, and $X_3$ her score on quiz 3. Then, for example, since three
of the 21 students got a 6 on quiz 1, $P(X_1 = 6) = \frac{3}{21} = \frac{1}{7}$. In the same
way, $P(X_2 = 6) = \frac{2}{21}$, since only 2 students got a 6 on quiz 2, and
$P(X_3 = 6) = 0$, since no student got a 6 on quiz 3. The distributions
of the three random variables are given below

Table 4

| x | 2 | 3 | 4 | 5 | 6 | 7 | 8 | 9 | 10 |
|---|---|---|---|---|---|---|---|---|---|
| $P(X_1 = x)$ | $\frac{1}{21}$ | $\frac{1}{21}$ | $\frac{1}{21}$ | $\frac{1}{21}$ | $\frac{3}{21}$ | $\frac{4}{21}$ | $\frac{5}{21}$ | $\frac{3}{21}$ | $\frac{2}{21}$ |

Table 5

| x | 2 | 3 | 4 | 5 | 6 | 7 | 8 | 9 | 10 |
|---|---|---|---|---|---|---|---|---|---|
| $P(X_2 = x)$ | $\frac{0}{21}$ | $\frac{1}{21}$ | $\frac{2}{21}$ | $\frac{1}{21}$ | $\frac{2}{21}$ | $\frac{7}{21}$ | $\frac{4}{21}$ | $\frac{2}{21}$ | $\frac{2}{21}$ |

Table 6

| x | 7 |
|---|---|
| $P(X_3 = x)$ | $\frac{21}{21}$ |

The expected value or expectation of $X_1$, as defined in Section 4.2, is $E(X_1) = 2(\frac{1}{21}) + 3(\frac{1}{21}) + \ldots + 10(\frac{2}{21}) = \frac{147}{21}$, which is also the mean score. Moreover, $E(X_2) = 7$ and $E(X_3) = 7$. It can be shown that this is always the case: given any finite list of numbers, consider the experiment of choosing one of the numbers at random. Let X be the random variable that assigns to each possible outcome of the experiment the number chosen. Then $E(X)$ is just the mean of the numbers in the list.

**Problem 1**

Forty-five people in a parapsychology experiment were each asked to think of a number from 1 to 10 and write it on a slip of paper. The response was as follows:

**Table 7**

| Number written | 1 | 2 | 3 | 4 | 5 | 6 | 7 | 8 | 9 | 10 |
|---|---|---|---|---|---|---|---|---|---|---|
| Number of people who wrote it | 9 | 3 | 2 | 5 | 5 | 2 | 4 | 6 | 1 | 8 |

(a) What is the mean of the numbers written?
(b) Consider the experiment of picking a slip at random. Let X be the random variable that assigns to each slip the number written on it. Find $E(X)$.

**Solution**

(a) The mean is $1 + 1 + \ldots + 2 + 2 + 2 + 3 + 3 + 4 + \ldots + 10 + \ldots +$ 10 divided by 45, where there are 9 1s, 3 2s,..., and 8 10s. In other words the mean is $1 \cdot 9 + 2 \cdot 3 + 3 \cdot 2 + 4 \cdot 5 + 5 \cdot 5 + 6 \cdot 2 + 7 \cdot 4 + 8 \cdot 6 + 9 \cdot 1 + 10 \cdot 8 = 243$ divided by 45: $\frac{243}{45} = 5.4$.

(b) By what was said before the problem, $E(X)$ is the same as the mean: $E(X) = 5.4$. We can also see this from the table above:

$$E(X) = 1P(X=1) + 2P(X=2) + 3P(X=3) + 4P(X=4) + 5P(X=5) +$$

$$6P(X=6) + 7P(X=7) + 8P(X=8) + 9P(X=9) + 10P(X=10) =$$

$$1\left(\frac{9}{45}\right) + 2\left(\frac{3}{45}\right) + 3\left(\frac{2}{45}\right) + 4\left(\frac{5}{45}\right) + 5\left(\frac{5}{45}\right)6\left(\frac{2}{45}\right) + 7\left(\frac{4}{45}\right) + 8\left(\frac{6}{45}\right) + 9\left(\frac{1}{45}\right) + 10\left(\frac{8}{45}\right) =$$

$$(9 \cdot 1 + 3 \cdot 2 + 2 \cdot 3 + 5 \cdot 4 + 5 \cdot 5 + 2 \cdot 6 + 4 \cdot 7 + 6 \cdot 8 + 1 \cdot 9 + 8 \cdot 10)/45 =$$

$$\frac{243}{45} = 5.4.$$

This should make it clear why the mean and the expectation are the same.

Returning to the three quizzes in Alan's class, we see that the
mean gives, in some sense, the "typical" or "expected" score, but it
tells nothing about how the scores were arranged so as to give the
mean. The scores in the first quiz were more spread out than those
on the second quiz, and the scores on the third quiz were not
spread out at all. It is useful to have a number that measures the
degree of spread of the scores. One such number, called the
**variance**, has been found to be especially important. To find the
variance of the scores:

Step 1   Find the mean of the scores.
Step 2   Subtract the mean from each score.
Step 3   Square the numbers obtained in Step 2.
Step 4   Find the mean of the numbers obtained in Step 3. This is the variance of the scores.

For quiz 1 the mean was 7. We calculate:

Table 8

For instance, $(-5)^2 = (-5)(-5) = 5 \cdot 5 = 5^2 = 25$.

| Score | Score − 7 | (Score − 7)$^2$ |
|-------|-----------|------------------|
| 2  | −5 | 25 |
| 3  | −4 | 16 |
| 4  | −3 | 9  |
| 5  | −2 | 4  |
| 6  | −1 | 1  |
| 6  | −1 | 1  |
| 6  | −1 | 1  |
| 7  | 0  | 0  |
| 7  | 0  | 0  |
| 7  | 0  | 0  |
| 7  | 0  | 0  |
| 8  | 1  | 1  |
| 8  | 1  | 1  |
| 8  | 1  | 1  |
| 8  | 1  | 1  |
| 8  | 1  | 1  |
| 9  | 2  | 4  |
| 9  | 2  | 4  |
| 9  | 2  | 4  |
| 10 | 3  | 9  |
| 10 | 3  | 9  |

TOTAL: 92,
Variance $= \frac{92}{21} \doteq 4.38$

We can shorten the calculation somewhat by combining like

Random Variables and Probability
Distributions

scores. We do this in calculating the variance for quiz 2:

Table 9

| Score | Frequency | Score−7 | (Score−7)² | Frequency×(Score−7)² |
|---|---|---|---|---|
| 3 | 1 | −4 | 16 | 16 |
| 4 | 2 | −3 | 9 | 18 |
| 5 | 1 | −2 | 4 | 4 |
| 6 | 2 | −1 | 1 | 2 |
| 7 | 7 | 0 | 0 | 0 |
| 8 | 4 | 1 | 1 | 4 |
| 9 | 2 | 2 | 4 | 8 |
| 10 | 2 | 3 | 9 | 18 |

TOTAL: 70,

Variance $=\frac{70}{21}=\frac{10}{3}\doteq 3.33$

For quiz 3 we have the score 7 with frequency 21; so we compute $21(7-7)^2=21\cdot 0=0$, and we find that the variance is $\frac{0}{21}$. Of course it's zero; the scores do not vary at all.

It may seem reasonable but rather arbitrary to use the square of the difference between the scores and the means in calculating the variance. Why not use some other power of this difference? For that matter, why use a power at all? There are two answers to these questions. First, other powers besides the second power (the square) are sometimes used, and they do provide further information about the spread of the data. Second and more importantly, mathematicians can prove useful theorems about the variance. We will explore some of the applications in the following section. For now let us observe merely that some other measures of the spread of data are used at times, but so far mathematicians have been unable to use these other measures as effectively as they have used the variance.

The first power, however, is not used, because it provides *no* information. See Exercise 7.

We have seen that the mean of a random variable is equal to its expectation. Thus, for example, the mean of the random variable $X_2$ of quiz 2 above is $E(X_2)=7$. We show now that the variance of $X_2$, which we calculated above, is equal to the expectation of $(X_2-7)^2$. The values of $(X_2-7)^2$ are, from column four of Table 9: 0, 1, 4, 9. and 16. Then, for example, $P((X_2-7)^2=4)=P(X_2=5)+P(X_2=9)=\frac{1}{21}+\frac{2}{21}=\frac{3}{21}$. The full calculation of $E((X_2=7)^2)$ appears in Table 10.

Table 10

| x | $P(X_2-7)^2=x)$ | $xP((X_2-7)^2=x)$ |
|---|---|---|
| 0 | $\frac{7}{21}$ | 0 |
| 1 | $\frac{6}{21}$ | $\frac{6}{21}$ |
| 4 | $\frac{3}{21}$ | $\frac{12}{21}$ |
| 9 | $\frac{4}{21}$ | $\frac{36}{21}$ |
| 16 | $\frac{1}{21}$ | $\frac{16}{21}$ |

TOTAL: $\frac{70}{21}=E((X_2-7)^2)=$ Variance

These results connecting mean and variance with expectation hold in general, as can be shown.

> Given any list of numbers, let X be the random variable for the experiment of picking a number on the list at random. Then, the mean of the numbers on the list is
>
> $$m = E(X) \qquad\qquad \textbf{1}$$
>
> and the variance of the numbers on the list is
>
> $$v = E\big((X-m)^2\big) \qquad\qquad \textbf{2}$$

**Problem 2**  The scores on the midterm exam in Alan's class were:

**Table 11**

| Score | 40 | 50 | 60 | 65 | 70 | 75 | 80 | 85 | 90 | 100 |
|---|---|---|---|---|---|---|---|---|---|---|
| Frequency | 1 | 1 | 1 | 2 | 3 | 6 | 2 | 3 | 1 | 1 |

Find the mean and variance.

**Solution**  The mean  $m = (40 \cdot 1 + 50 \cdot 1 + 60 \cdot 1 + 65 \cdot 2 + 70 \cdot 3 + 75 \cdot 6 + 80 \cdot 2 + 85 \cdot 3 + 90 \cdot 1 + 100 \cdot 1)/21 = \frac{1545}{21} \doteq 74$.

The variance  $v = (34^2 \cdot 1 + 24^2 \cdot 1 + 14^2 \cdot 1 + 9^2 \cdot 2 + 4^2 \cdot 3 + 1^2 \cdot 6 + 6^2 \cdot 3 + 11^2 \cdot 1 + 16^2 \cdot 1 + 26^2 \cdot 1)/21 = \frac{3,305}{21} \doteq 157$.

The **standard deviation** of a list of numbers is the square root of the variance:

$$s = \sqrt{v} \qquad\qquad \textbf{3}$$

For square roots, see Table I, Appendix B, p. 514.

Thus, the standard deviation of midterm scores in Alan's class is $s = \sqrt{157} \doteq 13$. Since the variance involves the squares of differences, taking the square root restores the scale of this measure to the scale of the original data. For instance if the data were a list of heights of students in inches, then the variance would be in square inches but the standard deviation would be in inches, like the heights themselves. So the standard deviation, s, really is a more "natural" measure of spread than is v.

We close with a note on "false accuracy." In the solution to Problem 2 we obtain $m = \frac{1,545}{21}$, which we calculated to be 74% to the nearest percent. A more accurate decimal approximation to $\frac{1545}{21}$ is 73.57%. But is there really any more accuracy in saying that the mean midterm grade was 73.57%? It is certainly true that 73.57 is a more accurate approximation to the mean of the numbers in the problem than is 74. But the numbers in the problem are not merely numbers; they are supposedly a measure of the students' achievement. As such, each test score is only an approximate measure of that student's knowledge. Even a very well designed and carefully graded exam is not likely to be able to gauge a student's knowledge to within less than 5%. In other words, a test score of 65 is *at best* telling us that the student has learned somewhere between 60 and 70% of the material.

Now, if a random variable X is measuring something to within an error of plus or minus c, then $X - c \leq X \leq X + c$. By results **3, 4, 5,** and **7** of the previous section. $E(X - c) \leq E(X) \leq E(X + c)$, $E(X) - E(c) \leq E(X) \leq E(X) + E(c)$, and $E(X) - c \leq E(X) \leq E(X) + c$. Thus, the mean value of the phenomenon being measured is only known to within plus or minus c. In the case of Problem 2, then, assuming the test scores are accurate to within 5%, the mean of 73.57 really only signifies that the average result is somewhere between about 69% and 79%. The mean score of 73.57 has no more useful accuracy than the mean score of 74; in fact, a more truthful mean would be "mid to low 70s."

The sort of false accuracy represented by the 73.57 mean above rarely occurs in reports of results of the so-called hard sciences, where detailed error estimates are usually given and substantiated. Unfortunately, false accuracy does occasionally appear in the social sciences, business, and popular writing. Let the reader beware.

**Exercises 4.3**

In Exercises 1 through 6 find the mean, variance, and standard deviation of each list of numbers. What can you conclude from a comparison of the results of Exercises 5 and 6?

1. $1, 3, 3, 3, 5, 5, 6, 6, 6, 6, 7, 9$.
2. $-6, -6, -4, -2, -2, -2, -2, -2, 0, 0, 0, 0, 0, 12, 17, 17$.

3.
| Number | $-\frac{4}{5}$ | 3 | $-\frac{1}{3}$ | $\frac{3}{4}$ | $-7$ | 16 |
|---|---|---|---|---|---|---|
| Frequency | 10 | 2 | 18 | 12 | 1 | 0 |

4.
| Number | $-\frac{4}{5}$ | 3 | $-\frac{1}{3}$ | $\frac{3}{4}$ | $-7$ | 16 |
|---|---|---|---|---|---|---|
| Frequency | 2 | 10 | 12 | 18 | 0 | 1 |

5. $1, 1, 3, 7$.
ᶜ6. $-1, 3, 5, 5$.

7. Let X be a random variable with mean m. Use equation **1** and equation **3** from Section 2 to show that $E(X - m) = 0$. Now see the marginal note on p. 260.

The **median** of a list of numbers is the "middle" number, which is found as follows. Arrange the numbers in nondecreasing order. If the number of numbers is odd, the middle number of the arrangement is the median. If the number of numbers is even, the mean of the two numbers

The number halfway between two numbers a and b is their mean, $(a + b)/2$.

on each side of the middle of the arrangement is the median. Examples:

$$\text{median} = 3$$
$$\downarrow$$
$$0, 1, 1, 1, 2, 3, 3, 3, 3, 4, 4, 5, 5$$

$$\text{median} = \tfrac{2+3}{2} = 2.5$$
$$\downarrow$$
$$0, 1, 1, 1, 2, 3, 3, 3, 3, 4$$

$$\text{median} = \tfrac{3+3}{2} = 3$$
$$\downarrow$$
$$1, 1, 2, 3, 3, 3, 3, 4$$

In Exercises 8 through 11 find the mean and the median of the given lists. What can you conclude about the relative size of the mean and the median?

8. $1, 2, 3, 4, 5$
9. $0, 2, 3, 4, 5$
10. $1, 2, 3, 4, 6$
11.

| Number | $-\frac{1}{3}$ | $-\frac{1}{2}$ | 0 | $\frac{2}{3}$ | $\frac{1}{2}$ |
|---|---|---|---|---|---|
| Frequency | 6 | 8 | 10 | 12 | 14 |

Let M be the median of a list of numbers. Let X be the random variable for the experiment of picking a number at random from the list. In each of Exercises 12 through 20, tell whether the statement made is true for every list of numbers, true for some lists but false for others, or never true. Give reasons or examples to support your answers.

12. $P(X < M) = \frac{1}{2}$.
13. $P(X \le M) = \frac{1}{2}$.
14. $P(X < M) = P(X > M)$.
15. $P(X \le M) = P(X \ge M)$.
16. $P(X < M)$ and $P(X > M)$ are each at most $\frac{1}{2}$.
17. $P(X \le M)$ and $P(X \ge M)$ are each at most $\frac{1}{2}$.
18. $P(X = M) > 0$.
19. There is always a number T such that $P(X < T)$ and $P(X > T)$ are at most $\frac{1}{2}$.
20. There is never more than one number T such that $P(X < T)$ and $P(X > T)$ are each at most $\frac{1}{2}$.

21. Let X be a random variable with variance v.
   *(a) Prove that $v = E(X^2) - (E(X))^2$.
   (b) State result (a) in words.
   (c) Check result (a) for the list $-3, -2, -2, 0, 1, 2, 2, 4$.
22. Use result (a) of Exercise 21 to prove that if c is a constant and X is a random variable then the variance of $X + c$ is the same as the variance of X.

Geologists actually use the 4th moment, called the *kurtosis* ("peakedness"), in studies of sand and gravel deposits.

Let X be a random variable with mean $m = E(X)$ and let n be a positive integer. The nth *central moment* of X is defined as $E((X - m)^n)$. Thus, the variance of X is the 2nd central moment of X. The following exercise refers to central moment.

23. PHE has some detailed data on a large sample of its so-called 200-gram meat patties. Find the 2nd, 3rd, and 4th moments of the data.

| Weight range (grams) | Percent of patties |
|---|---|
| $185\frac{1}{2}$–$195\frac{1}{2}$ | 8 |
| $195\frac{1}{2}$–$205\frac{1}{2}$ | 18 |
| $205\frac{1}{2}$–$215\frac{1}{2}$ | 12 |
| $215\frac{1}{2}$–$225\frac{1}{2}$ | 15 |
| $225\frac{1}{2}$–$235\frac{1}{2}$ | 21 |
| $235\frac{1}{2}$–$245\frac{1}{2}$ | 19 |
| $245\frac{1}{2}$–$255\frac{1}{2}$ | 7 |

(The patties are weighted to the nearest whole gram.)

**Section 4.4**
**The Binomial and**
**Geometric Distributions**

Life is filled with success-failure situations. Janet feels that she has a 40% chance of success in getting a raise this month. In his weekly dice game, Alan knows that the probability is $\frac{8}{36}$ that he will have success (that is, get a 7 or 11) on the first throw. The AC testing lab believes that 95% of the tent fabric it receives is satisfactory. Thus, it expects a given piece of fabric to fail its test only about 5% of the time. A success-failure situation is an experiment with exactly two outcomes, called a **trial**. For such experiments we will follow the standard practice of calling one outcome **success** and the other **failure** even in cases when these words are neither appropriate nor meaningful. For example, we can regard the flip of a balanced coin as a trial if we agree (for no particular reason) to call one of the possible outcomes success and the other failure. Note that any experiment with two or more outcomes can be converted into a trial in many different ways: simply regard some of the possible outcomes as successes and the others as failures.

Perhaps *guilty* and *not guilty* would more appropriate designations for the outcomes of a trial.

Problem 1

Solution

If the card is chosen at random from a regular 52-card deck, then there are $2^{52} = 4,503,599,627,370,496$, different correct answers to this problem.

Convert the experiment "pick a card, any card" into a trial. Here are three different possible answers.
(i) Let success be "a heart is chosen." Now when I pick a card there are only 2 possible results: either the card is a heart or it is not a heart.
(ii) Let success be "an ace is chosen." The sample space for this trial is {ace, not ace}.
(iii) Call "the 3 of spades is chosen" success and call "the 3 of spades is not chosen" failure.

In this section we will discuss experiments which consist of a sequence of trials. For example, AC performs such an experiment each time it receives a shipment of fabric. The lab selects 20 different swatches of material at random and tests them. Each of the 20 tests is a trial in which success means that the fabric passes inspection. If more than one of these trials results in failure, the entire batch is rejected. In another example, Janet gave a written exam to 5 junior programmers on 5 different days. In each of the 5 trials success meant that the programmer passed the exam and failure meant just that. For a more theoretical example, consider the experiment of throwing 4 balanced dice and counting the number of dice that show 3 or higher. This experiment may be regarded as a sequence of 4 trials. In each trial one die is thrown and success is the outcome "3 or more."

There are two useful sample spaces for such experiments. The simplest is a list of numbers $0, 1, 2, \ldots$ that indicate the number of successes that occur. For example, if 2 of the 4 dice come up 3 or higher then the outcome "2" occurs. However, for the moment we will be concerned with the much larger sample space consisting of all possible lists of the outcomes of each trial. For example, in the experiment of throwing 4 dice we would list sixteen 4-tuples $(—,—,—,—)$, where "success" or " failure" is written in each blank depending upon the outcome on the particular die (the result on the first die is recorded in the first blank, and so on). An event such as "success occurs on trial 4" would consist of all 4-tuples with success in the fourth blank:

|  |  |
|---|---|
| $(S, S, S, S)$ | $(F, S, S, S)$ |
| $(S, S, F, S)$ | $(F, S, F, S)$ |
| $(S, F, S, S)$ | $(F, F, S, S)$ |
| $(S, F, F, S)$ | $(F, F, F, S)$ |

*We will discuss this sample space later in this section.*

*In this list S denotes success and F denotes failure.*

For an experiment with more than 4 trials, we need much longer lists. While we do not care how many trials are involved in the experiment, it will be convenient to make certain other assumptions. We will limit ourselves to so-called **Bernoulli trials**, as described below.

*The list of all possible outcomes in the 20-trial AC fabric test experiment would contain 1,048,576 elements. Fortunately, we will never need to write out any of these sample spaces.*

*Jacques Bernoulli I (1654–1705) was the first to describe this model.*

> A Bernoulli trials experiment is any experiment that can be regarded as a sequence of trials in which (1) the probability of success is the same for each trial and (2) the event of success on any given trial is independent of the outcomes of all previous trials.

Here S denotes success (the die comes up 3 or more) and F denotes failure (the die comes up 1 or 2).

It is easy to draw a tree diagram for a Bernoulli trials experiment: each branch splits into two branches, namely "success" or "failure." Here for example, is the diagram for the dice experiment described on page 265.

Figure 1

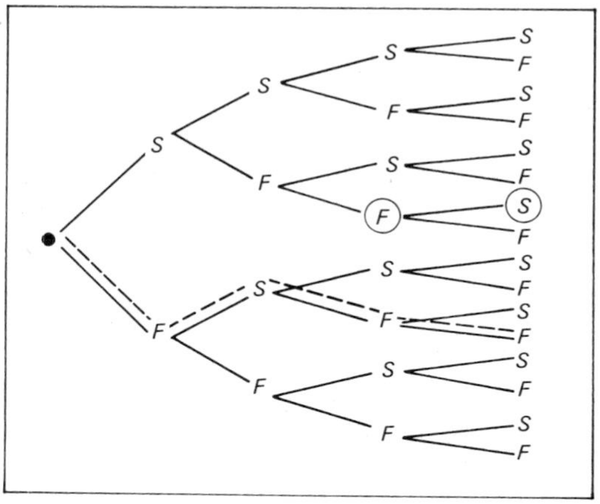

The chance of success on each trial is $\frac{4}{6} = \frac{2}{3}$, and the chance of failure is $1 - \frac{2}{3} = \frac{1}{3}$. Now consider, for example, the branches between the circled entries in Figure 1. What probability do we write on this branch? In a general multistage process the probability on this branch is

See Section 3.2, if needed.

$$P(\text{success on trial 4} \mid \text{success on trial 1}$$
$$\text{and failure on trials 2 and 3})$$

By condition (2) of the definition of Bernoulli trials this is simply P(success on trial 4), since the event "success on trial 4" is independent of the event "success on trial 1 and failure on trials 2 and 3." Moreover by condition (1) of the definition we have, in our example, P(success on trial 4) $= \frac{2}{3}$. Thus, the probability for the branch in question is $\frac{2}{3}$. In the same way we see that the probability for every branch that ends with S is $\frac{2}{3}$ and the probability for every branch that ends with F is $\frac{1}{3}$. In other words, every branch of Figure 1 that slants up should have $\frac{2}{3}$ on it and every branch that slants down should have $\frac{1}{3}$ on it.

While we may not be able to rigorously prove that the conditions required for a Bernoulli trials experiment hold in a given "real world" situation, it is often the case that we feel rather certain that they do. In the fabric test at AC, for instance, if the 20 swatches are selected at random, so that the fabric selected for one swatch does not affect the choice of another swatch, then the Bernoulli trials experiment model should be relevant. In fact the definition of independence given in Section 1.5 tries to capture this idea of "no effect" in a mathematically useful way. For the remainder of this text we will declare events to be *independent* if it is "obvious" that they have no effect on one another.

As we saw in Section 1.5, it is possible for an event A to have an effect on the event B but for A and B to be independent. What we are saying here is if A has no effect of any kind on B then *certainly* A and B are independent.

While there are cases in which it is difficult to use the definition of Bernoulli trials, a clear understanding of your practical situation and of the mathematical model presented here will generally enable you to decide whether or not the Bernoulli trials experiment model is appropriate.

It is obvious that, when I throw four balanced dice and count how many come up 3 or more, I am conducting a Bernoulli trials experiment. Here the probability of success on any trial is $\frac{2}{3}$ and the result on one die does not affect the results on the other dice. The AC example is also a Bernoulli trials experiment. We do not know the exact probability of selecting a good swatch of fabric from a batch. Yet if we select at random, then this probability will be the same for each of the 20 trials. We have already remarked that these trials are independent. Janet thought that she was conducting a Bernoulli trials experiment when she examined the five programmers. However, she later discovered that both requirements for Bernoulli trials were violated. In the first place, two of the programmers were much better trained and so had a higher probability of success. In the second place, she caught all of them discussing the exam before some of them had taken it, so the trials were not independent.

We are assuming that the batch is so large that removing one small swatch does not significantly affect the relative proportions of good and bad fabric.

**Problem 2**

I throw 4 balanced dice. What is the probability that exactly 3 of the dice come up 1 or 2?

**Solution**

Referring to Figure 1, we are looking for sequences of 4 trials in which there are exactly 3 failures, and hence 1 success. One such sequence is shown by the dotted line: failure on first trial and success on second trial and failure on third trial and failure on fourth trial. We may abbreviate this: $F_1 \cap S_2 \cap F_3 \cap F_4$. What is the probability of this particular sequence? Since $F_1 \cap S_2 \cap F_3$ and $F_4$ are independent, we have

In Equation **11** of Section 1.5 take $A = F_1 \cap S_2 \cap F_3, B = F_4$.

$$P(F_1 \cap S_2 \cap F_3 \cap F_4) = P(F_1 \cap S_2 \cap F_3)P(F_4) \qquad \mathbf{1}$$

by equation **11** of Section 1.5. Since $F_1 \cap S_2$ and $F_3$ are independent, we have

Now take $A = F_1 \cap S_2, B = F_3$.

$$P(F_1 \cap S_2 \cap F_3) = P(F_1 \cap S_2)P(F_3) \qquad \mathbf{2}$$

Finally, since $F_1$ and $S_2$ are independent,

$$P(F_1 \cap S_2) = P(F_1)P(S_2) \qquad \qquad \textbf{3}$$

Then from equations **4** and **3** we have

$$P(F_1 \cap S_2 \cap F_3) = P(F_1)P(S_2)P(F_3) \qquad \qquad \textbf{4}$$

and from equations **5** and **2**,

$$P(F_1 \cap S_2 \cap F_3 \cap F_4) = P(F_1)P(S_2)P(F_3)P(F_4) \qquad \qquad \textbf{5}$$

There are 3 other sequences of trials having 3 failures and and 1 success. Their probabilities are:

$$P(F_1 \cap F_2 \cap F_3 \cap S_4) = P(F_1)P(F_2)P(F_3)P(S_4) \qquad \qquad \textbf{6}$$

$$P(F_1 \cap F_2 \cap S_3 \cap F_4) = P(F_1)P(F_2)P(S_3)P(F_4) \qquad \qquad \textbf{7}$$

$$P(S_1 \cap F_2 \cap F_3 \cap F_4) = P(S_1)P(F_2)P(F_3)P(F_4) \qquad \qquad \textbf{8}$$

Now each pair of events in equations **5, 6, 7,** and **8** are disjoint, and they comprise a partition of the event "three failures and one

*Recall equation **4**, Section 3.2.*

success." Thus, the probability we seek is the sum of the probabilities of these events. The probability of success in any one trial is $\frac{2}{3}$ and that of failure is $\frac{1}{3}$; that is, $P(S_1) = P(S_2) = P(S_3) = P(S_4) = \frac{2}{3}$ and $P(F_1) = P(F_2) = P(F_3) = P(F_4) = \frac{1}{3}$. Then the right-hand side of equation **5** is $(\frac{1}{3})(\frac{2}{3})(\frac{1}{3})(\frac{1}{3}) = (\frac{1}{3})^3(\frac{2}{3})$. In fact, the right-hand side of each of equations **5, 6, 7,** and **8** is the product of three $\frac{1}{3}$'s and one $\frac{2}{3}$, that is, $(\frac{1}{3})^3(\frac{2}{3})$. Then the answer to our problem is simply $4(\frac{1}{3})^3(\frac{2}{3})$ $= 4(\frac{1}{27})(\frac{2}{3}) = \frac{8}{81} \doteq 0.10$.

This sort of repetition of fractions occurs in all computations for Bernoulli trials experiments. We take advantage of this fact in the following problem.

*Problem 3*

Six balanced dice are thrown. What is the probability that exactly 2 of the dice come up at least 5?

*Solution*

This is a Bernoulli trials experiment with 6 trials, probability of success $p = P(\text{at least } 5) = P(5, 6) = \frac{1}{6} + \frac{1}{6} = \frac{1}{3}$, and probability of failure $1 - p = \frac{2}{3}$.

We do not really need to list every sequence of outcomes with exactly two successes. Each such sequence will contain two successes, each with probability $\frac{1}{3}$, and four failures, each with probability $\frac{2}{3}$. Thus, the probability of each possible outcome is the product of the fractions $\frac{1}{3}, \frac{1}{3}, \frac{2}{3}, \frac{2}{3}, \frac{2}{3}, \frac{2}{3}$ in some order. Since the order in which fractions are multiplied is irrelevant, each of these products is equal to $(\frac{1}{3})^2(\frac{2}{3})^4$. How many possible outcomes are there? There are six trials and we must choose two of them to be

*The symbol $C_r^n$ was defined in Section 1.4.*

successes. There are $C_2^6$ such choices. Once we have decided which

In Problem 2 we had to select one of the four trials as success. There were $C_1^4 = 4$ possible outcomes each with probability $(\frac{1}{3})^3(\frac{2}{3})$.

two of the six trials are to be successes, we have determined the outcome: the remaining four trials must be failures. Thus, there are $C_2^6 = 15$ possible outcomes, each with probability $(\frac{1}{3})^2(\frac{2}{3})^4$. The required probability is $15(\frac{1}{3})^2(\frac{2}{3})^4 = 15 \times \frac{16}{729} = \frac{240}{729} = \frac{80}{243} \doteq .329$.

We can apply the method of Problems 2 and 3 to any Bernoulli trials experiment with a fixed number of trials. Suppose there are n trials. In a Bernoulli trials experiment, the probability of success is the same for each trial. Let this probability be p. Since "failure" is "not success," the probability of failure is $1 - p$. Finally, let k be one of the numbers $0, 1, 2, \ldots, n$. If an outcome has exactly k successes, then it must have exactly $n - k$ failures. In a Bernoulli trials experiment, the outcomes of the trials are independent. Thus, by calculations like those in Problem 2, the probability of each of these outcomes is the product of k p's and $n - k$ $(1 - p)$'s, that is, $p^k(1 - p)^{n-k}$. There are $C_k^n$ ways to choose the k trials that result in success. Each such choice completely determines the outcome, since all the trials not selected must be failures. It follows that the probability of exactly k successes is $C_k^n p^k(1 - p)^{n-k}$.

This formula holds in the "extreme" cases where we are interested in the probability of no successes ($k = 0$) or in the probability of all successes ($k = n$). In these cases we must interpret $C_0^n$, $p^0$ and $(1 - p)^0$ as 1. This interpretation is always made, and it can be justified mathematically.

> In a Bernoulli trials experiment with n trials in which the probability of success is p, the probability of exactly k successes is
>
> $$C_k^n p^k(1 - p)^{n-k}$$

**9**

**Problem 4**

Janet made up another exam and gave it to all five programmers at the same time. Assuming each programmer has a 60% chance of passing, what is the probability that at least 4 programmers pass?

**Solution**

Now Janet does have a Bernoulli trials experiment, with $n = 5$ and $p = 0.6$. Then by equation **9**, P (at least 4 pass) = P (exactly 4 successes) + P (exactly 5 successes) = $P(k = 4) + P(k = 5) = C_4^5(0.6)^4 (1 - 0.6)^1 + C_5^5(0.6)^5 (1 - 0.6)^0 = 5(0.6)^4 (0.4) + 1(0.6)^5 = 0.25920 + 0.07776 = 0.33696$.

**Problem 5**

AC receives a batch of tent fabric which in the past has failed its test 8 times out of 10 on the average. If they test 6 swatches, selected at random, what are the chances that at least 1 swatch passes the test?

**Solution**

In this Bernoulli trials experiment, $n = 6$ and $p = 1 - \frac{8}{10} = 0.2$. The hard way: P (at least one success) = $P(k = 1) + P(k = 2) + P(k = 3)$

$+ P(k = 4) + P(k = 5) + P(k = 6) = C_1^6 (0.2)(0.8)^5 + C_2^6 (0.2)^2 (0.8)^4 + C_3^6 (0.2)^3 (0.8)^3 + C_4^6 (0.2)^4 (0.8)^2 + C_5^6 (0.2)^5 (0.8) + C_6^6 (0.2)^6 (0.8)^0 = 0.737856$, Phew! And now for the easy way: P(at least one success) $= 1 - P$ (not at least one success) $= 1 - P$ (no success) $= 1 - P(k = 0)$ $= 1 - C_0^6 (0.2)^0 (0.8)^6 = 1 - 0.262144 = 0.737856$. The moral: don't forget the results in Chapter 1; they might come in handy.

If we regard each sequence of n trials as a *single* performance of a Bernoulli trials experiment, and if we regard the number of successes as the outcome of the performance, then the sample space is $S = \{0, 1, 2, \ldots, n\}$ and the probability distribution is:

| Possible outcomes | Probability |
|---|---|
| 0 | $C_0^n p^0 (1 - p)^{n-0} = (1 - p)^n$ |
| 1 | $C_1^n p^1 (1 - p)^{n-1} = np(1 - p)^n$ |
| 2 | $C_2^n p^2 (1 - p)^{n-2} = \frac{1}{2} n(n-1) p^2 (1 - p)^{n-2}$ |
| . | . |
| . | . |
| . | . |
| n − 1 | $C_{n-1}^n p^{n-1} (1 - p)^1 = np^{n-1}(1 - p)$ |
| n | $C_n^n p^n (1 - p)^0 = p^n$ |

It is called the binomial distribution because each product on the right involves a binomial coefficient $C_r^n$. (See the beginning of the next section.)

This probability distribution is called the **binomial distribution** for n and p. Thus, the distribution of the random variable that gives the number of successes in a Bernoulli trials experiment with n trials and success probability p is the binomial distribution for n and p.

**Problem 6**  Find, to 3D accuracy, the binomial distribution for $n = 9, p = 0.2$.

For calculation of $C_r^n$ see page 32.

| k | Probability | 3D |
|---|---|---|
| 0 | $C_0^9 (0.2)^0 (0.8)^9 = (0.8)^9$ | 0.134 |
| 1 | $C_1^9 (0.2)^1 (0.8)^8 = 9(0.2)(0.8)^8$ | 0.302 |
| 2 | $C_2^9 (0.2)^2 (0.8)^7 = 36(0.2)^2 (0.8)^7$ | 0.302 |
| 3 | $C_3^9 (0.2)^3 (0.8)^6 = 84(0.2)^3 (0.8)^6$ | 0.176 |
| 4 | $C_4^9 (0.2)^4 (0.8)^5 = 126(0.2)^4 (0.8)^5$ | 0.066 |
| 5 | $C_5^9 (0.2)^5 (0.8)^4 = 126(0.2)^5 (0.8)^4$ | 0.017 |
| 6 | $C_6^9 (0.2)^6 (0.8)^3 = 84(0.2)^6 (0.8)^3$ | 0.003 |
| 7 | $C_7^9 (0.2)^7 (0.8)^2 = 36(0.2)^7 (0.8)^2$ | 0.000 |
| 8 | $C_8^9 (0.2)^8 (0.8)^1 = 9(0.2)^8 (0.8)$ | 0.000 |
| 9 | $C_9^9 (0.2)^9 (0.8)^0 = (0.2)^9$ | 0.000 |

The last three entries in the right-hand column are not zero, but they are zero to *three decimal places*. For instance, the last entry is $(0.2)^9 = 0.000000512 \doteq 0.000$.

**Problem 7**  The president of AC overheard the president of AK bragging that his company had improved the spot-welding process for pack frames that AC abandoned last year. "When we gave up the process," she told Janet, "the chances of a spot-weld failure were 20%. Now that AK guy claims that the chances are less than 10% that more than 3 of its welds on a single frame will fail. An AK frame has nine spot welds. Has he really improved the process?" Suppose weld failures on a given frame are independent. Then the construction of each frame is a Bernoulli trials experiment with $n = 9$. In AC's experience they found $p = 0.20$; so the chances of more than 3 weld failures at AC would be P(more than 3 successes) $= 1 - $P(less than 4 successes) $= 1 - ($P(0) $+$ P(1) $+$ P(2) $+$ P(3)). By the table in the solution to Problem 6, this is $1 - (0.134 + 0.302 + 0.302 + 0.176) = 1.000 - 0.914 = 0.086$, which is less than 10%. It appears that AK has not made any improvement in the process.

**Solution**

Don't forget that the outcomes of a trial are called "success" and "failure" depending upon the application we have in mind, without regard to the nature of the trial. Here it is convenient to call the outcome "weld failure" success.

A Bernoulli trials experiment need not have a fixed total number of trials, as we see in the next problem.

**Problem 8**

Alan has decided to keep tossing a balanced die until it comes up 5. What are the chances that this will take
  (a) exactly 4 tosses?
  (b) at most 4 tosses?
  (c) at least 4 tosses?

**Solution**

This is a Bernoulli trials experiment with $p = P(5) = \frac{1}{6}$.

(a) To take exactly 4 tosses, Alan must fail in trials 1, 2, and 3, and succeed in trial 4. In the notation of Problem 2, this probability is $P(F_1 \cap F_2 \cap F_3 \cap S_4) = P(F_1)P(F_2)P(F_3)P(S_4) = (\frac{5}{6})^3(\frac{1}{6}) = \frac{125}{1296} \doteq 0.096$.

(b) P(it takes at most 4 tosses) $=$ P(it takes exactly 1 toss) $+$ P(2) $+$ P(3) $+$ P(4) $= (\frac{1}{6}) + (\frac{5}{6})(\frac{1}{6}) + (\frac{5}{6})^2(\frac{1}{6}) + (\frac{5}{6})^3(\frac{1}{6}) = \frac{1}{6} + \frac{5}{36} + \frac{25}{216} + \frac{125}{1296} = \frac{671}{1296} \doteq 0.518$.

(c) P(it takes at least 4 tosses) $= 1 - $P(it takes fewer than 4 tosses) $= 1 - ($P(1) $+$ P(2) $+$ P(3)) $= 1 - [\frac{1}{6} + (\frac{5}{6})(\frac{1}{6}) + (\frac{5}{6})^2(\frac{1}{6})] = 1 - \frac{91}{216} = \frac{125}{216} \doteq 0.579$.

The general result is easily obtained.

Here if $k = 1$ we must, as before, take $(1 - p)^0$ to be 1.

> In a Bernoulli trials experiment in which the probability of success is p and the number of trials is (potentially) unlimited, the probability that the first success occurs on trial number k is
> $$(1-p)^{k-1}p$$

For a situation like this the sample space for the experiment "see how many trials it takes to get a success" is $S = \{1, 2, 3, \ldots\}$, the set of all positive integers. Thus, we have, for a moment, left the realm of *finite* probability, since S is an infinite set. The probability distribution for S is

| | |
|---|---|
| 1 | p |
| 2 | $(1-p)p$ |
| 3 | $(1-p)^2 p$ |
| . | . |
| . | . |
| . | . |
| k | $(1-p)^{k-1}p$ |
| . | . |
| . | . |
| . | . |

(and so on forever)

*Why* is it called a geometric progression? Ask your instructor, or consult an algebra text—for example, *Intermediate Algebra* by Martin Zuckerman (New York: Norton, 1976), p. 579.

This is known as the **geometric distribution**, because the numbers in the second column (the probabilities) form a geometric progression.

**Exercises 4.4**

In Exercises 1 through 4, determine which are Bernoulli trials experiments and explain why the others are not Bernoulli trials experiments.

1. Six people are to be asked if they favor an amendment. If the first 3 say no, we will not count any more nos until we receive a yes.
2. Six people are to be asked if they favor Zarba for mayor. Since Zarba is known to be much more popular on the East side than on the West side, balance will be achieved by asking 3 people on each side.
3. Eight people chosen at random from the population are asked if they prefer AC parkas over all other brands.
4. A drug that is claimed to raise blood pressure is administered to 12 patients who suffer from low blood pressure.

In Exercises 5 through 12, 6 balanced dice, marked as usual, are tossed. Find the probabilities of the events described.

5. Exactly 4 dice come up 2.
6. At least 4 dice come up 2.
7. At most 2 dice come up 4.
8. An even number of dice come up 5.
9. An odd number of dice come up even.
10. No more than 7 dice come up 7.
11. No less than 7 dice come up 1.
12. At least 3 and at most 5 dice come up at least 3 and at most 5.

13. A balanced coin is flipped 6 times. Find the largest number k such that the probability of getting at least k heads is $\frac{1}{2}$ or more.

14. A balanced die is tossed 5 times. Find the largest number k such that the probability of at most k dice coming up greater than 4 is less than $\frac{1}{2}$.

15. Write, to 3-decimal-place accuracy, the binomial distribution for $n = 7$, $p = \frac{1}{2}$.

16. The Phlint Drug Company hopes to market a cure for baldness with the slogan, "It may not be perfect, but it causes a noticeable improvement in 20% of bald men." Before marketing the drug, they want to be at least 80% sure their claim is reasonable. They administer the drug to 10 bald male volunteers. At least how many must show improvement in order for PDC to market the drug under this slogan?

17. A balanced coin is flipped repeatedly. What are the chances that the first head appears on the seventh flip?

18. A balanced coin is flipped repeatedly. What is the probability that the first head appears on or before the fifth flip?

*19 Again and again the deck is shuffled, and a card is chosen and returned to the deck. How many times must this be done before the probability that a face card has been picked on 1 or more draws is at least 90%?

*20. I roll a balanced die and then flip as many balanced coins as the number of spots that turn up. For example, if the die shows 4, I flip 4 coins.

   (a) What is the probability that the coins flipped will all come up showing heads?

   (b) If all the coins show heads, what is the probability that the die showed an even number?

   (c) Suppose one third or less of the coins come up tails. What is the probability that exactly 1 tail came up?

21. Past experience indicates that I get about $\frac{2}{3}$ of the problems I work correct. In fact, I never spend more time on a problem than I need to just guess the answer. Thus, I learn practically nothing from working a problem so that the probability I will work a problem correctly is always $\frac{2}{3}$. What is the probability that I will pass an exam (get a 60 or better) if it has 5 problems, each of which count 20. Assume that I do not ever show any work; so that partial credit is out of the question.

## Section 4.5
## The Normal Distribution

Before introducing the normal distribution we must continue our discussion of the binomial distribution. We begin with an important application of the counting techniques of Section 1.1 to elementary algebra.

Suppose x and y are numbers and that n is a positive whole number. We want to calculate $(x + y)^n$, that is $(x+y)(x+y)(x+y)\cdots(x+y)$, where there are n factors in all. For small values of n this is not hard to do. Thus, $(x+y)^1$ is just $x+y$.

To find $(x+y)^2$ we multiply $x+y$ by $x+y$:

|  |  |
|---|---|
| $x+y$ | line 1 |
| $x+y$ | line 2 |
| $x^2+xy$ | line 3 |
| $xy+y^2$ | line 4 |
| $x^2+2xy+y^2$ | line 5 |

In this calculation we multiplied each term in line 1, namely x and y, by the first term in line 2, namely x, to get line 3. Then we multiplied each term in line 1 by the second term in line 2 to get line 4. Notice that the common terms xy in lines 3 and 4 were placed in the same column. We then added the terms in lines 3 and 4 to get the answer in line 5: $(x+y)^2=x^2+2xy+y^2$. To find $(x+y)^3$ we multiply $(x+y)^2$, as just found, by $x+y$:

$$
\begin{array}{l}
x^2+2xy\ +y^2 \\
\underline{\hspace{1.5cm}x\ +y} \\
x^3+2x^2y+\ xy^2 \\
\underline{\hspace{0.6cm}x^2y+2xy^2+y^3} \\
x^3+3x^2y+3xy^2+y^3
\end{array}
$$

These calculations are just one way to "multiply out" the expressions $(x+y)^2$ and $(x+y)^3$. In general, to calculate $(x+y)^n = (x+y)(x+y)\ldots(x+y)$, we choose either x or y from each of the n factors and multiply them together. Then we add the results. Consider, for instance, $(x+y)^4=(x+y)(x+y)(x+y)(x+y)$. If we choose x from each factor and multiply, we get $xxxx=x^4$. This is the only way to get $x^4$. If we choose x from the first three factors, choose y from the fourth factor, and then multiply, we get $x^3y$. Are there other ways to get $x^3y$? Of course. We could, for example, choose x from factors one, two, and four and y from factor three. How many ways are there to choose three xs from the four factors? There are $C_3^4=4$ ways. Thus, the term $x^3y$ occurs $C_3^4$ times. If we choose exactly two xs, then we must choose two ys and we get the term $xxyy=x^2y^2$. We get this term $C_2^4=6$ times. The complete computation of $(x+y)^4$ is shown in the tabulation below.

| **CALCULATION OF $(x+y)^4$** | | |
|---|---|---|
| **Number of xs** | **Resulting term** | **Number of times term is obtained** |
| 4 | $x^4$ | $C_4^4=1$ |
| 3 | $x^3y$ | $C_3^4=4$ |
| 2 | $x^2y^2$ | $C_2^4=6$ |
| 1 | $xy^3$ | $C_1^4=4$ |
| 0 | $y^4$ | $C_0^4=1$ |

Adding $1x^4$, $4x^3y$, $6x^2y^2$, $4xy^3$, and $1y^4$ we obtain $(x+y)^4 = x^4 + 4x^3y + 6x^2y^2 + 4xy^3 + y^4$, which we may check by multiplying $(x+y)^3$, as found before, by $x+y$:

$$
\begin{array}{r}
x^3 + 3x^2y + 3xy^2 + y^3 \\
x+y \\
\hline
x^4 + 3x^3y + 3x^2y^2 + xy^3 \\
x^3y + 3x^2y^2 + 3xy^3 + y^4 \\
\hline
x^4 + 4x^3y + 6x^2y^2 + 4xy^3 + y^4 = (x+y)^4 \checkmark
\end{array}
$$

The same sort of computation can be carried out for $(x+y)^n$, where n is any positive whole number.

| CALCULATION OF $(x+y)^n$ | | |
|---|---|---|
| Number of x's chosen | Resulting term | Number of times term is obtained |
| n | $x^n$ | $C_n^n$ |
| n − 1 | $x^{n-1}y$ | $C_{n-1}^n$ |
| n − 2 | $x^{n-2}y^2$ | $C_{n-2}^n$ |
| . | | . |
| . | . | . |
| . | . | . |
| 2 | $x^2y^{n-2}$ | $C_2^n$ |
| 1 | $xy^{n-1}$ | $C_1^n$ |
| 0 | $y^n$ | $C_0^n$ |

Adding these terms the indicated number of times we obtain

$$(x+y)^n = C_n^n x^n + C_{n-1}^n x^{n-1}y + C_{n-2}^n x^{n-2}y^2 + \ldots$$
$$+ C_2^n x^2 y^{n-2} + C_1^n xy^n + C_0^n y^n \qquad \mathbf{1}$$

The numbers $C_k^n$ are for this reason often called **binomial coefficients**. And this is why the **binomial distribution** of the last section is so called.

The expression $x+y$ is called a **binomial** in algebra. Equation **1** is known as the **binomial theorem**. The right side of equation **1** is called the **binomial expansion** of $(x+y)^n$.

It can be shown that the binomial theorem is true for all values of x and y.

Problem 1   In the binomial expansion of $(x+y)^9$, what is the term involving:

(a) $x^4y^5$?       (b) $x^2y^7$?

Solution   We use the binomial theorem with $n=9$.

(a) The term is $C_4^9 x^4 y^5 = 126 x^4 y^5$.
(b) The term is $C_2^9 x^2 y^7 = 36 x^2 y^7$.

Now this is not a book about algebra, but as we shall see we will use the binomial theorem to obtain formulas for the mean, variance, and standard deviation of the binomial distribution.

Another example: Suppose that the manager of the Bartlesville, OK, PHE store believes that 3 out of 5 customers prefer mustard on their hamburgers. If 10 people order hamburgers, she would expect $10 \cdot \frac{3}{5} = 6$ of them to request mustard.

In a Bernoulli trials experiment it would seem that the expected number of successes should equal the number of trials times the probability of success. For example if a balanced die is tossed 6 times and if "success" is defined as "less than 3," then the number of successes we expect should be $6P(\text{less than } 3) = 6(\frac{1}{3}) = 2$. Is this the result we actually obtain from the formal definition of expectation? Here the random variable X is the number of successes, the number of trials is $n = 6$, and the probability of success is $p = \frac{1}{3}$. Recall that the probability of exactly k successes in n trials is $C_k^n p^k (1-p)^{n-k}$, which in this case is $C_k^6 (\frac{1}{3})^k (\frac{2}{3})^{6-k}$. Then:

$$E(X) = 0P(X=0) + 1P(X=1) + 2P(X=2) + 3P(X=3) +$$

$$4P(X=4) + 5P(X=5) + 6P(X=6) =$$

$$0C_0^6 \left(\tfrac{1}{3}\right)^0 \left(\tfrac{2}{3}\right)^6 + 1C_1^6 \left(\tfrac{1}{3}\right)^1 \left(\tfrac{2}{3}\right)^5 +$$

$$2C_2^6 \left(\tfrac{1}{3}\right)^2 \left(\tfrac{2}{3}\right)^4 + 3C_3^6 \left(\tfrac{1}{3}\right)^3 \left(\tfrac{2}{3}\right)^3 +$$

$$4C_4^6 \left(\tfrac{1}{3}\right)^4 \left(\tfrac{2}{3}\right)^2 + 5C_5^6 \left(\tfrac{1}{3}\right)^5 \left(\tfrac{2}{3}\right)^1 + 6C_6^6 \left(\tfrac{1}{3}\right)^6 \left(\tfrac{2}{3}\right)^0 =$$

$$6\left(\tfrac{1}{3}\right)\left[ \left(\tfrac{2}{3}\right)^5 + 5\left(\tfrac{1}{3}\right)\left(\tfrac{2}{3}\right)^4 + \tfrac{5 \cdot 4}{2 \cdot 1}\left(\tfrac{1}{3}\right)^2 \left(\tfrac{2}{3}\right)^3 +$$

$$\tfrac{5 \cdot 4 \cdot 3}{3 \cdot 2 \cdot 1}\left(\tfrac{1}{2}\right)^3 \left(\tfrac{2}{3}\right)^2 + \tfrac{5 \cdot 4 \cdot 3 \cdot 2}{4 \cdot 3 \cdot 2 \cdot 1}\left(\tfrac{1}{3}\right)^4 \left(\tfrac{2}{3}\right) + \left(\tfrac{1}{3}\right)^5 \right] =$$

$$6\left(\tfrac{1}{3}\right)\left[ \left(\tfrac{2}{3}\right)^5 + C_1^5 \left(\tfrac{2}{3}\right)^4 \left(\tfrac{1}{3}\right)^3 + C_2^5 \left(\tfrac{2}{3}\right)^3 \left(\tfrac{1}{3}\right)^2 + C_3^5 \left(\tfrac{2}{3}\right)^2 \left(\tfrac{1}{3}\right)^3 + C_4^5 \left(\tfrac{2}{3}\right)\left(\tfrac{1}{3}\right)^4 + \left(\tfrac{1}{3}\right)^5 \right]$$

In equation **1**, set $n = 5$, $x = \frac{2}{3}$, $y = \frac{1}{3}$, and recall the formula for $C_k^5$.

Now the last expression in square brackets is just the binomial expansion of $(\frac{2}{3} + \frac{1}{3})^5$. Hence, $E(X) = 6(\frac{1}{3})(\frac{2}{3} + \frac{1}{3})^5 = 6(\frac{1}{3})(1)^5 = 6(\frac{1}{3}) = 2$.

So the result we thought should be true really is true in this case. It can be shown that this result is true in general for Bernoulli trials.

> In a Bernoulli trials experiment with n trials and probability of success p on each trial, let X be the number of successes. Then **2**
> $$E(X) = np$$

**Problem 2**

In a single performance of an experiment, 7 balanced coins are flipped. The performance is a success if at least 6 coins come up heads. The experiment is performed 96 times. How many successes are to be expected?

**Solution**

Each performance of the experiment is itself a Bernoulli trials experiment with $n = 7$, $p = \frac{1}{2}$. The probability of success on a performance is P(at least 6 heads) $= C_3^7(\frac{1}{2})^6(\frac{1}{2})^1 + C_7^7(\frac{1}{2})^7 = \frac{8}{128} = \frac{1}{16}$. The repeated performances also form a Bernoulli trials experiment with n $=96$ and p $= \frac{1}{16}$. Then the expected number of successes is np $= 96(\frac{1}{16}) = 6$.

Recall from Section 4.3 that the mean number of successes in any experiment is the same as the expectation of the random variable X defined above: m $=$ E(X). Thus, for a Bernoulli trials experiment, m $=$ np. Recall also from Section 4.3 that the variance of a random variable X is v $=$ E((X $-$ m)$^2$). Multiplying this out we have:

$$E(X^2 - 2mX + m^2) = E(X^2) - E(2mX) + E(m^2) =$$

**Here we are using equations 2, 3, 4, and 7 of Section 4.2.**

$$E(X^2) - 2mE(X) + m^2 = E(X^2) - 2m \cdot m + m^2 =$$

$$E(X^2) - 2m^2 + m^2 = E(X^2) - m^2.$$

Thus, by equation **2**,

$$v = E(X^2) - (np)^2 \qquad\qquad \textbf{3}$$

It remains to evaluate E(X$^2$). As an example we do this for the die experiment described above, in which n $=6$ and p $= \frac{1}{3}$. The values of X are $0, 1, 2, 3, 4, 5, 6$; so the values of X$^2$ are $0, 1, 4, 9, 16, 25, 36$.

**In general for any number k, $k^2 = k + k(k-1)$.**

To help in the calculation we rewrite these numbers in the form 0, 1, $1 + 2 \cdot 1$, $3 + 3 \cdot 2$, $4 + 4 \cdot 3$, $5 + 5 \cdot 4$, $6 + 6 \cdot 5$. Then

$$E(X^2) = 0P(X^2 = 0) + 1P(X^2 = 1) + 4P(X^2 = 4) + 9P(X^2 = 9) +$$

$$16P(X^2 = 16) + 25P(X^2 = 25) + 36P(X^2 = 36) =$$

$$0P(X = 0) + 1P(X = 1) + (2 + 2 \cdot 1)P(X = 2) + (3 + 3 \cdot 2)P(X = 3) +$$

$$(4 + 4 \cdot 3)P(X = 4) + (5 + 5 \cdot 4)P(X = 5) + (6 + 6 \cdot 5)P(X = 6) =$$

$$\left[ 0P(X = 0) + 1P(X = 1) + 2P(X = 2) + 3P(X = 3) + 4P(X = 4) + 5P(X = 5) + 6P(X = 6) \right] +$$

$$\left[ 2 \cdot 1C_2^6(\tfrac{1}{3})^2(\tfrac{2}{3})^4 + 3 \cdot 2C_3^6(\tfrac{1}{3})^3(\tfrac{2}{3})^3 + 4 \cdot 3C_4^6(\tfrac{1}{3})^4(\tfrac{2}{3})^2 + 5 \cdot 4C_5^6(\tfrac{1}{3})^5(\tfrac{2}{3})^1 + 6 \cdot 5C_6^6(\tfrac{1}{3})^6(\tfrac{2}{3})^0 \right] =$$

**The first square brackets above contain just E(X) $=$ np $= 6(\frac{1}{3})$.**

$$E(X) + 2 \cdot 1\tfrac{6 \cdot 5}{2 \cdot 1}(\tfrac{1}{3})^2(\tfrac{2}{3})^4 + 3 \cdot 2\tfrac{6 \cdot 5 \cdot 4}{3 \cdot 2 \cdot 1}(\tfrac{1}{3})^3(\tfrac{2}{3})^3 + 4 \cdot 3\tfrac{6 \cdot 5 \cdot 4 \cdot 3}{4 \cdot 3 \cdot 2 \cdot 1}(\tfrac{1}{3})^4(\tfrac{2}{3})^2 +$$

$$5 \cdot 4\tfrac{6 \cdot 5 \cdot 4 \cdot 3 \cdot 2}{5 \cdot 4 \cdot 3 \cdot 2 \cdot 1}(\tfrac{1}{3})^5(\tfrac{2}{3})^1 + 6 \cdot 5\tfrac{6 \cdot 5 \cdot 4 \cdot 3 \cdot 2 \cdot 1}{6 \cdot 5 \cdot 4 \cdot 3 \cdot 2 \cdot 1}(\tfrac{1}{3})^6(\tfrac{2}{3})^0 =$$

$$6(\tfrac{1}{3}) + 6 \cdot 5(\tfrac{1}{3})^2 \left[ (\tfrac{2}{3})^4 + \tfrac{4}{1}(\tfrac{1}{3})(\tfrac{2}{3})^3 + \tfrac{4 \cdot 3}{2 \cdot 1}(\tfrac{1}{3})^2(\tfrac{2}{3})^2 + \tfrac{4 \cdot 3 \cdot 2}{3 \cdot 2 \cdot 1}(\tfrac{1}{3})^3(\tfrac{2}{3})^1 + \tfrac{4 \cdot 3 \cdot 2 \cdot 1}{4 \cdot 3 \cdot 2 \cdot 1}(\tfrac{1}{3})^4(\tfrac{2}{3})^0 \right] =$$

**Here we have used the binomial theorem with x $= \frac{2}{3}$, y $= \frac{1}{3}$, and n $= 4$.**

$$6(\tfrac{1}{3}) + 6 \cdot 5(\tfrac{1}{3})^2 \left[ (\tfrac{2}{3}) + (\tfrac{1}{3}) \right]^4 = 6(\tfrac{1}{3}) + 6 \cdot 5(\tfrac{1}{3})^2 [1]^4 = 6(\tfrac{1}{3}) + 6 \cdot 5(\tfrac{1}{3})^2.$$

Finally, by equation **3**, $v = 6(\frac{1}{3}) + 6 \cdot 5(\frac{1}{3})^2 - [6(\frac{1}{3})]^2 =$

$$6(\tfrac{1}{3})\left[1 + 5(\tfrac{1}{3}) - 6(\tfrac{1}{3})\right] = 6(\tfrac{1}{3})(1 - \tfrac{1}{3}) = 2(\tfrac{2}{3}) = \tfrac{4}{3}.$$

The standard deviation (equation **3** of Section 4.3) is then $s = \sqrt{\frac{4}{3}}$ $\doteq 1.15$. Note that $v = 6(\frac{1}{3})(1 - \frac{1}{3}) = np(1-p)$ in this case. Proceeding just as above, we can obtain the following general results.

Recall from p. 270 that the probability distribution of the random variable giving the number of successes in a Bernoulli trials experiment is the binomial distribution. Thus, these formulas give m, v, and s for the binomial distribution for n and p.

In a Bernoulli trials experiment with n trials and probability of success p, the mean number of successes is
$$m = np, \qquad\qquad \textbf{4}$$
the variance is
$$v = np(1-p), \qquad\qquad \textbf{5}$$
and the standard deviation is
$$s = \sqrt{np(1-p)} \qquad\qquad \textbf{6}$$

**Problem 3**

The stoves are turned over to a group of cub scouts from New York.

Twenty AC camp stoves are selected at random and subjected to rigorous tests high in the Catskill mountains. In the past, 12 stoves have typically passed the test. How many stoves have to pass the test in order for the result of this year's test to be within 1 standard deviation of the typical past results?

**Solution**

Assuming the stoves are all alike, this is a Bernoulli trials situation with $n = 20$. The mean, from past experience, is $m = 12$. Then by equation **4**, $12 = 20p$; so $p = \frac{12}{20} = \frac{3}{5}$ and hence $1 - p = \frac{2}{5}$. Then, by equation **6**, $s = \sqrt{20(\frac{3}{5})(\frac{2}{5})} = \sqrt{\frac{24}{5}} = \sqrt{4.8} \doteq 2.2$. In order to be within one standard deviation of the mean, the number of stoves that pass the test must be between $12 - 2.2$ and $12 + 2.2$. Discarding fractions, we see that between 10 and 14 stoves should pass the test.

Alan had studied the unit on Bernoulli trials quite carefully in his course at LC and had worked out a fairly large number of exercises. Not only did he get $9\frac{1}{2}$ out of 10 on the weekly quiz on that unit, but he actually felt he understood and could use the concepts. One morning at AC he overheard the procurement manager say to Janet, "We ordered four hundred dozen (4,800) gaskets from a new supplier who gave us a good price. They said that some of the gaskets would be defective on close inspection but that three-quarters of them would be fine. Actually, we ended up rejecting 1,245 gaskets. I know we should have expected 1,200

This was Alan's finest hour as a probabilist. Unfortunately, he did not keep up his good work and he ended the course at LC with a C average.

defective gaskets, but is 1,245 reasonably close to 1,200 in this case?"

Alan ran back to the warehouse and began writing on a cardboard carton. "Suppose the gaskets were selected at random from a huge stock, $\frac{3}{4}$ of which were perfect. Then this is a Bernoulli trials experiment with n=4,800 and p=$\frac{3}{4}$. The mean is m=np=4,800·$\frac{3}{4}$=3,600 good gaskets, or 1,200 defective, as the manager said. To find out whether 1,245 is reasonable, we need to find the probability that the number of defectives is at least 45 away from 1,200, that is, the probability that the number of good gaskets is at least 45 away from 3,600: P(k ≤ 3,600−45 or k ≥ 3,600 +45). This probability is 1 minus the probability that k is within 44 of 3,600:  P(3,556 ≤ k ≤ 3,644) = P(k = 3,556) + P(k = 3,557) + ... + P(3,644)." He moved to a larger carton and wrote, "P(3,556)=$C_{3,556}^{4,800}(\frac{3}{4})^{3,556}(\frac{1}{4})^{4,800-3,556}$. This would take a year to figure out," he thought, "and after that would come P(3,557), P(3,558), and so on. It's impossible without a computer, and our computer is shut down this week."

He walked back to the office hoping to hear Janet explain all this to the manager, but he arrived just in time to see her look up from a book on her desk and say to the manager, "It's not reasonably close if you assume the $\frac{3}{4}$ figure to be accurate. The probability of being 45 or more away from the mean is only 0.13."

Histograms first appear on p. 238.

How did Janet do it? She used the **normal approximation** to the binomial distribution. If we were to draw a histogram of the binomial distribution with n=4,800, p=$\frac{3}{4}$ it would look like a "spike" (Figure 2), of height about 0.013, at k=3,600.

Figure 2

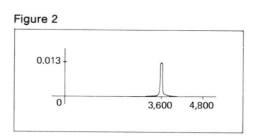

The "spike" doesn't quite drop to zero but, for example, at 3,500 and 3,700 the height of the histogram is less than $\frac{1}{10,000}$. To get a better view, let's enlarge part of Figure 2 (Figure 3). There are so many bars in the histogram that it looks like a smooth curve.

**Figure 3**

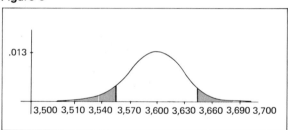

The standard deviation of this distribution is

$$s = \sqrt{4{,}800\left(\tfrac{3}{4}\right)\left(\tfrac{1}{4}\right)} = \sqrt{900} = 30.$$

We have marked the scale around 3,600 in units of 30. The manager wants to know the probability of being at least $1\tfrac{1}{2}$ standard deviations away from the mean, since 45 is $1\tfrac{1}{2}$ times 30. Since bars in this histogram have width one, this probability is equal to the area of the shaded region of Figure 3, which is about 0.13.

**Figure 4**

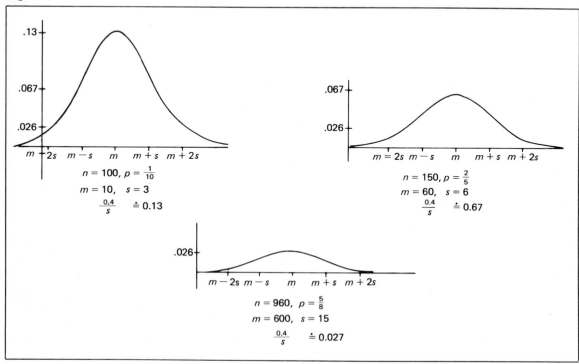

Histograms for binomial distributions with large n and various values of p (Figure 4) are all very similar to Figure 3 in the following ways: (1) they have a peak value of about 0.4/s at the mean, where s is the standard deviation; (2) they are symmetric about the mean; that is, they fall off to the left of the mean in the same way as to the right; (3) they drop practically to zero in 3 standard deviations on each side of the mean. For small values of n the histograms only vaguely resemble this curve, but, as n gets large, the resemblance becomes very close. For instance for $p = \frac{2}{5}$ and $n = 2, 5, 10$, we have (Figure 5):

Figure 5

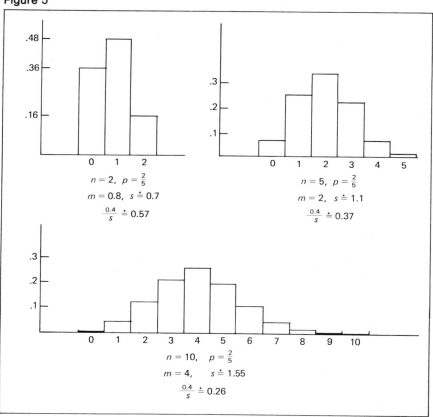

Tables II and III in Appendix B list values of the normal distribution with mean 0 and standard deviation 1. In order to apply these tables to a binomial distribution (or other distribution) that has a different mean and/or standard deviation, it is necessary to introduce a new variable z. Given a random variable X whose distribution has mean m and standard deviation s, the value of z corresponding to $X=k$ is the number of standard deviations k is from m. Thus,

$$z = \frac{k-m}{s} \qquad \qquad 7$$

The number z will be positive if $k>m$ and negative if $k<m$. The value of z is called the **z-score** corresponding to k.

The value of a binomial random variable is a whole number between 0 and n inclusive. In Figure 5, for example, the first distribution illustrated takes on three values: 0, 1, 2. However, the way the graph is drawn, each value is represented by a bar of width one, from $\frac{1}{2}$ unit less than the value to $\frac{1}{2}$ unit more. The binomial variable itself does not take on these fractional values. Nevertheless, since the normal distribution does take on all values, we will increase our accuracy by using z-scores corresponding to the sides of the histogram bars.

**Problem 4**  Compute the z-scores for the distribution with $n=5$ and $p=\frac{2}{5}$, shown in Figure 5.

**Solution**  We are interested in the z-scores corresponding to the ends of each bar, namely, $k = -\frac{1}{2}, \frac{1}{2}, 1\frac{1}{2}, 2\frac{1}{2}, 3\frac{1}{2}, 4\frac{1}{2}, 5\frac{1}{2}$. We have $m=2$ and $s \doteq 1.1$. By formula **7** the z-score corresponding to $k = -\frac{1}{2}$ is

$$z = \frac{-\frac{1}{2}-2}{1.1} = \frac{-2.5}{1.1} \doteq -2.3.$$

That is, for this distribution, the value $-\frac{1}{2}$ is about 2.3 standard deviations to the left of the mean. For $k = \frac{1}{2}$ we have

$$z = \frac{\frac{1}{2}-2}{1.1} = \frac{-1.5}{1.1} \doteq -1.4$$

As a final example we compute the z-score for $k = 2\frac{1}{2}$ to be

$$z = \frac{2\frac{1}{2}-2}{1.1} = \frac{.5}{1.1} \doteq .45$$

The other values in the following table were calculated in the same way.

| k | $-\frac{1}{2}$ | $\frac{1}{2}$ | $1\frac{1}{2}$ | $2\frac{1}{2}$ | $3\frac{1}{2}$ | $4\frac{1}{2}$ | $5\frac{1}{2}$ |
|---|---|---|---|---|---|---|---|
| z | $-2.3$ | $-1.4$ | $-.5$ | $.5$ | $1.4$ | $2.3$ | $3.2$ |

If the three graphs in Figure 5 were plotted using the z-scores instead of the values of k on the horizontal axis, they would all look almost the same, namely, like Figure 6. In fact it can be shown that every binomial distribution with $p \neq 0$ and $p \neq 1$ and with n sufficiently large has a graph closely resembling Figure 6, when z-scores are used on the horizontal axis. Abraham de

**Figure 6**

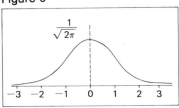

For the record, the formula for the curve is

$$f(z) = \frac{1}{\sqrt{2\pi}} e^{-z^2/2}$$

where $e \doteq 2.7183$. This result was

stated by de Moivre only for binomial distributions with $p = \frac{1}{2}$. It was later proven by Laplace for all p. The number $\pi$ ("pi"), as you may recall, is the area of a circle of radius 1; $\pi \doteq 3.1416$.

The normal curve is also often called the **bell-shaped curve**, though its resemblance to a bell is rather superficial.

The preparation of tables such as these requires calculus and lots of computation. Much more extensive tables of areas under the normal curve may be found in most college libraries. Some pocket calculators have a program that gives these values.

Moivre, in 1733, and Pierre Laplace, in 1812, discovered a formula for the smooth curve that the binomial distributions seem to be approximating. The formula is rather complicated, but we make no direct use of it. We do, however, mention that the mysterious number 0.4 that keeps cropping up is really $\dfrac{1}{\sqrt{2\pi}} \doteq 0.3989$.

The curve of Figure 6 is known as the normal approximation to the binomial distribution, or simply as the **normal distribution** or the **normal curve**.

Since problems in binomial distributions can be stated in terms of areas of histograms, they can be solved approximately with the normal distribution. Moreover, it has been observed that many other probability experiments which do not appear to be Bernoulli trials have histograms that are closely approximated by the normal distribution. Such experiments are said to be **approximately normally distributed**. (They are especially so termed by those who enjoy using long words.)

In order to make use of all this we have to learn how to find areas under the normal curve. The way to do this is refreshingly easy: use Tables II and III in Appendix B. In addition to these tables we must use the fact that the normal curve (Figure 6) is symmetric about the vertical line through 0.

**Problem 5**   Find the area under the normal curve for each of the following ranges of z.

(a) $0 \le z \le 2.7$

(b) $z \ge 1.3$

(c) $1.9 \le z \le 2.2$

(d) $-0.7 \le z \le 0$

(e) $-1.6 \le z \le 1.6$

(f) $-2.1 \le z \le 0.4$

(g) $-3.2 \le z \le -2.5$

(h) $z \le -0.2$

(i) $z \le 1.5$

(j) $z \ge -1.0$

(k) $z \le -0.3$ or $2.0 \le z \le 3.0$

**Solution**

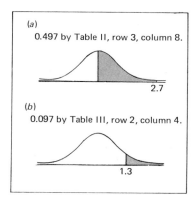

(a)
0.497 by Table II, row 3, column 8.

2.7

(b)
0.097 by Table III, row 2, column 4.

1.3

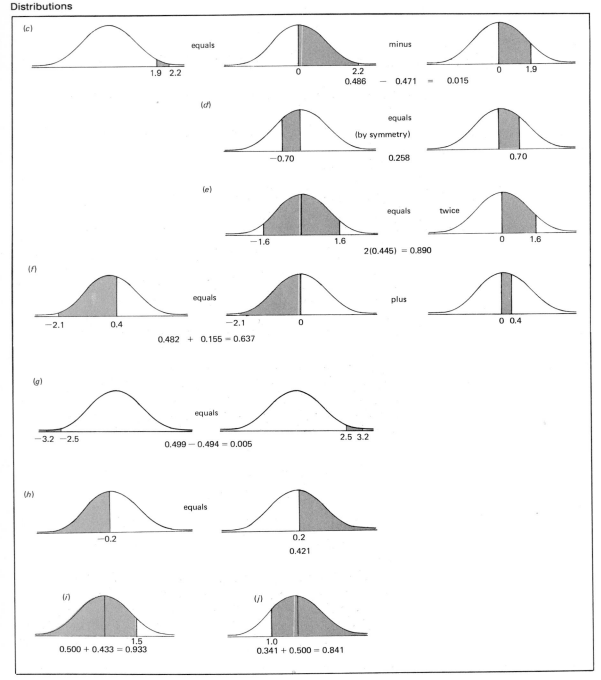

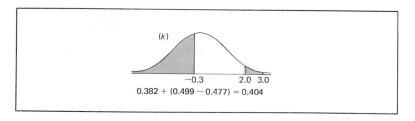

$$0.382 + (0.499 - 0.477) = 0.404$$

Now we can use the normal curve to solve problems.

**Problem 6**  Use the normal approximation to the binomial distribution to find the following probabilities for a Bernoulli trials experiment with $n=5$ and $p=\frac{2}{5}$.

(a) $P(2 \le k \le 4)$
(b) $P(k \le 3)$
(c) $P(4 \le k)$
(d) $P(k=2)$

**Solution**  In Problem 4 we computed all the relevant $z$-scores.

(a) Here we are interested in the area of bars 2, 3, and 4 in the histogram of Figure 5. Since these bars begin at $1\frac{1}{2}$ and end at $4\frac{1}{2}$, it will actually be necessary for us to compute $P(1\frac{1}{2} \le k \le 4\frac{1}{2}) = P(-.5 \le z \le 2.3)$. From Table II we calculate this probability: $0.192 + 0.489 = 0.681$. The exact value is 0.653 to three decimal places.

(b) $P(k \le 3) = P(k \le 3\frac{1}{2}) = P(z \le 1.4) = 0.500 + 0.419 = 0.919$.

(c) $P(4 \le k) = P(3\frac{1}{2} \le k) = P(1.4 \le z) = 0.081$.

(d) $P(k=2)$. In this case we are to calculate the area of one bar in the histogram: the bar from $1\frac{1}{2}$ to $2\frac{1}{2}$. Thus, we have $P(k=2) = P(1\frac{1}{2} \le k \le 2\frac{1}{2}) = P(-.5 \le z \le .5) = 2(0.192) = 0.384$. The exact value is 0.346 to three decimal places.

Of course, in Problem 6 it is relatively easy to compute the exact values. For example, in (d) $P(k=2) = C_2^5(\frac{2}{5})^2(\frac{3}{5})^3 = \frac{216}{625}$. In the next problem we apply the normal approximation to a case where direct calculation is not practical.

**Problem 7**  Solve the procurement manager's problem pp. 278–79.
**Solution**  By Alan's analysis, which was substantially the same as Janet's, we are to find $P(k \le 3{,}555$ or $k \ge 3{,}645)$ for a binomial distribution with $n=4{,}800, p=\frac{3}{4}$. Since histogram bars run from $\frac{1}{2}$ before k to $\frac{1}{2}$ after k, this means we seek the area for $k \le 3{,}554.5$ plus the area for $k \ge 3{,}644.5$. Now $m=np=3{,}600$ and $s=\sqrt{np(1-p)} = 30$, so in

the approximating normal distribution we need to find the area for
$z \leq (3{,}554.5 - 3{,}600) / 30$   or   $z \geq (3{,}644.5 - 3{,}600) / 30$, that is,
$z \leq -1.48$ or $z \geq 1.48$, or, since our tables are not really very detailed,
$z \leq -1.5$ or $z \geq 1.5$.

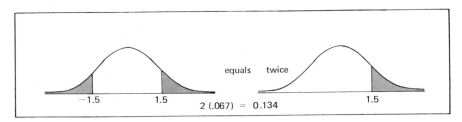

equals   twice

−1.5        1.5            1.5

2 (.067) = 0.134

Guess what book Janet looked up from.

And so $2(0.067) \doteq 0.13$, as Janet said.

**Problem 8**  If a fair coin is flipped one million times, what is the probability of
its coming up heads at least 505,000 times?

**Solution**  Here $n = 1{,}000{,}000$, $p = \frac{1}{2}$, and $m = 500{,}000$, $1 - p = \frac{1}{2}$ and $s =$

Actually, $k \geq 504{,}999.5$, but the difference is negligible.

$\sqrt{250{,}000} = 500$. Then $k \geq 505{,}000$ means the same thing as $z \geq$
$(505{,}000 - 500{,}000)/500 = 10$. Since $P(z \geq 3.9)$ is 0.000 to three decimals, we certainly have $P(z \geq 10) \doteq 0.000$. Thus, if in a million flips
you got 505,000 or more heads, you could be quite sure that the
coin was *not* fair.

**Problem 9**  If the heights to the nearest centimeter of the males at LC are
normally distributed with mean 175 cm and standard deviation
8 cm, about what percent of the LC males are:
(a) 180 cm. tall?
(b) under 160 cm. tall?
(c) between 165 and 195 cm. tall?

**Solution**  $179.5 \leq k \leq 180.5$, so
(a) $(179.5 - 175)/8 \leq z \leq (180.5 - 175)/8$.  $P(0.6 \leq z \leq 0.7) = 0.258 - 0.226 = 0.032$; about 3%.
(b) Now $z \leq (159.5 - 175)/8$. $P(z \leq -1.9) = 0.029$; also about 3%.
(c) $(164.5 - 175)/8 \leq z \leq (195.5 - 175)/8$,  $P(-1.3 \leq z \leq 2.6) = 0.403 + 0.495 \doteq 90\%$.

**Exercises 4.5**

1. Write the binomial expansion of $(x+y)^8$.
2. Write the binomial expansion of $(x+y)^{10}$.
3. In $(x+y)^{12}$ what is the term involving $x^7$?
4. In $(x+y)^{12}$ what is the term involving $y^3$?

In Exercises 5 through 8 find the mean m, variance v, and standard deviation s for the number of successes in the Bernoulli trials experiment given.

5. $n=10, p=\frac{1}{4}$
6. $n=100, p=\frac{1}{40}$
7. $n=1{,}000, p=\frac{351}{500}$
8. $n=1{,}000{,}000, p=\frac{1}{2}$

In Exercises 9 and 10 compute the z-scores associated to the given value in a distribution with given mean, m, and standard deviation s.

9. (a) $k=7.3, m=0, s=1$
   (b) $k=10, m=6, s=2$
   (c) $k=-2, m=6, s=2$
   (d) $k=13, m=6, s=2$
   (e) $k=5, m=-4, s=12$
10. (a) $k=5, m=0, s=1$
    (b) $k=19, m=10, s=3$
    (c) $k=-8, m=10, s=3$
    (d) $k=3, m=10, s=3$
    (e) $k=4, m=-2, s=\frac{1}{2}$

In Exercises 11 through 16 find the indicated Bernoulli trials probabilities and the normal approximation probabilities, to three decimals.

11. $n=4, p=\frac{1}{2}, k=0, 2, 3$.
12. $n=8, p=\frac{1}{4}, k=2, 3, 4$.
13. $n=10, p=\frac{1}{10}, k=0, 5, 10$.
14. $n=10, p=\frac{1}{2}, k=0, 5, 7$.
15. $n=20, p=\frac{1}{5}, k=0, 2, 4, 8$.
16. $n=20, p=\frac{1}{2}, k=8, 9, 10, 11$.

In Exercises 17 through 28, use the normal approximation to find the indicated binomial probabilities for $n=1{,}800$ and $p=\frac{2}{3}$.

17. $P(1{,}100 \le k \le 1{,}180)$.
18. $P(1{,}180 \le k \le 1{,}340)$.
19. $P(1{,}290 \le k)$.
20. $P(1{,}210 \le k)$.
21. $P(k \le 1{,}240)$.
22. $P(k=1{,}800)$.
23. $P(1{,}180 \le k \le 1{,}220)$.
24. $P(k \le 1{,}100)$.
25. $P(k \le 1{,}190 \text{ or } k \ge 1{,}210)$.
26. $P(k \le 1{,}120 \text{ or } k \ge 1{,}280)$.
27. $P(1{,}160 \le k \le 1{,}170 \text{ or } 1{,}180 \le k \le 1{,}190)$.
28. $P(1{,}200 \le k \text{ or } 1{,}800 \ge k \ge 1{,}170)$.
29. In a Bernoulli trials experiment with 16,000 trials and probability $\frac{9}{10}$ of success, what is the largest number k for which it is more likely than not that at least k successes occur?
30. In a Bernoulli trials experiment with 16,000 trials and probability $\frac{1}{10}$

of success, what is the largest number k for which the probability of k or fewer successes is less than one-half?

31. A survey commissioned by Petaluma Hamburger Emporium indicates that the average American has visited a PHE store 22 times in the past year, with a standard deviation of 4 visits. You have been asked to estimate how many Americans will visit a PHE store more than 27 times this year. Assume there are 200 million Americans. Write down all the other assumptions you need to make, and make your estimate.

32. I plan to buy a truckload of electrical equipment from a manufacturer who claims that, at most, 5% of the items are defective. I select 100 items at random and find 7 to be defective. If I assume the manufacturer is telling the truth, what are the chances of my selecting such a sample?

*33. Assume that some numerical data with mean 1,114 are normally distributed and that $15\frac{1}{2}\%$ of the data occur between the mean and 1,135. What percentage of the data occurs between 1,120 and 1,150?

---

**Section 4.6
The Poisson
Distribution**

In this brief section we introduce another probability distribution, which, although it was discovered long ago, has only recently (i.e., in this century!) been recognized as one of considerable importance.

In the previous section we stated, rather vaguely, that the normal approximation for a binomial distribution is good when n is large. How good is it, and how large must n be? That depends on the value of p. If p is near $\frac{1}{2}$, the normal approximation will give results accurate to two decimal places for n ≥ 3. In general if the variance $v = np(1-p) \geq 3$, then satisfactory results will be obtained. If, for example, p = 0.02, then np(1 - p) ≥ 3 for n ≥ 154. If, say, p = 0.02 and n = 50, then the normal approximation would be inaccurate in some problems, but exact calculation would still be very hard. Is there any way out? Yes, the **Poisson** approximation works well for small p. The formula uses the mean m = np of the distribution and runs as follows.

Simeon-Denis Poisson (1781–1840) published this result in 1837.

$$C_k^n p^k (1-p)^{n-k} \doteq m^k / (e^m k!) \qquad \textbf{1}$$

k! = k(k − 1)...2·1 and 0! = 1, as defined on page 30. Recall from page 282 that e ≐ 2.7183.

As with the normal curve, this is a fancy formula, which need not concern us greatly. Table IV in Appendix B contains some values of the expression on the right side of equation **1** for various values of m and k.

Problem 1

We have used Table IV, Part A, row
6, columns 1 and 2.

In a Bernoulli trials experiment with $n = 50, p = 0.02$, estimate the
probability of at least 2 successes.

The mean $m = np = 1.0$. Then $P(k \geq 2) = 1 - (P(k=0) + P(k=1)) = 1 - (0.368 + 0.368) = 0.264$. The probability of at least 2 successes is
about 0.26.

In order to apply Poisson's formula we need to know only the
mean m and the number of successes k. If we can determine m
(for example, by observation or experimentation), then we can
apply this formula without knowing n and p.

Problem 2

Solution

Conceivably n could be the total
number of salespeople who exist now
or will exist later, and p the probability that on a chosen hour one will be
at AC. That is not very practical.

Salespeople show up at random in the AC main office. In a typical
hour 6 of them show up. President Pennypincher wants to make
the office large enough to accommodate "as many salespersons as
come in." But on 1 or 2 occasions over 15 salespeople have come
in at once. She can't make the office *that* large without spending a
fortune. How large should she make the office so as to be 90% sure
of accommodating as many salespeople as come in?

We can't consider this as a Bernoulli trials experiment. What
would n mean? or p? Consider the experiment "select a business
hour at random and count the number of salespeople in the
office." We are given that the mean outcome of this experiment is
$m = 6$. It can be shown that it is reasonable to assume that the
probability P(k) of exactly k salespeople showing up in a randomly
chosen hour is given (approximately) by Poisson's expression
(equation **1**). Then the office should be large enough to accom-
modate k people, where k is the smallest integer such that $P(0) + P(1) + \ldots + P(k)$ is at least .90. From the 6.0 row of Table IV, Part B,
Appendix B, we find $P(0) + P(1) + \ldots + P(8) = 0.849$, and $P(0) + P(1) + \ldots + P(8) + P(9) = 0.918$. Thus, $k = 9$. Build an office to hold
9 visitors and, unless things change, you'll be 91% certain of not
having overcrowding on an hour when you happen to look in.

If a Bernoulli trials experiment has p close to zero, so that
Poisson's formula applies, and yet $np(1-p)$ is large enough for the
normal curve approximation also to apply, then it can be shown
that the two approximations will be just about the same. Two
common rules of thumb for using normal and Poisson approximations to the binomial distribution are: Use the normal approxima-
tion if either $p \leq \frac{1}{2}$ and $np > 5$, or $p > \frac{1}{2}$ and $n(1-p) > 5$. Use the
Poisson approximation if $p \leq 0.05$ and $n \geq 100$.

We have watched Janet, and occasionally Alan, apply most of
the probability theory presented in this book to problems of a

practical nature, although the data given were generally simpler and briefer than in the real world. We close this section with a problem that arose at AC, stated in its original, imprecise form. As usual, we minimize the discussion of methods for gathering data (such as survey design) and the techniques for implementing decisions (follow-up studies). These important topics are more appropriate for books on management and marketing.

**Problem 3**

The executives at AC complain that they waste too much time waiting to get an outside telephone line.

**Solution**

There are forty-two executives, each with a telephone that connects with the switchboard, which has 4 outside lines. A survey of the executives yields the following information: (1) the mean number of minutes per hour that an executive spends on outside line calls he or she has placed, not including time spent waiting for a line, is 6; (2) the mean number of minutes an executive spends per hour on phone calls made to him or her from outside is 4; (3) every executive would be satisfied with having a 95% chance of getting an outside line whenever he or she wants it. It seems reasonable to assume: (a) the events of any one phone's being busy with an outside call are independent, (b) the probabilities of each phone's being able to get an outside line are the same. With these assumptions and survey results the experiment "pick a phone at random and see if it is on an outside call" is a Bernoulli trials experiment with $n = 42$ and $p = (6+4)/60 = \frac{1}{6}$. If $K$ is the smallest number of outside lines that will satisfy the executives, then $P(k \le K)$ is the probability that at most $K$ lines are in use on outside calls. Hence, $K$ is the smallest number for which $P(k \le K) \ge 0.95$. Since $v = 42(\frac{1}{6})(\frac{5}{6}) = \frac{35}{6} > 3$, we may use either the normal approximation or Poisson's approximation, with $m = 7$, $s = \sqrt{210}/6 \doteq 2.4$. From Table II, Appendix B, $P(z \le 1.6) = 0.945$, $P(z \le 1.7) = 0.955$. Thus, we need $z = (K-m)/s = (K-7)/2.4 = 1.7$, and hence $K - 7 = (2.4)(1.7) = 4.08$, $K = 11.08$. From Table IV, Part B, $P(k \le 11) = 0.945$, $P(k \le 12) = 0.971$. Recommendation: add 7 outside lines to the 4 already in use.

AC is an employee-owned company, so it is not surprising to see the employees settle for less than a 100% success rate on telephone service. Forty-two outside lines would cost a lot.

The mean number of minutes a phone is on an outside line is 6 (outgoing) + 4 (incoming) = 10 for each 60-minute hour. Thus, $p = \frac{10}{60} = \frac{1}{6}$.

Before Poisson's formula can be applied to a practical problem the mean $m$ must, of course, be determined, at least approximately. Most practical problems of this type involve occurrences at various times. A convenient unit of time is chosen (one hour in Problems 2 and 3). Then $m$ is the mean number of occurrences per hour. This can be found approximately from a large number of observations. In Problem 2, for example, the office manager checked the front office on 40 different hours chosen at random during a few months with the following results (Table 12).

Table 12

| Number of salespeople | 0 | 1 | 2 | 3 | 4 | 5 | 6 | 7 | 8 | 9 | 10 |
|---|---|---|---|---|---|---|---|---|---|---|---|
| Number of hours | 7 | 2 | 0 | 3 | 6 | 4 | 3 | 2 | 2 | 3 | 1 |

| Number of salespeople | 11 | 12 | 13 | 14 | 15 | 16 | 17 | 18 or more |
|---|---|---|---|---|---|---|---|---|
| Number of hours | 1 | 1 | 0 | 2 | 0 | 2 | 1 | 0 |

We read, for instance, that on two occasions the manager found 16 salespersons jamming the office.

The mean of these data is, by the methods of Section 4.3, $(0 \cdot 7 + 1 \cdot 2 + 2 \cdot 0 + 3 \cdot 3 + \ldots + 17 \cdot 1 + 18 \cdot 0)/(7 + 2 + 0 + 3 + \ldots + 1 + 0) = \frac{240}{40} = 6$. This does not mean that m is exactly 6, since only 40 hours were sampled. But if the basic assumption that the salespeople arrived at random is correct, then the sample mean of 6 is probably close to the (unknown) mean.

**Exercises 4.6**

In Exercises 1 through 6 use the Poisson approximation to find the following binomial distribution probabilities, where n = number of trials, p = probability of success on a given trial, and k = number of successes.
1. P(k = 13); n = 800; p = 0.01.
2. P(k ≥ 14); n = 1,600; p = 0.02.
3. P(k in {1,2}); n = 1,600; p = 0.00025.
4. P(4 ≤ k ≤ 8); n = 50,000; p = 0.00002.
5. P(k ≠ 0); n = 100; p = 0.05.
6. P(k is odd); n = 857; p = 0.0035.

In Exercises 7 through 10 assume that the experiment's possible outcomes have a Poisson distribution.

See Exercise 7.

7. Cars arrive at the entrance of the parking lot of the Grosse Point, Michigan, PHE store at the average rate of 6 per minute during a typical Saturday afternoon. If 10 or more cars arrive in the same minute, serious congestion results. What are the chances of this happening?
8. By widening the entrances and making certain other changes, the PHE store manager can increase the ability of his parking lot to handle a sudden rush of cars without serious congestion. If he wants to reduce the chances of serious congestion to at most 5%, how many cars should it be able to handle per minute?
9. I have a poorly printed unauthorized edition of *The Hobbit*, by J.R.R. Tolkien. I selected 9 pages at random and examined them carefully for misprints, with the following results.

| Page | 8 | 22 | 27 | 41 | 76 | 109 | 161 | 184 | 209 |
|---|---|---|---|---|---|---|---|---|---|
| Number of misprints | 6 | 3 | 5 | 0 | 8 | 6 | 7 | 6 | 4 |

See Exercise 9.

Based on this, what are my chances of selecting an error-free page?
10. Find the smallest number for which I can say with 99% certainty that no page in my *Hobbit* has more than that number of errors.

**Section 4.7
Summary**

A random variable is a rule that assigns a number to each possible outcome of an experiment. If the possible outcomes are themselves numbers, the random variable may be represented graphically by a histogram. The average value or mean of a random variable is called its expectation. The variance and standard deviation of a random variable serve to further describe the distribution of its values.

The random variable giving the number of successes in a fixed number, n, of independent trials has a binomial probability distribution. For n sufficiently large a binomial distribution is approximated by the normal distribution and by a Poisson distribution. These distributions have many uses beyond their application to binomial distributions.

---
**TERMS**
---

Random variable, page 234
Histogram, page 238
Joint probability, page 244
Expectation, page 250
Mean, page 257
Standard deviation, page 261
Bernoulli trials experiment, page 265
Binomial distribution, page 270
Geometric distribution, page 272
Normal distribution, page 283
Poisson distribution, page 288

---
**FORMULAS AND COMPUTATIONAL TECHNIQUES**
---

Independence of two random variables, page 245
Expectation, pages 250–255
Bernoulli trials, pages 269, 271
Mean of binomial distribution, page 278
Standard deviation of binomial distribution , page 278

**Review Exercises**     Read the summary above and refer back to the chapter. Then work these exercises without looking back again. All these exercises are answered in Appendix C.

Exercises 1 through 6 refer to the following table of weights of third-grade girls in Hicksville, NY.

| Weight | Number of girls |
|--------|-----------------|
| 30.5–35.5 | 7 |
| 35.5–40.5 | 10 |
| 40.5–45.5 | 11 |
| 45.5–50.5 | 15 |
| 50.5–55.5 | 14 |
| 55.5–60.5 | 9 |
| 60.5–65.5 | 10 |
| 65.5–70.5 | 4 |
| 70.5–75.5 | 2 |

1. Describe the experiment and random variable X for this table.
2. Draw a histogram of X.
3. Compute:
   (a) $P(46 \le X \le 70)$
   (b) $P(X \le 55)$
   (c) $P(X \ge 65)$
4. Find the expectation of X and the mean weight m of the girls.
5. Find the variance and standard deviation of X.

6. Suppose all the weights in the table are 10% too low. Recompute m.
7. Draw a histogram of the binomial distribution with $n=6, p=\frac{1}{4}$.
8. What is the probability that a balanced coin flipped 5,000 times comes up tails between 2,440 and 2,470 times (inclusive)?
9. Adult IQs are normally distributed with mean 100 and standard deviation 22. What percentage of adults has IQs of 150 or more?
10. Suppose a random variable k has a Poisson distribution with mean 1.5. Find $P(1 \le k \le 4)$.

**Supplementary Exercises**     1. As a promotion, a company mails out 8 million circulars, each with a different number. Mr. Piccalilli has selected 15,031 numbers in advance for prizes, as follows: first prize, $25,000 plus $100 a month for life; 2 second prizes of $10,000; 3 third prizes of $5,000; 5 fourth prizes of $1,000; 20 fifth prizes of $500; 5,000 sixth prizes of $10; 10,000 seventh prizes of $5. In order to be eligible for a prize you must put a 13¢ stamp on the circular and mail it back. How much longer (in years) would you have to live in order for this to be a worthwhile investment?

2. Give examples of events A and B in the toss of a balanced die such that:

(a) $P(A \cap B) < P(A)P(B)$
(b) $P(A \cap B) = P(A)P(B)$
(c) $P(A \cap B) > P(A)P(B)$.

3. Last year the average gross by camping stores in New England of various AC products was as follows: packs, \$940; sleeping bags, \$2,280; camp stoves, \$1,485; rain gear, \$960; tents, \$8,880. Next year the prices on each of these items will go up 10%. It is predicted that sales volume of sleeping bags, rain gear, and tents will increase 15%, camp stoves will decrease 5%, and packs will stay the same.

(a) Introduce an experiment and 5 random variables and express last year's total average gross on the 5 AC items as expectations.
(b) Express next year's predicted average total gross on the 5 AC items as expectations.
(c) Calculate the expectations in (b).

For a review of absolute value, see Appendix A, Section 9.

4. Let X be a random variable with mean m. The **mean absolute deviation** of X is defined to be $E(|X - m|)$. Find the mean, the mean absolute deviation, the variance, the standard deviation, and the third and fourth central moments of each of the following tables of data.

(a) $1, 2, 3, 5, 7, 11, 13, 17, 19$.
(b) $1, 1, 2, 2, 3, 3, 5, 5, 7$.
(c) $1, 2, 2, 3, 3, 3, 5, 5, 5$.
(d)

| Number | $-5$ | $-3$ | $0$ | $2$ | $4$ |
|---|---|---|---|---|---|
| Frequency | 4 | 5 | 8 | 4 | 6 |

5. Let $m(X)$ be the mean of a random variable X. Prove that, if X and Y are random variables on the same experiment and if a and b are numbers, then $m(aX + bY) = am(X) + bm(Y)$.

6. Let $s(X)$ be the standard deviation of a random variable and let the symbol k denote a positive number. Use Exercise 5 to prove that $s(kX) = ks(X)$.

7. Suppose the random variable X assigns the same number c to every possible outcome. In the notation of Exercises 5 and 6, what are $m(X)$ and $s(X)$?

*8. Let X and Y be independent variables on the same experiment. Prove, in the notation of Exercises 5 and 6, that $(s(X + Y))^2 = (s(X))^2 + (s(Y))^2$.

9. Verify the result in the previous exercise for Problem 15, page 247.

10. A roulette wheel has 38 equally likely positions: $0, 1, 2, \ldots, 36, 00$. What are the chances that in 9 spins the ball lands on a number above 30 at least 8 times?

*11. How small (to two decimals) must the probability of success on 1 of 5 Bernoulli trials be in order for the probability of at most 2 successes to be at least 0.90?

12. Two balanced coins are simultaneously flipped 484 times. How many times would we expect them both to come up tails?

13. Use equation **1**, p. 250, to calculate the expected number of successes in a Bernoulli trials experiment with $n = 7$ and $p = \frac{1}{4}$. Compare your answer with the answer obtained from equation **2**, p. 276.

*14. I play a gambling game in which I flip a balanced coin until I get heads. My winnings are determined by the following chart.

Table

| Flip on which first heads appears | Winnings |
|---|---|
| 1 | 1 |
| 2 | 2 |
| 3 | 4 |
| 4 | 8 |
| 5 | 16 |
| . | . |
| . | . |
| . | . |
| $n+1$ | $2^n$ |

(a) What is the probability that I first get heads on the nth flip?

(b) What is the value of each term of the expression

$$E(X) = 1P(X=1) + 2P(X=2) + 4P(X=3) + 8P(X=4) + \dots$$

where X is the number of the flip on which the first head appears?

(c) What can you conclude about your expected winnings?

*15. Prove the equation

$$C_n^n + C_{n-1}^n + C_{n-2}^n + \dots + C_2^n + C_1^n + C_0^n = 2^n$$

in the following two ways:

(a) by the binomial theorem

(b) by counting subsets of a set of n objects in two ways

The remainder of the exercises deal with the independence of three events.

When we say that *three* events A, B, C are independent, not only do we mean that each event is independent of each other event, but we also require that each event be independent of the other two together. That is, we require each of the following six pairs of events to be independent:

| | |
|---|---|
| A and B | A and B∩C |
| A and C | B and A∩C |
| B and C | C and A∩B |

You might think, for example, that, if A and B are independent and A and C are independent, then A and B∩C must be independent. It might seem that if A and B∩C are independent then A and B must be independent and A and C must be independent. In fact, neither of these conjectures is true, as we see in Exercise 16.

16. Toss a balanced die, marked as usual.
    (a) Define the events A, B, and C by the following conditions: A = "multiple of 3"; B = "less than 4"; C = "even." Show that A and B are independent, that A and C are independent, and that A and B∩C are not independent.
    (b) Now let A = "multiple of 3"; B = "neither 2 nor 4"; C = "neither 2 nor 3." Show that A and B∩C are independent and that neither A and B nor A and C are independent.

17. A survey of preferences of AC parkas, sleeping bags, and raincoats in Colorado shows: 40% prefer AC parkas, 30% prefer AC sleeping bags, 20% prefer AC raincoats, 15% prefer both AC parkas and sleeping bags, 10% prefer both AC parkas and raincoats, 10% prefer both AC sleeping bags and raincoats, and 9% prefer all three products. Assuming an error of at most 4% in each result, could these events be independent?

See Exercise 20, Section 1.5.
18. Suppose A, B, C are independent, $P(A) = \frac{1}{3}$, $P(B) = \frac{1}{4}$, and $P(C) = \frac{1}{5}$. Find each of $P(\sim A \cap B \cap C)$, $P(A \cap \sim B \cap C)$, $P(A \cap B \cap \sim C)$, $P(A \cap \sim B \cap \sim C)$, $P(\sim A \cap B \cap \sim C)$, $P(\sim A \cap \sim B \cap C)$, and $P(\sim A \cap \sim B \cap \sim C)$.

*19. The only reason that I will not get back to my desk on time after my break is that I might meet one of my three Dutch friends, Aart, Betje, or Cyriel, at the coffee wagon. When the efficiency expert studied our company, he determined that the probability of my meeting Aart is 0.12, Betje is 0.35, and Cyriel is 0.27. What is the probability that I will get back to my desk on time? Assume that the events of my meeting one of my friends are independent.

20. A balanced die has two faces marked 1, two marked 2, and two marked 3. Find three events A, B, C in the experiment of tossing the die such that $P(A \cap B) = P(A)P(B)$, $P(A \cap C) = P(A)P(C)$, $P(B \cap C) = P(B)P(C)$, but A, B, C, are not independent.

21. Consider the following three events in the roll of two balanced dice:

$$A = \{3, 5, 7\}, B = \{2, 3, 11, 12\}, C = \{4, 5, 10, 11\}$$

Which of the following collections of events are independent?
    (a) A, B
    (b) B, C
    (c) A, C
    (d) A, B, C

22. A balanced die, marked as usual, is tossed. Check the following for independence.
    (a) "even," "multiple of 3," "6"
    (b) "odd," "at least 5," "at most 6"
    *(c) Part (b) is not too satisfactory, but it is the best that can be done. Show that, if three events in the toss of a balanced die, marked as usual, are independent, then at least one of the events must be certain.

# Chapter 5
# Linear
# Programming

Although the word "programming" in LP does not refer to computer programming, Janet's computer is programmed to use Linear Programming. In Section 6 of Chapter 6 we will discuss the use of computers in LP. Until that time we will present only problems that are small enough to be worked by hand.

Appalachian Creations is like most big corporations in that it bases many of its important business decisions on data obtained through the use of Linear Programming (LP). Most important LP problems involve minimizing costs or maximizing profits. In the 1930s, when AC was a one-family operation, the company was small enough for its founder, Thomas Black, to rely on his good business sense to make the right decisions. But now AC uses hundreds of raw materials with prices that fluctuate weekly. They make over 500 items and no human being could keep track of all the delicate interrelationships. At AC, only the computer in Janet's department is equipped with a sufficiently large memory to handle this task.

The principal technique presented in this chapter is the *simplex method*, which was invented by George Dantzig in 1947. We introduce this technique in Section 5.2. Most LP problems require some preliminary modifications before they are ready to be solved by the simplex method. These modifications are discussed in Sections 5.4 and 5.6. In Sections 5.1 and 5.3, we provide an explanation of how the simplex method works. In Section 5.5, the simplex method is applied to practical problems. Section 5.6 contains a presentation of a technique called the dual variable check, which will verify that you have found the correct answer to a Linear Programming problem.

The simplex method and all these modifications use the same operations with rows as Gauss-Jordan reduction does.

## Section 5.1
## Introduction to
## Linear Programming

When the management at Appalachian Creations chose Burlington, Vermont, as the site for its new factory for the production of high-quality down jackets and sleeping bags, it first asked a team of investigators to file a preliminary report on the proposed operation. This report revealed the following four facts.

(1) While rip-stop nylon, zippers, snaps, and thread were readily available, high-quality goose down was not. It seemed best to

A person-hour of work is one hour worked by one person. For example, if 3 women worked from 9:00 to 11:00 and 2 men worked from 10:00 to 11:00, a total of 8 person-hours of work was done $(3 \times 2 + 2 \times 1 = 8)$.

order down through a Norwegian distributor, who could guarantee delivery of 600 pounds a week.

(2) The planned size of the planned factory limited the staff to 30 workers. There would be no problem in hiring 30 skilled people; however, they would provide only $30 \times 40 = 1,200$ person-hours of work each week.

(3) The proposed jacket required 2 pounds of down and 6 hours of work, while the sleeping bag required 3 pounds of down and 4 hours of work.

(4) In order to satisfy the stockholders, the company should make $3 net profit on each jacket and $4 net profit on each sleeping bag produced.

The problem for management was to determine a "program" for production of jackets and sleeping bags at the greatest possible profit. This problem exemplifies a typical **linear programming** situation: how should one utilize limited resources (in this case down and time) to produce an optimum situation (in this case the greatest total profit)? It is obvious that this type of problem will arise in essentially every production situation. Of course, in most applications to real life there will be more than two resources and two commodities.

We tabulate the facts in the preliminary report in Table 1. Such tables will prove to be useful as an intermediate step between a practical problem and its mathematical formulation.

Table 1

|  | Per jacket | Per sleeping bag | Total available |
|---|---|---|---|
| Down | 2 lbs. | 3 lbs. | 600 lbs. |
| Time | 6 hrs. | 4 hrs. | 1,200 hrs. |
| Profit | $3 | $4 |  |

Since we are asked to find the number of jackets and the number of sleeping bags to be produced, it would seem natural to let $x_1$ represent the number of jackets and $x_2$ represent the number of sleeping bags. However, in view of the large numbers in the last column of the table, we choose instead to let

$x_1 =$ the number of hundreds of jackets produced each week

$x_2 =$ the number of hundreds of bags produced each week

An answer like $x_1 = 3$ and $x_2 = 2$ will then mean: make 300 jackets and 200 sleeping bags each week.

Notice that, since each jacket requires 2 pounds of down, $x_1$ hundred jackets will use $2x_1$ hundred pounds of down. Similarly, $x_2$ hundred sleeping bags will use $3x_2$ hundred pounds of down.

The symbols $\leq$ (less than or equal)
and $\geq$ (greater than or equal) are
discussed in Appendix A, Section 8.

Thus, the total down consumption will be $2x_1 + 3x_2$ hundred
pounds per week. Since there are only 6 hundred pounds of down
available, $2x_1 + 3x_2$ must be no more then 6, i.e.

$$2x_1 + 3x_2 \leq 6 \qquad\qquad \textbf{1}$$

Likewise, making $x_1$ hundred jackets uses $6x_1$ hundred hours, and
$4x_2$ hundred hours will be used to make $x_2$ hundred sleeping bags.
Since only 12 hundred hours of time are available each week, the
total weekly time consumption, $6x_1 + 4x_2$, must not exceed 12:

$$6x_1 + 4x_2 \leq 12 \qquad\qquad \textbf{2}$$

The profit on $x_1$ hundred jackets will amount to $3x_1$ hundred
dollars. On $x_2$ hundred sleeping bags the profit will be $4x_2$ hundred
dollars. The total profit will be the sum $3x_1 + 4x_2$, which we denote
by y.

The profit $y = 3x_1 + 4x_2$ varies depending upon the choice of
$x_1$ and $x_2$. For instance, choosing $x_1 = 1$ and $x_2 = 2$ results in the
profit $y = 3 \cdot 1 + 4 \cdot 2 = 11$ hundred dollars. Our aim is to find $x_1$ and
$x_2$ so that $2x_1 + 3x_2 \leq 6$, $6x_1 + 4x_2 \leq 12$, and y had the largest value
possible. Thus, choosing $x_1 = 1$ and $x_2 = 2$ is unacceptable since
$2 \cdot 1 + 3 \cdot 2 = 8 \geq 6$, which violates inequality **1**. An example of an
acceptable choice is $x_1 = 1$ and $x_2 = 1$. With this choice we have
$2 \cdot 1 + 3 \cdot 1 = 5 \leq 6$ and $6 \cdot 1 + 4 \cdot 1 = 10 \leq 12$, so that inequalities **1** and

Other acceptable choices may result
in a greater profit.

**2** are satisfied with a profit of $3 \cdot 1 + 4 \cdot 1 = 7$ hundred dollars.

We are now ready to illustrate the standard format for
presenting a mathematically formulated LP problem:

Maximize

$$y = 3x_1 + 4x_2 \qquad\qquad \textbf{3}$$

subject to

$$x_1 \geq 0, \quad x_2 \geq 0 \qquad\qquad \textbf{4}$$

$$2x_1 + 3x_2 \leq 6 \qquad\qquad \textbf{5}$$

$$6x_1 + 4x_2 \leq 12 \qquad\qquad \textbf{6}$$

Before our methods can be applied to find a solution of a practical
problem, it is necessary to present the information in the above
form. The instruction, "Maximize $y = 3x_1 + 4x_2$ subject to ..." is an
abbreviation for the phrase "Find $x_1$ and $x_2$ such that $3x_1 + 4x_2$ is
as large as possible and such that ..."

The variable y is called the **objective variable**, since the object
of the problem is to maximize y. While it is obvious in our case
that $x_1$ and $x_2$ cannot be negative this fact must be expressed

formally as in **4** above. The inequalities **5** and **6** are called **constraints**.

You may wonder why we do not treat this problem like the ones presented in Chapter 2. Can we not determine how many jackets and sleeping bags we should make to use up all the available down and all the available time? Why not simply solve the system

$$\left[ \begin{array}{l} 2x_1 + 3x_2 = 6 \\ 6x_1 + 4x_2 = 12 \end{array} \right]$$

Answer: $x_1 = \frac{6}{5}, x_2 = \frac{6}{5}$. The value $x_1 = \frac{6}{5}$ means: make $\frac{6}{5} \cdot 100 = 120$ jackets.
Check:

$$2\left(\tfrac{6}{5}\right) + 3\left(\tfrac{6}{5}\right) = (12+18)/5 = 6 \checkmark$$
$$6\left(\tfrac{6}{5}\right) + 4\left(\tfrac{6}{5}\right) = (36+24)/5 = 12 \checkmark$$

obtaining $x_1 = \frac{6}{5}$, that is, 120 jackets, and $x_2 = \frac{6}{5}$, that is, 120 sleeping bags? At this point it is difficult to raise an objection to this approach, since we will soon discover that problems of this size can often be solved in this way. As we will verify later, the solution $x_1 = \frac{6}{5}$, $x_2 = \frac{6}{5}$ does indeed produce the maximum profit $y = 3 \cdot \frac{6}{5} + 4 \cdot \frac{6}{5} = \frac{42}{5} = 8.4$, that is, $840.

This method of solution is, however, unlikely to work for any but the simplest of LP problems. Suppose, for instance, that in our problem there had also been a constraint on the supply of rip-stop nylon, say $3x_1 + 5x_2 \le 7$. The resulting system

$$\left[ \begin{array}{l} 2x_1 + 3x_2 = 6 \\ 6x_1 + 4x_2 = 12 \\ 3x_1 + 5x_2 = 7 \end{array} \right]$$

Since any solution to this system must satisfy all three equations, the only possible answer is $x_1 = \frac{6}{5}, x_2 = \frac{6}{5}$ as before. However, $3\left(\tfrac{6}{5}\right) + 5\left(\tfrac{6}{5}\right) = 9\tfrac{3}{5} \ne 7$.

is inconsistent, in the sense that it has no solutions at all, and hence the above "method" fails. In this extended problem, as in many practical LP problems, it is impossible to use all the time and material available. We are then in a new mathematical situation, more complicated than that of Chapter 2.

In this section we will develop a technique which uses geometry to solve any linear programming problem with only two variables $x_1$ and $x_2$. The rest of the chapter is concerned with an algebraic method which will solve linear programming problems involving any number of variables.

Why are problems of this sort called linear programming problems? First, the goal of such problems is to obtain a good *program* of production, that is, a set of instructions such as "make

120 jackets and 120 sleeping bags per week." Second, we will
confine ourselves to problems that can be expressed mathematically by using only *linear* forms, such as those encountered in
Chapter 2. The word "programming" in LP does not have to do
with computer programming.

In seeking a solution to our LP problem we note that, since
only two variables are involved, we can hope to use our knowledge
of coordinates to interpret the problem graphically. Our plan is
first to make a graph showing all points $(x_1, x_2)$ that satisfy
inequalities **4**, **5**, and **6**. We will then develop a technique for
quickly determining which of these points yields the maximum
value for y.

Since the problem involves several inequalities, we must learn
how to graph an inequality.

**Graphing Inequalities**

To find all points $(x_1, x_2)$ that satisfy $2x_1 + 3x_2 \le 6$, we begin by
graphing the *equation* $2x_1 + 3x_2 = 6$. From Section 2.1 we know that
this graph is a line (Figure 1). Now it can be shown that the graph
of the inequality $2x_1 + 3x_2 \le 6$ will be one of the two half-planes
bounded by this line. It will either be the **lower half-plane**, consisting of all points on or below this line, or else the **upper half-plane**,
consisting of all points on or above this line. The origin $(0, 0)$
satisfies our inequality, since $2 \cdot 0 + 3 \cdot 0 = 0 \le 6$, so the origin belongs to the graph of our inequality. We see then from Figure 1
that the graph is the lower half-plane (Figure 2).

This same technique is used to graph any inequality of the
form $ax_1 + bx_2 \le c$ or the form $ax_1 + bx_2 \ge c$, where a and b are not
both zero, as we see in the following examples.

Figure 1

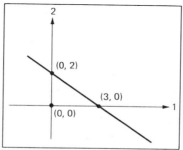

Figure 2

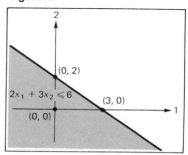

**Problem 1**

**Solution**

Graph the inequality $3x_1 - 2x_2 \leq 6$.
First we graph the line $3x_1 - 2x_2 = 6$. Since $(0,0)$ satisfies the inequality, and the origin is *above* the line, the graph is the upper half-plane. (Figure 3.)

**Figure 3**

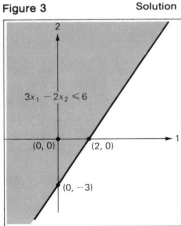

$3x_1 - 2x_2 \leq 6$

$(0, 0)$   $(2, 0)$

$(0, -3)$

**Problem 2**

**Solution**

Graph the inequality $2x_1 + \frac{7}{2}x_2 \geq 14$.
First we graph the line $2x_1 + \frac{7}{2}x_2 = 14$. Since the origin does *not* satisfy the inequality ($2 \cdot 0 + \frac{7}{2} \cdot 0$ is not $\geq 14$), the graph must be the half-plane that does *not* contain the origin, that is, the upper half-plane (see Figure 4).

**Figure 4**

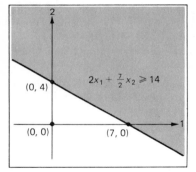

$(0, 4)$

$2x_1 + \frac{7}{2}x_2 \geq 14$

$(0, 0)$   $(7, 0)$

**Problem 3**

**Solution**

Graph the inequality $4x_1 - 5x_2 \geq 0$.
First we graph the line $4x_1 - 5x_2 = 0$. Since the line passes through the origin, we cannot use $(0,0)$ to help us determine which half-plane is the answer; instead, we may use any point that is not on this line. For easy computation we choose $(0,1)$. This point does not satisfy the inequality ($4 \cdot 0 - 5 \cdot 1 = -5$, which is not $\geq 0$); hence, the graph is the lower half-plane (see Figure 5).

**Figure 5**

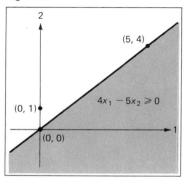

$(5, 4)$

$(0, 1)$

$4x_1 - 5x_2 \geq 0$

$(0, 0)$

In Section 5.6 we will show how to deal with problems in which the inequalities $x_1 \geq 0$, $x_2 \geq 0$ are not assumed.

There are two linear inequalities that occur in every standard format LP problem: $x_1 \geq 0$ and $x_2 \geq 0$. These simple inequalities are graphed in Figures 6 and 7, respectively. In Figure 6 the terms "upper" or "lower" are inappropriate; the graph in Figure 6 is a **right half-plane**.

Figure 6

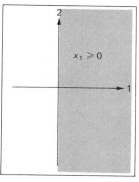

Figure 7

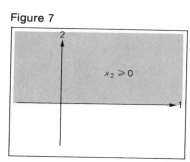

**Graphing a Region of Feasibility**

In the AC example above, a feasible solution would satisfy inequalities **4**, **5**, and **6**.

Mathematicians call the set of all points common to a number of regions the **intersection** of the regions. Thus, the region of feasibility is the intersection of all the half-planes determined by the constraints.

A point $(x_1, x_2)$ that satisfies all the conditions of an LP problem is called a **feasible solution** of the problem. The **region of feasibility** of a problem consists of all points that are feasible solutions. To graph this region for our problem, we first use the technique described above to graph each of the inequalities **4**, **5**, and **6**. We have already graphed inequalities **4** (Figures 6 and 7) and inequality **5** (Figure 2). The graph of inequality **6** appears in Figure 8. The graph of the region of feasibility consists of the points that these graphs have in common, as shown in Figure 9. Notice that we have labeled the constraint boundary lines **5** and **6**, after the inequalities from which they arose.

Figure 8

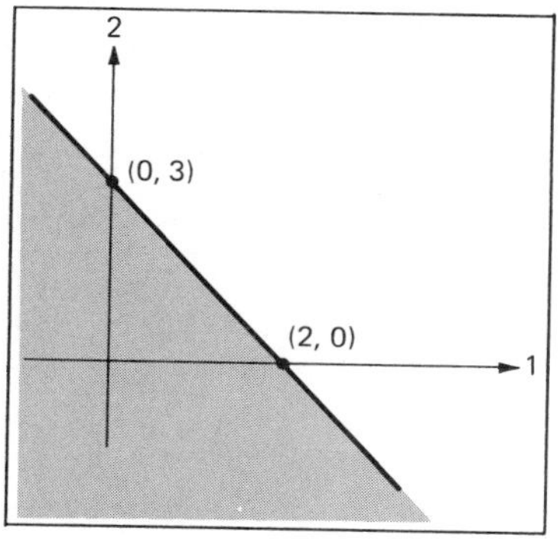

Figure 9

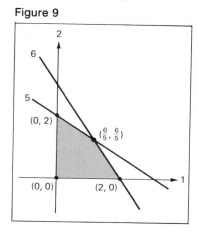

Corner points are called **extreme points** in many treatments of linear programming.

Our region of feasibility has four **corner points**: $(0,0)$, $(0,2)$, $(2,0)$, and $(\frac{6}{5},\frac{6}{5})$. The first three of these points were found when we graphed the inequalities. The fourth point is the intersection of lines **5** and **6**, found by solving the system of equations for these lines:

$$\left[\begin{array}{l} 2x_1 + 3x_2 = 6 \\ 6x_1 + 4x_2 = 12 \end{array}\right]$$

We will see that determining the corners is important, since an optimal solution to the problem will always be found at some corner of the region of feasibility. Before we see why this is the case, we will investigate a few other examples. Note that, while some linear programming problems in two variables have more complicated regions of feasibility, the process of graphing the region and locating the corners is always essentially the same.

The inequalities $x_1 \geq 0$ and $x_2 \geq 0$ restrict us to the **positive quadrant** of the plane (Figure 10). In the following problems we draw each constraint graph in the positive quadrant and locate the corner points by solving the appropriate systems.

**Figure 10**

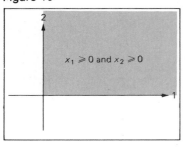

$x_1 \geqslant 0$ and $x_2 \geqslant 0$

The positive quadrant is also referred to as the **first quadrant**.

**Problem 4**  Draw the region of feasibility determined by the inequalities

$$x_1 \geq 0,\ x_2 \geq 0$$
$$-2x_1 + 3x_2 \leq 6 \qquad\qquad\qquad \textbf{7}$$
$$x_1 - 4x_2 \leq 4 \qquad\qquad\qquad \textbf{8}$$

**Solution**  See Figure 11, where the lines with equations $-2x_1 + 3x_2 = 6$ and $x_1 - 4x_2 = 4$ have been labeled **7** and **8** respectively. The region of feasibility is *unbounded*, since, given any distance, there are points in the region whose distance from the origin is greater than the given distance.

Since, as we will see, the solution of an LP problem will occur at a corner point and since the corner points can be found by solving the given equations simultaneously in pairs, the necessity of graphing may not be apparent. However in this problem the intersection of lines **7** and **8** yields neither a corner point nor a feasible solution. It is not easy to notice that this intersection is irrelevant by inspecting the given inequalities. In general, one should graph the lines first and then solve only those systems of equations that yield corner points of the region of feasibility.

**Figure 11**

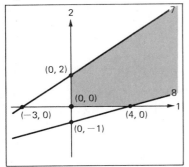

**Problem 5**   Draw the region of feasibility determined by the inequalities

$$x_1 \geq 0, \, x_2 \geq 0, \, -2x_1 + 3x_2 \geq 6, \, x_1 - 4x_2 \geq 4 \, .$$

**Solution**   The lines we use here are the same as in the previous problem (Figure 11). However, in this case we are interested in the points that are simultaneously above line **7**, below line **8**, and in the positive quadrant. That there are no such points is apparent from Figure 11. Thus, there is no such region or, as mathematicians would say, the region is **empty**. A situation like this occurs in practice whenever conditions of such stringency are placed on a problem that all possible solutions are ruled out.

**Problem 6**   Draw the region of feasibility determined by the inequalities.

$$x_1 \geq 0, \, x_2 \geq 0$$

$$x_1 - x_2 \leq 1 \qquad\qquad \textbf{9}$$

$$x_1 + x_2 \leq 3 \qquad\qquad \textbf{10}$$

$$3x_1 + x_2 \leq 6 \qquad\qquad \textbf{11}$$

**Answer**   See Figure 12.

**Problem 7**   Draw the region of feasibility determined by $x_1 \geq 0, \, x_2 \geq 0$

$$2x_1 - x_2 \geq 1 \qquad\qquad \textbf{12}$$

$$-x_1 + 2x_2 \geq 1 \qquad\qquad \textbf{13}$$

$$x_1 + x_2 \leq 5 \qquad\qquad \textbf{14}$$

**Answer**   See Figure 13. Notice that the requirements $x_1 \geq 0$ and $x_2 \geq 0$ are unnecessary, in view of constraints **12** and **13**.

**Extreme Point Theorem**   We now return to our discussion of the AC problem. In Figure 9 we used all of the inequalities to determine the feasible region. The question remains as to how to interpret the objective variable $y = 3x_1 + 4x_2$ geometrically. Assigning different values to y yields different lines. For example, when $y = 4$, we obtain the line $4 = 3x_1 + 4x_2$. A different value, say $y = 5$, gives a different line,

Figure 12

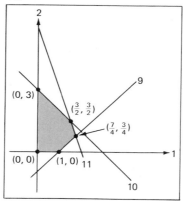

Figure 13

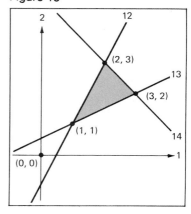

It is obvious that this system has no solution: if a pair of numbers $(x_1, x_2)$ satisfies the first equation, then $3x_1 + 4x_2 = 4 \neq 5$, and it fails to satisfy the second equation. Since the lines have no point in common, they must not cross one another.

the line with equation $5 = 3x_1 + 4x_2$. Since the system

$$\begin{bmatrix} 3x_1 + 4x_2 = 4 \\ 3x_1 + 4x_2 = 5 \end{bmatrix}$$

has no solution, these lines are parallel. In fact, no matter what value we assign to y, we get a line that is parallel to these two. We see from Figure 14 that, the larger the value we assign to y, the farther the line is from the origin. Every point in the plane is on exactly one of the lines $3x_1 + 4x_2 = y$. For example, the point $(2, 3)$ is on the line $y = 3 \cdot 2 + 4 \cdot 3 = 18$, that is, on the line $3x_1 + 4x_2 = 18$.

Now let us return to the graph in Figure 9. Draw the "y-lines" that pass through the corners of the regions of feasibility (see Figure 15). Recall that we want y to be as large as is feasible. The largest of these y-values occurs at the corner $(\frac{6}{5}, \frac{6}{5})$, where $y = 3 \cdot \frac{6}{5} + 4 \cdot \frac{6}{5} = \frac{42}{5}$. For any larger value of y, the corresponding line lies beyond the region of feasibility: no point on it satisfies the conditions of the problem. For example, the dashed line $y = 3x_1 + 4x_2 = 12$ in Figure 15 is such a line. Thus, the largest value of y that is yielded by a feasible solution occurs at the point with $x_1 = \frac{6}{5}$ and $x_2 = \frac{6}{5}$, which, as we noted before, corresponds to making $\frac{6}{5}$ hundred or 120 jackets and $\frac{6}{5}$ hundred or 120 sleeping bags. It can be shown that in all such problems the largest value of y occurs at a corner.

The extreme point theorem is also valid for problems involving three variables. For problems with four or more variables graphs and other visual interpretations are difficult. Nevertheless, mathematicians use geometric terminology in higher dimensional settings, and the extreme point theorem is applicable to all linear programming problems when suitably interpreted.

---

**EXTREME POINT THEOREM**

In any linear programming problem, an optimal value of the objective variable occurs at a corner point of the region of feasibility (unless, of course, there is no optimal value).

---

Figure 14

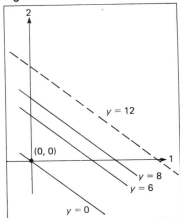

Figure 15

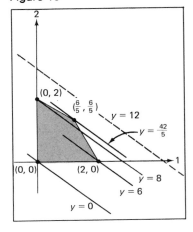

The extreme point theorem is true for all LP problems whether they are maximization or minimization problems (in the latter, the optimal value is the *smallest* value yielded by a feasible solution). This result also holds for problems involving more than two variables. The corner point theorem is the basis for the flow chart below.

**Geometrical Method for Solving
a Two-Variable LP Problem in
Standard Format**

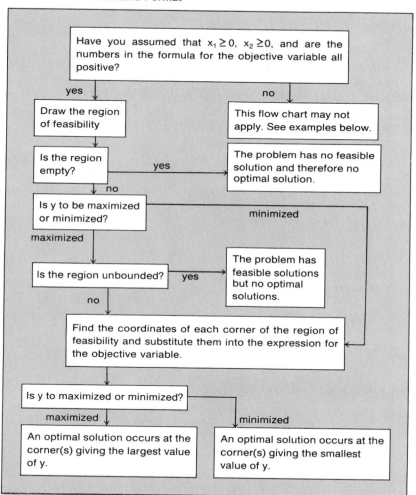

We have required here that $x_1 \geq 0$ and $x_2 \geq 0$ be part of the input data and that all the numbers occurring in the formula for the objective variables be positive. These requirements are satisfied in many practical applications, since, in these cases, the x's usually measure physical quantities. The technique of graphing particular lines corresponding to various values of y is slightly more difficult than the technique presented in the flow chart, but it will work for any two-variable LP problem, not just those to which the flow chart applies.

**Problem 8** Maximize $y = 6x_1 + x_2$ subject to the constraints of Problem 6:

$$x_1 \geq 0, x_2 \geq 0$$
$$x_1 - x_2 \leq 1$$
$$x_1 + x_2 \leq 3$$
$$3x_1 + x_2 \leq 6$$

**Solution** We have already drawn the region of feasibility and found the corner points in Figure 12, p.305. Substituting these points into the formula for y results in Table 2.

**Table 2**

| Corner point | y-value |
| --- | --- |
| $(0,0)$ | 0 |
| $(0,3)$ | 3 |
| $(\frac{3}{2}, \frac{3}{2})$ | $\frac{21}{2} = 10\frac{1}{2}$ |
| $(\frac{7}{4}, \frac{3}{4})$ | $\frac{45}{4} = 11\frac{1}{4}$ |
| $(1,0)$ | 6 |

Sometimes it may be hard to tell which y-value is largest without a calculator. For example, which is larger: $\frac{12}{29}$ or $\frac{5}{12}$? For help in making such determinations, see Appendix A, Section 8.

The largest of the y-values so obtained is $y = \frac{45}{4}$. Thus, the answer is $x_1 = \frac{7}{4}$, $x_2 = \frac{3}{4}$, and $y = \frac{45}{4}$.

**Problem 9** Maximize $y = 2x_1 + 3x_2$ subject to

$$x_1 \geq 0, x_2 \geq 0$$
$$-2x_1 + 3x_2 \leq 6$$
$$x_1 - 4x_2 \leq 4$$

**Solution** The region of feasibility (Figure 11, p. 304) is unbounded; hence, the problem has no maximum solution.

**Problem 10** Minimize (i.e., find the smallest value of) $y = 2x_1 + 5x_2$ subject to

$$x_1 \geq 0, x_2 \geq 0$$
$$-2x_1 + 3x_2 \geq 6$$
$$x_1 - 4x_2 \geq 4$$

The region of feasibility is in no way affected by the formula for the objective variable.

**Solution** By Problem 5, the region of feasibility is empty; hence, there is no solution.

**Problem 11** Minimize $y = 2x_1 + 5x_2$ subject to

$$x_1 \geq 0, x_2 \geq 0$$
$$x_1 + x_2 \geq 3 \qquad \text{15}$$
$$2x_1 + x_2 \geq 4 \qquad \text{16}$$
$$2x_1 + 5x_2 \geq 10 \qquad \text{17}$$

Solution We draw the region of feasibility and find its corner points (Figure 16). Substitution into the equation for the objective variable yields Table 3.

Figure 16 Table 3

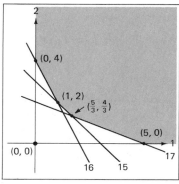

| Corner point | y-value |
|---|---|
| (0, 4) | 20 |
| (1, 2) | 12 |
| $(\frac{5}{3}, \frac{4}{3})$ | 10 |
| (5, 0) | 10 |

Thus, we find two minimum solutions: $x_1 = \frac{5}{3}$, $x_2 = \frac{4}{3}$ with $y = 10$ and $x_1 = 5$, $x_2 = 0$ with $y = 10$. Actually there are even more than two minimum solutions in this case. It can be shown that any point on the line segment joining the points $(5, 0)$ and $(\frac{5}{3}, \frac{4}{3})$ will also yield another minimum solution.

The following two problems are included so as to indicate techniques for handling cases to which the flow chart does not apply.

Problem 12 Find the maximum and minimum values of $y = x_1 - x_2$ subject to

$$x_1 \geq 0, x_2 \geq 0$$

$$-3x_1 + x_2 \leq 3 \qquad\qquad \mathbf{18}$$

$$2x_1 - x_2 \leq 2 \qquad\qquad \mathbf{19}$$

Figure 17 Solution The flow chart does not apply, since the objective variable contains a negative number (the $-1$ before $x_2$). The graph of the feasible region is shown in Figure 17. The line $y = 1$ passes through the corner point $(1, 0)$. For any larger value of $y$ (such as $y = 2$), the y-line misses the region. Thus, the maximum solution is: $x_1 = 1$, $x_2 = 0$, $y = 1$. The line $y = -3$ passes through the corner point $(0, 3)$, but, for every smaller value of $y$ (such as $y = -4$), the y-line also intersects the region. Thus, there is no minimum solution.

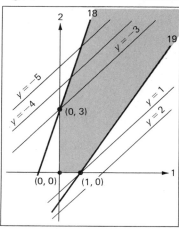

Problem 13 Find the maximum and minimum values of $y = x_1 + x_2$ subject to

$$-x_1 + 2x_2 \leq 2 \qquad\qquad \mathbf{20}$$

$$2x_1 - x_2 \leq 2 \qquad\qquad \mathbf{21}$$

**Figure 18**            Solution

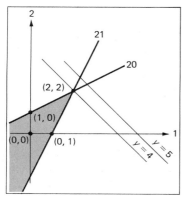

We cannot use the flow chart because we are not told that $x_1 \geq 0$ and $x_2 \geq 0$. The feasible region is shown in Figure 18. The region has only one corner point: $(2,2)$. It is clear from the two y-lines drawn above that the maximum solution is $x_1 = 2$, $x_2 = 2$, $y = 4$ and that there is no minimum solution.

Exercises 5.1          In Exercises 1 through 6, graph the indicated inequality.

1. $2x_1 + x_2 \leq 6$
2. $2x_1 + x_2 \geq -2$
3. $x_1 - 2x_2 \leq 4$
4. $3x_1 + 4x_2 \leq -12$
5. $-2x_1 + 3x_2 \geq 0$
6. $x_1 + x_2 \geq 0$

In Exercises 7 through 13, graph the region determined by (all) the specified conditions.

7. $x_1 \geq 0, x_2 \geq 0.$
   $x_1 + x_2 \leq 3$
   $x_1 + 2x_2 \leq 4$

8. $x_1 \geq 0, x_2 \geq 0$
   $x_1 + x_2 \geq 3$
   $2x_1 + 5x_2 \geq 10$

9. $x_1 \geq 0, x_2 \geq 0$
   $3x_1 + 8x_2 \leq 24$
   $4x_1 + 5x_2 \leq 20$
   $6x_1 + 4x_2 \leq 24$

10. $x_1 \geq 0, x_2 \geq 0$
    $4x_1 + x_2 \geq 4$
    $x_1 + x_2 \geq 3$
    $x_1 + 2x_2 \geq 4$

11. $5x_1 - x_2 \geq -8$
    $x_1 - 5x_2 \leq 8$
    $x_1 + x_2 \leq 2$

12. $2x_1 + x_2 \leq 6$
    $x_1 + 6x_2 \geq 6$
    $x_1 + x_2 \geq -2$

13. $x_1 + x_2 \geq 4$
    $2x_1 + x_2 \leq 4$
    $x_1 + 2x_2 \leq 4$

Thus, in 14(a), for instance, you are to maximize $y = 3x_1 + 2x_2$, subject to $x_1 \geq 0$, $x_2 \geq 0$, $x_1 + x_2 \leq 3$, and $x_1 + 2x_2 \leq 4$.

14. Maximize the following objective variables subject to the conditions listed in Exercise 7 above:
    (a) $y = 3x_1 + 2x_2$ (b) $y = 2x_1 + 3x_2$ (c) $y = x_1 + 4x_2$
15. Minimize the following objective variables subject to the conditions listed in Exercise 8 above:
    (a) $y = 2x_1 + 3x_2$ (b) $y = x_1 + 6x_2$ (c) $y = 3x_1 + x_2$

16. Maximize the following objective variables subject to the conditions listed in Exercise 9 above:
    (a) $y = 4x_1 + 4x_2$ (b) $y = 2x_1 + 7x_2$ (c) $y = 7x_1 + 10x_2$
    (d) $y = x_1 + 3x_2$

17. Minimize the following objective variables subject to the conditions listed in Exercise 10 above:
    (a) $y = 2x_1 + 3x_2$ (b) $y = 3x_1 + 2x_2$ (c) $y = x_1 + 5x_2$ (d) $y = 5x_1 + x_2$

$^C$18. Maximize $y = 3x_1 + x_2$ subject to $x_1 \geq 0$, $x_2 \geq 0$, and $x_1 + 2x_2 \leq 4$, $x_1 + x_2 \leq 2$, $4x_1 + 3x_2 \leq 12$.

19. Maximize and minimize the following objective variables subject to the conditions listed in Exercise 11 above:
    (a) $y = 2x_1 - x_2$
    (b) $y = 3x_1 + 4x_2$
    (c) $y = x_1$ (in other words, $y = x_1 + 0x_2$)
    (d) $y = x_2$

For example, in 19(a) you are to work two separate problems: (i) Maximize $2x_1 - x_2$ subject to the conditions listed in Exercise 11 and (ii) minimize $2x_1 - x_2$ subject to the conditions listed in Exercise 11.

20. Maximize and minimize the following objective variables subject to the conditions listed in Exercise 12 above:
    (a) $y = 2x_1 - x_2$
    (b) $y = 2x_1 + 3x_2$
    (c) $y = 3x_1 + 2x_2$
    (d) $y = 3x_1 + x_2$

21. Maximize and minimize the following objective variables subject to the conditions listed in Exercise 13 above:
    (a) $y = 3x_1 + 2x_2$
    (b) $y = x_1 - x_2$
    (c) $y = 5x_1 + 2x_2$

22. Maximize $y = -x_1 + x_2$ subject to $x_1 \geq 0$, $x_2 \geq 0$, and $3x_1 + 2x_2 \leq 6$, $2x_1 + 3x_2 \leq 6$.

23. Minimize $y = x_1 + x_2$ subject to $x_1 \geq 0$, $x_2 \geq 0$, and $3x_1 + 2x_2 \leq 6$, $2x_1 + 3x_2 \leq 6$.

24. Maximize $y = x_1 + 2x_2$ subject to $x_1 \geq 0$, $x_2 \geq 0$, and $-x_1 + x_2 \leq 2$, $x_1 - x_2 \leq 2$.

25. Minimize $y = x_1 - 2x_2$ subject to $x_1 \geq 0$, $x_2 \geq 0$, and $-x_1 + x_2 \leq 2$, $x_1 - x_2 \leq 2$.

26. (a) Minimize $y = x_1 + x_2$ subject to $x_1 \geq 0$, $x_2 \geq 0$, $3x_1 + 2x_2 \geq 12$, $x_1 + 5x_2 \geq 10$.
    (b) Maximize $y = -x_1 - x_2$ subject to $x_1 \geq 0$, $x_2 \geq 0$, $3x_1 + 2x_2 \geq 12$, $x_1 + 5x_2 \geq 10$.

27. (a) Find the maximum and minimum values of $y = 6x_1 + x_2$ subject to $4x_1 + 3x_2 \geq 22$, $3x_1 - 2x_2 \leq 8$, $x_1 + 5x_2 \leq 31$.
    (b) Find the maximum and minimum values of $y = x_1 + 7x_2$ subject to the same conditions as in (a).

28. (a) Find the maximum and minimum values of $y = 3x_1 + 2x_2$ subject to $x_1 \geq 0$, $x_2 \geq 0$, $9x_1 + 5x_2 \leq 45$, $2x_1 + 6x_2 \geq 12$, $2x_1 + x_2 \geq 4$.
    (b) Find the maximum and minimum values of $y = -x_1 + x_2$ subject to the same conditions as in (a).

29. Find the maximum and minimum values of $y = 3x_1 + 2x_2$ subject to $x_1 \geq 0$, $x_2 \geq 0$, $x_1 + x_2 \leq 1$, $-x_1 + x_2 \geq 2$.

30. (a) Find the maximum and minimum values of $y = 3x_1 + 2x_2$ subject to $x_1 \geq 0$, $x_2 \geq 0$, $-x_1 + x_2 \leq 1$, $x_1 - x_2 \geq 1$.
    (b) Find the maximum and minimum values of $y = 2x_1 - 3x_2$ subject to the same conditions as in (a).

31. Find the maximum and minimum values of $y = x_1 + x_2$ subject to $-x_1 \leq 2$, $-x_2 \leq 2$, $x_1 \leq 2$, $x_2 \leq 2$.

32. In the original AC example presented in this section we mentioned that the problem would be slightly more complicated if supplies of rip-stop nylon became limited. Well, it happened exactly as we predicted on page 300 of the text. Solve this more complicated problem.

33. In Problem 5 of Section 2.2, page 71 we discussed how AC should use its factories to fill orders exactly. Recall that, in one day of operation, the Springfield factory makes 3 jackets and 6 pair of down booties while the Waterbury factory makes 4 jackets and 5 pairs of booties. Suppose it costs $120 a day to operate each factory. How many days should each factory be operated to produce *at least* enough merchandise to fill the following orders at minimum cost?
    (a) 29 jackets, 52 booties (pairs)
    (b) 11 jackets, 16 booties
    (c) 1 jackets, no booties
    (d) no jackets, 5 booties

*34. Sighed the shoemaker to his wife, "We are ruined! The rent is due tomorrow at noon. Even though it's only 6 A.M., according to my calculations we'll be $17.00 short of the absolute minimum we need to pay the rent and buy new materials. If we don't pay the rent we'll be evicted; if we don't buy new materials we'll have to close down. What am I to do?" His wife replied, "You mean that, working full time from now until tomorrow noon, you will not be able to convert 7,000 sq. cm. of materials into enough merchandise to save us? Men's shoes require 600 sq. cm. of material and 2 hours of time and sell for $15. Women's shoes require 400 sq. cm. of material and 3 hours of time and sell for $12. You should have plenty of time and materials to make enough shoes. Besides all that, we have back orders for 50 pairs of men's shoes and 25 pairs of women's shoes. We'll sell all we make immediately." It took exactly 1 hour for him to explain enough linear programming to convince her that there was no hope. They left immediately to tell her parents the sad news. When they left 2 elves came out of nowhere. One said to the other, "It only takes us 1 hour to make a pair of men's shoes and 2 hours to make a pair of women's shoes. I think we can save them." When the shoemaker and his wife returned the next day at noon, the elves had just finished their work. The shoemaker saw what they had done and done and exclaimed, "We're saved. Let's give all the extra money to the elves." How much money did the shoemaker give the elves?

35. In a well-run PHE store a cheeseburger requires 5 oz. of meat, 0.7 oz. of cheese, and 3 person-minutes of preparation time, while a superburger requires 7 oz. of meat, 0.6 oz. of cheese, and 11 person-minutes of preparation time. Suppose the store has 21 lbs. 14 oz. of meat, 2 lbs. 10 oz. of cheese, and $5\frac{1}{2}$ hours worth of person-minutes of available preparation time. Each cheeseburger sold produces a profit of 10 cents, and each superburger a profit of 40 cents.

    (a) Introduce appropriate variables and units of measure, then write the problem as an LP problem in standard format.

    (b) How many cheeseburgers and superburgers should they make to maximize their profit?

    (c) How much meat, cheese, and time will be left over?

c36. The technique presented in this section can also be used to solve an LP problem involving an equality constraint. Solve the following problem graphically.

Maximize $y = 3x_1 + 2x_2$ subject to

$$x_1 \geq 0, x_2 \geq 0$$
$$x_1 + x_2 \leq 5$$
$$3x_1 + 7x_2 \geq 21$$
$$-x_1 + x_2 = 2$$

## Section 5.2
## The Simplex Method

In Section 5.5 we will discuss how to derive the appropriate system of inequalities from a given collection of data.

In this section we will describe the matrix form of the simplex method as it applies to a large class of LP maximization problems. Minimization problems will be treated in Section 5.4. It is important to be able to solve practical problems in which you have been given only the raw data, but in this section we will assume that the step from the raw data to their formulation as a system of inequalities has already been taken.

### Geometric Introduction

Almost all linear programming problems in the real world involve more than two variables. If our solution technique for LP problems in two variables is to have practical value, it must be adapted to LP problems in three, four, or more variables. To this end, consider the following rather simple LP problem in three variables:

Maximize

$$y = 5x_1 + 4x_2 + 8x_3 \qquad \textbf{1}$$

subject to

$$x_1 \geq 0, x_2 \geq 0, x_3 \geq 0 \qquad \textbf{2}$$
$$2x_1 + 2x_2 + 3x_3 \leq 6 \qquad \textbf{3}$$

Figure 19

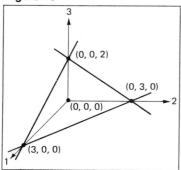

Figure 20

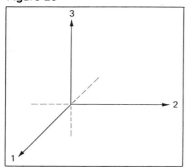

Figure 21                     Table 4

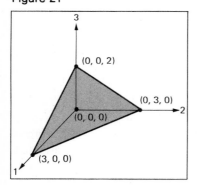

See the discussion following Problem 4 in Section 5.1.

In order to approach this problem geometrically we must employ coordinates in three-dimensional space, as introduced in Section 5 of Chapter 2. The reader is not expected to become proficient in the use of these coordinates; this discussion is being presented as introduction to and motivation for the purely computational method which follows.

In Section 5.1 we learned that a linear inequality in two variables represents a half-plane. Similarly, it can be shown that a linear inequality in three variables represents a **half-space**. For example, inequality **3** above represents the lower half-space bounded by the plane $2x_1 + 2x_2 + 3x_3 = 6$ (Figure 19). This half-space consists of all points on or below this plane. Recall that in Section 5.1 we said that the "background inequalities" $x_1 \geq 0$, $x_2 \geq 0$ represent the positive quadrant (Figure 10 in Section 5.1). Similarly (in space) the inequalities in condition **2** above represent **the positive octant** (Figure 20). The region of feasibility of our problem consists of all points common to the graphs in these two figures, that is, the solid pyramid of Figure 21. This region has four corner points: $(0,0,0), (3,0,0), (0,3,0)$, and $(0,0,2)$. According to the extreme point theorem, p. 306, the maximum value of the objective variable (Equation **1**) can be found by checking values at each of these points, which we do in Table 4.

| Corner point | y-value |
| --- | --- |
| $(0,0,0)$ | 0 |
| $(3,0,0)$ | 15 |
| $(0,3,0)$ | 12 |
| $(0,0,2)$ | 16 |

The answer is $x_1 = 0$, $x_2 = 0$, $x_3 = 2$, and $y = 16$.

That was easy, but it was easy because there was only one constraint and the problem was bounded. In a three-variable LP problem involving more constraints, the region of feasibility may be more complicated than the region shown in Figure 21. It might, for example, look like the region in Figure 22. In a region as complex as that in Figure 22, there are many corner points, and they may be hard to find. Solving the equations three at a time will not work, for the same reason that solving them two at a time did not work in the two-variable case. Also, even after the corner points are found, there may be a great number of them, and the labor of substituting their coordinate matrices into the formula for y may be considerable. The simplex method was created to surmount all these difficulties.

Figure 22

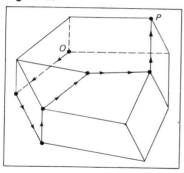

In the region of feasibility shown in Figure 22, some pairs of corner points are joined by an edge, where two boundary planes intersect. The idea of the simplex method is to begin at a feasible corner and travel along these edges from corner to corner, always increasing the value of y, until a corner is reached at which y attains a maximum value. It can be shown that we will have reached a maximum corner when moving to any adjacent corner causes no increase in the value of y. Figure 22 shows an example of such a path (marked with arrows), leading from the origin O to a maximum point P.

### The Matrix Form of the Simplex Method

To use the technique presented in this chapter we must assume that a feasible corner point is known. Methods for determining such a point, which also use the simplex method, are described in Section 5.4.

The method that we are about to describe is a compact matrix version of the geometric approach suggested above. It is remarkably simple and can be used effectively even if the user does not understand why it works. In the next section we will relate the algebraic and geometric approaches and briefly describe why the matrix technique works.

This technique will solve almost any LP maximization problem that arises in applications. We illustrate it with the following example:

Problem 1

Maximize

$$y = 3x_1 + 4x_2 + 7x_3 \qquad\qquad \textbf{4}$$

subject to

$$x_1 \geq 0, x_2 \geq 0, x_3 \geq 0 \qquad\qquad \textbf{5}$$
$$x_1 + 2x_2 + 4x_3 \leq 3 \qquad\qquad \textbf{6}$$
$$x_1 + x_2 + 2x_3 \leq 2 \qquad\qquad \textbf{7}$$
$$2x_1 + 3x_2 + 8x_3 \leq 7 \qquad\qquad \textbf{8}$$

Before setting up the matrix that we will use in solving this problem, we introduce some convenient terminology. Recall that inequalities **6**, **7**, and **8** are called constraints. The numbers multiplying the variables in these constraints make up the **constraint matrix** of the problem:

The term **bound** is usually used in linear programming to refer to a bound on a variable. For example, in our case, 0 is a bound for $x_1$. A better term for the numbers 3, 2, and 7 in inequalities **6**, **7**, and **8** would be **right-hand side**. When dealing with computers or persons familiar with LP, be careful of confusion that may result from our use of the word *bound*.

$$\begin{bmatrix} 1 & 2 & 4 \\ 1 & 1 & 2 \\ 2 & 3 & 8 \end{bmatrix} \qquad\qquad \textbf{9}$$

The **bounds** are the numbers on the right side of the inequality signs in inequalities **6**, **7**, and **8**. These numbers make up the **bound**

**matrix** of the problem:

$$\begin{bmatrix} 3 \\ 2 \\ 7 \end{bmatrix}$$                                          **10**

The numbers multiplying $x_1$, $x_2$, and $x_3$ in the formula for the objective variable (equation **4**) make up the **objective matrix** of the problem:

$$\begin{bmatrix} 3 & 4 & 7 \end{bmatrix}$$                                          **11**

The matrix form of the simplex method as presented in this section does not apply to all maximization LP problems. Before setting up a problem, we must make sure that the following three conditions are satisfied.

Condition 1      The problem must stipulate that all the x's that occur in it are greater than or equal to zero; that is, the inequalities $x_1 \geq 0$, $x_2 \geq 0$, etc., must appear.

Condition 2      All constraints must contain $\leq$ signs rather than $\geq$ signs or $=$ signs. Constraints such as $3x_1 + 2x_2 \geq 2$ or $x_1 - x_2 = 5$ must not be among the conditions to be met.

Condition 3      All the entries in the bound matrix must be greater than or equal to zero. A problem with a constraint such as $3x_1 + 2x_2 + x_3 \leq -2$ cannot be considered.

Note that no condition is required for the objective matrix.

If one or more of these conditions are not satisfied, then the matrix form of the simplex method as given in this section does not apply. Care must be taken, since most problems can be set up and "solved" whether or not they meet the conditions. The trouble is that when the conditions are not met the techniques will generally yield wrong answers. If these conditions are not met, the problem must be subjected to some preliminary modifications. If Condition 1 is not met, the problem has **unrestricted variables** (see Section 5.6). If Condition 2 is not met, the problem has **mixed constraints** (see Section 5.4). If Condition 3 is not met, the problem must be subjected to Phase I (see Section 5.4). In Problem 1 above, however, all three conditions are met.

The matrix for this problem is set up in four steps as follows.

(1) Write the constraint matrix:

$$\begin{bmatrix} 1 & 2 & 4 \\ 1 & 1 & 2 \\ 2 & 3 & 8 \end{bmatrix}$$

Recall that an identity matrix (see p. 127) is a square matrix with 1s on the main (NW to SE) diagonal and 0s everywhere else.

(2) To its right, write the identity matrix that has the same number of rows as the constraint matrix—in this case, three rows:

$$\begin{bmatrix} 1 & 2 & 4 & 1 & 0 & 0 \\ 1 & 1 & 2 & 0 & 1 & 0 \\ 2 & 3 & 8 & 0 & 0 & 1 \end{bmatrix}$$

(3) To the right of the identity matrix, write the bound matrix:

$$\begin{bmatrix} 1 & 2 & 4 & 1 & 0 & 0 & 3 \\ 1 & 1 & 2 & 0 & 1 & 0 & 2 \\ 2 & 3 & 8 & 0 & 0 & 1 & 7 \end{bmatrix}$$

(4) Below the constraint matrix, write the objective matrix; fill out this row with zeros:

$$\begin{bmatrix} 1 & 2 & 4 & 1 & 0 & 0 & 3 \\ 1 & 1 & 2 & 0 & 1 & 0 & 2 \\ 2 & 3 & 8 & 0 & 0 & 1 & 7 \\ 3 & 4 & 7 & 0 & 0 & 0 & 0 \end{bmatrix} \qquad \textbf{12}$$

Matrix **12** is the matrix on which the simplex method will operate.

If we ignore the identity matrix and the bottom row, this matrix is the matrix of the system

$$\begin{bmatrix} x_1 + 2x_2 + 4x_3 = 3 \\ x_1 + x_2 + 2x_3 = 2 \\ 2x_1 + 3x_2 + 8x_3 = 7 \end{bmatrix}$$

The identity matrix is needed to account for the fact that we are dealing with inequalities rather than the equations. Its presence is easily explained through the introduction of slack variables (see Section 5.3). Matrix **12** is, of course, the matrix for a system of equations that is closely related to our system of inequalities. The matrix form of the simplex method is just Gauss-Jordan reduction modified to account for the fact that our object is not just to solve a system of equations but rather to solve a system of equations *and* to maximize the objective variable.

The flow chart on the next page summarizes the above discussion and contains the necessary modifications of Gauss-Jordan reduction. We suggest that after glancing over this chart the reader work through the solution of Problem 1 presented below, referring to the chart as required.

## The Simplex Method for an LP
## Maximization Problem

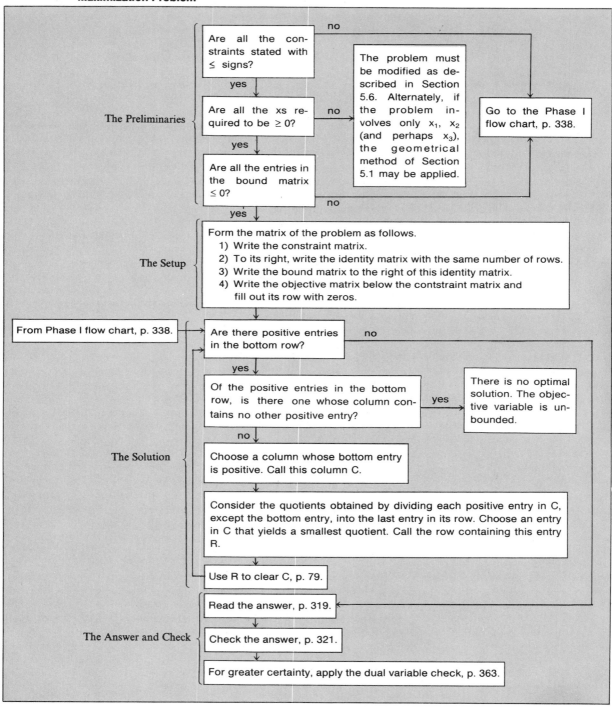

The Preliminaries

Are all the constraints stated with $\leq$ signs?

yes

Are all the xs required to be $\geq 0$?

yes

Are all the entries in the bound matrix $\leq 0$?

yes

no → The problem must be modified as described in Section 5.6. Alternately, if the problem involves only $x_1$, $x_2$ (and perhaps $x_3$), the geometrical method of Section 5.1 may be applied.

Go to the Phase I flow chart, p. 338.

The Setup

Form the matrix of the problem as follows.
1) Write the constraint matrix.
2) To its right, write the identity matrix with the same number of rows.
3) Write the bound matrix to the right of this identity matrix.
4) Write the objective matrix below the contstraint matrix and fill out its row with zeros.

From Phase I flow chart, p. 338.

The Solution

Are there positive entries in the bottom row?

no

yes

Of the positive entries in the bottom row, is there one whose column contains no other positive entry?

yes → There is no optimal solution. The objective variable is unbounded.

no

Choose a column whose bottom entry is positive. Call this column C.

Consider the quotients obtained by dividing each positive entry in C, except the bottom entry, into the last entry in its row. Choose an entry in C that yields a smallest quotient. Call the row containing this entry R.

Use R to clear C, p. 79.

The Answer and Check

Read the answer, p. 319.

Check the answer, p. 321.

For greater certainty, apply the dual variable check, p. 363.

As our first illustration of the flow chart, we complete the solution of Problem 1. We have already checked the preliminaries, completed the set up, and obtained the first matrix:

$$R\begin{bmatrix} 1 & 2 & 4 & 1 & 0 & 0 & 3 \\ 1 & 1 & 2 & 0 & 1 & 0 & 2 \\ 2 & 3 & 8 & 0 & 0 & 1 & 7 \\ 3 & 4 & 7 & 0 & 0 & 0 & 0 \end{bmatrix}$$
$$\phantom{R}C$$

**13**

The bottom row contains three positive entries, each of whose columns contain other positive entries. We arbitrarily choose the first such column to be C. We divide all but the last positive entry in C into the last entry in its row: $3 \div 1 = 3$, $2 \div 1 = 2$, $7 \div 2 = 3\frac{1}{2}$. The smallest of these quotients is the second one; hence, we must choose R to be the second row. We use R to clear C and obtain:

$$\begin{matrix} R_1 - R_2 \\ \\ R_3 - 2R_2 \\ R_4 - 3R_2 \end{matrix}\begin{bmatrix} 0 & 1 & 2 & 1 & -1 & 0 & 1 \\ 1 & 1 & 2 & 0 & 1 & 0 & 2 \\ 0 & 1 & 4 & 0 & -2 & 1 & 3 \\ 0 & 1 & 1 & 0 & -3 & 0 & -6 \end{bmatrix}$$

**14**

The bottom row of this matrix contains two positive entries. We choose the first column because it looks as if it will result in easier arithmetic when we clear. The quotients are $1 \div 1 = 1$, $2 \div 1 = 2$, and $3 \div 1 = 3$, so we now choose R to be $R_1$. Clearing, we obtain

$$\begin{bmatrix} 0 & 1 & 2 & 1 & -1 & 0 & 1 \\ 1 & 0 & 0 & -1 & 2 & 0 & 1 \\ 0 & 0 & 2 & -1 & -1 & 1 & 2 \\ 0 & 0 & -1 & -1 & -2 & 0 & -7 \end{bmatrix}$$

**15**

Since the bottom row of this matrix contains no positive entries, we are ready to read the answer.

**Reading the Answer**    When we began, matrix **12** contained an identity matrix above a row of zeros:

$$\begin{bmatrix} 1 & 2 & 4 & 1 & 0 & 0 & 3 \\ 1 & 1 & 2 & 0 & 1 & 0 & 2 \\ 2 & 3 & 8 & 0 & 0 & 1 & 7 \\ 3 & 4 & 7 & 0 & 0 & 0 & 0 \end{bmatrix}$$

Each time a column was cleared, a column of this matrix was

relocated. In the final matrix, matrix **15**, we have

$$\begin{bmatrix} \boxed{0} & \boxed{1} & 2 & 1 & -1 & \boxed{0} & 1 \\ \boxed{1} & \boxed{0} & 0 & -1 & 2 & \boxed{0} & 1 \\ \boxed{0} & \boxed{0} & 2 & -1 & -1 & \boxed{1} & 2 \\ \boxed{0} & \boxed{0} & -1 & -1 & -2 & \boxed{0} & -7 \end{bmatrix}$$

The first two columns of the identity matrix have been moved and now appear in reverse order, as the first two columns of the final matrix.

We now proceed as follows.

(1) Write $x_1$ above $C_1$, $x_2$ above $C_2$, and so on. In our case we write:

$$\begin{array}{ccc} x_1 & x_2 & x_3 \\ \end{array}$$
$$\begin{bmatrix} 0 & 1 & 2 & 1 & -1 & 0 & 1 \\ 1 & 0 & 0 & -1 & 2 & 0 & 1 \\ 0 & 0 & 2 & -1 & -1 & 1 & 2 \\ 0 & 0 & -1 & -1 & -2 & 0 & -7 \end{bmatrix} \quad \textbf{16}$$

(2) Variables that do not occur above columns of the relocated identity matrix are set to zero; that is, variables that do not occur above columns that you actually cleared are zero. In our case: $x_3 = 0$.

(3) The value of each remaining variable occurs in the last column opposite the 1 in the column of that variable. In our case:

$$\begin{array}{ccc} x_1 & x_2 & x_3 \\ \end{array}$$
$$\begin{bmatrix} 0 & ① & 2 & 1 & -1 & 0 & 1 \\ ① & 0 & 0 & -1 & 2 & 0 & 1 \\ 0 & 0 & 2 & -1 & -1 & 1 & 2 \\ 0 & 0 & -1 & -1 & -2 & 0 & -7 \end{bmatrix} \begin{array}{l} x_2 = 1 \\ x_1 = 1 \end{array} \quad \textbf{17}$$

(4) The maximum value of the objective variable y is the number in the lower right corner (the southeast corner) of the final matrix, *with the sign changed*. In our case, the maximum value is $y = 7$.

The other columns of the final matrix contain some extra information about the solution, which may be useful. We will discuss this in the next section.

One Final Remark    There are problems in which the final matrix presents several choices of columns for the relocated identity matrix. While no such problem appears in this text, the following technique will enable you to solve any problem you might encounter.

**Locating the Cleared Columns**

In the final matrix, place a * below each column that ends in zero, contains a 1, and has all other entries zero. For each column of the original identity matrix, choose a starred column that has its 1 in the same row. The columns so chosen are the cleared columns. For example in the final matrix

$$\begin{bmatrix} 1 & 1 & 0 & 3 \\ 0 & 0 & 1 & 2 \\ 0 & 0 & 0 & -6 \end{bmatrix}$$
$$\quad * \quad * \quad *$$

we could designate $C_1$ and $C_3$ to be cleared (whence $x_1 = 3$, $x_2 = 0$, $x_3 = 2$, $y = 6$). Clearing $C_2$, which requires no work in this case, results in unclearing $C_1$. Now the cleared columns are $C_2$ and $C_3$

*Both of these answers are correct.* (whence $x_1 = 0$, $x_2 = 3$, $x_3 = 2$, and $y = 6$). Applying the simplex method involved no work, although it did change the answer (but not the value of the objective variable).

We will not discuss problems such as this, with multiple solutions. As with linear equations, if an LP problem has two or more answers, then it has infinitely many. However, it is a more complicated matter to describe them all. The interested reader is referred to *Matrix Methods in Finite Mathematics* by S. C. Althoen and R. J. Bumcrot, Section 6–4, pp. 332–344.

**Checking the Answer**

Step 1

*In Section 5.6 we present a more reliable check: the dual variable check.*

Substitute the solution into the equation for the objective variable. Does it yield the negative of the number in the southeast corner of the final matrix?

In Problem 1, p. 315, we have $y = 3 \cdot 1 + 4 \cdot 1 + 7 \cdot 0 = 7 \checkmark$

Step 2

Substitute the solution into each constraint. Is it satisfied? In our case we have

$$1 \cdot 1 + 2 \cdot 1 + 4 \cdot 0 = 3 \leq 3 \checkmark$$
$$1 \cdot 1 + 1 \cdot 1 + 2 \cdot 0 = 2 \leq 2 \checkmark$$
$$2 \cdot 1 + 3 \cdot 1 + 8 \cdot 0 = 5 \leq 7 \checkmark$$

so our solution checks.

Warning

While each solution should certainly be subjected to the previous check, it is possible that an incorrect solution will also check. (See Problem 5 below.) This check is no guarantee that your answer is right. However, if it fails, your answer is certainly wrong.

**Problem 2**    Maximize $y = 3x_1 + 6x_2 + 4x_3 - 4x_4$ subject to

$$x_1 \geq 0, x_2 \geq 0, x_3 \geq 0, x_4 \geq 0$$
$$x_1 + 2x_2 + x_3 - 3x_4 \leq 2$$
$$x_1 - x_2 + 3x_3 + 5x_4 \leq 1$$
$$-x_1 + 4x_2 - 2x_3 + x_4 \leq 10$$

**Solution**    All constraints are with $\leq$ signs, all x's are $\geq 0$, and all bounds are $\geq 0$, so we set up the matrix:

$$\begin{bmatrix} 1 & 2^* & 1 & -3 & 1 & 0 & 0 & 2 \\ 1 & -1 & 3 & 5 & 0 & 1 & 0 & 1 \\ -1 & 4 & -2 & 1 & 0 & 0 & 1 & 10 \\ 3 & 6 & 4 & -4 & 0 & 0 & 0 & 0 \end{bmatrix}$$

Since the first three columns end with positive entries, any of them could have been chosen C.

Say we choose the second column to be C. Then the quotients $2 \div 2 = 1$, $10 \div 4 = \frac{5}{2}$ tell us to choose R to be $R_1$. This choice of C and R is indicated by the \*. (Note that we did not consider the quotient $1 \div -1$, since $-1$ is not positive.) The result after clearing is:

$$\begin{bmatrix} \frac{1}{2} & 1 & \frac{1}{2} & -\frac{3}{2} & \frac{1}{2} & 0 & 0 & 1 \\ \frac{3}{2} & 0 & \frac{7}{2} & \frac{7}{2}^* & \frac{1}{2} & 1 & 0 & 2 \\ -3 & 0 & -4 & 7 & -2 & 0 & 1 & 6 \\ 0 & 0 & 1 & 5 & -3 & 0 & 0 & -6 \end{bmatrix}$$

$C_3$ is also an acceptable choice for C.

Say we now take C to be $C_4$; then we must choose R to be $R_2$, as indicated by the \*. Clearing yields:

$$\begin{array}{cccccccc} x_1 & x_2 & x_3 & x_4 & & & & \\ \end{array}$$
$$\begin{bmatrix} \frac{8}{7} & 1 & 2 & 0 & \frac{5}{7} & \frac{3}{7} & 0 & \frac{13}{7} \\ \frac{3}{7} & 0 & 1 & 1 & \frac{1}{7} & \frac{2}{7} & 0 & \frac{4}{7} \\ -6 & 0 & -11 & 0 & -3 & -2 & 1 & 2 \\ -\frac{15}{7} & 0 & -4 & 0 & -\frac{26}{7} & -\frac{10}{7} & 0 & -\frac{62}{7} \end{bmatrix}$$

In the second step, if we had let C be $C_3$, it would have taken one more step to reach this answer. After some practice you can often see which choice of C in each step will be best.

The bottom row of this matrix contains no positive entries, so it is the final matrix. We label the first four columns as shown and read the answer: $x_1 = 0, x_2 = \frac{13}{7}, x_3 = 0, x_4 = \frac{4}{7}, y = \frac{62}{7}$. (Be sure to check this answer.)

**Problem 3**    Maximize $y = x_1 - x_2$ subject to

$$x_1 \geq 0, x_2 \geq 0, x_3 \geq 0$$
$$x_1 - 2x_2 \qquad \leq 2$$
$$2x_1 - 3x_2 - x_3 \leq 6$$
$$x_1 - 3x_2 + x_3 \leq 1$$

Solution

The * in this matrix indicates the row and column that will be used to obtain the *next* matrix. The * is inserted after the matrix has been written and the first part of the solution procedure has been applied to it. This convention is employed throughout this chapter.

Figure 23

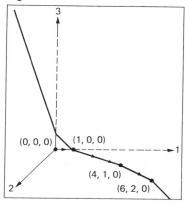

Notice that Step 1 of the checking procedure described above can be applied to each matrix obtained in the simplex method. This is a good way to check for arithmetic errors at each step.

It is not necessary to apply the simplex method again; we are merely illustrating a point.

Graphs of planes in three-dimensional space are difficult to draw. While Figure 23 does accurately indicate the edges of the region of feasibility, it is not readily apparent how we obtained it. In fact it took a lot of time, rough drafts, and patience. Since we are using the figure only as an illustration of the simplex method, we will not spend any time explaining how to obtain such graphs. If you master the techniques of Chapter 2 you will be able to draw such graphs provided you have enough patience, paper, and time.

The problem meets all three conditions. The first matrix is

$$\begin{bmatrix} 1 & -2 & 0 & 1 & 0 & 0 & 2 \\ 2 & -3 & -1 & 0 & 1 & 0 & 6 \\ 1^* & -3 & 1 & 0 & 0 & 1 & 1 \\ 1 & -1 & 0 & 0 & 0 & 0 & 0 \end{bmatrix} \qquad \textbf{18}$$

Since the last row has only one positive entry there is only one choice for C: column 1. After checking the ratios, we find that R must be the third row. Clearing yields

$$\begin{bmatrix} 0 & 1^* & -1 & 1 & 0 & -1 & 1 \\ 0 & 3 & -3 & 0 & 1 & -2 & 4 \\ 1 & -3 & 1 & 0 & 0 & 1 & 1 \\ 0 & 2 & -1 & 0 & 0 & -1 & -1 \end{bmatrix} \qquad \textbf{19}$$

Again there is only one choice for C. Checking quotients, we let R be the first row. Clearing yields

$$\begin{bmatrix} 0 & 1 & -1 & 1 & 0 & -1 & 1 \\ 0 & 0 & 0 & -3 & 1 & 1 & 1 \\ 1 & 0 & -2 & 3 & 0 & -2 & 4 \\ 0 & 0 & 1 & -2 & 0 & 1 & -3 \end{bmatrix} \qquad \textbf{20}$$

Column three of this matrix has a positive bottom entry but no other positive entries. Thus, according to the flow chart, there is no maximum, because the objective variable is unbounded.

It is always possible to read the answer as explained on page 319 before you have completed the simplex method. The intermediate answers will be feasible but not optimal. For example, in matrix **18** the first three columns are not cleared so the answer is simply $x_1 = 0$, $x_2 = 0$, $x_3 = 0$, and $y = 0$. Graphically, we are at the point $(0, 0, 0)$. In matrix **19** we read that $x_1 = 1$, $x_2 = 0$, $x_3 = 0$, and $y = 1$. We have moved to the point $(1, 0, 0)$. In matrix **20** we have moved to the point $(4, 1, 0)$. We could ignore the information given by the third column and apply the simplex method again to matrix **20**, by clearing the sixth column. The result is:

$$\begin{bmatrix} 0 & 1 & -1 & -2 & 1 & 0 & 2 \\ 0 & 0 & 0 & -3 & 1 & 1 & 1 \\ 1 & 0 & -2 & -3 & 2 & 0 & 6 \\ 0 & 0 & 1 & 1 & -1 & 0 & -4 \end{bmatrix}$$

Now we have $x_1 = 6$, $x_2 = 2$, $x_3 = 0$, and $y = 4$. We are at the point $(6, 2, 0)$. In Figure 23 we have graphed the edges of the planes that bound the region of feasibility and have indicated the path the simplex method followed.

We can see from Figure 23 that the region is unbounded. In fact we can actually prove it. We happen to know that $(x_1, \frac{2}{3}x_1, 0)$ is a solution for any positive choice for $x_1$. We show this by a direct check.

First Constraint

$$x_1 - 2x_2 = x_2 - 2\left(\tfrac{2}{3}x_1\right)$$
$$= x_2 - \tfrac{4}{3}x_1$$
$$= -\tfrac{1}{3}x_1 \leq 0 < 2$$

Second Constraint

$$2x_1 - 3x_2 - x_3 = 2x_1 - 3\left(\tfrac{2}{3}x_1\right) - 0$$
$$= 2x_1 - 2x_1$$
$$= 0 < 6$$

Third Constraint

$$x_1 - 3x_2 + x_3 = x_1 - 3\left(\tfrac{2}{3}x_1\right) + 0$$
$$= x_1 - 2x_1$$
$$= -x_1 \leq 0 < 1$$

Finally, for this solution, $y = x_1 - x_2 = x_1 - \tfrac{2}{3}x_1 = \tfrac{1}{3}x_1$. Thus, we can make $y$ as large as we want by taking $x_1$ to be a sufficiently large number. For instance, if we want $y$ to be 10,000,000,000, we simply let $x_1 = 30,000,000,000$. The reader may check that (30,000,000,000, 20,000,000,000, 0) is a solution for which $y = 10,000,000,000$.

**Problem 4**    Maximize $y = 3x_1 + 4x_2$ subject to

$$x_1 \geq 0, x_2 \geq 0$$
$$2x_1 + 3x_2 \leq 6$$
$$6x_1 + 4x_2 \leq 12$$

**Solution**    This is the problem introduced at the beginning of Section 5.1. It meets all conditions and is set up as follows.

$$\begin{bmatrix} 2 & 3^* & 1 & 0 & 6 \\ 6 & 4 & 0 & 1 & 12 \\ 3 & 4 & 0 & 0 & 0 \end{bmatrix}$$

The first application yields:

$$\begin{bmatrix} \tfrac{2}{3} & 1 & \tfrac{1}{3} & 0 & 2 \\ \tfrac{10}{3}^* & 0 & -\tfrac{4}{3} & 1 & 4 \\ \tfrac{1}{3} & 0 & -\tfrac{4}{3} & 0 & -8 \end{bmatrix}$$

The second application yields:

$$\begin{bmatrix} 0 & 1 & \frac{3}{5} & -\frac{1}{5} & \frac{6}{5} \\ 1 & 0 & -\frac{2}{5} & \frac{3}{10} & \frac{6}{5} \\ 0 & 0 & -\frac{6}{5} & -\frac{1}{10} & -\frac{42}{5} \end{bmatrix}$$

The answer is $x_1 = \frac{6}{5}$ and $x_2 = \frac{6}{5}$; the maximum is $y = \frac{42}{5}$. This agrees with our previous answer.

**Problem 5**  Maximize $y = 2x_1 + x_2$ subject to

$$x_1 \geq 0, x_2 \geq 0,$$
$$-x_1 + x_2 \leq 2$$
$$3x_1 + 2x_2 \geq 14$$
$$x_1 - x_2 \leq 3$$

**Solution**  Since the second constraint violates Condition 2, the matrix method does not apply and we must find some other way to handle this problem. The fact that there are two variables suggests a geometric approach. The graph in Figure 24 shows that the region of feasibility is unbounded and that there is no maximum. If we had ignored the fact that Condition 2 is violated and had used the matrix method anyway by setting up the matrix

**Figure 24**

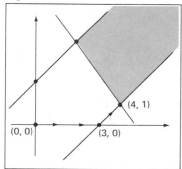

$$\begin{bmatrix} -1 & 1 & 1 & 0 & 0 & 2 \\ 3 & 2 & 0 & 1 & 0 & 14 \\ 1 & -1 & 0 & 0 & 1 & 3 \\ 2 & 1 & 0 & 0 & 0 & 0 \end{bmatrix}$$

then, in two steps, we would obtain the final matrix

$$\begin{bmatrix} 0 & 0 & 1 & 0 & 1 & 5 \\ 0 & 1 & 0 & \frac{1}{5} & -\frac{3}{5} & 1 \\ 1 & 0 & 0 & \frac{1}{5} & \frac{2}{5} & 4 \\ 0 & 0 & 0 & -\frac{3}{5} & -\frac{1}{5} & -9 \end{bmatrix}$$

and the apparent solution $x_1 = 4$, $x_2 = 1$, and $y = 9$. It is easy to verify that this answer "checks." However, as we have seen, it is incorrect.

**Additional Checks and Shortcuts**  The most common errors in the use of the simplex method will be avoided if the user will keep in mind the following simple facts.

(1) A column that is to be cleared must have a positive last entry.
(2) The entry that is used to clear a column must also be positive.
(3) Throughout the entire process, all the entries in the   last
column, except the bottom entry, are always $\geq 0$.
(4) The number in the southeast corner is zero at the first step and
becomes more negative (or stays the same) after each subsequent step.

Most of the shortcuts in Section 4 of Chapter 2 do *not* apply
here. However, you may if you wish multiply any row except the
last by a *positive* number without changing the answer. You may
also postpone changing the nonzero entry in a cleared column into
a 1 until reading the answer. The most effective shortcut is to
decide which column to clear on the basis of a quick look ahead to
see the effect of various choices on the last row.

You can even multiply the last row by
a *positive* number. However, if you do
so, you must divide the value of the
objective variable by the same positive number before you read the
answer.

**Exercises 5.2**

1. Maximize $y = 3x_1 + 4x_2$ subject to $x_1 \geq 0$, $x_2 \geq 0$, $x_1 + x_2 \leq 3$, $x_1 + 2x_2 \leq 4$.
2. Maximize $y = 5x_1 + 12x_2$ subject to $x_1 \geq 0$, $x_2 \geq 0$, $x_1 + 2x_2 \leq 3$, $2x_1 + 5x_2 \leq 7$.
3. Maximize $y = 2x_1 + 3x_2$ subject to $x_1 \geq 0$, $x_2 \geq 0$, $x_1 + x_2 \leq 2$, $x_1 + 4x_2 \leq 4$.
4. Maximize $y = x_1 + x_2$ subject to $x_1 \geq 0$, $x_2 \geq 0$, $-x_1 + x_2 \leq 1$, $3x_1 + x_2 \leq 9$.
$^c$5. Maximize $y = 2x_1 + x_2$ subject to $x_1 \geq 0$, $x_2 \geq 0$, $-x_1 + x_2 \leq 1$, $x_1 + x_2 \geq 2$, $4x_1 - x_2 \leq 4$.
6. Maximize $y = 3x_1 + 2x_2$ subject to $x_1 \geq 0$, $x_2 \geq 0$, $x_1 + x_2 \leq 4$, $x_1 - 2x_2 \leq 2$.
$^c$7. Maximize $y = -2x_1 - 3x_2$ subject to $x_1 \geq 0$, $x_2 \geq 0$, $-x_1 + x_2 \leq 2$, $x_1 + x_2 \leq 2$.
8. Maximize $y = x_1 + 2x_2$ subject to $x_1 \geq 0$, $x_2 \geq 0$, $4x_1 + x_2 \leq 5$, $8x_1 + 7x_2 \leq 9$.
$^c$9. Maximize $y = 3x_1 + 2x_2$ subject to $x_1 \geq 0$, $x_2 \geq 0$, $-x_1 + x_2 \leq 2$, $x_1 - 2x_2 \leq 4$.
10. Maximize $y = 2x_1 + x_2$ subject to $x_1 \geq 0$, $x_2 \geq 0$, $-x_1 + x_2 \leq 1$, $x_1 + x_2 \leq 2$, $4x_1 - x_2 \leq 4$.
11. Maximize $y = x_1 + 2x_2$ subject to $x_1 \geq 0$, $x_2 \geq 0$, $-2x_1 + x_2 \leq 2$, $x_1 - x_2 \leq 1$, $-x_1 + 2x_2 \leq 8$, $x_2 \leq 3$.
12. Maximize $y = x_1 + x_2$ subject to $x_1 \geq 0$, $x_2 \geq 0$, $-x_1 + 3x_2 \leq 4$, $x_1 - x_2 \leq 2$, $2x_1 - x_2 \leq 6$.
13. Maximize $y = 3x_1 + 2x_2$ subject to $0 \leq x_1 \leq 3$, $0 \leq x_2 \leq 4$.
14. Maximize $y = 7x_1 + 5x_2$ subject to $x_1 \geq 0$, $x_2 \geq 0$, $x_1 - 2x_2 \leq 2$, $-3x_1 + x_2 \leq 3$, $4x_1 - 4x_2 \leq 9$.
$^c$15. Maximize $y = -x_1 + x_2$ subject to $x_2 \geq 0$, $-x_1 - x_2 \leq -3$, $2x_1 - x_2 \leq -4$, $x_2 \leq 6$.

16. Maximize $y = 6x_1 + 4x_2 + 5x_3$ subject to $x_1 \geq 0$, $x_2 \geq 0$, $x_3 \geq 0$, $2x_1 + 3x_2 + x_3 \leq 5$, $x_1 + 2x_2 + 2x_3 \leq 3$.

17. Maximize $y = 12x_1 + 16x_2 + 6x_3$ subject to $x_1 \geq 0$, $x_2 \geq 0$, $x_3 \geq 0$, $2x_1 + x_2 + 2x_3 \leq 6$, $3x_1 + 8x_2 + 5x_3 \leq 22$, $2x_1 + 2x_2 + 3x_3 \leq 12$.

18. Maximize $y = 6x_1 + 7x_2 + 8x_3$ subject to $x_1 \geq 0$, $x_2 \geq 0$, $x_3 \geq 0$, $3x_1 + 7x_2 + 5x_3 \leq 15$, $x_1 + x_2 + x_3 \leq 4$, $2x_1 + 4x_2 + 5x_3 \leq 11$.

19. Maximize $y = 7x_1 + 5x_2 + 6x_3$ subject to $x_1 \geq 0$, $x_2 \geq 0$, $x_3 \geq 0$, $x_1 + x_2 - x_3 \leq 3$, $x_1 + 2x_2 + x_3 \leq 8$, $x_1 + x_2 \leq 5$.

20. Maximize $y = 3x_1 + 4x_2 + 2x_3$ subject to $x_1 \geq 0$, $x_2 \geq 0$, $x_3 \geq 0$, $3x_1 + x_2 + x_3 \leq 6$, $x_1 + 2x_2 + x_3 \leq 6$, $x_1 + x_2 + x_3 \leq 4$.

21. Maximize $y = 3x_1 - x_2 + 9x_3$ subject to $x_1 \geq 0$, $x_2 \geq 0$, $x_3 \geq 0$, $2x_1 - x_2 \leq 6$, $x_1 - x_2 + x_3 \leq 2$, $3x_1 - 6x_3 \leq 14$.

22. Maximize $y = 7x_1 + 5x_2 + 3x_3$ subject to $x_1 \geq 0$, $x_2 \geq 0$, $x_3 \geq 0$, $x_1 + 2x_2 + 4x_3 \leq 5$, $6x_1 + 4x_2 + 3x_3 \leq 4$, $x_1 + 3x_2 + 8x_3 \leq 7$.

23. Maximize $y = 6x_1 + 13x_2 + 4x_3 + 5x_4$ subject to $x_1 \geq 0$, $x_2 \geq 0$, $x_3 \geq 0$, $x_4 \geq 0$, $3x_1 + 2x_2 + 2x_3 + 3x_4 \leq 8$, $2x_1 + 4x_2 + x_3 + 4x_4 \leq 4$, $x_1 + 3x_2 + x_3 + 2x_4 \leq 3$, $4x_1 + 8x_2 + 3x_3 + 7x_4 \leq 15$.

24. Maximize $y = 2x_1 + 3x_2 + 4x_3$ subject to $x_1 \geq 0$, $x_2 \geq 0$, $x_3 \geq 0$, $2x_1 + 2x_2 + x_3 \leq 1$, $2x_1 + 3x_2 + 2x_3 \leq 5$, $x_1 + x_2 + x_3 \leq 2$, $2x_1 + 3x_2 + x_3 \leq 2$.

25. Maximize $y = 5x_1 + 4x_2 + 2x_3 + 3x_4$ subject to $x_1 \geq 0$, $x_2 \geq 0$, $x_3 \geq 0$, $x_4 \geq 0$, $2x_1 + x_2 + 3x_3 + 6x_4 \leq 5$, $3x_1 + 3x_2 + 2x_3 \leq 2$, $4x_1 + 2x_2 + x_3 + 4x_4 \leq 9$.

26. Maximize $y = 2x_1 + 3x_2 - x_3 + x_4$ subject to $x_1 \geq 0$, $x_2 \geq 0$, $x_3 \geq 0$, $x_4 \geq 0$, $2x_1 - x_2 + 3x_3 + x_4 \leq 2$, $3x_1 - 2x_2 + 8x_3 - x_4 \leq 7$, $x_1 - 3x_2 + x_3 - 7x_4 \leq 8$.

c27. Maximize $y = -2x_1 - x_2 - 4x_3 - 2x_4$ subject to $x_1 \geq 0$, $x_2 \geq 0$, $x_3 \geq 0$, $x_4 \geq 0$, $3x_1 + x_2 - x_3 + 4x_4 \leq 7$, $x_1 + 3x_2 - 3x_3 + x_4 \leq 2$, $2x_1 - 3x_2 + x_3 - 2x_4 \leq 8$, $-x_1 + 4x_2 - 3x_3 + 5x_4 \leq 9$.

28. Maximize $y = 6x_1 + 18x_2 + 11x_3 - 5x_4$ subject to $x_1 \geq 0$, $x_2 \geq 0$, $x_3 \geq 0$, $x_4 \geq 0$, $2x_1 + 6x_2 + 3x_3 - 2x_4 \leq 3$, $2x_1 + 3x_2 + x_3 - x_4 \leq 2$, $4x_1 + x_3 - 2x_4 \leq 5$.

29. Maximize $y = 4x_1 + 8x_2 + 6x_3$ subject to $x_1 \geq 0$, $x_2 \geq 0$, $x_3 \geq 0$, $2x_1 + 2x_2 - x_3 \leq 4$, $5x_1 + 4x_2 + 5x_3 \leq 24$, $3x_1 + 8x_2 + 2x_3 \leq 10$, $3x_1 + 2x_2 + 3x_3 \leq 14$.

30. Maximize $y = x_1 + x_2 + x_3 + x_4$ subject to $x_1 \geq 0$, $x_2 \geq 0$, $x_3 \geq 0$, $x_4 \geq 0$, $x_1 + x_2 + x_3 \leq 3$, $x_2 + x_3 + x_4 \leq 4$, $x_1 + x_3 + x_4 \leq 5$, $x_1 + x_2 + x_4 \leq 6$.

31. Maximize $y = x_1 + x_2 + x_3 + x_4 + x_5$ subject to $x_1 \geq 0$, $x_2 \geq 0$, $x_3 \geq 0$, $x_4 \geq 0$, $x_5 \geq 0$, $x_1 + x_2 \leq 1$, $x_2 + x_3 \leq 2$, $x_3 + x_4 \leq 3$, $x_4 + x_5 \leq 4$.

32. (a) Given an LP maximization problem with 5 variables (not counting the objective variable) and 6 constraints, what is the size of the matrix set up in the simplex method?

    (b) In general, if you know how many constraints and how many variables (not including the objective variable) an LP maximization problem has, how do you determine the size of the matrix set up in the simplex method?

33. (a) Last week I worked an LP maximization problem with 7 vari-

ables. Much to my surprise, all the variables except two turned out to be nonzero. What is the fewest number of constraints that the problem could have had?

(b) In general, how can you determine the size of the smallest problem with a given number of nonzero variables in the answer?

34. Create an LP maximization problem with 4 variables and 3 constraints with the answer $x_1 = x_2 = 0$, $x_3 = 2$, $x_4 = 0$, $y = 8$.

35. In some of their early attempts to use the simplex method, the PHE directors were rather unsophisticated. By failing to specify all constraints, they sometimes got correct but useless answers. In planning the fishfeast dinner, for example, they first attempted to use LP techniques as follows: A fishfeast consists of fish, fries, and slaw. Fish costs 21¢ per 3 oz. serving, fries cost 18¢ per 3 oz. serving, and slaw costs 14¢ per 3 oz. serving. If a fishfeast must cost no more than $1.26, how much of each food should be used to produce a feast of the greatest weight? First use the geometric method to solve this problem. Then use the simplex method.

36. Use the geometric method to solve the problem: Maximize $y = 4x_1 + x_2 + 2x_3$ subject to $x_1 \geq 0$, $x_2 \geq 0$, $x_3 \geq 0$, $6x_1 + 2x_2 + 3x_3 \leq 6$, $2x_1 + 2x_2 + x_3 \leq 4$. Use the simplex method to check your answer.

37. Use the geometric method to solve the problem: Maximize $y = 3x_1 + x_2 + x_3 + 4x_4$ subject to $x_1 \geq 0$, $x_2 \geq 0$, $x_3 \geq 0$, $x_4 \geq 0$, and $2x_1 + x_2 + 3x_3 + 2x_4 \leq 12$. Use the simplex method to check your answer.

| **Section 5.3**<br>**The Algebra of**<br>**the Simplex Method** | In this section we will attempt to remove some of the mystery from the simplex method as it was presented in the previous section. As an example we return to Problem 1 of the previous section. We will explain how we arrived at the initial matrix of an LP problem and we will show how to get more information from the final matrix than we have obtained so far. |
|---|---|

Maximize

$$y = 3x_1 + 4x_2 + 7x_3 \qquad\qquad\qquad 1$$

subject to

$$x_1 \geq 0,\ x_2 \geq 0,\ x_3 \geq 0, \qquad\qquad\qquad 2$$

$$x_1 + 2x_2 + 4x_3 \leq 3 \qquad\qquad\qquad 3$$

$$x_1 + x_2 + 2x_3 \leq 2 \qquad\qquad\qquad 4$$

$$2x_1 + 3x_2 + 8x_3 \leq 7 \qquad\qquad\qquad 5$$

Since the algebraic techniques of Chapter 2 apply only to equalities and not to inequalities, we will need to reformulate this problem in terms of equalities in order to be able to use our previous work. We do this by introducing one new variable in each inequality.

If we find a feasible solution $(x_1, x_2, x_3)$ to the problem, it is likely that, in constraint **3**, for example, $x_1 + 2x_2 + 4x_3$ will not be exactly equal to 3. For example, the solution $x_1 = 1$, $x_2 = \frac{1}{2}$, $x_3 = 0$ yields $x_1 + 2x_2 + 4x_3 = 2 < 3$. A new variable, $x_4$, is assigned the task of making up the difference between $x_1 + 2x_2 + 4x_3$ and 3. Thus, for the solution $(1, \frac{1}{2}, 0)$, $x_4$ would be $3 - 2 = 1$. In general, if we know the numerical values of $x_1$, $x_2$, and $x_3$, we will be able to determine $x_4$ as the quantity left over, that is,

$$x_4 = 3 - (x_1 + 2x_2 + 4x_3)$$

While the value of $x_4$ changes as we change the values of $x_1$, $x_2$, and $x_3$, we have arranged matters so that it is always true that

$$x_1 + 2x_2 + 4x_3 + x_4 = 3$$

A variable such as $x_4$ is often called a **slack variable**, since it takes up all the slack in an inequality. While $x_4$ may be zero, it will never be negative, since the constraint $x_1 + 2x_2 + 4x_3 \leq 3$ guarantees that there will be some (or exactly no) slack.

We do the same thing for the other two inequalities, introducing new variables $x_5$ and $x_6$ to take up the slack in them. We now have the following system of linear equations.

$$\begin{bmatrix} x_1 + 2x_2 + 4x_3 + x_4 && = 3 \\ x_1 + x_2 + 2x_3 && + x_5 && = 2 \\ 2x_1 + 3x_2 + 8x_3 && + x_6 = 7 \end{bmatrix} \qquad \textbf{6}$$

The new variables $x_4$, $x_5$, and $x_6$ are generally not related to one another. In practical applications they can often be given physical interpretations as representing leftover resources, unused machine time, and so on. It will be convenient to have these new variables occur in the expression for the objective variable. However, since leftover resources contribute nothing to profit, the value of these new variables should not affect the value of the objective variable. We resolve this situation by rewriting the objective variable as

$$y = 3x_1 + 4x_2 + 7x_3 + 0x_4 + 0x_5 + 0x_6 \qquad \textbf{7}$$

While the new variables appear in the formula for y, the zeros multiplying them guarantee that they will not affect its value.

Matrix **12** in Section 5.2, which we used in solving the problem, is just the matrix of system **6** followed by the coefficients of the objective variable (Equation 7):

$$\begin{bmatrix} 1 & 2 & 4 & 1 & 0 & 0 & 3 \\ 1 & 1 & 2 & 0 & 1 & 0 & 2 \\ 2 & 3 & 8 & 0 & 0 & 1 & 7 \\ 3 & 4 & 7 & 0 & 0 & 0 & 0 \end{bmatrix} \qquad \textbf{8}$$

For reasons that will become clear in the second part of this section, we insert 0 in the southeast corner at address (4,7).

Once the manipulations of the simplex method were completed and we had the final matrix, (matrix **15** in Section 5.2), we began by writing $x_1$ above $C_1$, $x_2$ above $C_2$, and so on. Now here, in contrast to matrix **17** in Section 5.2, we will also write the slack variables $x_4$, $x_5$, and $x_6$ above the appropriate columns. We obtain

$$\begin{array}{ccccccc} x_1 & x_2 & x_3 & x_4 & x_5 & x_6 & \end{array}$$
$$\begin{bmatrix} 0 & 1 & 2 & 1 & -1 & 0 & 1 \\ 1 & 0 & 0 & -1 & 2 & 0 & 1 \\ 0 & 0 & 2 & -1 & -1 & 1 & 2 \\ 0 & 0 & -1 & -1 & -2 & 0 & -7 \end{bmatrix} \quad x_6 = 2 \qquad \textbf{9}$$

We can read not only the values of the original variables $x_1 = 1$, $x_2 = 1$, $x_3 = 0$, $y = 7$, as explained on page 319 but also the values of the slack variables $x_4 = 0$, $x_5 = 0$, $x_6 = 2$. These values are borne out in the check of our solution made on page 321; inequality **3** has slack of $x_4 = 0$; inequality **4** has slack of $x_5 = 0$; inequality **5** has slack of $x_6 = 2$.

In order to illustrate more precisely the details of the simplex method, we will now solve one rather simple problem in accordance with the geometrical instructions of Section 5.1 and then translate each step of the solution into matrix methods. This illustration is provided for those readers who may be interested in the algebraic details behind the simplex method. Those who are interested only in practical methods may omit the rest of this section and go on to Exercise 4.

We will solve the following problem.
Maximize
$$y = 2x_1 + x_2$$
subject to
$$x_1 \geq 0, x_2 \geq 0$$
$$-x_1 + x_2 \leq 2$$
$$3x_1 + 2x_2 \leq 14$$
$$x_1 - x_2 \leq 3$$

We need three slack variables: $x_3$, $x_4$, $x_5$. These transform our constraint inequalities into the system of equalities

$$\begin{bmatrix} -x_1 + x_2 + x_3 & & = 2 \\ 3x_1 + 2x_2 & + x_4 & = 14 \\ x_1 - x_2 & + x_5 = 3 \\ 2x_1 + x_2 & - y \end{bmatrix} = 0 \qquad \begin{matrix} \mathbf{10} \\ \mathbf{11} \\ \mathbf{12} \\ \mathbf{13} \end{matrix}$$

Note the unusual alignment of equation **13**. Since y never occurs in any equation except the last, we can place y in the same column as the right-hand sides of the constraints. Moreover, since the right-hand side of the last equation is always 0, we do not need to carry this information along in each step. Thus, we place the right-side bracket as shown above.

Now y is a dependent variable. At each corner of the region of feasibility that we visit, the numerical value of y will be determined, and its negative will be the entry in the southeast corner of the matrix of the system. The simplex method starts at the corner $(0,0)$, at which the value of y in this problem, as in every standard LP problem, is 0. Since $-0=0$, we enter 0 in the southeast corner. Then the first matrix for our solution is:

*The negative of a number n is $-n$.*

$$\begin{bmatrix} -1 & 1 & 1 & 0 & 0 & 2 \\ 3 & 2 & 0 & 1 & 0 & 14 \\ 1 & -1 & 0 & 0 & 1 & 3 \\ 2 & 1 & 0 & 0 & 0 & 0 \end{bmatrix} \qquad \mathbf{14}$$

Note that this is the matrix we would obtain for this problem from the "setup" part of the flow chart on page 318.

In the formula for the objective variable, $y = 2x_1 + x_2$, we see that an increase in either $x_1$ or $x_2$ will cause y to increase. We arbitrarily decide to move along the 1-axis by increasing $x_1$ and holding $x_2 = 0$. As we do this, the variables $x_3$, $x_4$, and $x_5$ will also change. We can see exactly what happens by setting $x_2 = 0$ in equations **10**, **11**, and **12**:

$$\begin{aligned} -x_1 + x_3 &= 2 \\ 3x_1 + x_4 &= 14 \\ x_1 + x_5 &= 3 \end{aligned}$$

and solving these equations for $x_3$, $x_4$, and $x_5$:

$$x_3 = 2 + x_1$$
$$x_4 = 14 - 3x_1$$
$$x_5 = 3 - x_1$$

From these equations we see that as $x_1$ gets larger so will $x_3$. However, $x_4$ and $x_5$ will decrease as we increase $x_1$. Remember that, to stay within the region of feasibility, we must keep $x_3 \geq 0$, $x_4 \geq 0$, and $x_5 \geq 0$. There is no problem about $x_3$, since it is also increasing. But $x_4$ decreases to zero when $14 - 3x_1 = 0$, that is, when $x_1 = \frac{14}{3} = 4\frac{2}{3}$. And $x_5$ decreases to zero when $3 - x_1 = 0$, that is, when $x_1 = 3$. Since $3 < 4\frac{2}{3}$, we must stop increasing $x_1$ when it hits 3. If we go beyond 3, $x_5$ would become negative and this would violate the constraint $x_5 \geq 0$.

Now these calculations can be done in matrix **14** without actually setting $x_2 = 0$ and rewriting equations **10**, **11**, and **12**. All we have really done is to divide the positive coefficients of $x_1$ in the constraint equations into the corresponding constants (obtaining in our case $\frac{14}{3} = 4\frac{2}{3}$ and $\frac{3}{1} = 3$) and then to choose the smallest ratio (3, in our case). This is precisely the content of the first four boxes on the left in the "solution" part of the flow chart on page 318. In our problem this has resulted in choosing $R = R_3$ of matrix **14**, having first chosen $C = C_1$.

Holding $x_2 = 0$ we now increase $x_1$ from 0 to 3. Geometrically, this means that we are moving along the edge of the region of feasibility (Figure 25) from the corner $(0,0)$ to the corner $(3,0)$. Setting $x_1 = 3$ and $x_2 = 0$ in equations **10**, **11**, **12**, and **13**, we now have $x_1 = 3$, $x_2 = 0$, $x_3 = 5$, $x_4 = 5$, $x_5 = 0$, with $y = 6$. Note that we have not yet changed matrix **14**.

We are now at the corner where $x_2 = 0$ and $x_5 = 0$. To move away from this corner along an edge we will hold one of the variables $x_2$ or $x_5$ at zero and increase the other one. How will this affect the value of $y$? In order to discover this we must first express $y$ in terms of $x_2$ and $x_5$; that is, we must work with our original equations so as to get an expression for $y$ involving only $x_2$ and $x_5$. To do this we subtract 2 times equation **12** from equation **13**:

$$(2x_1 + x_2) - 2(x_1 - x_2 + x_5) = y - 2 \cdot 3$$
$$3x_2 - 2x_5 = y - 6 \qquad \textbf{13}'$$

We see from this equation that $y$ increases when $x_2$ increases but that $y$ decreases when $x_5$ increases. If we are to continue to increase $y$, we should therefore hold $x_5 = 0$ (the smallest allowable value) and increase $x_2$. How will $x_1$, $x_3$, and $x_4$ change as $x_5 = 0$ and

**Figure 25**

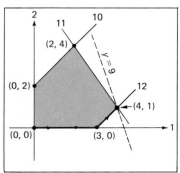

$x_2$ increases? To answer this question, we must find expressions for $x_1$, $x_3$, and $x_4$ in terms of $x_2$. But as we discovered from the previous step, we do not actually set $x_5 = 0$ and write out these expressions. It is enough to change equations **10**, **11**, and **12** into a system of three equations **10'**, **11'**, and **12'** in which each equation involves $x_2$, $x_5$, and one more variable (a different variable in each equation). Equation **12** is already such an equation, since it involves only $x_2$, $x_5$, and $x_1$, so we may rename it **12'** and use it to help obtain the new system. Adding equation **12'** to equation **10**, subtracting 3 times equation **12'** from equation **11**, and copying equation **13'**, we obtain the system

$$\begin{bmatrix} x_3 + & x_5 = 5 \\ 5x_2 & +x_4 - 3x_5 = 5 \\ x_1 - x_2 & + x_5 = 3 \\ 3x_2 & -2x_5 = y - 6 \end{bmatrix} \qquad \begin{array}{l} \textbf{10'} \\ \textbf{11'} \\ \textbf{12'} \\ \textbf{13'} \end{array}$$

The matrix of this system is

The value of $y$ for the solution $x_2 = 0$, $x_5 = 0$ is 6. As before, we write the negative of this value in the southeast corner.

$$\begin{bmatrix} 0 & 0 & 1 & 0 & 1 & 5 \\ 0 & 5 & 0 & 1 & -3 & 5 \\ 1 & -1 & 0 & 0 & 1 & 3 \\ 0 & 3 & 0 & 0 & -2 & -6 \end{bmatrix} \qquad \textbf{15}$$

Note that matrix **15** is obtained from matrix **14** by using $R = R_3$ to clear $C = C_1$, just as required in the last box in the "solution" part of the flow chart on page 318.

Now, holding $x_5 = 0$ and increasing $x_2$, we see from equation **10'** that $x_3$ does not change; we see from equation **11'** that $x_4$ decreases to zero when $x_2$ increases to $\frac{5}{5} = 1$, and we see from equation **12'** that $x_1$ increases. Thus, we increase $x_2$ from 0 to 1, moving along the edge of Figure 25, from $(3,0)$ to $(4,1)$, and we then have $x_1 = 4$, $x_2 = 1$, $x_3 = 5$, $x_4 = 0$, $x_5 = 0$, with $y = 9$. We have now gone again through the first four boxes in the "solution" part of the flow chart on page 318 and have selected $C = C_2$ and $R = R_2$ of matrix **15**.

At our present corner we have $x_4 = 0$ and $x_5 = 0$. To move away from this corner along an edge we must hold one of the variables $x_4$ or $x_5$ at zero and increase the other one. In order to discover how this will affect $y$, we must find an expression for $y$ involving only $x_4$ and $x_5$. This we do by subtracting $\frac{3}{5}$ times equation **11'** from equation **13'** to obtain

$$-\tfrac{3}{5}x_4 - \tfrac{1}{5}x_5 = y - 9$$

From this equation we see that increasing either $x_4$ or $x_5$ will decrease $y$. We have arrived at the corner where $y$ is maximum!

Had we followed the flow chart on page 318 and used $R_2$ of matrix **15** to clear $C_2$, we would have obtained

$$\begin{bmatrix} 0 & 0 & 1 & 0 & 1 & 5 \\ 0 & 1 & 0 & \frac{1}{5} & -\frac{3}{5} & 1 \\ 1 & 0 & 0 & \frac{1}{5} & \frac{2}{5} & 4 \\ 0 & 0 & 0 & -\frac{3}{5} & -\frac{1}{5} & -9 \end{bmatrix} \qquad \textbf{16}$$

which corresponds to the system

$$\begin{bmatrix} & & x_3 & & + & x_5 = 5 \\ & x_2 & & + \frac{1}{5}x_4 & - \frac{3}{5}x_5 = 1 \\ x_1 & & & + \frac{1}{5}x_4 & + \frac{2}{5}x_5 = 4 \\ & & & - \frac{3}{5}x_4 & - \frac{1}{5}x_5 = y - 9 \end{bmatrix}$$

Since $x_4 = x_5 = 0$ places us at the corner where y is maximum, we set $x_4 = x_5 = 0$ in this system to obtain $x_3 = 5$, $x_2 = 1$, $x_1 = 4$, and $0 = y - 9$; or $y = 9$, as before.

**Exercises 5.3**

1. Explain the box on the right in the "solution" part of the flow chart, page 318.
2. Go back to the illustrative problem, on page 330, start by holding $x_1 = 0$ and increasing $x_2$, and carry through the discussion, with references to Figure 25, showing that the final answer is reached in 3 moves.
3. Carry through a discussion similar to the one above for the PHE burger problem set up in the solution to Exercise 35 in Section 5.1.
4. (a) What are the values of the slack variables in the solution to Problem 2, page 322?
   (b) What are the values of the slack variables in the solution to Problem 4, page 324?
   (c) What does the answer to (b) mean in relation to the first example discussed in Section 5.1, pages 297–99?

**Section 5.4
Phase I,
Mixed Constraints,
and Minimization**

Problems that do not satisfy Condition 1 will be discussed in Section 5.6.

In this section we describe the preliminary modifications which must be made before applying the simplex method to a linear programming problem that does not satisfy Conditions 2 or 3 of Section 5.2, page 316. After doing this, it becomes an easy matter to solve most practical linear programming problems.

**Introduction to
Mixed Constraints**

The operations research group at Appalachian Creations was about to tackle the following simple LP problem. Chemicals A and B are to be mixed to make a new type of sunscreen. Sale of 1 oz.

of A, when included in the mixture, yields a \$3 profit and sale of 1 oz. of B in the mixture yields a \$4 profit. Each ounce of A contains 3 milligrams (mg) of a harmful chemical; each ounce of B contains 5 mg of the chemical. If a tube of the mixture can weigh at most 4 oz. and contain at most 15 mg of the bad chemical, how does AC maximize profit?

It was routine for the staff to set up this problem. Let $x_1$, $x_2$ be the number of ounces of A, B, respectively, in a tube. The staff were required to

Maximize

$$y = 3x_1 + 4x_2$$

subject to

$$x_1 \geq 0, x_2 \geq 0,$$

$$x_1 + x_2 \leq 4 \qquad \qquad \mathbf{1}$$

$$3x_1 + 5x_2 \leq 15 \qquad \qquad \mathbf{2}$$

Just as they were about to start using the simplex method, the following memo arrived: "One oz. fluid A contains 1 g (gram) of a very beneficial chemical, and each oz. of B contains 2 g of the chemical. Every tube must contain at least 2 g of this stuff in order for us to mount a good ad campaign." In terms of the above notation, this meant that there was now an additional constraint:

$$x_1 + 2x_2 \geq 2 \qquad \qquad \mathbf{3}$$

This shook them up a little. The flow chart in Section 5.2 does not allow a constraint like constraint **3** (with a $\geq$ sign) in an LP maximization problem. Fortunately this problem involves only two variables. Thus, the staff was able to graph the region of feasibility (Figure 26), check the corner points, and find the answer: $x_1 = \frac{5}{2}$, $x_2 = \frac{3}{2}$, $y = \frac{27}{2}$. So each tube should contain 2.5 oz. of A and 1.5 oz. of B, for a profit of \$13.50.

But the staff continued to worry. What if they were given an LP maximization problem with more than two variables that had mixed constraints, that is, where some constraints had $\leq$ signs, some had $\geq$ signs, and maybe even some had $=$ signs?

**Figure 26**

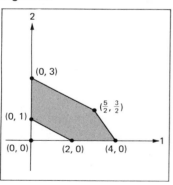

**A Simple Technique**

See Appendix A, Sections 8 and 10.

First we must learn how to reverse inequality signs by multiplying by $-1$. The effect of such a multiplication on an inequality is to change $\leq$ to $\geq$ and $\geq$ to $\leq$.

**Problem 1**

Rewrite the constraint

$$4x_1 - 3x_2 + \tfrac{2}{3}x_3 \geq \tfrac{5}{2} \qquad \qquad \mathbf{4}$$

as an equivalent constraint involving a $\leq$ sign.

Solution  Multiply both sides of constraint **4** by $-1$; then $\geq$ must be changed to $\leq$:

$$-4x_1 + 3x_2 - \tfrac{2}{3}x_3 \leq -\tfrac{5}{2}$$

Phase I  We are now able to rewrite the sunscreen problem so that all constraints conform to Condition 2 of Section 5.2.

Maximize

$$y = 3x_1 + 4x_2$$

subject to

$$x_1 \geq 0, x_2 \geq 0$$
$$x_1 + x_2 \leq 4$$
$$3x_1 + 5x_2 \leq 15$$
$$-x_1 - 2x_2 \leq -2$$

However, the third constraint fails to satisfy Condition 3. Condition 3 is important because it guarantees that the origin is a feasible point; that is, since 0 is less than any positive number, substituting 0 for each variable will make the left side of each constraint 0. This will satisfy the constraint, unless, of course, the constraint bound is negative.

The simplex method begins with a feasible point and moves along the edges of the feasible region until it finds the corner at which the objective variable is optimized. In Section 5.2 we always set out from the origin. In the original AC example in this section, the first matrix for the simplex method is

$$\begin{bmatrix} 1 & 1 & 1 & 0 & 4 \\ 3 & 5 & 0 & 1 & 15 \\ 3 & 4 & 0 & 0 & 0 \end{bmatrix}$$

If we read the answer from this matrix, we see immediately that $x_1 = 0$, $x_2 = 0$, since their columns are uncleared. For the modified problem, the matrix is

$$\begin{bmatrix} 1 & 1 & 1 & 0 & 0 & 4 \\ 3 & 5 & 0 & 1 & 0 & 15 \\ -1 & -2 & 0 & 0 & 1 & -2 \\ 3 & 4 & 0 & 0 & 0 & 0 \end{bmatrix}$$

The answer still reads $x_1 = 0$, $x_2 = 0$, but this time such a result is unacceptable, since it is not feasible.

Checking the graph (Figure 26), we notice that there is an edge leading from the origin to a corner of the feasible region. In fact, we could travel away from $(0,0)$ along either axis to reach such a corner. Since the simplex method moves along edges, is it possible to modify the technique so that it can find a first feasible solution? Yes, it is. The new technique, which we now illustrate, is called Phase I. See the flow chart on the next page.

**Problem 2**  Maximize $y = 3x_1 + 4x_2$ subject to

$$x_1 \geq 0, x_2 \geq 0$$

$$x_1 + x_2 \leq 4$$

$$3x_1 + 5x_2 \leq 15$$

$$x_1 + 2x_2 \geq 2$$

**Solution 1**  We have already set up the first matrix:

$$
\begin{array}{c}
\phantom{R} \\
\phantom{R} \\
R \\
\phantom{R}
\end{array}
\begin{bmatrix}
\phantom{-}1 & \phantom{-}1 & 1 & 0 & 0 & \phantom{-}4 \\
\phantom{-}3 & \phantom{-}5 & 0 & 1 & 0 & \phantom{-}15 \\
-1^* & -2 & 0 & 0 & 1 & -2 \\
\phantom{-}3 & \phantom{-}4 & 0 & 0 & 0 & \phantom{-}0
\end{bmatrix}
\begin{array}{c} C \\ \phantom{x} \\ \phantom{x} \\ \phantom{x} \end{array}
$$

The flow chart instructs us to ignore the last row, consider all the rows with negative last entries, and choose R to be one of these rows. In this case only $R_3$ has a negative last entry so we must let R be $R_3$. We next pick a negative entry in R. We arbitrarily choose the $-1$. Thus, C is $C_1$. We use R to clear C:

$$
\begin{bmatrix}
0 & -1 & 1 & 0 & 1^* & 2 \\
0 & -1 & 0 & 1 & 3 & 9 \\
1 & 2 & 0 & 0 & -1 & 2 \\
0 & -2 & 0 & 0 & 3 & -6
\end{bmatrix}
$$

Now there are no negative entries (except the bottom entry) in the last column. We apply the familiar simplex method.

$$
\begin{bmatrix}
0 & -1 & 1 & 0 & 1 & 2 \\
0 & 2^* & -3 & 1 & 0 & 3 \\
1 & 1 & 1 & 0 & 0 & 4 \\
0 & 1 & -3 & 0 & 0 & -12
\end{bmatrix}
$$

**5**

$$
\begin{bmatrix}
0 & 0 & -\frac{1}{2} & \frac{1}{2} & 1 & \frac{7}{2} \\
0 & 1 & -\frac{3}{2} & \frac{1}{2} & 0 & \frac{3}{2} \\
1 & 0 & \frac{5}{2} & -\frac{1}{2} & 0 & \frac{5}{2} \\
0 & 0 & -\frac{3}{2} & -\frac{1}{2} & 0 & -\frac{27}{2}
\end{bmatrix}
$$

from which we read the answer

$$x_1 = \tfrac{5}{2}, \ x_2 = \tfrac{3}{2}, \text{ and } y = \tfrac{27}{2}$$

as before.

**Phase I: Finding an Initial
Feasible Solution for a
Maximization Problem**

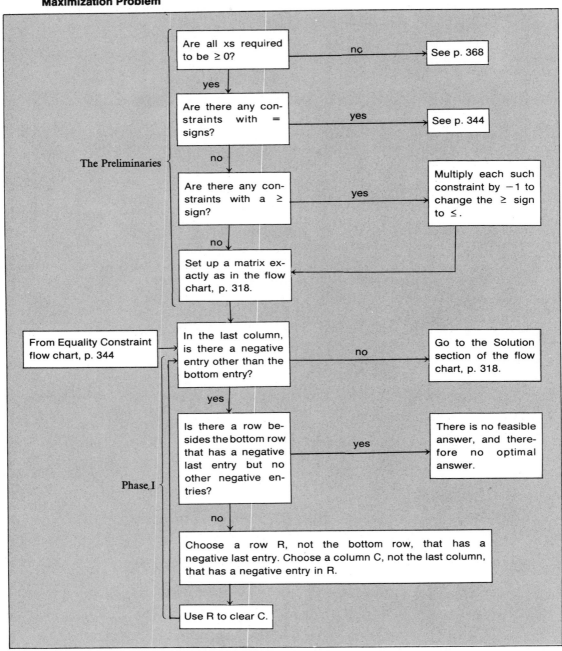

Problem 3    Maximize $y = -3x_1 - 2x_2$ subject to

$$x_1 \geq 0, x_2 \geq 0,$$

$$-x_1 + 4x_2 \geq 14 \qquad \textbf{6}$$

$$-x_1 + 2x_2 \geq 6 \qquad \textbf{7}$$

$$x_1 + 2x_2 \geq 2 \qquad \textbf{8}$$

Solution    We must first multiply each constraint by $-1$.

$$x_1 - 4x_2 \leq -14$$

$$x_1 - 2x_2 \leq -6$$

$$-x_1 - 2x_2 \leq -2$$

Here is one solution. As usual we will use a * to indicate the entry we are using to clear.

We could have used any of the first three rows for R. Having chosen the third row, we also could have used the $(3,2)$ entry instead of the $(3,1)$ entry.

$$\begin{bmatrix} 1 & -4 & 1 & 0 & 0 & -14 \\ 1 & -2 & 0 & 1 & 0 & -6 \\ -1^* & -2 & 0 & 0 & 1 & -2 \\ -3 & -2 & 0 & 0 & 0 & 0 \end{bmatrix} \qquad \textbf{9}$$

We are at the corner $x_1 = 0$, $x_2 = 0$, with $y = 0$.

We could also let $R_1$ be R, but, once we let $R = R_2$, we have no other choice for the *.

$$\begin{bmatrix} 0 & -6 & 1 & 0 & 1 & -16 \\ 0 & -4^* & 0 & 1 & 1 & -8 \\ 1 & 2 & 0 & 0 & -1 & 2 \\ 0 & 4 & 0 & 0 & -3 & 6 \end{bmatrix} \qquad \textbf{10}$$

We have moved to the corner $x_1 = 2$, $x_2 = 0$ with $y = -6$. Don't forget that the value of y is the entry in the southeast corner *with its sign changed*.

We could also choose $R_1$ to be R.

$$\begin{bmatrix} 0 & 0 & 1 & -\frac{3}{2} & -\frac{1}{2} & -4 \\ 0 & 4 & 0 & -1 & -1 & 8 \\ 1 & 0 & 0 & \frac{1}{2} & -\frac{1}{2}^* & -2 \\ 0 & 0 & 0 & 1 & -2 & -2 \end{bmatrix} \qquad \textbf{11}$$

There is no reason to divide $R_2$ by 4 yet. We are now at the corner $x_1 = -2$, $x_2 = \frac{8}{4} = 2$, and $y = -2$.

There is no other choice for R, but we could let $C = C_4$.

$$\begin{bmatrix} -1^* & 0 & 1 & -2 & 0 & -2 \\ -2 & 4 & 0 & -2 & 0 & 12 \\ -2 & 0 & 0 & -1 & 1 & 4 \\ -4 & 0 & 0 & -1 & 0 & 6 \end{bmatrix} \qquad \textbf{12}$$

We have moved to the corner $x_1 = 0$, $x_2 = \frac{12}{4} = 3$, with $y = -6$.

$$\begin{bmatrix} 1 & 0 & -1 & 2* & 0 & 2 \\ 0 & 4 & -2 & 2 & 0 & 16 \\ 0 & 0 & -2 & 3 & 1 & 8 \\ 0 & 0 & -4 & 7 & 0 & 14 \end{bmatrix}$$ **13**

Now $x_1 = 2$, $x_2 = \frac{16}{4} = 4$, and $y = -14$.

$$\begin{bmatrix} 0 & & 2 & 0 & 2 \\ 4 & & 0 & 0 & 14 \\ 0 & & 0 & 1 & 5 \\ -\frac{7}{2} & 0 & -\frac{1}{2} & 0 & 0 & 7 \end{bmatrix}$$ **14**

We don't need the other entries to tell us that $x_1 = 0$, $x_2 = \frac{7}{2}$, and $y = -7$ is the final answer.

We are now applying the regular simplex method.

**Figure 27**

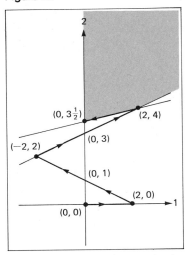

It is easier to apply the simplex method than it is to prove that constraint **8** is redundant. We can see this from Figure 27, but, if you have already drawn Figure 27, why not simply use the corner point theorem and avoid the simplex method altogether?

The geometric method (presented in Section 5.1) is usually the quickest way to solve problems with only two variables.

We make five interesting observations from the graph of this problem (Figure 27).

(1) The third constraint is *redundant*; that is, it is unnecessary in the presence of the first two constraints.
(2) The region of feasibility is unbounded, but the maximization problem has a solution anyway, because the entries in the objective matrix are negative.
(3) We can actually see the path that the simplex method followed to find the optimal corner. Note that it visits every corner in the figure. The geometric method would have been much quicker, but we cannot tell that by just looking at the problem.
(4) It seems silly to visit the corners $(2,0)$, $(-2,2)$, and $(2,4)$. Could we not simply go straight up the 2-axis? Yes, although it is easier to see what we should have done now that we have solved the problem: we should have made the other choices in matrices **9** and **12**. If we had somehow noticed that constraint **8** was redundant, then, by omitting it, we could have simplified the problem.
(5) Once we reached a corner of the region of feasibility, namely $(2,4)$, we finished the problem with Phase II, the ordinary simplex method. You can often shorten the work by looking ahead a little bit. For example, rework Problem 3 but this time start by letting R be $R_1$.

**Minimization Problems**    Phase I can also be used to solve minimization problems.

Problem 4    Minimize $y = 2x_1 + 3x_2 + 7x_3$ subject to

$$x_1 \geq 0, x_2 \geq 0, x_3 \geq 0,$$
$$x_1 + x_2 + 2x_3 \geq 3$$
$$x_1 + 2x_2 + 3x_3 \geq 4$$
$$2x_1 + 4x_2 + 8x_3 \geq 7$$

Solution    Consider the variable $y'$, which is the negative of the objective variable $y$:

$$y' = -2x_1 - 3x_2 - 7x_3$$

The larger we make this variable, the smaller we make $y$. For example, if we increase $y'$ from $-20$ to $-10$, we decrease $y$ from 20 to 10. Thus, if we maximize $y'$ we will have minimized $y$. Therefore, corresponding to the above minimization problem there is a maximization problem, namely

Maximize

$$y' = -2x_1 - 3x_2 - 7x_3$$

subject to

$$x_1 \geq 0, x_2 \geq 0, x_3 \geq 0,$$
$$x_1 + x_2 + 2x_3 \geq 3$$
$$x_1 + 2x_2 + 3x_3 \geq 4$$
$$2x_1 + 4x_2 + 8x_3 \geq 7$$

Now every constraint violates Condition 2. We multiply $-1$ through each constraint and set up the initial matrix:

$$\begin{bmatrix} -1 & -1 & -2 & 1 & 0 & 0 & -3 \\ -1 & -2 & -3 & 0 & 1 & 0 & -4 \\ -2^* & -4 & -8 & 0 & 0 & 1 & -7 \\ -2 & -3 & -7 & 0 & 0 & 0 & 0 \end{bmatrix}$$

There are three negative numbers in the last column. We arbitrarily let R be $R_3$.

We now have a choice of any of the first three columns. We arbitrarily select $C_1$. Clearing yields the matrix

$$\begin{bmatrix} 0 & 1 & 2 & 1 & 0 & -\frac{1}{2} & \frac{1}{2} \\ 0 & 0 & 1 & 0 & 1 & -\frac{1}{2}^* & -\frac{1}{2} \\ 1 & 2 & 4 & 0 & 0 & -\frac{1}{2} & \frac{7}{2} \\ 0 & 1 & 1 & 0 & 0 & -1 & 7 \end{bmatrix}$$

We must use Phase I again. This time we have no choice. We must let $R_2 = R$ and $C_6 = C$. We then obtain

$$\begin{bmatrix} 0 & 1^* & 1 & 1 & -1 & 0 & 1 \\ 0 & 0 & -2 & 0 & -2 & 1 & 1 \\ 1 & 2 & 3 & 0 & -1 & 0 & 4 \\ 0 & 1 & -1 & 0 & -2 & 0 & 8 \end{bmatrix}$$

Now we are ready to apply the ordinary simplex method.

$$\begin{bmatrix} 0 & 1 & 1 & 1 & -1 & 0 & 1 \\ 0 & 0 & -2 & 0 & -2 & 1 & 1 \\ 1 & 0 & 1 & -2 & 1 & 0 & 2 \\ 0 & 0 & -2 & -1 & -1 & 0 & 7 \end{bmatrix}$$

Since all the entries (except the last) in the bottom row are zero or negative, we can read the answer.

Warning We have just solved a maximization problem. We read the *maximization* answer:

$$x_1 = 2, x_2 = 1, x_3 = 0, y' = -7$$

To relate this to our minimization problem, we simply change the sign of $y'$: The answer to the minimization problem is then

$$x_1 = 2, x_2 = 1, x_3 = 0, y = 7$$

We do not need a whole new flow chart for a minimization problem in linear programming. The following sentence is sufficient.

> To minimize the objective variable, maximize its negative.

Equality Constraints If one or more of the constraints is an equation rather than an inequality, one simply omits the appropriate slack variables. Recall from Section 5.3 that we used slack variables to change each inequality into an equality. If we already have an equality, we merely omit the slack variable by deleting a column from the identity matrix. For example, look at this problem.

Problem 5 Maximize $y = 7x_1 + 2x_2$ subject to

$$x_1 \geq 0, \quad x_2 \geq 0$$
$$8x_1 + 3x_2 \leq 24$$
$$x_1 + x_2 \leq 4$$
$$-x_1 + x_2 = 2$$

Solution    We need only two slack variables, $x_3$ and $x_4$:

$$\begin{bmatrix} 8x_1 + 3x_2 + x_3 & = 24 \\ x_1 + x_2 & + x_4 = 4 \\ -x_1 + x_2 & = 2 \end{bmatrix}$$ **15**

The initial matrix is

$$\begin{bmatrix} 8 & 3 & 1 & 0 & 24 \\ 1 & 1 & 0 & 1 & 4 \\ -1 & 1^* & 0 & 0 & 2 \\ 7 & 2 & 0 & 0 & 0 \end{bmatrix}$$

Be careful! Direct application of the simplex method here will generally fail, because, while this problem does not require three slack variables, it can be shown that Phase I and the simplex method require the presence of all three columns of the identity matrix. (They may appear in any order.)

The difficulty is that we can not be sure that there is any solution at all to the system of equations represented by system **15**. Phase I begins with a solution to the system of equations represented by the matrix and moves to a feasible solution for the Linear Programming problem. Once we have a feasible solution, the simplex method can move from it to an optimal solution. In system **15** if we set $x_1 = 0$, $x_2 = 0$, $x_3 = 24$, $x_4 = 4$, then the third equation will not be satisfied. Fortunately it is easy to change a problem into the form required by Phase I: use *any* entries to clear columns so as to obtain, in any order, the missing columns of the identity matrix. If this cannot be done, then the original problem has no feasible, and therefore no optimal, solution. All this is summarized in the following flow chart.

As our first application of this flow chart we complete the solution of Problem 5. In our case we need a third column for the identity matrix. We arbitrarily choose the second column and use the third row to clear it. The result is:

$$\begin{bmatrix} 11 & 0 & 1 & 0 & 18 \\ 2^* & 0 & 0 & 1 & 2 \\ -1 & 1 & 0 & 0 & 2 \\ 9 & 0 & 0 & 0 & -4 \end{bmatrix}$$

There is no need for Phase I. We merely apply the simplex method:

$$\begin{bmatrix} 0 & 0 & 1 & -\frac{11}{2} & 7 \\ 1 & 0 & 0 & \frac{1}{2} & 1 \\ 0 & 1 & 0 & \frac{1}{2} & 3 \\ 0 & 0 & 0 & -\frac{9}{2} & -13 \end{bmatrix}$$

We obtain $x_1 = 1$, $x_2 = 3$, $y = 13$.

---

A matrix presents a feasible solution if its last column contains no negative entries (except perhaps the last) and if it contains the columns of an identity matrix (of the correct size) in any order.

The difficulty in system **15** can occur only if an equality constraint is present. In matrix **9**, for example, the answer $x_1 = 0$, $x_2 = 0$, $x_3 = -14$, $x_4 = -6$, $x_5 = -2$, is a solution for the system of equations it represents.

It is always pointless to use an entry in the last row to clear a column.

We could also have used the $(3, 1)$ entry.

**Flow Chart for
a Problem with
Equality Constraints**

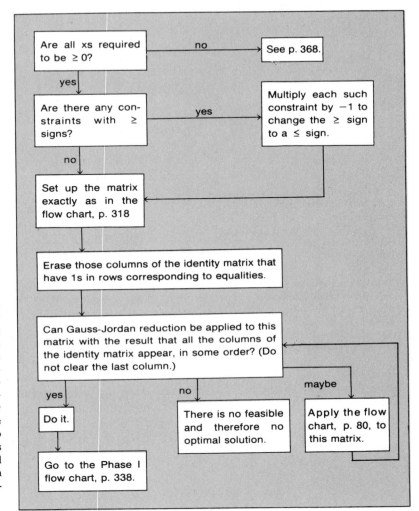

When applying this technique to problems not in this text it may happen that an entire row of zeros appears somewhere above the last row. If this happens, it means that the set of equality constraints has multiple solutions. In this case it is necessary to modify the flow chart procedure: *Whenever an entire row of zeros appears, erase it.* This will reduce the size of the matrix. (We hesitate to mention the following rather frivolous special case. If the last row is all zeros, then the maximum or minimum is zero, provided there are any feasible solutions at all.)

Problem 6    Maximize $y = 2x_1 + x_2$ subject to

$$x_1 \geq 0, x_2 \geq 0$$
$$3x_1 + 2x_2 \leq 6$$
$$x_1 - x_2 = 4$$

Solution    The initial matrix is

$$\begin{bmatrix} 3 & 2 & 1 & 6 \\ 1^* & -1 & 0 & 4 \\ 2 & 1 & 0 & 0 \end{bmatrix}$$

Figure 28

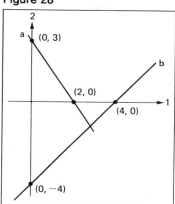

We obtain the second column for the identity matrix by using the second row to clear the first column:

$$\begin{bmatrix} 0 & 5 & 1 & -6 \\ 1 & -1 & 0 & 4 \\ 0 & 3 & 0 & -8 \end{bmatrix}$$

The $-6$ tells us to use Phase I. The fact that there are no other negative entries in its row tells us that there is no feasible and, therefore, no optimal solution. This is easy to see geometrically (Figure 28). There are no points in the positive quadrant that are below line **a**: $3x_1 + 2x_2 = 6$ and on line **b**: $x_1 - x_2 = 4$.

**Problem 7**   Maximize $y = 2x_1 - x_2 + x_3$ subject to

$$x_1 \geq 0, x_2 \geq 0, x_3 \geq 0,$$
$$3x_1 - x_2 + 2x_3 = \quad 7$$
$$x_1 - x_2 + x_3 = -2$$
$$4x_1 - 2x_2 + 3x_3 = \quad 3$$
$$x_1 - 4x_2 + x_3 \leq \quad 7.$$

**Solution**   We set up the matrix

$$\begin{bmatrix} 3 & -1 & 2 & 0 & 7 \\ 1^* & -1 & 1 & 0 & -2 \\ 4 & -2 & 3 & 0 & 3 \\ 1 & -4 & 1 & 1 & 7 \\ 2 & -1 & 1 & 0 & 0 \end{bmatrix}$$

and then try to obtain the missing 3 columns of the identity matrix.

$$\begin{bmatrix} 0 & 2 & -1 & 0 & 13 \\ 1 & -1 & 1 & 0 & -2 \\ 0 & 2 & -1^* & 0 & 11 \\ 0 & -3 & 0 & 1 & 9 \\ 0 & 1 & -1 & 0 & 4 \end{bmatrix}$$

$$\begin{bmatrix} 0 & 0 & 0 & 0 & 2 \\ 1 & 1 & 0 & 0 & 9 \\ 0 & -2 & 1 & 0 & -11 \\ 0 & -3 & 0 & 1 & 9 \\ 0 & -1 & 0 & 0 & -7 \end{bmatrix}$$

Since we cannot clear the last column we must clear column 2. But we cannot use $R_1$ (since the $(1,2)$ entry is 0) and if we use any other rows to clear $C_2$ we will simply be interchanging columns of the identity matrix.

The first row of this matrix tells us that the system is inconsistent. Hence, there is no solution. In any event we certainly cannot expect to obtain the first column of the $4 \times 4$ identity matrix. Thus, our original problem has no feasible, and therefore no optimal, solution.

Minimization with mixed constraints is accomplished as before by maximizing the negative of the objective variable.

Problem 8  Minimize $y = 5x_1 + 6x_2$ subject to

$$x_1 \geq 0, x_2 \geq 0$$
$$-2x_1 + x_2 = -2$$
$$2x_1 + 3x_2 \geq 6$$
$$3x_1 + 5x_2 \geq 15$$

Solution  We convert to the equivalent maximization problem: maximize $y' = -5x_1 - 6x_2$ subject to

$$x_1 \geq 0, x_2 \geq 0$$
$$-2x_1 + x_2 = -2$$
$$2x_1 + 3x_2 \geq 6$$
$$3x_1 + 5x_2 \leq 15$$

Next, we multiply $-1$ through the second constraint so that it satisfies Condition 2. The matrix is

$$\begin{bmatrix} -2 & 1^* & 0 & 0 & -2 \\ -2 & -3 & 1 & 0 & -6 \\ 3 & 5 & 0 & 1 & 15 \\ -5 & -6 & 0 & 0 & 0 \end{bmatrix}$$

First, we must generate the missing column of the identity matrix. We could use $R_1$ to clear either of the first two columns of this matrix. It will be easier to clear the second column.

$$\begin{bmatrix} -2 & 1 & 0 & 0 & -2 \\ -8^* & 0 & 1 & 0 & -12 \\ 13 & 0 & 0 & 1 & 25 \\ -17 & 0 & 0 & 0 & -12 \end{bmatrix}$$

$$\begin{bmatrix} 0 & 1 & -\frac{1}{4} & 0 & 1 \\ 8 & 0 & 1 & 0 & 12 \\ 0 & 0 & \frac{13}{8} & 1 & \frac{11}{2} \\ 0 & 0 & -\frac{17}{8} & 0 & \frac{27}{2} \end{bmatrix}$$

The answer to this maximization problem is

$$x_1 = \tfrac{3}{2}, \; x_2 = 1, \; y' = -\tfrac{27}{2}$$

Thus, the answer to the minimization problem is

$$x_1 = \tfrac{3}{2}, \; x_2 = 1, \; y = \tfrac{27}{2}.$$

Sometimes Phase I will require fewer steps if you do the following.

(i) Pick a row with a negative last entry.
(ii) Pick a negative entry in that row.
(iii) Consider the positive entries in the column of the entry chosen in step (ii).
(iv) Use one of these positive entries to clear the column.

Of course, you will want to use the positive entry that yields the smallest quotient when divided into the entry at the end of its row. There is no point in introducing *new* negative entries in the last column.

#### One Final Remark

The book *Matrix Methods in Finite Mathematics*, by the same authors, contains (p. 323) a detailed treatment of the version of Phase I described in the previous two paragraphs. This slightly more complicated version of Phase I is guaranteed not to cycle.

Although it is extremely unlikely, it is possible for the simplex method or Phase I, as presented in this book, to *cycle*, that is, to go on forever. There are ways to modify the simplex method to guarantee that cycling will not occur. However, cycling is so rare that even computers are generally not programmed to avoid it. In hand computation you will notice that you are cycling if you keep returning to the same matrix. If this happens, try clearing a different column. It is difficult to find problems that cycle. Even if you find one, you will have to cycle willfully. No problem ever forces you to cycle.

#### Exercises 5.4

By **standard format constraint** we mean an inequality such as

$$3x_1 - 2x_2 + x_3 \leq 17$$

where the left side involves a sum of variables, the inequality sign is $\leq$, and the right side is a single number.

In Exercises 1 and 2, convert the given constraints to standard format constraints.

1. (a) $-x_1 + 2x_2 \geq -4$
   (b) $3x_1 + x_2 - 4x_3 - x_4 \geq -2$
   (c) $2x_1 - x_3 \geq x_2 + 2x_4 - x_5 - 7$
   (d) $2 \quad x_1 + 3x_2 - 5x_3$
   (e) $x_1 + 2x_2 - 8 \geq 2x_1 - x_3 + 5$
2. (a) $3x_1 - x_2 \geq -2$
   (b) $x_1 + 2x_2 \geq x_3 - 2x_4 + 5$
   (c) $3x_1 - 2x_2 \geq x_1 + 3x_2 - x_3 + 2x_4 - 7$
   (d) $8x_1 - 3x_2 \leq 2x_3 - x_4 - 9$
   (e) $9 - 2x_3 + x_4 - x_1 \geq 8 - x_1 + 2x_2 + x_4$

Use Phase I and the simplex method to solve the following linear programming problems. You may already have solved some of these exercises geometrically in Section 5.1. If so, try to relate each step in the matrix solution to your graph; that is, determine which corner point you are visiting after each column is cleared.

3. Maximize $y = x_1 + 4x_2$ subject to $x_1 \geq 0$, $x_2 \geq 0$, and $x_1 + x_2 \geq 2$, $x_1 + 2x_2 \leq 3$.

This is almost Exercise 27(a) of Section 5.1, p. 311.

This is almost Exercise 27(b) of Section 5.1, p. 311.

The region in this problem is the same as in Exercise 28 of Section 5.1, p. 311.

This is almost Exercise 21(a) of Section 5.1, p. 311.

This is Problem 5 of Section 5.2, p. 325.

This is almost Exercise 15(a) of Section 5.1, p. 310.

This is almost Exercise 17(b) of Section 5.1, p. 311.

This is almost Exercise 27(a) of Section 5.1, p. 311.

4. Maximize $y = 3x_1 + x_2$ subject to $x_1 \geq 0$, $x_2 \geq 0$, and $x_1 + 2x_2 \geq 4$, $x_1 + x_2 \leq 3$.

5. Maximize $y = 6x_1 + x_2$ subject to $x_1 \geq 0$, $x_2 \geq 0$, $4x_1 + 3x_2 \geq 22$, $3x_1 - 2x_2 \geq 8$, $x_1 + 5x_2 \leq 31$.

6. Maximize $y = x_1 + 7x_2$ subject to $x_1 \geq 0$, $x_2 \geq 0$, $4x_1 + 3x_2 \geq 22$, $3x_1 - 2x_2 \leq 8$, $x_1 + 5x_2 \leq 31$.

7. Maximize $y = 3x_1 + x_2$ subject to $x_1 \geq 0$, $x_2 \geq 0$, $9x_1 + 5x_2 \leq 45$, $2x_1 + 6x_2 \geq 12$, $2x_1 + x_2 \geq 4$.

8. Maximize $y = 2x_1 + 5x_2$ subject to $x_1 \geq 0$, $x_2 \geq 0$, $x_1 + x_2 \leq 1$, $2x_1 + x_2 \geq 4$.

9. Maximize $y = 3x_1 + 2x_2$ subject to $x_1 \geq 0$, $x_2 \geq 0$, $x_1 + x_2 \geq 4$, $2x_1 + x_2 \leq 4$, $x_1 + 2x_2 \leq 4$.

10. Maximize $y = 4x_1 + 7x_2$ subject to $x_1 \geq 0$, $x_2 \geq 0$, $x_1 - 2x_2 \leq 4$, $2x_1 + x_2 \geq 4$

11. Maximize $y = 2x_1 + x_2$ subject to $x_1 \geq 0$, $x_2 \geq 0$, $-x_1 + x_2 \leq 2$, $3x_1 + 2x_2 \geq 14$, $x_1 - x_2 \leq 3$.

C12. Maximize $y = x_1 + x_2$ subject to $1 \leq x_1 \leq 2$ and $1 \leq x_2 \leq 2$.

13. Maximize $y = 4x_1 + 6x_2 + 7x_3$ subject to $x_1 \geq 0$, $x_2 \geq 0$, $x_3 \geq 0$, $x_1 + 2x_2 - 4x_3 \geq 1$, $2x_1 + x_2 + 2x_3 \leq 4$, $-x_1 + 3x_2 + 4x_3 \leq 6$.

14. Maximize $y = 4x_1 + 5x_2 + 8x_3$ subject to $x_1 \geq 0$, $x_2 \geq 0$, $x_3 \geq 0$, $x_1 + 2x_2 - x_3 \geq 2$, $2x_1 + 3x_2 + 3x_3 \leq 6$, $x_1 + 2x_2 + 4x_3 \leq 9$.

15. Maximize $y = 2x_1 + 7x_2 + 6x_3$ subject to $x_1 \geq 0$, $x_2 \geq 0$, $x_3 \geq 0$, $2x_1 + x_2 + 4x_3 \geq 2$, $x_1 + 3x_2 + x_3 \geq 4$, $x_1 + 3x_2 + 2x_3 \leq 11$.

16. Maximize $y = 6x_1 + 8x_2 + 10x_3$ subject to $x_1 \geq 0$, $x_2 \geq 0$, $x_3 \geq 0$, $4x_1 + 7x_2 + 9x_3 \geq 1$, $2x_1 + 5x_2 + 2x_3 \geq 3$, $2x_1 + 4x_2 + 3x_3 \leq 4$.

17. Maximize $y = 3x_1 + 4x_2 + 6x_3$ subject to $x_1 \geq 0$, $x_2 \geq 0$, $x_3 \geq 0$, $3x_1 + 5x_2 + 7x_3 \leq 2$, $2x_1 + 8x_2 + x_3 \leq 8$, $3x_1 + 4x_2 + 5x_3 \geq 3$.

18. Maximize $y = 8x_1 + 9x_2 + 12x_3$ subject to $x_1 \geq 0$, $x_2 \geq 0$, $x_3 \geq 0$, $2x_1 + 3x_2 + 4x_3 \leq 6$, $4x_1 + x_2 + 3x_3 \geq 7$, $2x_1 + 5x_2 + x_3 \leq 9$, $2x_1 + 5x_2 + 6x_3 \geq 7$.

19. Maximize $y = 4x_1 + 3x_2 + 4x_3$ subject to $x_1 \geq 0$, $x_2 \geq 0$, $x_3 \geq 0$, $4x_1 - 2x_2 + 2x_3 \geq 2$, $x_1 - 3x_2 + 2x_3 \leq 3$, $3x_1 - 2x_2 \leq 4$.

20. Maximize $y = 2x_1 + 9x_2 + 7x_3 + 7x_4$ subject to $x_1 \geq 0$, $x_2 \geq 0$, $x_3 \geq 0$, $x_4 \geq 0$, $2x_1 + 5x_2 + 4x_3 + x_4 \geq 2$, $x_1 + 4x_2 - 3x_3 + 4x_4 \geq -3$, $x_1 + 2x_2 + 2x_3 + x_4 \leq 4$.

21. Minimize $y = 2x_1 + 3x_2$ subject to $x_1 \geq 0$, $x_2 \geq 0$, $x_1 + x_2 \geq 3$, $2x_1 + 5x_2 \geq 10$.

22. Minimize $y = 4x_1 + 2x_2$ subject to $x_1 \geq 0$, $x_2 \geq 0$, $x_1 + x_2 \geq 2$, $4x_1 + x_2 \geq 4$.

23. Minimize $y = 9x_1 + x_2$ subject to $x_1 \geq 0$, $x_2 \geq 0$, $x_1 + x_2 \geq 1$, $3x_1 - x_2 \geq 1$.

24. Minimize $y = 3x_1 + 2x_2$ subject to $x_1 \geq 0$, $x_2 \geq 0$, $4x_1 + x_2 \geq 4$, $x_1 + x_2 \geq 3$, $x_1 + 2x_2 \geq 4$.

25. Minimize $y = 2x_1 + 3x_2$ subject to $x_1 \geq 0$, $x_2 \geq 0$, $x_1 + 4x_2 \geq 4$, $4x_1 + x_2 \geq 4$, $x_1 + x_2 \geq 3$.

26. Minimize $y = 6x_1 + x_2$ subject to $x_1 \geq 0$, $x_2 \geq 0$, $4x_1 + 3x_2 \geq 22$, $3x_1 - 2x_2 \leq 8$, $x_1 + 5x_2 \leq 31$.

C27. Minimize $y = 30x_1 + 51x_2$ subject to $x_1 \geq 0$, $x_2 \geq 0$, $2x_1 + x_2 \geq 16$, $x_1 + 2x_2 \geq 11$, $x_1 + x_2 \leq 9$.

This is Exercise 25 of Section 5.1, p.
311.

This is almost Exercise 21(b) of Section 5.1, p. 311.

28. Minimize $y = x_1 + x_2$ subject to $x_1 \geq 0$, $x_2 \geq 0$, $x_1 + 5x_2 \geq 5$, $x_1 + 2x_2 \geq 4$, $3x_1 + 2x_2 \geq 6$.

29. Minimize $y = x_1 - 2x_2$ subject to $x_1 \geq 0$, $x_2 \geq 0$, $-x_1 + x_2 \leq 2$, $x_1 - x_2 \leq 2$.

30. Minimize $y = x_1 - x_2$ subject to $x_1 \geq 0$, $x_2 \geq 0$, $x_1 + x_2 \geq 4$, $2x_1 + x_2 \leq 4$, $x_1 + 2x_2 \leq 4$.

31. Minimize $y = 3x_1 + 8x_2 + 5x_3$ subject to $x_1 \geq 0$, $x_2 \geq 0$, $x_3 \geq 0$, $x_1 + x_2 + x_3 \geq 7$, $x_1 + 2x_2 + x_3 \geq 5$, $-x_1 + x_2 \geq 6$.

32. Minimize $y = 2x_1 + 3x_2 + 7x_3$ subject to $x_1 \geq 0$, $x_2 \geq 0$, $x_3 \geq 0$, $x_1 + 2x_2 + 3x_3 \geq 4$, $2x_1 + 4x_2 + 8x_3 \geq 7$, $x_1 + x_2 + 2x_3 \geq 3$.

33. Minimize $y = 8x_1 + 4x_2 + 9x_3$ subject to $x_1 \geq 0$, $x_2 \geq 0$, $x_3 \geq 0$, $3x_1 - 2x_2 + 2x_3 \geq 4$, $-2x_1 + x_2 + 2x_3 \geq 5$, $2x_1 + 4x_2 + 3x_3 \geq 5$.

34. Minimize $y = -x_1 + 4x_2 + 6x_3$ subject to $x_1 \geq 0$, $x_2 \geq 0$, $x_3 \geq 0$, $-x_1 + 2x_2 - x_3 \geq 4$, $-2x_1 + x_2 + 3x_3 \geq 6$, $4x_1 + 2x_2 + 4x_3 \geq 7$.

*35. A complicated pilot study involving trading of certain frozen food items between stores in PHEM, the model PHE company, has led to the necessity to minimize $y = 6x_1 + 3x_2 + 2x_3 + 4x_4$, where $x_1$, $x_2$, $x_3$, and $x_4$ must not be negative, subject to the conditions $2x_2 + x_3 \geq x_1 + x_4 + 3$, $x_2 + x_3 - 4 \geq 2x_1 + 3x_4$, $2(x_1 + x_2) \geq 3x_3 - 2x_4 + 2$, and $4 - 3x_1 - 2x_3 \leq x_4 - 3x_2$. Do it.

C36. Minimize $y = x_1 + x_2 + x_3$ subject to $1 \leq x_1 \leq 2$, $1 \leq x_2 \leq 2$, $1 \leq x_3 \leq 2$.

37. Maximize $y = 3x_1 + 2x_2$ subject to $x_1 \geq 0$, $x_2 \geq 0$, $x_1 + x_2 = 3$, $2x_1 + x_2 \leq 4$.

38. Maximize $y = 4x_1 + 2x_2$ subject to $x_1 \geq 0$, $x_2 \geq 0$, $3x_1 + 2x_2 \geq 6$, $x_1 + x_2 = 3$, $3x_1 + x_2 \leq 8$.

39. Minimize $y = 3x_1 - x_2$ subject to $x_1 \geq 0$, $x_2 \geq 0$, $x_1 + x_2 = 3$, $3x_1 + x_2 \leq 6$, $3x_1 + 2x_2 \geq 7$.

This is Exercise 36 of Section 5.1, p.
313.

40. Maximize $y = 3x_1 + 2x_2$ subject to $x_1 \geq 0$, $x_2 \geq 0$, $x_1 + x_2 \leq 5$, $3x_1 + 7x_2 \geq 21$, $-x_1 + x_2 = 2$.

41. Minimize $y = 3x_1 + 2x_2$ subject to $x_1 \geq 0$, $x_2 \geq 0$, $x_1 + x_2 \leq 5$, $3x_1 + 7x_2 \geq 21$, $-x_1 + x_2 = 2$.

42. Minimize $y = x_1 - x_2 + 2x_3$ subject to $x_1 \geq 0$, $x_2 \geq 0$, $x_3 \geq 0$, $2x_1 - 3x_2 + x_3 = 2$, $x_1 - x_2 + x_3 \geq 7$, $3x_1 - 2x_2 + x_3 \leq 10$.

43. Maximize $y = 3x_1 + 4x_2 + x_3 + 2x_4$ subject to $x_1 \geq 0$, $x_2 \geq 0$, $x_3 \geq 0$, $x_4 \geq 0$, $7x_1 + 3x_2 + x_3 + 2x_4 \leq 14$, $x_1 + 2x_2 + x_3 + 2x_4 = 6$.

44. Maximize $y = x_1 + 2x_2$ subject to $x_1 \geq 0$, $x_2 \geq 0$, $x_1 + x_2 = 2$, $3x_1 + x_2 \leq 3$, $x_1 + 2x_2 \geq 6$.

45. Minimize $y = x_1 - x_2$ subject to $x_1 \geq 0$, $x_2 \geq 0$, $2x_1 + 3x_2 = 5$, $3x_1 - x_2 \geq 6$, $2x_1 + 2x_2 = 4$, $4x_1 + x_2 = 6$.

## Section 5.5 Linear Programming at Appalachian Creations

In this section we present and solve three problems that came up recently at Appalachain Creations, Inc. While our discussion and analysis of these problems is rather complete, it should be pointed out that this is a mathematics book and not a management text. What we are really presenting here is the "middle part" of these problems. The first part, concerned with recognition of the problem and the collection of data, and the last part, concerned with presentation and implementation of the solution, are best discussed in courses in management techniques. These "outer parts" of linear programming obviously vary greatly from company to company, and in the final analysis they can only be learned through actual experience. The "middle part" however is a piece of

## ABSTRACT MATHEMATICS

and as such it is essentially the same for *all* types of problems. Hence, it can really be learned from this book!

**Problem 1**  The technical climbing division of AC believes it can sell the following quantities of the following items: pitons, 800; carabiners, 600; nuts, 1,000; ascenders, 90. These beliefs may be somewhat optimistic; at any rate the company has decided as a matter of policy to order no more than these quantities. The company has 4 possible sources for these items, all of them small factories in Switzerland that operate up to 32 hours a week. In one full week, the factory at Visp produces 300 pitons, 200 carabiners, and 40 ascenders; the factory at Brig produces 200 pitons, 200 carabiners, 400 nuts, and 40 ascenders; the factory at Ayer produces 100 pitons, 400 carabiners, 300 nuts, and 20 ascenders; and the factory at Binn produces 400 pitons, 400 nuts, and 20 ascenders. The price structure at the factories is such that sale of one week's production from Visp results in a profit of $300 for AC, and sale of one week's production from Brig, Ayer, and Binn results in a profit of $600, $800, and $400, respectively. How long should each factory work so as to produce the maximum profit?

**Solution**  Let us agree to measure pitons, carabiners, and nuts in units of 100 each, ascenders in units of 10, and profit in units of $100. The data above may then be tabulated as shown in Table 5.

**Table 5**

| Product | Factory | | | | Constraint |
| --- | --- | --- | --- | --- | --- |
| | **Visp** | **Brig** | **Ayer** | **Binn** | |
| Pitons | 3 | 2 | 1 | 4 | at most 8 |
| Carabiners | 2 | 2 | 4 | 0 | at most 6 |
| Nuts | 0 | 4 | 3 | 4 | at most 10 |
| Ascenders | 4 | 4 | 2 | 2 | at most 9 |
| Profit | 3 | 6 | 8 | 4 | maximize |

Let $x_1$ be the number of weeks the Visp factory operates and let $x_2$, $x_3$, $x_4$ be the number of weeks the factories operate at Brig, Ayer, and Binn, respectively. Let y be the total profit. Then we are to maximize

$$y = 3x_1 + 6x_2 + 8x_3 + 4x_4$$

**1**

subject to

$$x_1 \geq 0, \; x_2 \geq 0, \; x_3 \geq 0, \; x_4 \geq 0$$

$$
\begin{array}{ll}
3x_1 + 2x_2 + \; x_3 + 4x_4 \leq 8 & \qquad 2 \\
2x_1 + 2x_2 + 4x_3 \qquad\; \leq 6 & \qquad 3 \\
\quad\; 4x_2 + 3x_3 + 4x_4 \leq 10 & \qquad 4 \\
4x_1 + 4x_2 + 2x_3 + 2x_4 \leq 9 & \qquad 5
\end{array}
$$

We apply the simplex method, which results in the following sequence of matrixes:

$$
\begin{bmatrix}
3 & 2 & 1^* & 4 & 1 & 0 & 0 & 0 & 8 \\
2 & 2 & 4^* & 0 & 0 & 1 & 0 & 0 & 6 \\
0 & 4 & 3 & 4 & 0 & 0 & 1 & 0 & 10 \\
4 & 4 & 2 & 2 & 0 & 0 & 0 & 1 & 9 \\
3 & 6 & 8 & 4 & 0 & 0 & 0 & 0 & 0
\end{bmatrix}
$$

$$
\begin{array}{l}
R_1 - \frac{1}{4}R_2 \\
\frac{1}{4}R_2 \\
R_3 - \frac{3}{4}R_2 \\
R_4 - \frac{1}{2}R_2 \\
R_5 - 2R_2
\end{array}
\begin{bmatrix}
\frac{5}{2} & \frac{3}{2} & 0 & 4 & 1 & -\frac{1}{4} & 0 & 0 & \frac{13}{2} \\
\frac{1}{2} & \frac{1}{2} & 1 & 0 & 0 & \frac{1}{4} & 0 & 0 & \frac{3}{2} \\
-\frac{3}{2} & \frac{5}{2} & 0 & 4^* & 0 & -\frac{3}{4} & 1 & 0 & \frac{11}{2} \\
3 & 3 & 0 & 2 & 0 & -\frac{1}{2} & 0 & 1 & 6 \\
-1 & 2 & 0 & 4 & 0 & -2 & 0 & 0 & -12
\end{bmatrix}
$$

$$
\begin{array}{l}
R_1 - R_3 \\
\; \\
\frac{1}{4}R_3 \\
R_4 - \frac{1}{2}R_3 \\
R_5 - R_3
\end{array}
\begin{bmatrix}
4^* & -1 & 0 & 0 & 1 & \frac{1}{2} & -1 & 0 & 1 \\
\frac{1}{2} & \frac{1}{2} & 1 & 0 & 0 & \frac{1}{4} & 0 & 0 & \frac{3}{2} \\
-\frac{3}{8} & \frac{5}{8} & 0 & 1 & 0 & -\frac{3}{16} & \frac{1}{4} & 0 & \frac{11}{8} \\
\frac{15}{4} & \frac{7}{4} & 0 & 0 & 0 & -\frac{1}{8} & -\frac{1}{2} & 1 & \frac{13}{4} \\
\frac{1}{2} & -\frac{1}{2} & 0 & 0 & 0 & -\frac{5}{4} & -1 & 0 & -\frac{35}{2}
\end{bmatrix}
$$

$$
\begin{array}{c}
\qquad\quad x_1 \;\; x_2 \;\; x_3 \;\; x_4 \;\; x_5 \;\;\; x_6 \;\;\; x_7 \;\; x_8 \\
\begin{array}{l}
\frac{1}{4}R_1 \\
R_2 - \frac{1}{8}R_1 \\
R_3 + \frac{3}{32}R_1 \\
R_4 - \frac{15}{16}R_1 \\
R_5 - \frac{1}{8}R_1
\end{array}
\begin{bmatrix}
1 & & 0 & 0 & & & & 0 & \frac{1}{4} \\
0 & & 1 & 0 & & & & 0 & \frac{11}{8} \\
0 & & 0 & 1 & & & & 0 & \frac{47}{32} \\
0 & & 0 & 0 & & & & 1 & \frac{37}{16} \\
0 & -\frac{3}{8} & 0 & 0 & -\frac{1}{8} & -\frac{21}{16} & -\frac{7}{8} & 0 & -\frac{141}{8}
\end{bmatrix}
\end{array}
$$

We do not actually need the (4,9) entry of this matrix. Nevertheless, it is always a good idea to compute the last column as a check that you have selected the right row to use for clearing. If you have chosen the wrong row, a negative number will appear above the last entry in the last column.

In this last matrix, we have illustrated a way to save computational labor. We calculated the bottom row first. Since the result indicated that this was the final matrix, we calculated only the cleared columns and the last column. The answer can be read from this incomplete final matrix: $y = \frac{141}{8}$, $x_1 = \frac{1}{4}$, $x_2 = 0$, $x_3 = \frac{11}{8}$, $x_4 = \frac{47}{32}$, and

The dual variable check, p. 363, could also be applied here.

slack variable values, $x_5 = x_6 = x_7 = 0$, $x_8 = \frac{37}{16}$. We substitute these values into **1** and constraints **2** through **5** above, and they check. For example, in constraint **5**: $4(\frac{1}{4}) + 4(0) + 2(\frac{11}{8}) + 2(\frac{47}{32}) = \frac{107}{16}$; $\frac{107}{16} +$ the slack $= \frac{107}{16} + \frac{37}{16} = 9$. The total number of ascenders is $(\frac{107}{16})(10) = 66\frac{7}{8}$; since a partially completed device will not be shipped, the company might receive only 66 ascenders. Since Binn, for example, works on a 32-hour week, it will work $\frac{47}{32}$ week $= 1$ week, 15 hours to fill the order. Recalling the other units in which we counted, we may express the final answer as follows: Order 8 hours production from Visp; none from Brig; 1 week, 12 hours from Ayer; and 1 week, 15 hours from Binn. The company will receive 800 pitons, 600 carabiners, 1,000 nuts, and 66 ascenders, which can be sold for a profit of a little less than $1,762.50 (a little less because of the uncompleted ascender).

**Problem 2** The managers at AC wish to blend their own brand of instant breakfast cereal for backpackers by mixing various quantities of the prepared mixes already on hand. They have consulted a nutritionist, who has recommended that a 6-person portion of their cereal should contain at least 3 oz. of raisins, 2 oz. of currants, and 2 oz. of nuts. Each 10-oz. package of each of the 5 kinds of prepared mixes they have on hand contains the portions of these ingredients listed in Table 6.

**Table 6**

| Type | Mix (oz. per package) | | | Cost (cents per package) |
|------|---------|------|----------|--------------------------|
|      | Raisins | Nuts | Currants |                          |
| A    | 1       | 2    | $\frac{1}{2}$ | 30 |
| B    | 2       | 1    | 2        | 90 |
| C    | 3       | 0    | 2        | 120 |
| D    | 1       | 1    | 3        | 70 |
| E    | 2       | 3    | 2        | 90 |

The last column of this table gives the cost to the company of each type of mix. How should they prepare the most economical cereal mix, how much of each food will be in each 6-person portion, how much will the portion weigh, and how much will the ingredients cost the company?

**Solution** Let $x_1, x_2, x_3, x_4, x_5$ be the number of 10-oz. packages of mix of type A, B, C, D, E, respectively, used to make one 6-person portion. Measure the cost $y$ in units of 10 cents. We are to minimize

$$y = 3x_1 + 9x_2 + 12x_3 + 7x_4 + 9x_5 \qquad \textbf{6}$$

subject to

$$x_1 \geq 0, \; x_2 \geq 0, \; x_3 \geq 0, \; x_4 \geq 0, \; x_5 \geq 0$$

$$x_1 + 2x_2 + 3x_3 + x_4 + 2x_5 \geq 3 \qquad \textbf{7}$$
$$2x_1 + x_2 + x_4 + 3x_5 \geq 2 \qquad \textbf{8}$$
$$\tfrac{1}{2}x_1 + 2x_2 + 2x_3 + 3x_4 + 2x_5 \geq 2 \qquad \textbf{9}$$

The simplex method yields the following sequence of matrices.

$$
\begin{bmatrix}
-1 & -2 & -3 & -1 & -2 & 1 & 0 & 0 & -3 \\
-2 & -1 & 0 & -1 & -3 & 0 & 1 & 0 & -2 \\
-\tfrac{1}{2}* & -2 & -2 & -3 & -2 & 0 & 0 & 1 & -2 \\
-3 & -9 & -12 & -7 & -9 & 0 & 0 & 0 & 0
\end{bmatrix}
$$

$$
\begin{array}{l}
R_1-2R_3 \\
R_2-4R_3 \\
-2R_3 \\
R_4-6R_3
\end{array}
\begin{bmatrix}
0 & 2 & 1 & 5* & 2 & 1 & 0 & -2 & 1 \\
0 & 7 & 8 & 11 & 5 & 0 & 1 & -4 & 6 \\
1 & 4 & 4 & 6 & 4 & 0 & 0 & -2 & 4 \\
0 & 3 & 0 & 11 & 3 & 0 & 0 & -6 & 12
\end{bmatrix}
$$

$$
\begin{array}{l}
\tfrac{1}{5}R_1 \\
R_2-\tfrac{11}{5}R_1 \\
R_3-\tfrac{6}{5}R_1 \\
R_4-\tfrac{11}{5}R_1
\end{array}
\begin{bmatrix}
0 & & 1 & & 0 & & & & \tfrac{1}{5} \\
0 & & 0 & & 1 & & & & \tfrac{19}{5} \\
1 & & 0 & & 0 & & & & \tfrac{14}{5} \\
0 & -\tfrac{7}{5} & -\tfrac{11}{5} & 0 & -\tfrac{7}{5} & -\tfrac{11}{5} & 0 & -\tfrac{8}{5} & \tfrac{49}{5}
\end{bmatrix}
$$

The answer: $x_1=\tfrac{14}{5}$, $x_4=\tfrac{1}{5}$, $x_2=x_3=x_4=0$, $y=\tfrac{49}{5}$. The answer checks when substituted into **6** and constraints **7**, **8**, and **9** above. The AC cereal contains, in one 6-person portion, 3 oz. of raisins, $\tfrac{29}{5}=5.8$ oz. of nuts, and 2 oz. of currants, which explains why they called it "the nuttiest breakfast on the trail." Such a portion is prepared from $(\tfrac{14}{5})(10)=28$ oz. of type A mix and $(\tfrac{1}{5})(10)=2$ oz. of type D; it weighs 30 oz. and costs the company $(\tfrac{49}{5})(10)\textcent=\$.98$.

**Problem 3**  After paying the biggest dividend ever, AC had $1,000,000 left to invest. Its investment analyst is extremely conservative. He suggests investing at least one-fourth in tax free municipal bonds at 5% interest. Over the past several years, AC has been trying to obtain controlling interest in Adirondack Knapsacks. Therefore, the analyst suggests investing at least 30% of the sum in AK's corporate bonds, preferred stock, and common stock. These pay 6%, 6%, and 5%, respectively. Nevertheless, he views AK stock as a risky investment, especially since AC is doing so well. He feels that AC should invest no more than half a million in stocks. On the other hand, the president of AC wants to own AK and insists that more be invested in stocks than in bonds. The analyst reluctantly agrees but tries to compensate by insisting they invest at least $100,000 more in a 4% savings account than in common stocks. How should AC invest the $1,000,000 so as to maximize its return and follow all the advice?

Solution  Let

$$x_1 = \text{number of dollars invested in municipal bonds}$$
$$x_2 = \text{number of dollars invested in corporate bonds}$$
$$x_3 = \text{number of dollars invested in preferred stock}$$
$$x_4 = \text{number of dollars invested in common stock}$$
$$x_5 = \text{number of dollars invested in savings accounts}$$

Constraint 1  At least $\frac{1}{4}$ in municipal bonds:

$$x_1 \geq 250,000$$

Constraint 2  At least 30% in corporate bonds, preferred stock, and common stock:

$$x_2 + x_3 + x_4 \geq 300,000$$

Constraint 3  No more than $\frac{1}{2}$ in stocks:

$$x_3 + x_4 \leq 500,000$$

Constraint 4  More invested in stocks than in bonds:

$$x_1 + x_2 \leq x_3 + x_4$$

Constraint 5  At least \$100,000 more in a savings account than in common stock:

$$x_4 + 100,000 \leq x_5$$

Constraint 6  Since they want to invest the entire \$1,000,000 we must also assume that

Strictly speaking constraint 4 should be

$$x_1 + x_2 < x_3 + x_4$$

If we really want to account for this, we could notice that, since you cannot buy less than 1¢ of stock, if $x_3 + x_4$ is bigger than $x_1 + x_2$, then it must be at least one cent bigger. Thus, we should assume

$$x_1 + x_2 \leq x_3 + x_4 + .01.$$

For this particular problem, it does not matter.

$$x_1 + x_2 + x_3 + x_4 + x_5 = 1,000,000$$

The objective variable is

$$y = .05x_1 + .06x_2 + .06x_3 + .05x_4 + .04x_5$$

To get numbers of manageable size for hand calculation we change to units of \$10,000 in the constraints, and to units of percentage in the objective variable. Then we are to maximize

$$y = 5x_1 + 6x_2 + 6x_3 + 5x_4 + 4x_5 \qquad \textbf{10}$$

subject to

$$x_1 \geq 0, \quad x_2 \geq 0, \quad x_3 \geq 0, \quad x_4 \geq 0, \quad x_5 \geq 0,$$

and

$$
\begin{array}{lll}
-x_1 & \leq -25 & \textbf{11} \\
-x_2 - x_3 - x_4 & \leq -30 & \textbf{12} \\
x_3 + x_4 & \leq 50 & \textbf{13} \\
x_1 + x_2 - x_3 - x_4 & \leq 0 & \textbf{14} \\
x_4 - x_5 \leq -10 & & \textbf{15} \\
x_1 + x_2 + x_3 + x_4 + x_5 = 100 & & \textbf{16}
\end{array}
$$

First we clear a column to get the $5 \times 5$ identity matrix, in scrambled order.

Phase I and the simplex method yield:

$$
\begin{bmatrix}
-1 & 0 & 0 & 0 & 0 & 1 & 0 & 0 & 0 & 0 & -25 \\
0 & -1 & -1 & -1 & 0 & 0 & 1 & 0 & 0 & 0 & -30 \\
0 & 0 & 1 & 1 & 0 & 0 & 0 & 1 & 0 & 0 & 50 \\
1 & 1 & -1 & -1 & 0 & 0 & 0 & 0 & 1 & 0 & 0 \\
0 & 0 & 0 & 1 & -1 & 0 & 0 & 0 & 0 & 1 & -10 \\
1 & 1 & 1 & 1 & 1^* & 0 & 0 & 0 & 0 & 0 & 100 \\
5 & 6 & 6 & 5 & 4 & 0 & 0 & 0 & 0 & 0 & 0
\end{bmatrix}
$$

$$
\begin{bmatrix}
-1 & 0 & 0 & 0 & 0 & 1 & 0 & 0 & 0 & 0 & -25 \\
0 & -1 & -1^* & -1 & 0 & 0 & 1 & 0 & 0 & 0 & -30 \\
0 & 0 & 1 & 1 & 0 & 0 & 0 & 1 & 0 & 0 & 50 \\
1 & 1 & -1 & -1 & 0 & 0 & 0 & 0 & 1 & 0 & 0 \\
1 & 1 & 1 & 2 & 0 & 0 & 0 & 0 & 0 & 1 & 90 \\
1 & 1 & 1 & 1 & 1 & 0 & 0 & 0 & 0 & 0 & 100 \\
1 & 2 & 2 & 1 & 0 & 0 & 0 & 0 & 0 & 0 & -400
\end{bmatrix}
$$

$$
\begin{bmatrix}
-1^* & 0 & 0 & 0 & 0 & 1 & 0 & 0 & 0 & 0 & -25 \\
0 & 1 & 1 & 1 & 0 & 0 & -1 & 0 & 0 & 0 & 30 \\
0 & -1 & 0 & 0 & 0 & 0 & 1 & 1 & 0 & 0 & 20 \\
1 & 2 & 0 & 0 & 0 & 0 & -1 & 0 & 1 & 0 & 30 \\
1 & 0 & 0 & 1 & 0 & 0 & 1 & 0 & 0 & 1 & 60 \\
1 & 0 & 0 & 0 & 1 & 0 & 1 & 0 & 0 & 0 & 70 \\
1 & 0 & 0 & -1 & 0 & 0 & 2 & 0 & 0 & 0 & -460
\end{bmatrix}
$$

$$
\begin{bmatrix}
1 & 0 & 0 & 0 & 0 & -1 & 0 & 0 & 0 & 0 & 25 \\
0 & 1 & 1 & 1 & 0 & 0 & -1 & 0 & 0 & 0 & 30 \\
0 & -1 & 0 & 0 & 0 & 0 & 1^* & 1 & 0 & 0 & 20 \\
0 & 2 & 0 & 0 & 0 & 1 & -1 & 0 & 1 & 0 & 5 \\
0 & 0 & 0 & 1 & 0 & 1 & 1 & 0 & 0 & 1 & 35 \\
0 & 0 & 0 & 0 & 1 & 1 & 1 & 0 & 0 & 0 & 45 \\
0 & 0 & 0 & -1 & 0 & 1 & 2 & 0 & 0 & 0 & -485
\end{bmatrix}
$$

$$
\begin{bmatrix}
1 & 0 & 0 & 0 & 0 & -1 & 0 & 0 & 0 & 0 & 25 \\
0 & 0 & 1 & 1 & 0 & 0 & 0 & 1 & 0 & 0 & 50 \\
0 & -1 & 0 & 0 & 0 & 0 & 1 & 1 & 0 & 0 & 20 \\
0 & 1 & 0 & 0 & 0 & 1 & 0 & 1 & 1 & 0 & 25 \\
0 & 1^* & 0 & 1 & 0 & 1 & 0 & -1 & 0 & 1 & 15 \\
0 & 1 & 0 & 0 & 1 & 1 & 0 & -1 & 0 & 0 & 25 \\
0 & 2 & 0 & -1 & 0 & 1 & 0 & -2 & 0 & 0 & -525
\end{bmatrix}
$$

$$
\begin{bmatrix}
1 & 0 & 0 & 0 & 0 & -1 & 0 & 0 & 0 & 0 & 25 \\
0 & 0 & 1 & 1 & 0 & 0 & 0 & 1 & 0 & 0 & 50 \\
0 & 0 & 0 & 1 & 0 & 1 & 1 & 0 & 0 & 1 & 35 \\
0 & 0 & 0 & -1 & 0 & 0 & 0 & 2 & 1 & -1 & 10 \\
0 & 1 & 0 & 1 & 0 & 1 & 0 & -1 & 0 & 1 & 15 \\
0 & 0 & 0 & -1 & 1 & 0 & 0 & 0 & 0 & -1 & 10 \\
0 & 0 & 0 & -3 & 0 & -1 & 0 & 0 & 0 & -2 & -555
\end{bmatrix}
$$

Returning to units of 1, the answer is: $x_1 = 250,000$, $x_2 = 150,000$, $x_3 = 500,000$, $x_4 = 0$, and $x_5 = 100,000$. The return on the investment will be 5.55% or $55,500.

**Exercises 5.5**

1. AC wishes to make a high-calorie candy by hardening a mixture of two syrups into a pellet. The syrups contain small quantities of two undesirable chemicals; call them A and B. Three grams (g) of syrup I contain 10 milligrams (mg) of A and 10 of B; 3 g of syrup II contain 10 mg of A and 40 of B; 3 g of I and II will deliver 20 and 30 calories, respectively. How should the syrups be mixed to produce a pellet with the greatest caloric content but with no more than 20 mg of A and 40 of B?

2. My doctor says I should take at least 20 mg of phlorotaste and 30 mg of lypollogin a day for the next 2 months. While the prescription she writes is for each of these in pure form, my druggist tells me that getting them already mixed together is much cheaper. In fact, 8 oz. of hyposin contains 1 mg of phlorotaste and 5 mg of lypollogin and costs $7. Eight oz. of eneron contains 7 mg of phlorotaste and 2 mg of lypollogin and costs $10. How many ounces of each of these should I buy to fill my needs at minimum cost?

I have been assured, by the way, that there is no danger of overdosage with these substances.

3. Our local toy company makes trucks, beach balls, music boxes, and tricycles from limited amounts of wood, vinyl plastic, and steel, according to Table 7. How many of each toy should they make to maximize their profit?

**Table 7**

|  | Wood | Vinyl plastic | Steel | Profit |
|---|---|---|---|---|
| Trucks | 1 | 0 | 1 | 2 |
| Beach balls | 0 | 3 | 0 | 1 |
| Music boxes | 4 | 2 | 2 | 5 |
| Tricycles | 0 | 0 | 2 | 2 |
| Supply | 22 | 15 | 16 | |

c4. "I don't know how much these two temporary secretarial services charge," said the AC personnel director, "but they charge the same rate per hour. We need to get 60 letters typed, 700 circulars copied, and 60 stencils cut by tomorrow. I am told that in 5 hours the Jiffy Service can type 30 letters, copy 100 circulars, and cut 20 stencils; the Rapid Service can type 20 letters, copy 700 circulars, and cut 30 stencils. What should I do?"

5. A manufacturer has orders for 3 items. These can be produced by 3 methods. In 1 hour, method 1 produces 2 As, 1 B, and 2 Cs. In 1 hour, method 2 produces 3 As, 8 Bs, and 5 Cs. In 1 hour, method 3 produces 2 As, 2 Bs, and 3 Cs. It costs $10 per hour to use method 1. It costs $22 per hour to use method 2. It costs $12 per hour to use

method 3. There are orders for 12 As, 16 Bs, and 16 Cs. While the orders must be met, overproduction is of no concern. How many hours should he use each method to fill the orders at minimum cost? What will this cost be?

6. "In testing boots," explained the AC research director, "it isn't the number of miles walked that matters but the type of footing encountered. We have spoken with our chief tester, who has described 3 different routes she knows in this area. Route A is 6 miles long. Three miles of this have a rocky footing, 4 miles are steep, and 5 miles are wet. Route B is 4 miles long with 1 mile rocky, 2 steep, and 1 wet. Route C is 6 miles long with 4 miles rocky, 3 steep, and 5 wet. We want to test these boots over at least 12 miles of rocky terrain, 20 of steep, and 8 of wet, while keeping the total mileage walked as low as we can. How can we do it?"

*7. Petaluma Hamburger Emporium is designing a fruit compote for its dessert offering, to be made with strawberries, apples, and peaches. One ladleful of uncooked strawberries costs 40¢, contains 2 milligrams (mg) salt, and, when cooked, has a volume of 3 cc and a weight of 1 oz. One ladleful of uncooked apples costs 30¢, contains no salt, and cooks down to 1 cc and 2 oz. The peaches are precooked; one ladleful costs 50¢, weighs 3 oz., has 3 mg of salt, and has a volume of 2 cc. A serving of compote should contain at least 4 mg salt and weigh at least 3 oz. For the sake of taste and appearance there is one more restriction: when one ladleful of strawberries is cooked and mixed with one ladleful of peaches, the resulting mix should have a volume of at least 5 cc more than the volume of one ladleful of cooked apples. In what proportions should the fruits be mixed to make the cheapest compote, and how much, per serving, will the compote cost?

8. I am in charge of three chemical factories which each produce four chemicals: narcolase, enervate, aureate, and coprolite. The Bismuth, North Dakota, factory produces 300 liters of narcolase, 100 of enervate, 200 of aureate, and 700 of coprolite per hour at a cost of $2,400 per hour. The liter-per-hour figures for the Wilkes-Barium, Pennsylvania, factory are 300 of narcolase, 600 of enervate, 100 of aureate, and 200 of coprolite, at an operating cost of $700 per hour. The corresponding figures for the Indiumapolis, Indiana, plant are 500, 800, 200, and 400 at a cost of $1,800. I have orders for 51,000 liters of narcolase and 20,000 liters of aureate, although I could produce more of either chemical. While I have no orders for enervate this week, it is an unavoidable byproduct. I have storage space for 86,000 liters, but I could produce less. I have orders for 46,000 liters of coprolite. Unfortunately, this chemical deteriorates rapidly, so I must produce exactly 46,000 liters. My problem is this: What is the cheapest way for me to meet my orders, yet not exceed the storage restrictions on enervate?

9. A manufacturer produces two types of prefabricated houses. The Basic is a one-bedroom house. The Deluxe has three bedrooms. He

also produces a garage that can be built onto either house. However, the garage is not sold separately. Thus, he must produce at least as many houses as garages. His production schedule is determined by orders and available labor. This month the figures are:

| Type | Order |
|------|-------|
| Basic | 10 |
| Deluxe | 5 |
| Garage | 12 |

It takes 100 person-hours to make a Basic, 160 person-hours to make a Deluxe, and 20 person-hours to make a garage. Unfortunately, he can obtain only 900-person hours of labor. He hopes to counteract the chronic labor shortage by buying some new, more sophisticated equipment. But he fears he will not be able to get the necessary bank loan if he does not show at least $10,000 profit this month. He makes $1,000 profit on the Basic, $2,000 profit on the Deluxe, and $500 profit on a garage. His main concern is losing business to the competition. Although nobody cares about getting his or her garage on time, he does want to produce as many houses as possible. What should he do? (Note: Since he cannot possibly fill his orders, the information in the above tabulation cannot be included in the mathematical formulation of this problem without eliminating all feasible solutions.)

He showed a $9,000 profit two months ago, but only a $7,000 profit last month.

10. A crooked politician peddles influence. Although some of his enemies believe that he is owned by the mob, this really is not true. He is just as happy selling his services to corporations or even to private citizens provided they have the cash. In the interest of fairness, he has a standard price for each favor: $5,000 if it is for a corporation, $500 for a private citizen, and $1,000 for organized crime. Now, organized crime has muscle, so they do not care who is elected. Private citizens and corporations want their man in office, so he wants to be sure to please them, especially around election time. He feels that he can do 30 favors a year and not have his actions appear out of line with those of his colleagues. The mob insists on at least 8 favors and he feels his health might suffer if he did not oblige. He does want to do more favors for corporations and private citizens than he does for the mob. To ease his conscience he likes to do at least 2 more favors for private citizens than for the mob and corporations combined. How should he behave so as to maximize graft?

11. The Taint It Pork? Company produces a meat substitute at factories in Secaucus, New Jersey, and Gary, Indiana. The only markets for their products so far are Willard's supermarkets in Winesburg, Ohio, and Sal Monela's Italian restaurant chain in the Ozarks. Winesburg orders 30 pounds a month and the Ozarks need 50 pounds a month. Each plant can produce 40 pounds a month. It costs different amounts to ship each one's product to each of its markets. These

costs are summarized in the following chart:

**Transportation Cost
per Pound**

| To/From | Winesburg | Ozarks |
|---------|-----------|--------|
| Secaucus | $2 | $5 |
| Gary | $3 | $4 |

How should they supply their demands to minimize their cost?

12. I have decided to quit buying dogfood for my 30-pound mutt, Sekhmet. Instead, I will feed her ordinary food. However, I do want her to have a proper diet. My main concerns are that she get at least 60 grams (g) of protein, at most 126 g of carbohydrates, at least 3,180 milligrams (mg) of calcium, and exactly 960 calories a day. I feel that, if I take care of these requirements, the others will be taken care of along the way. Anyway, I am willing to buy vitamin and mineral supplements, if I have to. I can get hamburger at 6¢ an ounce. To get more calcium, I will mix this with powdered milk at 15¢ a cup and eggs at 7¢ each. Here is the relevant chart of food values.

| | Protein | Carbohydrates | Calories | Calcium |
|---|---------|---------------|----------|---------|
| Hamburger (1 oz.) | 8 g | 0 g | 60 | 3 mg |
| Powdered milk (1 cup) | 20 | 35 | 240 | 870 |
| Egg | 6 | 0 | 78 | 27 |

Which selection of foods meets my needs at minimum cost?

13. My doctor feels that I should be on a low-sodium diet. He also insists that I get my cholesterol intake down to no more than 1,000 milligrams (mg) per week. I do avoid eggs, but I drink 4 cups of milk a week at 34 mg of cholesterol per cup, though no sodium. I am not a vegetarian and I would like to eat meat. I am concerned that I get at least 260 grams (g) of protein a week. The milk provides only 36 g per week. I also want to be certain I get at least 70 mg of iron per week. I decide to include beef, chicken, and pork in my diet.

**Nutritional Value
per Ounce**

| | Sodium | Cholesterol | Protein | Iron |
|---|--------|-------------|---------|------|
| Beef | 17 mg | 27 mg | 7 g | 3 mg |
| Chicken | 22 | 21 | 9 | $\frac{1}{2}$ |
| Pork | 18 | 24 | 8 | 1 |

In summary, I want my meat eating to involve

(i)    as little sodium as possible
(ii)   at least 70 mg of iron per week
(iii)  at least 224 g of protein per week
(iv)   no more than 864 mg of cholesterol per week.

How much of each of these 3 foods should I eat to guarantee this?

14. After I received the $30,000 check from my uncle's estate, I decided to get some advice from my friends about investing it. Marcia said she knew how I squandered money. She felt I should invest it all.

Fran thought that I should invest at least one-third in tax-free municipal bonds. When I told Mary that I was going to invest some in stocks, she said, "Well, make sure you put at least twice as much in preferred stock as in common stock." Ruth was even more upset. She said, "You'll lose everything in the market. Please put at least $1,000 more in a savings account than in stocks." All this sounded fine to me. My investment analyst said, "I can get municipal bonds at 5%, preferred stock at 7%, and common stock at 5%, and you can get a toaster if you open a 4% savings account at the bank around the corner." How should I arrange my investment portfolio to maximize my interest yield while following everyone's advice?

[c]15. A certain textbook writer needed a linear programming problem of the maximization type. He thought about natural resources. How many fish could be stocked in a lake with limited nutrients and space? "No, why not farm management?" he thought. "OK, a farmer produces beef cattle, pigs, and chickens for respective profits of ... . Hmmm, I don't know anything at all about farming. So what—I'll make up numbers; nobody's going to notice." Here is his exercise.

"15. A farmer produces beef cattle, pigs, and chickens for respective profits of $100, $50, and $27 per animal. She grows food for these animals on a 40-acre farm. A cow requires 3 acres of grass, food for a pig can be grown on 1 acre, and one chicken's feed can be grown on a half acre. What's left over she plants in sweet corn at a profit of $30 an acre. Each cow this farmer produces yields about 80 pounds of beef and each pig yields 30 pounds of pork. The farmer wants to have at least 450 pounds of meat, not including chicken, for her own personal consumption. Each acre she plants in animal food requires 50 hours of work per year, and each acre of sweet corn requires 75 hours of work per year. She has only 700 hours a year for field work. How many of each type animal should she produce and how much sweet corn should she plant?"

Solve this problem.

We told you the writer knew nothing of farming!

## Section 5.6
## The Dual Variable Check and Unrestricted Variables

The material on unrestricted variables may be read before the dual variable check.

The dual variable check will not tell you whether or not the problem has multiple solutions. An answer that checks may be only one of infinitely many that check.

The dual variable check is an interesting procedure for checking the answer to a linear programming problem. Given any LP problem, there is a closely related LP problem called its **dual**. Once we have solved both problems, there is a very easy technique that will check *both* answers. While the check does use these two answers, it does not matter how they were obtained. Whether you use the simplex method, a geometric method, wild guessing, or divine inspiration, an answer that checks is correct.

In describing how to set up the dual problem, it will be convenient to use the matrix operation of transposing. Recall from Section 3.4 that, given a matrix, one obtains its **transpose** by switching its rows and columns, as in the following example.

Problem 1

Find the transpose of the matrix $\begin{bmatrix} 2 & 1 \\ 3 & 4 \\ 5 & 7 \end{bmatrix}$

Solution  The matrix has three rows: 2  1; 3  4; and 5  7. We form a new matrix which has these rows as columns:

$$\begin{bmatrix} 2 & 3 & 5 \\ 1 & 4 & 7 \end{bmatrix}$$

Thus, the first row becomes the first column, and so forth. This new matrix is the transpose of the original matrix. The original matrix has two columns: $\begin{matrix} 2 \\ 3 \\ 5 \end{matrix}$ and $\begin{matrix} 1 \\ 4 \\ 7 \end{matrix}$. We could also have formed the transposed matrix by writing these columns as rows:

$$\begin{bmatrix} 2 & 3 & 5 \\ 1 & 4 & 7 \end{bmatrix}$$

Problem 2  Find the transposes of the following matrices:

$$\begin{bmatrix} 1 & 1 & 2 \\ 2 & 1 & 3 \\ 4 & 2 & 8 \end{bmatrix}, \begin{bmatrix} 3 & 2 & 7 \end{bmatrix}, \text{and} \begin{bmatrix} 5 \\ 4 \\ 10 \end{bmatrix}$$

Answer  The respective transposes are $\begin{bmatrix} 1 & 2 & 4 \\ 1 & 1 & 2 \\ 2 & 3 & 8 \end{bmatrix}, \begin{bmatrix} 3 \\ 2 \\ 7 \end{bmatrix}, \text{and} \begin{bmatrix} 5 & 4 & 10 \end{bmatrix}$

We are ready to set up the dual problem for LP problems that do not have equality constraints or unrestricted variables. A **standard LP maximization problem** is an LP maximization problem in which all constraints involve $\leq$ and all variables are required to be $\geq 0$. A **standard LP minimization problem** is an LP problem in which all constraints involve $\geq$ and all variables are required to be $\geq 0$.

*Note that we do not require the constraint bounds to be nonnegative.*

---

To FORM THE DUAL OF A GIVEN STANDARD LP PROBLEM:

(1) If the given problem is a standard LP maximization problem, the dual will be a standard LP minimization problem.

If the given problem is a standard LP minimization problem, the dual will be a standard LP maximization problem.

(2) The dual constraint matrix is the transpose of the given constraint matrix.

(3) The dual objective matrix is the transpose of the given bound matrix.

(4) The dual bound matrix is the transpose of the given objective matrix.

---

Problem 3    Write the dual problem for each of the given problems.

(a) Maximize $y = 3x_1 + 2x_2 + 7x_3$ subject to

$$x_1 \geq 0, x_2 \geq 0, x_3 \geq 0$$
$$x_1 + x_2 + 2x_3 \leq 5$$
$$2x_1 + x_2 + 3x_3 \leq 4$$
$$4x_1 + 2x_2 + 8x_3 \leq 10$$

(b) Minimize $y = x_1 - x_2$ subject to

$$x_1 \geq 0, x_2 \geq 0$$
$$2x_1 + x_2 \geq 1$$
$$3x_1 + 4x_2 \leq 7$$
$$5x_1 + 7x_2 \geq -3$$

Solution    (a) The given problem is a standard maximization problem with constraint matrix

$$\begin{bmatrix} 1 & 1 & 2 \\ 2 & 1 & 3 \\ 4 & 2 & 8 \end{bmatrix}$$

objective matrix

$$\begin{bmatrix} 3 & 2 & 7 \end{bmatrix}$$

and bound matrix

$$\begin{bmatrix} 5 \\ 4 \\ 10 \end{bmatrix}$$

We found the transposes of these matrices in Problem 2. The dual problem is the standard minimization problem: Minimize $y = 5x_1 + 4x_2 + 10x_3$ subject to

$$x_1 \geq 0, x_2 \geq 0, x_3 \geq 0$$
$$x_1 + 2x_2 + 4x_3 \geq 3$$
$$x_1 + x_2 + 2x_3 \geq 2$$
$$2x_1 + 3x_2 + 8x_3 \geq 7.$$

(b) This problem is not a standard LP minimization problem. However, it requires only one slight modification in constraint **2**: Minimize $y = x_1 - x_2$ subject to

$$x_1 \geq 0, x_2 \geq 0$$
$$2x_1 + x_2 \geq 1$$
$$-3x_1 - 4x_2 \geq -7$$
$$5x_1 + 7x_2 \geq -3$$

The constraint, objective, and bound matrices, are, respectively

$$\begin{bmatrix} 2 & 1 \\ -3 & -4 \\ 5 & 7 \end{bmatrix}, [1 \quad -1], \begin{bmatrix} 1 \\ -7 \\ -3 \end{bmatrix}.$$

The respective transposes are $\begin{bmatrix} 2 & -3 & 5 \\ 1 & -4 & 7 \end{bmatrix}, \begin{bmatrix} 1 \\ -1 \end{bmatrix}, [1 \; -7 \; -3]$.

The dual problem is

Maximize $x_1 - 7x_2 - 3x_3$ subject to

$$x_1 \geq 0, x_2 \geq 0, x_3 \geq 0$$
$$2x_1 - 3x_2 + 5x_3 \leq 1$$
$$x_1 - 4x_2 + 7x_3 \leq -1$$

Here are two observations about the dual problem.

(1) The dual has the same number of inequalities as the given problem has variables and the same number of variables as the given problem has inequalities.
(2) The dual of the dual problem is the given problem.

We are now ready to state the dual variable check.

---

### THE DUAL VARIABLE CHECK

If feasible solutions to a given problem and its dual give the same value to their respective objective variables, then each feasible solution is optimal.

---

It can be shown that the dual variable check applies to the more general LP problems presented below as well as to standard LP problems. We will first illustrate this procedure for the two standard problems given in Problem 3.

Problem 4  (a) Verify that $x_1 = 0$, $x_2 = 1$, $x_3 = 1$, and $y = 9$ is a solution to the maximization problem in Problem 3(a).
(b) Verify that $x_1 = 0$, $x_2 = \frac{7}{4}$ and $y = -\frac{7}{4}$ is a solution to the minimization problem in Problem 3(b).

Solution  (a) We must first solve the dual minimization problem. We believe the answer to be $x_1 = 0, x_2 = 1, x_3 = \frac{1}{2}, y = 9$. There are three steps in the dual variable check.

(1) Is the maximization answer feasible? In the first place each

variable is $\geq 0$. Next we substitute

$$1(0)+1(1)+2(1)=3 \ \leq \ 5 \ \checkmark$$
$$2(0)+1(1)+3(1)=4 \ \leq \ 4 \ \checkmark$$
$$4(0)+2(1)+8(1)=10 \leq 10 \ \checkmark$$

(2) Is the minimization answer feasible? In the first place, each variable is $\geq 0$. Next we substitute:

$$1(0)+2(1)+4\left(\tfrac{1}{2}\right)=4 \geq 3 \ \checkmark$$
$$1(0)+1(1)+2\left(\tfrac{1}{2}\right)=2 \geq 2 \ \checkmark$$
$$2(0)+3(1)+8\left(\tfrac{1}{2}\right)=7 \geq 7 \ \checkmark$$

(3) Does each answer give the same numerical value to its respective objective variable?

Maximization: $3(0)+2(1)+7(1)=9$
Minimization: $5(0)+4(1)+10\left(\tfrac{1}{2}\right)=9$

In each case we get 9, so our answers check.

(b) If you solve the dual maximization problem you should get the answer $x_1=0$, $x_2=\tfrac{1}{4}$, $x_3=0$, and $y=-\tfrac{7}{4}$. We apply the same three checks as in part (a):

(1) Min. feasible? First, each variable has been assigned a value $\geq 0$. Then:

$$2(0)+1\left(\tfrac{7}{4}\right)= \ \tfrac{7}{4} \geq 1 \ \checkmark$$
$$3(0)+4\left(\tfrac{7}{4}\right)= \ 7 \leq 7 \ \checkmark$$
$$5(0)+7\left(\tfrac{7}{4}\right)= \tfrac{49}{4} \geq -3 \ \checkmark$$

(2) Max. feasible? First, each variable has been assigned a value $\geq 0$. Then:

$$2(0)-3\left(\tfrac{1}{4}\right)+5(0)= -\tfrac{3}{4} \leq 1 \ \checkmark$$
$$1(0)-4\left(\tfrac{1}{4}\right)+7(0)= -1 \leq -1 \ \checkmark$$

(3) Same values?

$$\text{Min: } 1(0)-1\left(\tfrac{7}{4}\right)=-\tfrac{7}{4}$$
$$\text{Max: } 1(0)-7\left(\tfrac{1}{4}\right)-3(0)=-\tfrac{7}{4} \ \checkmark$$

Therefore, each answer is correct.

In case a linear programming problem has no solution, the following check applies.

> If either a given problem or its dual has no feasible solution, then neither problem has an optimal solution.

From a practical standpoint, this check is not quite as satisfactory. It is possible to incorrectly "solve" both a problem and its dual. If these errors lead you to believe that neither problem has an optimal solution, when in fact they do have optimal solutions, then this check verifies your errors. Try not to commit errors in solving *both* problems.

**Problem 5**

Minimize $y = x_1 - 2x_2$ subject to

$$x_1 \geq 0, x_2 \geq 0$$
$$x_1 + x_2 \leq 1$$
$$2x_1 + 3x_2 \geq 6$$

**Solution**

In obtaining the first matrix we have multiplied the second constraint and the expression for the objective variable by $-1$. We will often do several steps at once to save space, and we advise the student to do likewise.

$$\begin{bmatrix} 1 & 1 & 1 & 0 & 1 \\ -2 & -3^* & 0 & 1 & -6 \\ -1 & 2 & 0 & 0 & 0 \end{bmatrix} \quad \begin{bmatrix} \frac{1}{3} & 0 & 1 & \frac{1}{3} & -1 \\ 2 & 3 & 0 & -1 & 6 \\ -\frac{7}{3} & 0 & 0 & \frac{2}{3} & -4 \end{bmatrix}$$

The first row of the matrix on the right tells us that there is no feasible solution for this problem; that is, the first row has a negative last entry but no other negative entries. The dual maximization problem is:

Maximize

$$y = -x_1 + 6x_2$$

subject to

$$-x_1 + 2x_2 \leq 1$$
$$-x_1 + 3x_2 \leq -2$$

$$\begin{bmatrix} -1 & 2 & 1 & 0 & 1 \\ -1^* & 3 & 0 & 1 & -2 \\ -1 & 6 & 0 & 0 & 0 \end{bmatrix} \quad \begin{bmatrix} 0 & -1 & 1 & -1 & 3 \\ 1 & -3 & 0 & -1 & 2 \\ 0 & 3 & 0 & -1 & 2 \end{bmatrix}$$

The second column of the matrix on the right tells us that there is no optimal solution for this problem; that is, the second column ends with a positive entry yet contains no other positive entries.

**A Shortcut For Standard LP Problems**

It happens to be easy to read the answer to the dual of a standard maximization problem directly from the final matrix of the solution of the maximization problem. Thus, we can solve a standard maximization problem and its dual simultaneously and apply the dual variable check immediately without having to work another problem. Also, duality can be used as an alternative method for solving standard minimization LP problems: simply set up and solve the dual maximization problem and then read the answer to the dual minimization problem from the final matrix, as explained below.

We will use this shortcut in our treatment of game theory in Section 6.3.

---

**TO READ THE DUAL MINIMIZATION ANSWER DIRECTLY FROM THE FINAL MAXIMIZATION MATRIX:**

(1) Write the letters $x_1, x_2$, etc., directly below the columns where the identity matrix *used* to be.

(2) The value of each particular x is the entry directly above it with the sign changed.

(3) The value of the optimized objective variable is the same as for the maximization problem, namely, the entry in the southeast corner with the sign changed.

---

When a computer is used to do the simplex method, it is usually instructed to work a problem *or* its dual, whichever has fewer rows.

For example, the final matrix for the standard maximization LP Problem 3(a) is

$$\begin{bmatrix} -1 & 0 & 0 & 1 & -2 & \frac{1}{2} & 2 \\ 2 & 1 & 0 & 0 & 4 & -\frac{3}{2} & 1 \\ 0 & 0 & 1 & 0 & -1 & \frac{1}{2} & 1 \\ -1 & 0 & 0 & 0 & -1 & -\frac{1}{2} & -9 \end{bmatrix}$$
$$\phantom{xxxxxxxxxxxxxx} x_1 \quad x_2 \quad x_3$$

from which we read the answer to the dual minimization problem: $x_1 = 0, x_2 = 1, x_3 = \frac{1}{2}, y = 9$.

**General LP Problems**

**Unrestricted variables** are variables that do not satisfy Condition 1, p. 316; that is, an unrestricted variable is a variable that is not assumed to be greater than or equal to zero.

By a constraint inequality we do *not* mean a preliminary restriction on a variable, such as $x_1 \quad 0$.

If a linear programming problem involves equality constraints or unrestricted variables, then its dual is slightly different. A **general LP maximization problem** is a maximization LP problem in which all the constraint inequalities are $\le$. A **general LP minimization problem** is an LP minimization problem in which all the constraint inequalities are $\ge$. Thus, "general" problems are like "standard" problems except (1) they may have some equality constraints, and (2) some of the variables may not be required to be $\ge 0$.

---

To Form the Dual of a Given General LP Problem:

(1) Pretend that all the equalities are inequalities (of the right type: $\leq$ for max.; $\geq$ for min.) and that all the variables are assumed to be $\geq 0$.

(2) Write the dual of this "standardized" LP problem.

(3) Number the constraints in each problem. (Label the first constraint (1), etc.)

(4) If a variable in the given problem is unrestricted, then in the dual problem change the constraint corresponding to its subscript into an equality.

(5) If a constraint in the given problem is an equality, then in the dual problem make the corresponding variable unrestricted.

---

**Problem 6**

Write the dual of each of the following problems:
(a) Maximize $y = x_1 + 2x_2$ subject to

(1)     $-2x_1 + x_2 \leq 3$
(2)     $x_1 + x_2 \leq -3$
(3)     $x_1 - 2x_2 \leq 3$

(b) Minimize $y = 2x_1 + 3x_2 + x_3$ subject to

$$x_2 \geq 0, x_3 \geq 0$$

(1)     $x_1 + x_2 - 3x_3 \geq -5$
(2)     $x_1 - 3x_2 + x_3 = 4$
(3)     $2x_1 - 12x_2 - 3x_3 \leq 6$
(4)     $-x_1 + 8x_2 + 4x_3 = 6$

**Solution**

(a) *If the variables were restricted,* the dual would be:
Minimize $y = 3x_1 - 3x_2 + 3x_3$ subject to

$$x_1 \geq 0, x_2 \geq 0, x_3 \geq 0$$

(1)     $-2x_1 + x_2 + x_3 \geq 1$
(2)     $x_1 + x_2 - 2x_3 \geq 2$

However, since $x_1$ is unrestricted in the given problem, constraint 1 becomes an equality, and since $x_2$ is unrestricted in the given problem, constraint 2 also becomes an equality.

Also, since each constraint in the given problem is an inequality, each variable in the dual is restricted. The dual is then:

Minimize $y = 3x_1 - 3x_2 + 3x_3$ subject to

$$x_1 \geq 0, x_2 \geq 0, x_3 \geq 0$$

$$-2x_1 + x_2 + x_3 = 1$$

$$x_1 + x_2 - 2x_3 = 2$$

(b) *If $x_1$ were restricted and constraints 2 and 4 were standard inequalities*, then the dual would be

Maximize $y = -5x_1 + 4x_2 - 6x_3 + 6x_4$ subject to

$$x_1 \geq 0, x_2 \geq 0, x_3 \geq 0, x_4 \geq 0$$

(1)      $x_1 + x_2 - 2x_3 - x_4 \leq 2$      (1)

(2)      $x_1 - 3x_2 + 12x_3 + 8x_4 \leq 3$

(3)      $-3x_1 + x_2 + 3x_3 + 4x_4 \leq 1$

We have multiplied constraint (3) above by $-1$.

However, in the given problem, variable $x_1$ was unrestricted. Thus, in the dual problem, inequality 1 will be an equality. Also, the given problem has two equalities: constraints 2 and 4. Thus, in the dual problem variables 2 and 4, that is $x_2$ and $x_4$, will be unrestricted. The dual is then:

Maximize $y = -5x_1 + 4x_2 - 6x_3 + 6x_4$ subject to

$$x_1 \geq 0, x_3 \geq 0$$

$$x_1 + x_2 - 2x_3 - x_4 = 2$$

$$x_1 - 3x_2 + 12x_3 + 8x_4 \leq 3$$

$$-3x_1 + x_2 + 3x_3 + 4x_4 \leq 1$$

**Unrestricted Variables**

Now in order to be able to apply the dual variable check to problems with equality constraints we must learn how to solve problems involving unrestricted variables. Fortunately, this is easy to do, although the rule may not make sense to you until you have examined the examples that follow it.

---

**RULE FOR UNRESTRICTED VARIABLES**
Replace each unrestricted variable x by a pair of restricted variables $x_p$ and $x_n$, where $x = x_p - x_n, x_p \geq 0, x_n \geq 0$.

---

Here $x_p$ denotes the "positive part" and $x_n$ denotes the "negative part." While $x_p$ and $x_n$ will both be restricted: $x_p \geq 0, x_n \geq 0$, we see that, if $x_n > x_p$, then x will be negative. For example, if $x_p = 0$ and

Since any number can be written as the difference of two nonnegative numbers, so can any variable.

$x_n = 3$, then $x_p - x_n = 0 - 3 = -3$. It can be shown that this substitution will enable us to obtain the answers to any general linear programming problem. If the original problem has no solution, we will discover that too.

Problem 7

This is Problem 6(a).

Maximize $y = x_1 + 2x_2$ subject to

$$-2x_1 + \phantom{2}x_2 \leq \phantom{-}3$$
$$x_1 + \phantom{2}x_2 \leq -3$$
$$x_1 - 2x_2 \leq \phantom{-}3$$

Solution

There are two unrestricted variables $x_1$ and $x_2$ so we substitute: $x_1 = x_{1p} - x_{1n}$ and $x_2 = x_{2p} - x_{2n}$. Our problem becomes:

Maximize $y = (x_{1p} - x_{1n}) + 2(x_{2p} - x_{2n})$ subject to

$$x_{1p} \geq 0, x_{1n} \geq 0, x_{2p} \geq 0, x_{2n} \geq 0$$
$$-2(x_{1p} - x_{1n}) + \phantom{2}(x_{2p} - x_{2n}) \leq 3$$
$$(x_{1p} - x_{1n}) + \phantom{2}(x_{2p} - x_{2n}) \leq -3$$
$$(x_{1p} - x_{1n}) - 2(x_{2p} - x_{2n}) \leq 3$$

If we remove the parentheses we obtain a standard problem in four variables.

Maximize $y = x_{1p} - x_{1n} + 2x_{2p} - 2x_{2n}$ subject to

$$x_{1p} \geq 0, x_{1n} \geq 0, x_{2p} \geq 0, x_{2n} \geq 0$$
$$-2x_{1p} + 2x_{1n} + \phantom{2}x_{2p} - \phantom{2}x_{2n} \leq 3$$
$$x_{1p} - \phantom{2}x_{1n} + \phantom{2}x_{2p} - \phantom{2}x_{2n} \leq -3$$
$$x_{1p} - \phantom{2}x_{1n} - 2x_{2p} + 2x_{2n} \leq 3.$$

The solution will involve Phase I.

Notice that in this matrix $C_2 = -C_1$ and $C_4 = -C_3$. There will always be this sort of "negative duplication" of columns in a problem involving unrestricted variables. It simplifies the matrix arithmetic somewhat.

$C_3$ is not cleared; it contains a *negative* 1.

$$\begin{bmatrix} -2 & 2 & 1 & -1 & 1 & 0 & 0 & 3 \\ 1 & -1 & 1 & -1^* & 0 & 1 & 0 & -3 \\ 1 & -1 & -2 & 2 & 0 & 0 & 1 & 3 \\ 1 & -1 & 2 & -2 & 0 & 0 & 0 & 0 \end{bmatrix}$$

$$\begin{bmatrix} -3 & 3 & 0 & 0 & 1 & -1 & 0 & 6 \\ -1 & 1 & -1 & 1 & 0 & -1 & 0 & 3 \\ 3 & -3^* & 0 & 0 & 0 & 2 & 1 & -3 \\ -1 & 1 & 0 & 0 & 0 & -2 & 0 & 6 \end{bmatrix}$$

$$\begin{bmatrix} 0 & 0 & 0 & 0 & 1 & 1 & 1^* & 3 \\ 0 & 0 & -1 & 1 & 0 & -\frac{1}{3} & \frac{1}{3} & 2 \\ -3 & 3 & 0 & 0 & 0 & -2 & -1 & 3 \\ 0 & 0 & 0 & 0 & 0 & -\frac{4}{3} & \frac{1}{3} & 5 \end{bmatrix}$$

Now on to Phase II, that is, the ordinary simplex method.

$$\begin{array}{cccc} x_{1p} & x_{1n} & x_{2p} & x_{2n} \end{array}$$

$$\begin{bmatrix} 0 & 0 & 0 & 0 & 1 & 1 & 1 & 3 \\ 0 & 0 & -1 & 1 & -\frac{1}{3} & -\frac{2}{3} & 0 & 1 \\ -3 & 3 & 0 & 0 & 1 & -1 & 0 & 6 \\ 0 & 0 & 0 & 0 & -\frac{1}{3} & -\frac{5}{3} & 0 & 4 \end{bmatrix}$$

The answer is $x_{1p}=0$, $x_{1n}=2$, $x_{2p}=0$, $x_{2n}=1$, and $y=-4$. Returning to our original problem we find that $x_1=x_{1p}-x_{1n}=0-2=-2$, $x_2=x_{2p}-x_{2n}=0-1=-1$. The answer is $x_1=-2$, $x_2=-1$, and $y=-4$.

While we could apply the dual variable check to the expanded problem and its dual, it is much easier to work with the dual of the original problem:

We obtained this dual in the solution to Problem 6(a).

Minimize $y=3x_1-3x_2+3x_3$ subject to
$$x_1 \geq 0, x_2 \geq 0, x_3 \geq 0$$
$$-2x_1+x_2+x_3=1$$
$$x_1+x_2-2x_3=2$$

Since all the variables are restricted, we simply apply the solution technique of Section 5.4:

$$\begin{bmatrix} -2 & 1^* & 1 & 1 \\ 1 & 1 & -2 & 2 \\ -3 & 3 & -3 & 0 \end{bmatrix} \quad \begin{bmatrix} -2 & 1 & 1 & 1 \\ 3 & 0 & -3^* & 1 \\ 3 & 0 & -6 & -3 \end{bmatrix}$$

$$\begin{array}{ccc} x_1 & x_2 & x_3 \end{array}$$

$$\begin{bmatrix} -1 & 1 & 0 & \frac{4}{3} \\ -1^* & 0 & 1 & -\frac{1}{3} \\ -3 & 0 & 0 & -5 \end{bmatrix} \quad \begin{bmatrix} 0 & 1 & -1 & \frac{5}{3} \\ 1 & 0 & -1 & \frac{1}{3} \\ 0 & 0 & -3 & -4 \end{bmatrix}$$

The solution is $x_1=\frac{1}{3}$, $x_2=\frac{5}{3}$, $x_3=0$, and $y=-4$.

The check:

(1) The max. answer is feasible:
$$-2(-2)+1(-1)= \quad 3 \leq \quad 3 \checkmark$$
$$1(-2)+1(-1)=-3 \leq -3 \checkmark$$
$$1(-2)-2(-1)= \quad 0 \leq \quad 3 \checkmark$$

(2) The min. answer is feasible:
$$\tfrac{1}{3} \geq 0, \tfrac{5}{3} \geq 0, 0 \geq 0 \checkmark$$
$$-2(\tfrac{1}{3})+1(\tfrac{5}{3})+1(0)=1=1 \checkmark$$
$$1(\tfrac{1}{3})+1(\tfrac{5}{3})-2(0)=2=2 \checkmark$$

(3) They give the same value to their objective variables:
Max.: $1(-2)+2(-1)=-4$
Min.: $3(\tfrac{1}{3})-3(\tfrac{5}{3})+3(0)=-4 \checkmark$

As a final example we solve Problem 6(b) and its dual.

Problem 8

Minimize $y = 2x_1 + 3x_2 + x_3$ subject to

$$x_2 \geq 0, x_3 \geq 0$$

$$-x_1 - \quad x_2 + 3x_3 \leq 5$$
$$x_1 - \quad 3x_2 + \quad x_3 = 4$$
$$2x_1 - 12x_2 - 3x_3 \leq 6$$
$$-x_1 + \quad 8x_2 + 4x_3 = 6$$

We have already reversed the first inequality.

Since $x_1$ is unrestricted, we must replace it by $x_{1p} - x_{1n}$. In the matrix this amounts to introducing a new column, $-C_1$, between $C_1$ and $C_2$:

$$\begin{bmatrix} -1 & 1 & -1 & 3 & 1 & 0 & 5 \\ 1^* & -1 & -3 & 1 & 0 & 0 & 4 \\ 2 & -2 & -12 & -3 & 0 & 1 & 6 \\ -1 & 1 & 8 & 4 & 0 & 0 & 6 \\ -2 & 2 & -3 & -1 & 0 & 0 & 0 \end{bmatrix}$$

$$\begin{bmatrix} 0 & 0 & -4 & 4 & 1 & 0 & 9 \\ 1 & -1 & -3 & 1 & 0 & 0 & 4 \\ 0 & 0 & -6 & -5 & 0 & 1 & -2 \\ 0 & 0 & 5^* & 5 & 0 & 0 & 10 \\ 0 & 0 & -9 & 1 & 0 & 0 & 8 \end{bmatrix}$$

We now have the columns of the identity matrix, $C_1, C_3, C_5, C_6$, and are ready to begin the simplex method.

$$\begin{bmatrix} 0 & 0 & 0 & 8 & 1 & 0 & 17 \\ 1 & -1 & 0 & 4 & 0 & 0 & 10 \\ 0 & 0 & 0 & 1 & 0 & 1 & 10 \\ 0 & 0 & 1 & 1^* & 0 & 0 & 2 \\ 0 & 0 & 0 & 10 & 0 & 0 & 26 \end{bmatrix}$$

$$\begin{matrix} x_{1p} & x_{1n} & x_2 & x_3 \end{matrix}$$

$$\begin{bmatrix} 0 & 0 & -8 & 0 & 1 & 0 & 1 \\ 1 & -1 & -4 & 0 & 0 & 0 & 2 \\ 0 & 0 & -1 & 0 & 0 & 1 & 8 \\ 0 & 0 & 1 & 1 & 0 & 0 & 2 \\ 0 & 0 & -10 & 0 & 0 & 0 & 6 \end{bmatrix}$$

The answer is $x_1 = 2 - 0 = 2, x_2 = 0, x_3 = 2$ with $y = 6$. We have already set up the dual in Problem 6(b):

Maximize $y = -5x_1 + 4x_2 - 6x_3 + 6x_4$ subject to

$$x_1 \geq 0, x_3 \geq 0$$

$$x_1 + \quad x_2 - \quad 2x_3 - \quad x_4 = 2$$
$$x_1 - 3x_2 + 12x_3 + 8x_4 \leq 3$$
$$-3x_1 + \quad x_2 + \quad 3x_3 + 4x_4 \leq 1$$

The solution:

$$
\begin{array}{cccccc}
x_1 & x_{2p} & x_{2n} & x_3 & x_{4p} & x_{4n} \\
\end{array}
$$

$$
\left[\begin{array}{ccccccccc}
1 & 1 & -1 & -2 & -1 & 1^* & 0 & 0 & 2 \\
1 & -3 & 3 & 12 & 8 & -8 & 1 & 0 & 3 \\
-3 & 1 & -1 & 3 & 4 & -4 & 0 & 1 & 1 \\
-5 & 4 & -4 & -6 & 6 & -6 & 0 & 0 & 0
\end{array}\right]
$$

$$
\left[\begin{array}{ccccccccc}
1 & 1 & -1 & -2 & -1 & 1 & 0 & 0 & 2 \\
9 & 5 & -5 & -4 & 0 & 0 & 1 & 0 & 19 \\
1 & 5^* & -5 & -5 & 0 & 0 & 0 & 1 & 9 \\
1 & 10 & -10 & -18 & 0 & 0 & 0 & 0 & 12
\end{array}\right]
$$

$$
\begin{array}{cccccc}
x_1 & x_{2p} & x_{2n} & x_3 & x_{4p} & x_{4n} \\
\end{array}
$$

$$
\left[\begin{array}{ccccccccc}
\frac{4}{5} & 0 & 0 & -1 & -1 & 1 & 0 & -\frac{1}{5} & \frac{1}{5} \\
8 & 0 & 0 & 1 & 0 & 0 & 1 & -1 & 10 \\
\frac{1}{5} & 1 & -1 & -1 & 0 & 0 & 0 & \frac{1}{5} & \frac{9}{5} \\
-1 & 0 & 0 & -8 & 0 & 0 & 0 & -2 & -6
\end{array}\right]
$$

The answer is $x_1 = 0, x_2 = \frac{9}{5} - 0 = \frac{9}{5}, x_3 = 0, x_4 = 0 - \frac{1}{5} = -\frac{1}{5}$ with $y = 6$,

(1) Max. feasible: $x_1 = 0 \geq 0, x_3 = 0 \geq 0 \checkmark$

$$1(0) + 1\left(\tfrac{9}{5}\right) - 2(0) - 1\left(-\tfrac{1}{5}\right) = \quad 2 = 2 \checkmark$$

$$1(0) - 3\left(\tfrac{9}{5}\right) + 2(0) + 8\left(-\tfrac{1}{5}\right) = -7 \leq 3 \checkmark$$

$$-3(0) + 1\left(\tfrac{9}{5}\right) + 3(0) + 4\left(-\tfrac{1}{5}\right) = \quad 1 \leq 1 \checkmark$$

(2) Min. feasible: $x_2 = 0 \geq 0, x_4 = 0 \geq 0 \checkmark$

$$-1(2) - \quad 1(0) + 3(2) = \quad 4 \leq 5 \checkmark$$

$$1(2) - \quad 3(0) + 1(2) = \quad 4 = 4 \checkmark$$

$$2(2) - 12(0) - 3(2) = -2 \leq 6 \checkmark$$

$$-1(2) + \quad 8(0) + 4(2) = \quad 6 = 6 \checkmark$$

(3) The objective variables:

$$\text{Max:} \ -5(0) + 4\left(\tfrac{9}{5}\right) - 6(0) + 6\left(-\tfrac{1}{5}\right) = 6$$

$$\text{Min:} \ 2(2) + 3(0) + 1(2) = 6 \checkmark$$

**An Economic Interpretation of Duality**

If a given linear programming problem arises from a story problem, you might expect that its dual linear programming problem can be interpreted as the mathematical formulation of a related story problem. This is in fact the case as we see in the following example.

The Almine Coal Company has four mines. Each mine produces 3 types of coal, as shown in Table 8. The company's problem is to fill its orders at minimum cost.

Table 8

| Mine | Daily coal production (in hundreds of tons) | | | Cost of operation (in thousands of dollars) |
|------|------|---|---|------|
| | Type | | | |
| | A | B | C | |
| I | 4 | 5 | 3 | 4 |
| II | 2 | 1 | 0 | 2 |
| III | 3 | 2 | 5 | 3 |
| IV | 4 | 2 | 6 | 3 |
| Orders | 20 | 30 | 40 | |

If we let $x_1$ be the number of days to operate mine I, $x_2$ the number of days to operate mine II, and so forth, we are led immediately to the following problem:

Minimize $y = 4x_1 + 2x_2 + 3x_3 + 3x_4$ subject to

$$x_1 \geq 0, x_2 \geq 0, x_3 \geq 0, x_4 \geq 0$$
$$4x_1 + 2x_2 + 3x_3 + 4x_4 \geq 20$$
$$5x_1 + x_2 + 2x_3 + 2x_4 \geq 30$$
$$3x_1 + 5x_3 + 6x_4 \geq 40$$

The managers of a private company, Kraye & Sons, have access to this information and feel they can mine coal more cheaply. However, they do not have the distribution capability of Almine. They decide to offer to operate Almine's facilities and then sell the coal, already sorted by type, to Almine. Kraye & Sons' problem is to find an offer, attractive to Almine, that produces the greatest profit for them. Suppose we let $x_1$ be the price to be charged for 100 tons of type A coal, $x_2$ the price for the same quantity of type B, and $x_3$ the price for type C. Since Almine needs 2,000 tons of type A, 3,000 tons of type B, and 4,000 tons of type C, Kraye's sales will generate a daily income of

*We are measuring prices in thousands of dollars.*

$$20x_1 + 30x_2 + 40x_3$$

thousand dollars. This is to be maximized.

Mine I produces 4 hundred tons of type A, 5 hundred tons of type B, and 3 hundred tons of type C. At prices $x_1$, $x_2$, and $x_3$ it would cost Almine $4x_1 + 5x_2 + 3x_3$ to buy this much coal from Kraye. Almine can obtain this much coal for $4,000 by operating the mine itself. Kraye cannot expect Almine to pay more than this for coal. Thus, it must set its prices so that

$$4x_1 + 5x_2 + 3x_3 \leq 4$$

A similar argument for each of the other mines forces Kraye to set prices so that

$$2x_1 + x_2 \quad\ \leq 2$$
$$3x_1 + 2x_2 + 5x_3 \leq 3$$
$$4x_1 + 2x_2 + 6x_3 \leq 3$$

In summary, its problem is to maximize $y = 20x_1 + 30x_2 + 40x_3$ subject to

$$x_1 \geq 0, x_2 \geq 0, x_3 \geq 0$$

$$4x_1 + 5x_2 + 3x_3 \leq 4$$
$$2x_1 + x_2 \quad\ \leq 2$$
$$3x_1 + 2x_2 + 5x_3 \leq 3$$
$$4x_1 + 2x_2 + 6x_3 \leq 3$$

We see that these problems are dual to each other. Since the optimal value for each problem will be the same, the best offer from Kraye's viewpoint will cost Almine exactly the same as mining the coal itself. Whether or not to accept the offer will be a matter of complete indifference, mathematically speaking.

**Exercises 5.6** Write the dual of each of the problems in 1 through 5.

1. Maximize $y = 2x_1 + 3x_2$ subject to

$$x_1 \geq 0, x_2 \geq 0$$
$$x_1 + x_2 \leq 2$$
$$x_1 + 4x_2 \leq 4$$

2. Maximize $y = 2x_1 + x_2$ subject to

$$x_1 \geq 0, x_2 \geq 0$$
$$-x_1 + x_2 \leq 1$$
$$x_1 + x_2 \geq 2$$
$$4x_1 - x_2 \leq 4$$

3. Minimize $y = 6x_1 + 22x_2 + 12x_3$ subject to

$$x_1 \geq 0, x_2 \geq 0, x_3 \geq 0$$
$$2x_1 + 3x_2 + 2x_3 \geq 12$$
$$x_1 + 8x_2 + 2x_3 \geq 16$$
$$2x_1 + 5x_2 + 3x_3 \geq 6$$

4. Minimize $y = 5x_1 + 2x_2 + 9x_3$ subject to

$$x_1 \geq 0, x_2 \geq 0, x_3 \geq 0$$
$$2x_1 \quad + 3x_2 + 4x_3 \geq 5$$
$$x_1 \quad + 3x_2 + 2x_3 \geq 4$$
$$3x_1 \quad + 2x_2 + \quad x_3 \geq 2$$
$$6x_1 \qquad\quad + 3x_3 \geq 3$$

5. Maximize $y = 3x_1 - 2x_2$ subject to

$$x_1 \geq 0, x_2 \geq 0$$
$$2x_1 - x_2 \leq -2$$
$$x_1 - 2x_2 \geq 2$$

6. Solve Exercise 1 and its dual and apply the dual variable check to your solution.
7. Solve Exercise 2 and its dual and apply the dual variable check to your solution.
8. Solve Exercise 3 and its dual and apply the dual variable check to your solution.
9. Solve Exercise 4 and its dual and apply the dual variable check to your solution.
10. Solve Exercise 5 and its dual and apply the dual variable check to your solution.

C11. Use matrix methods to solve Exercise 19(b) in Section 5.1.

In Exercises 12 through 21 solve the given problem and its dual and apply the dual variable check.

12. Maximize $y = 2x_1 + 3x_2 - x_3$ subject to

$$x_1 \geq 0, x_3 \geq 0$$
$$x_1 \quad + x_2 \quad - x_3 \geq 1$$
$$x_1 \quad - 3x_2 \quad + x_3 = 4$$
$$2x_1 - 12x_2 - 3x_3 \leq 6$$
$$-x_1 \quad + 8x_2 + 4x_3 = 6$$

13. Minimize $y = 2x_1 - 3x_2 + 3x_3$ subject to

$$x_2 \geq 0, x_3 \geq 0$$
$$x_2 + \quad x_3 = \quad 7$$
$$-x_1 + x_2 - 2x_3 \leq -8$$
$$-x_1 + x_2 - \quad x_3 \geq 5$$

14. Maximize $y = 3x_1 - x_2 + 4x_3$ subject to

$$x_1 \geq 0, x_2 \geq 0, x_3 \geq 0$$
$$2x_1 \quad - x_2 - x_3 \geq \quad 1$$
$$x_1 - 2x_2 - x_3 \leq -1$$
$$3x_1 \quad - x_2 + x_3 \geq -2$$

15. Maximize $y = x_1 - 2x_2 + 2x_3$ subject to

$$x_1 \geq 0, x_2 \geq 0, x_3 \geq 0$$

$$x_1 + 2x_2 - x_3 \geq 2$$
$$3x_1 - 2x_2 + 2x_3 \leq 4$$
$$-x_1 - 2x_2 + 4x_3 \leq -4$$

16. Maximize $y = x_1 - 2x_2 + 2x_3$ subject to

$$x_1 \geq 0, x_2 \geq 0, x_3 \geq 0$$

$$x_1 + 2x_2 - x_3 = 2$$
$$3x_1 - 2x_2 + 3x_3 \leq 4$$
$$-x_1 - 2x_2 - 2x_3 \leq -4$$

17. Maximize $y = 2x_1 - 3x_2 + 3x_3$ subject to

$$x_2 \geq 0, x_3 \geq 0$$

$$x_2 + x_3 = 7$$
$$-x_1 + x_2 - 2x_3 \leq 8$$
$$-x_1 + x_2 - x_3 \geq 5$$

18. Minimize $y = -x_1 - 4x_2 + 6x_3 - 6x_4$ subject to

$$x_1 \geq 0, x_4 \geq 0$$

$$x_1 + x_2 - 2x_3 - x_4 = 2$$
$$x_1 - 3x_2 + 12x_3 + 8x_4 \leq 3$$
$$-3x_1 - x_2 - 3x_3 - 4x_4 \geq 1$$

19. Maximize $y = -3x_1 - x_2 - 2x_3$ subject to

$$x_1 \geq 0$$

$$x_1 + x_2 + x_3 \geq -8$$
$$2x_1 - x_2 - 3x_3 \leq 6$$
$$-3x_1 + x_2 - x_3 \geq 6$$

20. Maximize $y = 2x_1 - 2x_2 + x_3 + 4x_4$ subject to

$$x_1 \geq 0, x_2 \geq 0, x_3 \geq 0$$

$$11x_1 + x_2 - x_3 - 3x_4 \geq 10$$
$$3x_1 + x_2 + 3x_3 - x_4 = 12$$
$$-x_1 + x_2 - x_3 + x_4 \leq 8$$

See pp. 372–74.  21. What is Kraye's best offer?

$^C$22. A door-to-door salesman of powered nutrients hears that I have started feeding ordinary food to my dog. He is aware of food values and prices as summarized in the following chart:

| | Protein | Carbohydrates | Calcium | Cost |
|---|---|---|---|---|
| Hamburger | 8g | 0g | 3mg | 6¢/oz. |
| Powdered milk | 20 | 35 | 870 | 15¢/cup |
| Eggs | 6 | 0 | 27 | 7¢ each |
| Requirements | at least 60g | at least 126g | at least 3,180mg | |

Note that the salesman is under the mistaken impression that I need *at least* 126 grams of carbohydrates. Compare Exercise 12 in Section 5.

He sells powdered protein, carbohydrates, and calcium. How much should he charge me for each of these ingredients so as to maximize his profit while making an offer which is attractive to me?

See Problem 11 in Section 5.

23. Yesterday, the president of the Taint It Pork? Company received a peculiar offer from the nearly bankrupt 10-4 Receivershipment Transport Company. This particular firm has a terrible reputation stemming from several court cases involving alleged theft of goods. The president of Taint It Pork? laughed at the prospect of using the services of such a shady company. However, he was soon confronted with an offer he could not refuse. The president of 10-4 said:

"I know you won't trust me with your goods so I'll buy your pork from you. At the Secaucus plant, I'll pay $x_1$ dollars a pound. At the Gary plant, I'll pay you $x_2$ dollars a pound. After I deliver the pork, I'll sell it back to you. I'll only charge you $x_3$ dollars a pound at Winesburg and $x_4$ dollars a pound in the Ozarks."

The president could not refuse the offer. After all, it was no more expensive than paying the usual transportation costs, which were:

**Transportation Cost per Pound**

| To/From | Winesburg | Ozarks |
| --- | --- | --- |
| Secaucus | $2 | $5 |
| Gary | $3 | $4 |

The 10-4 company agreed to buy all 40 pounds of production at Secaucus and all 40 pounds of production at Gary. They were going to sell 30 pounds at Winesburg and 50 pounds in the Ozarks so that both these demands would be met. Find prices $x_1$, $x_2$, $x_3$, and $x_4$, that maximize profit for 10-4.

## Section 7 Summary

*Calculus can sometimes be used to convert nonlinear constraints into linear ones.*

Optimization is very important in business and engineering. In many practical situations all the constraints in a problem are linear or can be closely approximated by linear constraints. The simplex method, which is merely a modification of Gauss-Jordan reduction, can be used to optimize a linear objective variable subject to linear constraints.

In Section 5.2 we described the basic simplex method for standard maximization LP problems in which all entries in the bound matrix are greater than or equal to 0. In Section 5.3 we discussed some of the reasons why the simplex method works. The same sort of reasoning will also help to explain why the modifications presented in Sections 5.4, 5.5, and 5.6 work.

In Section 5.4 we adapted the simplex method to handle mixed constraints. This first modification is called Phase I. Geometrically, Phase I moves the problem to a corner of the region of feasibility from which the regular simplex method can move to the final answer.

In Section 5.5 we formulated a few simple story problems to give some indication of possible practical applications. Section 5.6 contains three ideas: the dual variable check, a new minimization technique (which is essential for our treatment of game theory in Section 6.3), and the modification for unrestricted variables.

Now that you are familiar with the simplex method, a few comments on mathematical modeling are in order. Just before this text was published, Janet decided to accept a job offer from a large data-processing firm. She is doing quite well there and feels that she has a greater opportunity for advancement.

She has kept in touch with her friends at AC and has agreed to relate an incident that happened there recently.

Janet: *So you want me to describe that $72,000 mistake made by that blonde guy they hired to replace me? Fine. AC decided to market a make-it-yourself sleeping-bag kit. Goose down for the kits was available in packets of five different sizes according to Table 9.*

Table 9

| Quantity of Down (in ounces) | Price |
|---|---|
| 1 | $ 1.75 |
| 2 | 3.00 |
| 4 | 5.50 |
| 8 | 10.50 |
| 16 | 20.00 |

*Synthetic fiber was available in packets of any size needed, at a cost of $.75 an ounce. While synthetic fiber is cheaper, 1 ounce of down has a volume of 600 cubic inches and 1 ounce of synthetic fiber has a volume of only 400 cubic inches. The larger the volume, the better the insulation. Somebody at AC got the idea of mixing down and synthetic fibers. They decided that the kit should produce a bag with at least 23,000 cubic inches of volume with no more than 50 ounces of down and synthetic fiber combined. Of course, they wanted to minimize their production costs. Here is how that guy solved the problem:*
*Let $x_1$ be the number of ounces of down and let $x_2$ be the number of ounces of synthetic fibers used. Then the volume constraint becomes*

$$600x_1 + 400x_2 \geq 23,000$$

*and the weight constraint becomes*

$$x_1 + x_2 \leq 50$$

*He had to minimize cost. The price seemed to vary. One ounce of* down cost $1.75 but 16 ounces of down cost $20.00, that is $1.25 an ounce. For no apparent reason, he decided to solve two problems, one in which the price was $1.75 an ounce, another in which he assumed the price was $1.25 an ounce. Synthetic fiber was easy—it was always $.75 an ounce. Here are the two problems:

PROBLEM 1

$$\text{Minimize } 1.75x_1 + .75x_2$$
$$\text{subject to } x_1 \geq 0, x_2 \geq 0,$$
$$600x_1 + 400x_2 \geq 23,000$$
$$x_1 + x_2 \leq 50$$

PROBLEM 2

$$\text{Minimize } 1.25x_1 + .75x_2$$
$$\text{subject to } x_1 \geq 0, x_2 \geq 0$$
$$600x_1 + 400x_2 \geq 23,000$$
$$x_1 + x_2 \leq 50$$

Figure 29

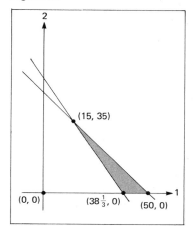

The region of feasibility is the same for each problem (see Figure 29). In Table 10 we use the corner point theorem to solve these problems.

Table 10

| Corner point | y-value for $1.75x_1 + .75x_2$ | y-value for $1.25x_1 + .75x_2$ |
|---|---|---|
| $(38\frac{1}{3}, 0)$ | $67.08\frac{1}{3}$ | $47.91\frac{2}{3}$ |
| $(15, 35)$ | 52.50 | 45.00 |
| $(50, 0)$ | 87.50 | 62.50 |

In either case the answer was the same: put 15 ounces of down and 35 ounces of synthetic fiber into the kit.

At the factories, the managers needed to put four packets of down into each kit:

| | |
|---|---|
| 1 oz. | $ 1.75 |
| 2 oz. | 3.00 |
| 4 oz. | 5.50 |
| 8 oz. | 10.50 |
| Total 15 oz. | 20.75 cost of down |
| 35 oz. | 26.25 cost of synthetic fiber |
| Total cost | $47.00 |

Since $47.00 was between the extremes $52.50 and $45.00 everybody was happy and, in fact, AC turned out 100 of these kits a day, 2,000 a *month, 24,000 a year for two years before somebody realized that if they used 16 ounces of down and 34 ounces of synthetic fiber the cost would be*

| | |
|---|---|
| 16 ounces of down | $20.00 |
| 34 ounces of synthetic fiber | 25.50 |
| Total | $45.50 |

*This saves $1.50 per kit or $72,000 over the two-year period. That's more than they paid in salary to that guy.*

> *It's easy to see what went wrong. Just consider the graph of down cost versus quantity:*

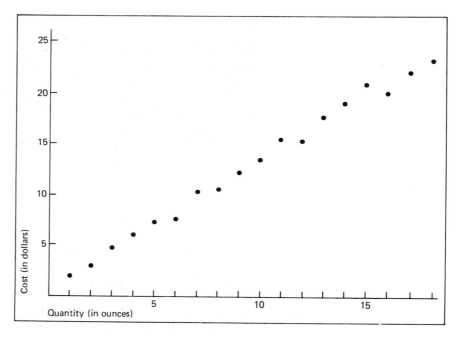

> *The points do not lie on a straight line, so a linear model is not appropriate. There are many problems in business for which the techniques of this text are not appropriate. It is essential that you understand your problem and understand the mathematics you are going to use to solve it.*

Many of the more sophisticated techniques are based upon methods presented in this text.

We: *Ms. Witherspoon, can you give some indication to our readers of exactly what a linear model is?*

J: *Suppose down cost $1.75 an ounce, no matter how many ounces you buy. Now the solution to Problem 1, use 15 ounces of down and 35* *ounces of synthetic fiber, is correct. But look at the graph of down quantity versus cost:*

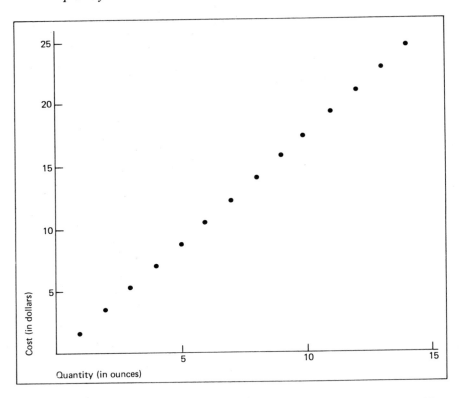

For some reason Janet refuses to come right out and say that a linear model is a geometric model involving straight lines and their higher dimensional analogs. (Straight lines were obtained by the formula $ax_1 + bx_2 = c$. If we extend to three dimensions (three variables) we obtain the formula for a plane: $ax_1 + bx_2 + cx_3 = d$.)

*There isn't any line. Sure, all the points lie on a line. But the problem itself asks, How much of each type of filling should be used? Lines, coordinates, systems of equations, feasible regions—none of those is mentioned.*

*It just happens that we can convert our real business problem to an abstract geometry problem. We "model" the aspects of the real problem which are important. We pretend the formula*

cost of $x_1$ ounces of down $= 1.75x_1$

*holds for any value of $x_1$, even, say, $x_1 = -3,700.938$. That value for $x_1$ may be acceptable in the geometric model but it is certainly unacceptable in the real world problem. A model train builder tries to mimic all the aspects of a real train. But he will fail. The geometric model builder tries to mimic all the important and relevant aspects of a problem at hand. In many cases she will be successful.*

*The reason that the blond guy failed was that he tried to use a linear model where such a model was inappropriate. There just isn't any simple formula for the cost of down. All we really have is Table 1. The blond guy tried to use a model that was so simple as to be irrelevant, so naturally his answer was irrelevant. In fact he's irrelevant. I told them not to hire...*

We:   *Thank you, Ms. Witherspoon.*

---

TERMS

---

Constraint matrix, page 315
Bound matrix, page 315
Objective matrix, page 316
Standard LP problem, page 361
Dual of a standard LP problem, page 361
General LP problem, page 366
Dual of a general LP problem, page 367

---

COMPUTATIONAL TECHNIQUES

---

Simplex method for maximization problems, page 318
How to read minimization answer from
   maximization matrix, page 366
Phase I, page 338
Simplex method for problems with
   equality constraints, page 344
Dual variable check, pages 363 and 365
Simplex method for minimization
   problems, page 342
Rule for problems with unrestricted variables, page 368.

**Review Exercises**  Look back over the chapter, then do the following exercises without looking back again. Answers to all these exercises are in Appendix C.

1. Graph the following inequalities
   (a) $2x_1 + 3x_2 \le 6$
   (b) $3x_1 + 2 \ge 4x_2 + x_1 + 14$
   (c) $x_1 + 2x_2 + 3x_3 \le 6$
2. Use the geometric method to maximize $y = 3x_1 + 4x_2$ subject to $x_1 \ge 0, x_2 \ge 0, x_1 + 2x_2 \le 5, x_1 + x_2 \le 4$.
3. Use the geometric method to find the maximum and minimum values of $y = x_1 + 2x_2$ subject to $2x_1 - x_2 \ge 2, 2x_1 - 3x_2 \le 6$.
4. Use the geometric method to find the maximum and minimum values of $y = -3x_1 + 5x_2$ subject to $x_1 + x_2 \le 2, 3x_1 - x_2 \ge -6, x_1 - 7x_2 \le 18$.
5. Use the simplex method to solve the following problems:
   (a) Maximize $y = 5x_1 + 2x_2$ subject to $x_1 \ge 0, x_2 \ge 0, 3x_1 + 2x_2 \le 6, 2x_1 - x_2 \le 3$.

(b) Minimize $y = 3x_1 + 4x_2$ subject to $x_1 \geq 0, x_2 \geq 0, x_1 + x_2 \geq 2,$ $-2x_1 + x_2 \geq 2, x_1 - 2x_2 \geq 2.$

6. Maximize $y = 3x_1 + 3x_2 + 4x_3 + 2x_4$ subject to $x_1 \geq 0, x_2 \geq 0, x_3 \geq 0,$ $x_4 \geq 0, 2x_1 + 4x_2 + 4x_3 + 2x_4 \leq 4, 3x_1 + 2x_2 + x_3 \leq 5, 2x_1 + 2x_2 + 3x_4 \leq 3,$ $x_1 + x_2 + 2x_3 + x_4 \leq 4.$

7. State and solve the dual problem for Exercise 6 above.

C8. The Titan Conglomerate needs 9 million gallons of fuel oil and 7 million gallons of gasoline. The Supergas refinery will deliver 40,000 gallons of oil and 80,000 gallons of gasoline for $110,000 a day. The Exxtrabig refinery will deliver 60,000 gallons of oil and 30,000 of gasoline for $70,000 a day. How does Titan get the best deal? How much does it pay?

9. A candy wholesaler has a supply of 6,000 rolls of mints, 10,000 gumballs, and 8,000 candy bars. She makes 4 types of boxes. Type A can accommodate 2 rolls of mints, 3 gumballs, and 2 candy bars; B holds 3 rolls of mints and 4 gumballs; C holds 2 rolls of mints, 2 gumballs, and 3 candy bars; D holds 6 rolls of mints only. The filled boxes can be wholesaled at a profit of 50, 30, 20, and 60 cents per box, respectively. There is one other matter. It is summer, and she is afraid that a power brownout is likely. Without refrigeration, all the candy bars will melt in her warehouse. So she must use up all the candy bars and get the boxes of candy out to the stores at once. Assuming that she uses up all the candy bars, how can she maximize profit?

10. Solve the following problem and its dual. Apply the dual variable check to your answers.

Minimize $y = x_1 - x_2 + 4x_3$ subject to $x_1 \geq 0, x_3 \geq 0, x_1 + x_2 + x_3 \geq 0,$ $2x_1 + x_2 \leq 12, x_1 + x_3 = 10.$

## Supplementary Exercises

1. Maximize $y = 7x_1 + 5x_2$ subject to $x_1 \geq 0, x_2 \geq 0, 7x_1 + 8x_2 \leq 9,$ $6x_1 + 7x_2 \leq 15.$

2. Minimize $y = 3x_1 + 5x_2$ subject to $x_1 \geq 0, x_2 \geq 0, 7x_1 + 6x_2 \geq 7,$ $8x_1 + 7x_2 \geq 5.$

3. Maximize $y = 5x_1 + 5x_2 + 7x_3$ subject to $x_1 \geq 0, x_2 \geq 0, x_3 \geq 0,$ $-2x_1 + x_2 + 3x_3 \leq 9, 3x_1 + 4x_3 \leq 6, 2x_1 + 4x_2 + 2x_3 \leq 2.$

4. Minimize $y = 9x_1 + 6x_2 + 2x_3$ subject to $x_1 \geq 0, x_2 \geq 0, x_3 \geq 0,$ $-2x_1 + 3x_2 + 2x_3 \geq 5, x_1 + 4x_3 \geq 5, 3x_1 + 4x_2 + 2x_3 \geq 7.$

5. Maximize $y = x_1 + 3x_2 + 6x_3 + 2x_4 + 2x_5$ subject to $x_1 \geq 0, x_2 \geq 0, x_3 \geq 0,$ $x_4 \geq 0, x_5 \geq 0, 3x_1 + 2x_2 - 6x_3 + 4x_4 + 5x_5 \leq 10, 2x_1 + 3x_3 + 5x_4 + 2x_5 \leq 8.$

6. Minimize $y = 10x_1 + 8x_2$ subject to $x_1 \geq 0, x_2 \geq 0, 3x_1 + 2x_2 \geq 1, 2x_1 \geq 0,$ $-6x_1 + 3x_2 \geq 6, 4x_1 + 5x_2 \geq 2, 5x_1 + 2x_2 \geq 2.$

7. Maximize $y = 4x_1 + 8x_2 + 12x_3$ subject to $x_1 \geq 0, x_2 \geq 0, x_3 \geq 0,$ $x_1 + 5x_2 + 9x_3 \leq 13, 2x_1 + 6x_2 + 10x_3 \leq 14, 3x_1 + 7x_2 + 11x_3 \leq 15.$

8. Minimize $y = 13x_1 + 14x_2 + 15x_3$ subject to $x_1 \geq 0, x_2 \geq 0, x_3 \geq 0,$ $x_1 + 2x_2 + 3x_3 \geq 4, 5x_1 + 6x_2 + 7x_3 \geq 8, 9x_1 + 10x_2 + 11x_3 \geq 12.$

9. Maximize $y = 6x_1 + 12x_2$ subject to $x_1 \geq 0, x_2 \geq 0, 2x_1 + 8x_2 \leq 14,$ $x_1 + 7x_2 \leq 13, 4x_1 + 10x_2 \leq 16, 3x_1 + 9x_2 \leq 15, 5x_1 + 11x_2 \leq 17.$

10. Minimize $y = 13x_1 + 14x_2 + 15x_3 + 16x_4 + 17x_5$ subject to $x_1 \geq 0, x_2 \geq 0$, $x_3 \geq 0, x_4 \geq 0, x_5 \geq 0, x_1 + 2x_2 + 3x_3 + 4x_4 + 5x_5 \geq 6$, $7x_1 + 8x_2 + 9x_3 + 10x_4 + 11x_5 \geq 12$.

11. Maximize $y = 3x_1 + 4x_2 + 5x_3 + 6x_4$ subject to $x_1 \geq 0, x_2 \geq 0, x_3 \geq 0$, $x_4 \geq 0, x_1 \leq 6, 2x_1 + x_2 \leq 5, 2x_2 + x_3 \leq 4, 2x_3 + x_4 \leq 3, 2x_4 \leq 2$.

12. Minimize $y = 6x_1 + 5x_2 + 4x_3 + 3x_4 + 2x_5$ subject to $x_1 \geq 0, x_2 \geq 0, x_3 \geq 0$, $x_4 \geq 0, x_5 \geq 0, x_1 + 2x_2 \geq 3 \ x_2 + 2x_3 \geq 4, x_3 \geq 2x_4 \geq 5, x_4 + 2x_5 \geq 6$.

*13. Maximize $y = 4x_1 + 5x_2 + 6x_3 + 7x_4$ subject to $x_1 \geq 0, \ x_2 \geq 0, \ x_3 \geq 0$, $x_4 \geq 0, 3x_4 \leq 7, 2x_1 + 3x_2 \leq 6, x_1 + 2x_2 + 3x_3 \leq 5, x_2 + 2x_3 + 3x_4 \leq 4$.

14. Minimize $y = 7x_1 + 6x_2 + 5x_3 + 4x_4$ subject to $x_1 \geq 0, x_2 \geq 0, x_3 \geq 0, x_4 \geq 0$, $3x_1 + 2x_2 + x_3 \geq 4, 3x_2 + 2x_3 + x_4 \geq 5, 3x_3 + 2x_4 \geq 6, x_4 \geq 7$.

15. There are 2 mines. One operation of mine I produces 1 ton of high-grade, 3 tons of medium-grade, and 5 tons of low-grade ore. One operation of mine II produces 2 tons of high-grade, 2 tons of medium-grade, and 2 tons of low-grade. The company makes $200 profit in one operation of mine I and $208 profit in one operation of mine II. Storage restrictions require that the company make no more than 88 tons of high-grade ore, 160 tons of medium-grade ore, and 200 tons of low-grade ore. How many operations of each mine should it make to maximize its profit and not exceed storage? What will the maximum profit be?

16. A manufacturer produces 4 products, each of which requires wood, plastic, and steel in its construction. A requires 2 units of wood, 1 unit of plastic, and 4 units of steel. B requires 1 unit of wood, 3 units of plastic, and 2 units of steel. C requires 3 units of wood, 2 units of plastic, and 1 unit of steel. D requires 6 units of wood, no units of plastic, and 3 units of steel. The manufacturer has only 5 units of wood, 2 units of plastic, and 9 units of steel. His profit is $5 on each A, $4 on each B, $2 on each C, and $3 on each D. How many of each item should he produce to maximize his profit, and what will his maximum profit be?

17. Two liquid vitamin supplements are available. Supplement 1 contains 2 units of vitamin A, 1 unit of vitamin B, and 1 unit of vitamin C per tablespoon. Supplement II contains 1 unit of vitamin A, 2 units of vitamin B, and 3 units of vitamin C per tablespoon. Each costs 30¢ per tablespoon. I need at least 3 units of vitamin A, 5 units of vitamin B, and 2 units of vitamin C. How can I meet my needs most economically, and what will be the minimum cost?

18. A company produces 3 items: A, B, and C. The main ingredients are materials I, II, and III. The company has only 7 units of I, 3 units of II, and 7 units of III. Each A requires 3 units of I, 1 unit of II, and 1 unit of III. Each B requires 5 units of 1, 2 units of II, and 6 units of III. Each C requires 1 unit of I, 1 unit of II, and 3 units of III. The profit is: $9 for each A, $4 for each B, and $6 for each C. How many of each item should the company produce to maximize its profit?

19. Minimize $y = 2x_1 + 2x_2$ subject to $x_1 \geq 0, x_2 \geq 0, -x_1 + x_2 \geq -2$, $x_1 + x_2 \leq -3$.

20. Maximize $y = 3x_1 + 2x_2$ subject to $x_1 \geq 0, x_2 \geq 0, 5x_1 + x_2 \leq 10$, $2x_1 + 2x_2 \leq 12, x_1 + x_2 \leq 12$.

21. Minimize $y = 2x_1 + x_2 + 8x_3 + 3x_4$ subject to $x_1 \geq 0, x_2 \geq 0, x_3 \geq 0$, $x_4 \geq 0, -2x_1 + x_2 - x_3 \geq 1, x_1 - x_2 + 2x_3 + x_4 \geq 2$.

22. Maximize $y = 2x_1 + 6x_2 + 5x_3$ subject to $x_1 \geq 0, x_2 \geq 0, x_3 \geq 0$, $5x_1 + 4x_2 + 9x_3 \leq 12, x_1 + 2x_2 + 4x_3 \leq 4, 4x_1 + x_2 + 5x_3 \leq 3$.

23. Minimize $y = 15x_1 + 4x_2 + 11x_3$ subject to $x_1 \geq 0, x_2 \geq 0, x_3 \geq 0$, $3x_1 + x_2 + 2x_3 \geq 6, 7x_1 + x_2 + 4x_3 \geq 7, 5x_1 + x_2 + 5x_3 \geq 8$.

24. Minimize $y = 6x_1 + 22x_2 + 12x_3$ subject to $x_1 \geq 0, x_2 \geq 0, x_3 \geq 0$, $2x_1 + 3x_2 + 2x_3 \geq 12, x_1 + 8x_2 + 2x_3 \geq 16, 2x_1 + 5x_2 + 3x_3 \geq 6$.

25. Maximize $y = 2x_1 + x_2$ subject to $-x_1 + x_2 \leq 1, x_1 - x_2 \leq 1, x_1 + x_2 \geq 4$, $x_1 + x_2 \leq 6$.

26. Maximize $y = 16x_1 + 11x_2 + 12x_3$ subject to $x_1 \geq 0, x_2 \geq 0, x_3 \geq 0$, $2x_1 + x_2 + x_3 \leq 30, x_1 + 2x_2 + 3x_3 \leq 51$.

27. Maximize $y = 3x_1 + 6x_2 + 4x_3 - 4x_4$ subject to $x_1 \geq 0, x_2 \geq 0, x_3 \geq 0$, $x_4 \geq 0, x_1 + 2x_2 + x_3 - 3x_4 \leq 2, x_1 - x_2 + 3x_3 + 5x_4 \leq 1$, $-x_1 + 4x_2 - 2x_3 + x_4 \leq 10$.

28. Minimize $y = 3x_1 + 8x_2 + 5x_3$ subject to $x_1 \geq 0, x_2 \geq 0, x_3 \geq 0$, $x_1 + x_2 + x_3 \geq 7, x_1 + 2x_2 + x_3 \geq 7, -x_1 + x_2 \geq 6$.

29. Minimize $y = 5x_1 + 2x_2 + 9x_3$ subject to $x_1 \geq 0, x_2 \geq 0, x_3 \geq 0$, $2x_1 + 3x_2 + 4x_3 \geq 5, x_1 + 3x_2 + 2x_3 \geq 4, 3x_1 + 2x_2 + x_3 \geq 2, 6x_1 + 3x_3 \geq 3$.

See Problem 7 of Section 2.2, p. 73.

30. Suppose each hour of operation of the Springfield factory costs $20 and each hour of operation of the Danbury factory costs $30. What is the cheapest way to fill the Falmouth order?

Solve the following two problems and their duals.

31. Maximize $y = 2x_1 - 2x_2 + x_3 + 4x_4$ subject to $x_1 \geq 0, x_2 \geq 0, x_3 \geq 0$, $11x_1 + x_2 - x_3 - 3x_4 \geq 10, 3x_1 + x_2 + 3x_3 - x_4 = 12, -x_1 + x_2 - x_3 + x_4 \leq 8$.

32. Minimize $y = 6x_1 + 8x_2 - 4x_3$ subject to $x_1 \geq 0, x_3 \geq 0, x_1 + x_2 \geq 2$, $-x_1 - x_3 = -1, 2x_1 + x_2 \geq 1, -x_2 - x_3 = -3$.

33. (a) In the 1950s PHE increased from 100 stores to 2,500. The relation between number of stores and total corporate profit is shown in part by the following tabulation.

| Number of stores | Annualized profit ($M) |
| --- | --- |
| 1,000 | 299 |
| 1,500 | 449 |
| 1,800 | 539 |
| 2,100 | 634 |
| 2,300 | 685 |
| 2,500 | 741 |

Plot these data on a graph. Does it seem reasonable to treat the study of the relation between stores and profit with a linear model?

(b) In the 1970s the corresponding results were, in part

| Number of stores | Annualized profit ($M) |
|---|---|
| 4,500 | 1,125 |
| 4,800 | 1,116 |
| 5,100 | 1,089 |
| 5,400 | 1,044 |
| 5,700 | 981 |

Plot these data on a graph. Is a linear model appropriate here?

34. Suppose a stone is thrown off a cliff and falls into a river. Do you think that a linear model could be used to describe its path?

35. When one quantity is directly proportional to another, can a linear model be used to describe the relation between the quantities?

36. Arrbeeyii Baseball Card Company (ABCC) sells two flavors of chewing gum each wrapped together with cards and iron-on cloth patches. The cards depict baseball players and their batting and pitching records. The patches represent each major league team. Regular flavor has 1 stick of gum, 3 different cards, and 1 team patch. Grape flavor has 1 stick of gum, 1 player card, and 2 different team patches.

(a) Each day ABCC receives 9,000 cards and 6,000 patches from the printer. How many packets of each flavor gum should they make each day to use up all the cards and patches?

(b) There are 14 teams in the American League and 12 teams in the National League. There are 650 different players represented on cards.

(i) How many different sets of patches can they make up for grape flavor gum?

(ii) How many different sets of player cards can they make up for regular flavor gum?

(iii) How many different sets of inserts can they make for each type of gum?

(iv) How many different ways can they rearrange the letters in their name?

ABCC is noted for its huge sticks of gum.

(c) Last Tuesday ABCC received only 4,000 ounces of gum base. Each stick of gum uses 1 ounce of gum base. Their profit on regular gum is 2¢ a stick, and on grape gum is 3¢ a stick. How many of each type of gum should they have made to maximize their profit?

# Chapter 6
# Further
# Topics

In the following six sections we have collected several independent topics, which can be investigated if time permits. Section 1 requires material covered in Chapter 1. Section 2 can be read anytime after Chapter 2. Section 3 uses the simplex method as developed in Section 6 of Chapter 5. Section 4 depends upon the ideas developed in Chapter 3. Section 5 is independent of the rest of the text. The section on computers relates to various parts of the text and can be consulted as needed.

## Section 6.1
## Poker, Scrabble® Brand Crossword Game, and Odds

In this section we investigate two popular games using the counting techniques of Chapter 1. Modern probability theory began with the careful study of games of chance, and this is still the most effective way to introduce the subject. No moral judgment should be made respecting the use of dice and cards in this book. They are merely a convenient and familiar source for experiments.

The basic poker deck consists of fifty-two cards. Each card has a **suit**: diamonds ♦, hearts ♥, clubs ♣, or spades ♠. Each card also has a **denomination**: Ace (A), 2, 3, 4, 5, 6, 7, 8, 9, 10, jack (J), queen (Q), or king (K). There is exactly one card for each choice of suit and denomination. The card with suit diamonds and denomination J, for example, is called the "jack of diamonds." The cards with suit diamonds or hearts are *red*; those with suit clubs or spades are *black*. The cards with denomination jack, queen, or king are *face cards* or *picture cards*. The order of the denominations, from lowest to highest, is: 2, 3, 4, 5, 6, 7, 8, 9, 10, J, Q, K, A. However an ace can be used as the lowest denomination or the highest denomination in a straight (see below).

The denomination of a card is often called its **number** or its **kind**. In this context, A, K, Q, J are numbers.

Sometimes one or more cards in a game will be designated as **wild cards**. This means that they may be declared by the player receiving them to be any card at all. The cards most often so designated are those with denomination 2 (the "deuces").

Sometimes one or two extra cards with no suit or denomination, called **jokers**, are added to the deck and used as wild cards.

A **hand** is a set of five cards that have been dealt to a player. It does not matter in what order the cards were received. The standard hands in poker are named as follows, in order of increasing value:

**Nothing:** None of the following.

**Pair:** Two cards of the same denomination and three cards with denominations different from each other and from the denomination of the pair. Example: J♥, J♠, 6♦, 8♦, 10♣.

**Two pair:** Two cards of the same denomination, two other cards of a second denomination, different from the first denomination, and another card of yet a third denomination. Example: 3♠, 3♦, 10♣, 10♦, A♥.

**Three of a kind:** Three cards of the same denomination, another card of a second denomination, and another card of yet a third denomination. Example: 9♦, 9♣, 9♥, K♠, 5♠.

**Straight:** Five cards, not all of the same suit, with consecutive denominations, Example: 8♠, 9♠, 10♠, J♥, Q♣.

**Flush:** Five cards of the same suit not with consecutive denominations. Example: 3♥, 5♥, A♥, 9♥, K♥.

**Full house:** Three cards of the same denomination and two other cards of a second denomination. Example: 6♣, 6♦, 6♥, K♥, K♣.

**Four of a kind:** Four cards of the same denomination and a fifth card of another denomination. Example: 5♥, 5♦, 5♠, 5♣, 10♦.

**Straight flush:** Five cards of the same suit with consecutive denominations. Example: A♦, 2♦, 3♦, 4♦, 5♦.

A **royal straight flush**, often called a **royal flush**, is a straight flush with denominations 10, J, Q, K, A.

**Five of a kind:** (Possible only with wild cards.) Five cards, one or more of which are wild, with all non-wild cards of the same denomination. Example: (with deuces wild) 2♥, 2♦, 7♠, 7♦, 7♣.

Unless specified in advance, a game is assumed to have no wild cards.

In *straight poker* and *five-card stud poker*, each player is dealt five cards. In *seven-card stud poker* each player is dealt seven cards from which he or she selects a hand of five. In *two-* (or *three-*) *card draw poker*, each player is dealt five cards. He or she may then discard up to two cards (or three, depending on what the players agree to) and be dealt replacements.

**Problem 1**

In straight poker what are the probabilities of being dealt each of the standard hands?

**Solution**

This is an experiment in which each possible outcome (hand) in the sample space S is equally likely, so the probability of an event (type of hand) H is $P(H) = n(H)/n(S)$. Since each hand is a combination of 5 cards,

$$n(S) = C_5^{52} = \frac{52 \cdot 51 \cdot 50 \cdot 49 \cdot 48}{5 \cdot 4 \cdot 3 \cdot 2 \cdot 1} = 2{,}598{,}960.$$

We must count $n(H)$ for each standard hand H.

**Straight flush.**

Only 10 denominations can be the highest denomination in a straight, namely, 5, 6, 7, 8, 9, 10, J, Q, K, A. To determine a straight flush we may (1) choose a suit, then (2) choose the denomination of the highest card. This can be done in $C_1^4 C_1^{10} = 4 \cdot 10 = 40$ ways, so there are 40 straight flushes.

**Four of a kind.**

(1) Pick a denomination, (2) pick 4 cards of the denomination, (3) pick a fifth card. $C_1^{13} C_4^4 C_1^{48} = 13 \cdot 1 \cdot 48 = 624$.

**Full house.**

(1) Pick a denomination for the three of a kind, (2) pick 3 cards of that denomination, (3) pick a second denomination for the pair, (4) pick 2 cards of that denomination. $C_1^{13} C_3^4 C_1^{12} C_2^4 = 13 \cdot 4 \cdot 12 \cdot 6 = 3{,}744$.

**Flush.**

(1) Pick a suit for the flush, (2) pick 5 cards from the chosen suit. But be careful! In poker a *straight* flush is not a flush. Therefore, we must subtract the straight flushes: $C_1^4 C_5^{13} - n(\text{straight flushes}) = 4 \cdot 1{,}287 - 40 = 4 \cdot 1{,}277 = 5{,}108$.

**Straight.**

(1) Pick a high card for the straight. (2) Once we have the highest card there are four possible choices for the next card, four for the next, and so on. But again we should not count straight flushes: $C_1^{40} \cdot 4^4 - n(\text{straight flushes}) = 40 \cdot 256 - 40 = 10{,}200$.

**Three of a kind.**

(1) Pick a denomination, (2) choose 3 cards of that denomination, (3) pick 2 different denominations from the 12 remaining denominations (4) and (5) pick a card of each of these denominations: $C_1^{13} \cdot C_3^4 \cdot C_2^{12} \cdot C_1^4 \cdot C_1^4 = 13 \cdot 4 \cdot 66 \cdot 4 \cdot 4 = 54{,}912$.

**Two pair.** (1) Pick 2 denominations, (2) pick a pair of one of these denominations, (3) pick a pair of the other denomination, (4) pick a fifth card of yet another denomination: $C_2^{13} \cdot C_2^4 \cdot C_2^4 \cdot C_1^{44} = 78 \cdot 6 \cdot 6 \cdot 44 = 123{,}552$.

**Pair.** (1) Pick a denomination, (2) pick a pair of that denomination, (3) pick 3 different denominations from the remaining 12 denominations, (4), (5), (6) pick 1 card of each of these 3 denominations: $C_1^{13} \cdot C_2^4 \cdot C_3^{12} \cdot C_1^4 \cdot C_1^4 \cdot C_1^4 = 13 \cdot 6 \cdot 220 \cdot 4 \cdot 4 \cdot 4 = 1{,}098{,}240$.

For the Nothing hands, see Problem 2(a) below.

With these counts it is a simple matter to tabulate the probabilities.

| Poker hand | Number | Probability | |
|---|---|---|---|
| Straight flush | 40 | $40/2{,}598{,}960 \doteq 1/65{,}000 \doteq 0.000015$ | |
| Four of a kind | 624 | $624/2{,}598{,}960 \doteq 1/4000$ | $\doteq 0.00024$ |
| Full house | 3,744 | $3{,}744/2{,}598{,}960 \doteq 1/700$ | $\doteq 0.00144$ |
| Flush | 5,108 | $5{,}108/2{,}598{,}960 \doteq 1/500$ | $\doteq 0.00197$ |
| Straight | 10,200 | $10{,}200/2{,}598{,}960 \doteq 1/250$ | $\doteq 0.00392$ |
| Three of a kind | 54,912 | $54{,}912/2{,}598{,}960 \doteq 1/50$ | $\doteq 0.0211$ |
| Two pair | 123,552 | $123{,}552/2{,}598{,}960 \doteq 1/20$ | $\doteq 0.0475$ |
| Pair | 1,098,240 | $1{,}098{,}240/2{,}598{,}960 \doteq 2/5$ | $\doteq 0.423$ |
| Total | 1,296,420 | | |

It is comforting to note that the usual ranking of poker hands is correct in the sense that higher ranked hands are less likely.

**Problem 2** (a) In the first hand of last Thursday's poker game, Alan got nothing. What is the probability of that?

(b) In the second hand "jacks or better" was required; that is, the person starting the bet had to have a hand at least as good as a pair of jacks. What are the chances that Alan could start the bid?

**Solution**

The high probability of getting nothing in poker explains why wild cards, drawing cards, and so forth, are often introduced.

Here is another count of the Nothing hands, which reconfirms our previous work. (1) Pick five different denominations, (2), (3), (4), (5), (6) pick one card of each denomination, but (7) don't pick the same suit for each card, and (8) throw out the straights:

$C_5^{13} \cdot (C_1^4 \cdot C_1^4 \cdot C_1^4 \cdot C_1^4 \cdot C_1^4 - C_1^4) - n(\text{straights})$
$= 1{,}287(4^5 - 4) - 10{,}200 = 1{,}302{,}540$ $\checkmark$.

(a) Since "nothing" is the complement of "something," P(nothing) $= 1 - $ P(something). From the table above we see that 1,296,420 hands contain something, so P(something) $=$ 1,296,420/2,598,960. Thus, P(nothing) $= 1 - $ 1,296,420/ 2,598,960 $=$ 1,302,540/2,598,960 $=$ 43,419/86,632 $=$ 0.501. Alan can expect nothing about half the time.

(b) We must first count the hands that contain a pair of jacks, queens, kings, or aces. (1) Pick one of the four denominations, (2) pick a pair of this denomination, (3) pick 3 different denominations from the 12 remaining denominations, (4), (5), (6) pick 1 card from each of these three denominations: $C_1^9 \cdot C_2^4 \cdot C_3^{12} \cdot C_1^4 \cdot C_1^4 \cdot C_1^4 = 9 \cdot 6 \cdot 220 \cdot 64 = 337{,}920$. Thus, there are 1,098,240 $-$ 337,920 $=$ 760,320 pairs below jacks. Hence,

$1,296,420 - 760,320 = 536,100$ hands contain jacks or better. The probability we want is $536,100/2,598,960 = 8,935/43,316 \doteq 0.206 \doteq \frac{1}{5}$.

In the second game of the evening deuces (twos) were wild. In the end Carl's three of a kind beat Alan's two pair. Whose hand was more likely?

Solution

This is rather complicated. You may want to read it later.

Without additional rules this is a very tedious problem, because each hand containing 1 or more wild cards can be interpreted in many ways. Since the game in question is a friendly one, let's assume each hand is interpreted as high as possible in "straight poker" (see the tabulation above). For example, the hand 2♦, 2♥, 7♦, 9♦, 10♥ would not be read as two pair or as three of a kind or as a 10-high straight but as a jack-high straight. Keeping this in mind we are ready to count the number of three-of-a-kind hands. If a hand contains 3 or 4 wild cards, it will be much better than three of a kind, so we count no such hands. If a hand contains exactly 2 wild cards, and its best interpretation is three of a kind, then the other 3 cards must be of different denominations, must not all have the same suit, and must not be part of a straight. There are $C_2^4$ ways to pick the wild cards. There are $C_1^4 \cdot C_1^4 \cdot C_1^4 - C_1^4$ ways to pick the suits of the non-wild cards, not all the same suit. The wild cards and the suits of the non-wild cards having beeen picked, there are $C_3^{12}$ ways to choose the denominations of the non-wild cards. But we must exclude those choices that produce straights. To do this we sort straights with exactly 2 wild cards according to the denomination of their lowest *non-wild* card. If the lowest non-wild card is an ace, then the denominations of the other two non-wild cards must be chosen from 3, 4, 5; so there are $C_2^3$ straights of this type. There are zero straights with lowest non-wild card of denomination 2, since deuces are wild. If the lowest non-wild card is 3, 4, 5, 6, 7, 8, 9, or 10, then the denominations of the other two non-wild cards must be chosen from the next 4 higher denominations; so there are $8 \cdot C_2^4$ straights of this type. If the lowest non-wild card is J, then one wild card must be used as 10 and the denominations of the other 2 non-wild cards must be chosen from Q, K, A, so there are $C_2^3$ straights of this type. If the lowest non-wild card is Q, then the wild cards must be used as 10, J, and the other 2 non-wild cards must be K, A; so there is 1 straight of this type. There are zero straights with lowest non-wild card K or A (counted high). Hence there are, in all,

$$C_2^4 \left( C_1^4 \cdot C_1^4 \cdot C_1^4 - C_1^4 \right) \left( C_3^{12} - C_2^3 - 0 - 8 \cdot C_2^4 - C_1^3 - 1 - 0 \right)$$

$$= 6(4 \cdot 4 \cdot 4 - 4)(220 - 3 - 0 - 8 \cdot 6 - 3 - 1 - 0) = 59,400$$

three-of-a-kind hands with exactly two wild deuces.

In order to get three of a kind with one wild card, exactly 2 of the other 4 cards must be of the same denomination. Thus, the number of such hands is $C_1^4(C_1^{12}C_2^4C_2^1C_1^4C_1^4) = 4 \cdot 12 \cdot 6 \cdot 55 \cdot 4 \cdot 4 = 253,440$. The number of three-of-a-kind hands with no wild cards is $C_1^{12}C_3^4C_2^1C_1^4C_1^4 = 12 \cdot 4 \cdot 55 \cdot 4 \cdot 4 = 42,240$. Thus, the number of three-of-a-kind hands is $59,400 + 253,440 + 42,240 = 355,080$.

Now a hand containing one or more wild cards cannot have two pair as its best interpretation. This is obvious if the hand has more than one wild card. If the hand has exactly one wild card and if it can be interpreted as two pair, then it must have at least one pair of non-wild cards. But then it would be interpreted as one of the 253,440 three-of-a-kind hands above. Thus, the only two-pair hands are those without wild cards, of which there are $C_2^{12}C_2^4C_2^4C_1^{40} = 66 \cdot 6 \cdot 6 \cdot 40 = 95,040$.

This is not surprising since we have agreed to give the best possible interpretation to a hand. Thus, a hand with a two will never be interpreted as a two-pair hand.

Thus, in this game two pair is less likely than three of a kind! Precisely, P(three of a kind) $= 2,959/21,658 \doteq 0.137$ and P(two pair) $= 396/10829 \doteq 0.037$; so the former is more than 3 times as likely as the latter.

**Problem 4**

SCRABBLE® Brand Crossword Game has 100 tiles marked as follows: 12 *E*s; 9 *A*s and *I*s; 8 *O*s; 6 *N*s, *R*s, and *T*s; 4 *D*s, *L*s, *S*s, and *U*s; 3 *G*s; 2 *B*s, *C*s, *F*s, *H*s, *M*s, *P*s, *V*s, *W*s, *Y*s, and blank tiles; and 1 *J*, *K*, *Q*, *X*, and *Z*. Seven tiles are drawn for the starting set. How many different starting sets are possible?

**Solution**

We will be counting combinations of 7 letters, some of which may be repeated various numbers of times. The following tabulation will be helpful.

| If you want to repeat a letter *at least* this many times | You may choose from this many different letters | |
|---|---|---|
| 7 | 4 | (*A, E, I, O*) |
| 6 | 7 | (*A, E, I, O, N, R, T*) |
| 5 | 7 | (*A, E, I, O, N, R, T*) |
| 4 | 11 | (*A, E, I, O, N, R, T, D, L, S, U*) |
| 3 | 12 | (*A, E, I, O, N, R, T, D, L, S, U, G*) |
| 2 | 22 | (all but *J, K, Q, X, Z*) |
| 1 | 27 | (all letters) |

We sort the starting sets according to size(s) of block(s) of repeating letters. For example, 7 means all 7 letters are the same; 3, 2, 2 means one letter repeated three times, another twice, and another twice. The count runs as follows.

| Size(s) of block(s) | Number of possible starting sets | | |
|---|---|---|---|
| 7 | (a) $C_1^4$ | = | 4 |
| 6, 1 | (b) $C_1^7 C_1^{26}$ | = | 182 |
| 5, 2 | $C_1^7 C_1^{21}$ | = | 147 |
| 5, 1, 1 | (c) $C_1^7 C_2^{26}$ | = | 2,275 |
| 4, 3 | $C_1^{11} \cdot C_1^{11}$ | = | 121 |
| 4, 2, 1 | $C_1^{11} \cdot C_1^{21} C_1^{25}$ | = | 5,775 |
| 4, 1, 1, 1 | $C_1^{11} \cdot C_3^{26}$ | = | 28,600 |
| 3, 3, 1 | $C_2^{12} \cdot C_1^{25}$ | = | 1,650 |
| 3, 2, 2 | $C_1^{12} \cdot C_2^{21}$ | = | 2,520 |
| 3, 2, 1, 1 | (d) $C_1^{12} \cdot C_1^{21} C_2^{25}$ | = | 75,600 |
| 3, 1, 1, 1, 1 | $C_1^{12} \cdot C_4^{26}$ | = | 179,400 |
| 2, 2, 2, 1 | $C_3^{22} \cdot C_1^{24}$ | = | 36,960 |
| 2, 2, 1, 1, 1 | $C_2^{22} \cdot C_3^{25}$ | = | 531,300 |
| 2, 1, 1, 1, 1, 1 | $C_1^{22} \cdot C_5^{26}$ | = | 1,447,160 |
| 1, 1, 1, 1, 1, 1, 1 | $C_7^{27}$ | = | 888,030 |

TOTAL: 3,199,724

(a) We must choose one of the 4 letters that can be used 7 times. It does not matter that, for example, there are $C_7^{12}$ ways to choose 7 Es; there is one starting set, EEEEEEE, in this count.

(b) Notice that the second factor is $C_1^{26}$, not $C_1^{27}$, since the choice of the letter to be used 6 times reduces by 1 the number of choices for the letter to be used one time.

(c) Choose the letter to be used 5 times. From the previous tabulation we see that there are 7 choices. Then choose 2 different letters each to be used once. While there are 27 letters which occur once, we have already chosen 1 letter to use 5 times. Thus, we have only 26 choices left.

(d) Choose a letter to be used 3 times; then a different letter to be used twice; then 2 different letters to be used once.

**Problem 5**

In Scrabble® Brand Crossword Game:
(a) What is the probability that your starting set is all Es?
(b) What is the probability that your starting set is all vowels (no blanks)?
(c) What is the probability that your starting set is all consonants (no blanks)?

**Solution**

The tiles themselves actually *are* all different; some just happen to contain the same letters.

Recall that $C_7^{12} = C_{12-7}^{12} = C_5^{12}$.

Imagine that all 100 tiles are different. There are $C_7^{100} = 16,007,560,800$ artificial outcomes, each equally likely.

(a) There are 12 Es and $C_7^{12}$ ways to choose 7 of them. Thus, there are $C_7^{12} = C_5^{12} = 792$ artificial outcomes with all Es. The probability that your starting set is all Es is $792/16,007,560,800 = 0.00000005$.

(b) There are 9 As, 12 Es, 9 Is, 8 Os, and 4 Us for a total of $9+12+9+8+4=42$ vowels. There are $C_7^{42} = 26,978,328$ artificial outcomes with all vowels; hence the probability is $C_7^{42}/C_7^{100} = (42 \cdot 41 \cdot 40 \cdot 39 \cdot 38 \cdot 37 \cdot 36) / (100 \cdot 99 \cdot 98 \cdot 97 \cdot 96 \cdot 95 \cdot 94) = (3 \cdot 41 \cdot 1 \cdot 13 \cdot 19 \cdot 37 \cdot 1)/(5 \cdot 11 \cdot 7 \cdot 97 \cdot 2 \cdot 95 \cdot 94) = 1,124,097/666,981,700 \doteq 0.00169$.

(c) There are $100 - n(\text{vowels}) - n(\text{blanks}) = 100 - 42 - 2 = 56$ consonants. Since $C_n^{56} = 231,917,400$, hence this probability is $C_7^{56}/C_7^{100} \doteq 0.0145$.

Probabilities connected with games are often expressed in terms of odds. The *odds for* an event A are the ratio of P(A) to P($\sim$A), expressed in integer form. If P(A) = $\frac{3}{5}$ for example, then the ratio of P(A) to P($\sim$A) is $\frac{3}{5}$ to $\frac{2}{5}$. Multiplying through by 5, we find that the odds for A are 3 to 2. Another way to understand odds is in terms of money bet and won. If P(A) = $\frac{3}{5}$, then a \$3 bet on A should pay \$5 if A occurs. Thus, a bet of \$3 should pay \$2 in net winnings, giving odds of 3 to 2.

These are the *fair* odds for A. The odds quoted by a gambling establishment are likely to include a percentage for "the house."

The *odds against* an event A are just the odds for $\sim$A. Thus, if the odds for A are 3 to 2, then the odds against A are 2 to 3.

Believe it or not, the odds *against* an event are often called, by gamblers, the odds *on* the event.

The general formulas are as follows.

---

CONVERSION OF PROBABILITY TO ODDS AND ODDS TO PROBABILITY

If P(A) = m/n, the (fair) odds for A are m to n − m and the (fair) odds against A are n − m to m.

If the (fair) odds for A are p to q, then P(A) = p/(p + q). If the (fair) odds against A are r to s, then P(A) = s/(r + s).

**1**

---

None of these results require that P be an equally likely distribution.

Problem 6　(a) The odds against Alan's being transferred to the Orono warehouse are 8 to 3. What's the probability that he will be sent?

(b) The probability that Alan will not get an A in his probability course is .82. What are the odds that he will get an A?

Solution　(a) In the notation of result **1**, r = 8 and s = 3, so P(Alan is sent to Orono) = $\frac{3}{11}$ $\doteq$ 0.273.

(b) P(Alan gets an A) = 1 − 0.82 = 0.18 = $\frac{18}{100}$ = $\frac{9}{50}$. In the notation of result **1**, m = 9 and n = 50. The odds that Alan will get an A are 9 to 50 − 9 or 9 to 41.

**Note:**　Odds are like fractions in the sense that odds of 9 to 41 are the same as odds of 18 to 82, and so on.

Exercises 6.1　Nicholas "Nick the Greek" Dandolos (1882–1966) was called king of the gamblers from 1928 to 1949. Prior to this, Arnold Rothstein had this role. The following description of their first meeting is taken from the book, *Nick the Greek King of the Gamblers*, by Cy

Rice (New York: Funk and Wagnalls, 1969) pp. 140–142. We have inserted numbers which refer to the questions that follow.

Nine hours ticked by. Nick was his usual fresh self. During the span of play he had eaten a small sandwich with the crusts cut off and had drunk the juice from two freshly squeezed oranges. After the first twenty-four hours he planned on a few sporadic sips of brandy.

By early morning he was ahead close to $700,000. Rothstein was also winning, but not substantially. Then, without warning, the fickle Goddess of Luck did an about-face and everything Nick tried turned sour. The poker proverb "Chips have no home" was proving its validity as his stack vanished, to be replenished by more buying.

Rothstein was growing richer, the chips building up before him. Infrequently Nick gazed searchingly at him and Rothstein stared back. It was strictly between the two of them now. They were heading for a showdown. The other players had been hit staggering blows and lacked the chips in this high-table-stakes game to raise or call when they should, often having to settle for part of the pot.

Stud hands were dealt. Nick had a king in the hole and a king up.[1] Rothstein had a queen of diamonds[2] showing. The other players had low cards. Nick sat to the left of the dealer. It was his bet. Not wanting to drive anyone out, he bet a modest $10,000. Two players called, and it was up to Rothstein.

Rothstein raised the pot $30,000.

Nick called. The other players passed, leaving only Nick and Rothstein to fight it out. Nick guessed that Rothstein had an ace in the hole, but no matter what card it was—even another queen—*he* had a good thing going and meant to nurse it along.

His next card was an eight and Rothstein received a nine of diamonds. He had two diamonds showing, but there was no cause for alarm. Nick didn't give a possible flush a second thought.[3] No player in his right mind, if he had three diamonds, would attempt to buck the percentages and try for two more. Not at the high stakes they were playing.

Nick bet another $10,000. Rothstein raised him $60,000. Nick just called.

For the next card Nick drew a five and Rothstein got a six of diamonds. Nick checked, and Rothstein counted out $90,000 in chips and calmly pushed them into the pot.

Nick picked up his half-smoked cigar from the ashtray and unhurriedly lit it. His concentration was on Rothstein's hands, which were resting on the table. They gave no clue. They were steady. Then Rothstein belched. It was a low belch, but to Nick, who hated unnecessary noise at a card game, it sounded like a canon had been fired.

The odds seemed heavily stacked in his favor. He summarized the situation. Rothstein either had a pair of queens or an ace—possibly an ace of diamonds, which gave him four of the same suit. Yet even if he did have the four diamonds, the odds against him drawing the fifth were great.[4]

The room was quiet. Everyone was watching Nick.

Nick called the $90,000 and raised the pot $188,500, every cent he had in front of him. Rothstein called. He still had chips left, but Nick was tapped out and the betting had ended.

There was $797,000 on the table, the biggest pot in the history of stud poker.

It was time for the final card. A seven of clubs fell to Nick, who stifled a yawn with the back of his hand. Rothstein was dealt a seven of diamonds.

Rothstein said, "Too bad you ran out of chips, Nick, or we could have made this an interesting pot."

Very slowly he turned his hole card over. It was an ace of diamonds, giving him a diamond flush.

Nick rose from the table. "Thank you, gentlemen, he said. "Once again it has been a pleasure."

Rothstein escorted him to the door. "You're a real sportsman," he complimented.

"Win without boasting. Lose without excuse," Nick said, quoting an American, Albert Payson Terhune.

---

We will suppose that a total of five players were involved but that no one was dealt any diamonds up except Rothstein. With these assumptions, ignoring the other players will have little effect on the answers.

1. (a) What is the probability of being dealt a pair of kings as your first 2 cards in stud poker?
   (b) What is the probability of being dealt 2 diamonds as your first 2 cards in stud poker?
2. (a) What is the probability that Rothstein has 2 diamonds given that he has 1 diamond?
   (b) What is the probability that Nick has 2 kings given that he has 1 king?
3. What is the probability that Rothstein will wind up with a flush given that he has 3 diamonds?
4. What are the odds against being dealt a fifth diamond given that you already have 4?
5. In seven-card stud poker you are dealt 7 cards and you select the best five-card hand from them. What is the probability that this best hand is a full house?
6. How many cards must you be dealt before it becomes certain that your hand contains a (five-card) flush?
7. How many cards can you be dealt and still not be able to select a standard (five-card) hand from them?
8. In five-card stud poker with 2 jokers in the deck, what is the probability that the best interpretation of your hand is a full house?
9. In draw poker if you hold, say, a 3, 4, 5, and 7 after discarding one card, you are trying to *fill an inside straight*, whereas if you hold, say, 4, 5, 6, and 7 you are trying to *fill an outside straight*. When Janet drew one card and lost to Alan's flush, she angrily threw her hand on the table: 3, 4, 5 of hearts, 6, 7 of spades. What are the odds that she had filled an inside straight?
10. What is the probability that the letters in your starting set in the Scrabble® Brand Crossword Game can be arranged to spell ABSTRACT?
11. How many different starting sets in the Scrabble® Brand Crossword Game consist entirely of vowels (no blanks)?
12. Use result **1** to convert a probability of m/n to odds and the resulting odds back to a probability.
13. Use result **1** to convert odds of p to q for A into a probability and the resulting probabilities back to odds.

## Section 6.2
## Matrix Inversion
## and Leontief Models

Matrix division is not a standard term in mathematics. We make temporary use of it here to help motivate the following discussion.

As a further application of Gauss-Jordan reduction we will develop the notion of matrix division. This operation is of interest to us for two reasons. First of all, having multiplied matrices in Chapter 2, we only naturally ask how to divide them. Second, in some cases matrix division can be used to solve systems of equations.

Let us consider the equation

$$\begin{bmatrix} 1 & 2 \\ 3 & 4 \end{bmatrix} \div \begin{bmatrix} 2 & 3 \\ 3 & 4 \end{bmatrix} = \begin{bmatrix} 2 & -1 \\ 0 & 1 \end{bmatrix} \qquad \mathbf{1}$$

The immediate question is: How did you get it? In order to answer this, we will consider the question, Why is equation **1** correct?

In ordinary arithmetic, you check an equation such as

$$32 \div 4 = 8 \qquad\qquad \textbf{2}$$

Although the order in which two numbers are multiplied is irrelevant (for example, $8 \times 4 = 32 = 4 \times 8$), the order of multiplication usually does make a difference with matrices. Thus, it is no real surprise that

$$\begin{bmatrix} 2 & 3 \\ 3 & 4 \end{bmatrix}\begin{bmatrix} 2 & -1 \\ 0 & 1 \end{bmatrix} = \begin{bmatrix} 4 & 1 \\ 6 & 1 \end{bmatrix}$$
$$\neq \begin{bmatrix} 1 & 2 \\ 3 & 4 \end{bmatrix}.$$

So we are really doing only a kind of "one-sided division." This is why the term "matrix division" is generally not used.

Recall that for two matrices to be equal all the corresponding entries must be equal.

by multiplying: $8 \times 4 = 32 \; \checkmark$. Let's try this with equation **1**:

$$\begin{bmatrix} 2 & -1 \\ 0 & 1 \end{bmatrix} \cdot \begin{bmatrix} 2 & 3 \\ 3 & 4 \end{bmatrix} = \begin{bmatrix} 1 & 2 \\ 3 & 4 \end{bmatrix} \; \checkmark$$

So we could solve the matrix equation

$$[?]\begin{bmatrix} 2 & 3 \\ 3 & 4 \end{bmatrix} = \begin{bmatrix} 1 & 2 \\ 3 & 4 \end{bmatrix}$$

to obtain the answer. If we let

$$[?] = \begin{bmatrix} w & x \\ y & z \end{bmatrix}$$

and multiply we obtain

$$\begin{bmatrix} w & x \\ y & z \end{bmatrix}\begin{bmatrix} 2 & 3 \\ 3 & 4 \end{bmatrix} = \begin{bmatrix} 2w+3x & 3w+4x \\ 2y+3z & 3y+4z \end{bmatrix} = \begin{bmatrix} 1 & 2 \\ 3 & 4 \end{bmatrix}$$

$$\text{or} \quad \begin{bmatrix} 2w+3x & = 1 \\ 3w+4x & = 2 \\ 2y+3z = 3 \\ 3y+4z = 4 \end{bmatrix}$$

If you solve this system, you will get the answer $w = 2$, $x = -1$, $y = 0$, and $z = 1$.

Of course, there is an easier way to go about this. You may remember that, in arithmetic, division is unnecessary in the sense that any division problem can be replaced by an equivalent multiplication problem. For example equation **2** can be replaced by

$$32 \times \tfrac{1}{4} = 8 \qquad\qquad \textbf{3}$$

that is, we "invert the divisor and multiply." So we could also replace equation **1** by an equivalent equation involving multiplication:

$$\begin{bmatrix} 1 & 2 \\ 3 & 4 \end{bmatrix} \times \dfrac{1}{\begin{bmatrix} 2 & 3 \\ 3 & 4 \end{bmatrix}} = \begin{bmatrix} 2 & -1 \\ 0 & 1 \end{bmatrix} \qquad\qquad \textbf{4}$$

Thus if we could "invert a matrix" we would be able to divide simply by multiplying by "1 over the divisor." Our next claim is that

$$\frac{1}{\begin{bmatrix} 2 & 3 \\ 3 & 4 \end{bmatrix}} = \begin{bmatrix} -4 & 3 \\ 3 & -2 \end{bmatrix}$$

**5**

Wrong, you say? Of course it is not quite correct since if we cross multiply we obtain

$$\begin{bmatrix} -4 & 3 \\ 3 & -2 \end{bmatrix} \begin{bmatrix} 2 & 3 \\ 3 & 4 \end{bmatrix} = 1$$

**6**

Equation **6** is incorrect since the product of two $2 \times 2$ matrices is another $2 \times 2$ matrix and not a number. Let's actually multiply out the left-hand side of equation **6**.

$$\begin{bmatrix} -4 & 3 \\ 3 & -2 \end{bmatrix} \begin{bmatrix} 2 & 3 \\ 3 & 4 \end{bmatrix} = \begin{bmatrix} 1 & 0 \\ 0 & 1 \end{bmatrix}$$

**7**

The matrix $\begin{bmatrix} 1 & 0 \\ 0 & 1 \end{bmatrix}$ is not equal to the number 1 but it does have the same effect in matrix multiplication that 1 has in number multiplication: it doesn't change what it is multiplied by.
For example,

$$\begin{bmatrix} 1 & 0 \\ 0 & 1 \end{bmatrix} \begin{bmatrix} 5 & 7 \\ -2 & 3 \end{bmatrix} = \begin{bmatrix} 5 & 7 \\ -2 & 3 \end{bmatrix}$$

$$\begin{bmatrix} 8 & 3 \\ 2 & 1 \end{bmatrix} \begin{bmatrix} 1 & 0 \\ 0 & 1 \end{bmatrix} = \begin{bmatrix} 8 & 3 \\ 2 & 1 \end{bmatrix}$$

$$\begin{bmatrix} 7 & 3 \\ 1 & 1 \\ -2 & 4 \end{bmatrix} \begin{bmatrix} 1 & 0 \\ 0 & 1 \end{bmatrix} = \begin{bmatrix} 7 & 3 \\ 1 & 1 \\ -2 & 4 \end{bmatrix}$$

We first met this matrix in Section 2.6.

The matrix $\begin{bmatrix} 1 & 0 \\ 0 & 1 \end{bmatrix}$ is called an **identity matrix**, since it preserves the identity of any matrix multiplied by it. In general, an identity matrix is a square matrix with 1s in the **main diagonal** (that is, the northwest-to-southeast diagonal) and 0s everywhere else. The $3 \times 3$, $4 \times 4$, and $5 \times 5$ identity matrices are, respectively,

If you multiply any of these identity matrices by any given matrix (of a size for which the multiplication will be defined) the answer is the given matrix.

$$\begin{bmatrix} 1 & 0 & 0 \\ 0 & 1 & 0 \\ 0 & 0 & 1 \end{bmatrix}, \begin{bmatrix} 1 & 0 & 0 & 0 \\ 0 & 1 & 0 & 0 \\ 0 & 0 & 1 & 0 \\ 0 & 0 & 0 & 1 \end{bmatrix}, \text{ and } \begin{bmatrix} 1 & 0 & 0 & 0 & 0 \\ 0 & 1 & 0 & 0 & 0 \\ 0 & 0 & 1 & 0 & 0 \\ 0 & 0 & 0 & 1 & 0 \\ 0 & 0 & 0 & 0 & 1 \end{bmatrix}$$

An **inverse** of the square matrix A is any matrix whose product with A (on either side) is an identity matrix of the same size as A.

For example, the matrix

$$\begin{bmatrix} 6 & -1 & -5 \\ -7 & 1 & 5 \\ -10 & 2 & 11 \end{bmatrix} \qquad \textbf{8}$$

is an inverse of the matrix

$$\begin{bmatrix} -1 & 1 & 0 \\ -27 & -16 & -5 \\ 4 & 2 & 1 \end{bmatrix} \qquad \textbf{9}$$

since

$$\begin{bmatrix} 6 & -1 & -5 \\ -7 & 1 & 5 \\ -10 & 2 & 11 \end{bmatrix} \begin{bmatrix} -1 & -1 & 0 \\ -27 & -16 & -5 \\ 4 & 2 & 1 \end{bmatrix} = \begin{bmatrix} 1 & 0 & 0 \\ 0 & 1 & 0 \\ 0 & 0 & 1 \end{bmatrix} \qquad \textbf{10}$$

Finally, we describe division of matrices as follows. *To divide one matrix by another, multiply the first matrix by the inverse of the second.* Thus, (making use of the inverse mentioned above):

$$\begin{bmatrix} 2 & 7 & 5 \\ -3 & 1 & 5 \\ 4 & 2 & 8 \end{bmatrix} \div \begin{bmatrix} -1 & -1 & 0 \\ -27 & -16 & -5 \\ 4 & 2 & 1 \end{bmatrix} =$$

$$\begin{bmatrix} 2 & 7 & 5 \\ -3 & 1 & 5 \\ 4 & 2 & 8 \end{bmatrix} \times \begin{bmatrix} 6 & -1 & -5 \\ -7 & 1 & 5 \\ -10 & 2 & 11 \end{bmatrix} = \begin{bmatrix} -87 & 15 & 80 \\ -75 & 14 & 75 \\ -70 & 14 & 78 \end{bmatrix}$$

Before we explain how to actually compute inverses there are several things which should be mentioned.

Recall from Section 6 of Chapter 2 that the order in which two matrices are multiplied usually makes a difference. It comes as a pleasant surprise then to note that besides equations **7** and **10** we also have

$$\begin{bmatrix} 2 & 3 \\ 3 & 4 \end{bmatrix} \begin{bmatrix} -4 & 3 \\ 3 & -2 \end{bmatrix} = \begin{bmatrix} 1 & 0 \\ 0 & 1 \end{bmatrix} \qquad \textbf{11}$$

and

$$\begin{bmatrix} -1 & -1 & 0 \\ -27 & -16 & -5 \\ 4 & 2 & 1 \end{bmatrix} \begin{bmatrix} 6 & -1 & 5 \\ -7 & 1 & 5 \\ -10 & 2 & 11 \end{bmatrix} = \begin{bmatrix} 1 & 0 & 0 \\ 0 & 1 & 0 \\ 0 & 0 & 1 \end{bmatrix} \qquad \textbf{12}$$

This is why matrix inversion *is* a standard term in mathematics.

In general, it can be shown that the product *in either order* of a square matrix and an inverse is the same identity matrix. In view of this, we can say that matrix **9**, is the inverse of matrix **8** as well as the other way around. In general, if we find two square matrices whose product is an identity matrix, then each matrix is an inverse of the other. For example, check that

$$\begin{bmatrix} 0 & 5 & -7 & 1 \\ -2 & 0 & 0 & 1 \\ 1 & -2 & 3 & -1 \\ 1 & -1 & 1 & 0 \end{bmatrix} \begin{bmatrix} 1 & 1 & 2 & 1 \\ 4 & 5 & 9 & 1 \\ 3 & 4 & 7 & 1 \\ 2 & 3 & 4 & 2 \end{bmatrix} = \begin{bmatrix} 1 & 0 & 0 & 0 \\ 0 & 1 & 0 & 0 \\ 0 & 0 & 1 & 0 \\ 0 & 0 & 0 & 1 \end{bmatrix} \quad \textbf{13}$$

This being true, we may say that the first matrix is an inverse of the second. We may also say that the second matrix is an inverse of the first and confidently write (although you may wish to check)

$$\begin{bmatrix} 1 & 1 & 2 & 1 \\ 4 & 5 & 9 & 1 \\ 3 & 4 & 7 & 1 \\ 2 & 3 & 4 & 2 \end{bmatrix} \begin{bmatrix} 0 & 5 & -7 & 1 \\ -2 & 0 & 0 & 1 \\ 1 & -2 & 3 & -1 \\ 1 & -1 & 1 & 0 \end{bmatrix} = \begin{bmatrix} 1 & 0 & 0 & 0 \\ 0 & 1 & 0 & 0 \\ 0 & 0 & 1 & 0 \\ 0 & 0 & 0 & 1 \end{bmatrix} \quad \textbf{14}$$

It can also be shown that a square matrix can have at most one inverse. Therefore from now on we will refer to *the* inverse. Exponential notation is usually used to denote the inverse of a matrix. For example the inverse of the matrix

$$\begin{bmatrix} 2 & 3 \\ 3 & 4 \end{bmatrix}$$

is denoted

$$\begin{bmatrix} 2 & 3 \\ 3 & 4 \end{bmatrix}^{-1}$$

From equation **11** we obtain

$$\begin{bmatrix} 2 & 3 \\ 3 & 4 \end{bmatrix}^{-1} = \begin{bmatrix} -4 & 3 \\ 3 & -2 \end{bmatrix}$$

Similarly, equation **12** may be rewritten

$$\begin{bmatrix} -1 & -1 & 0 \\ -27 & -16 & -5 \\ 4 & 2 & 1 \end{bmatrix}^{-1} = \begin{bmatrix} 6 & -1 & 0 \\ -7 & 1 & 5 \\ -10 & 2 & 11 \end{bmatrix}$$

or

$$\begin{bmatrix} 6 & -1 & 0 \\ -7 & 1 & 5 \\ -10 & 2 & 11 \end{bmatrix}^{-1} = \begin{bmatrix} -1 & -1 & 0 \\ -27 & -16 & -5 \\ 4 & 2 & 1 \end{bmatrix}$$

Notice that we have been discussing the inverses of *square* matrices only. For example,

$$\begin{bmatrix} 1 & 2 & -1 \\ 2 & 2 & 3 \end{bmatrix} \begin{bmatrix} -9 & -3 \\ 6 & 2 \\ 2 & 1 \end{bmatrix} = \begin{bmatrix} 1 & 0 \\ 0 & 1 \end{bmatrix} \qquad\qquad \textbf{15}$$

but

$$\begin{bmatrix} -9 & -3 \\ 6 & 2 \\ 2 & 1 \end{bmatrix} \begin{bmatrix} 1 & 2 & -1 \\ 2 & 2 & 3 \end{bmatrix} = \begin{bmatrix} -15 & -24 & 0 \\ 10 & 16 & 0 \\ 4 & 6 & 1 \end{bmatrix} \qquad \textbf{16}$$

Thus, the two matrices on the left side of equation **15**, are, we might say, "semi-inverses" of each other. Also, a given non-square matrix may have many such "semi-inverses." For example, compare equation **15** with

$$\begin{bmatrix} 1 & 2 & -1 \\ 2 & 2 & 3 \end{bmatrix} \begin{bmatrix} 3 & 1 \\ -\frac{3}{2} & -\frac{1}{2} \\ -1 & 0 \end{bmatrix} = \begin{bmatrix} 1 & 0 \\ 0 & 1 \end{bmatrix} \qquad\qquad \textbf{17}$$

We shall avoid these difficulties by declaring, simply, that *non-square matrices do not have inverses.*

Do not think that every square matrix has an inverse. Consider, for example, the matrix

$$\begin{bmatrix} 1 & 2 \\ 0 & 0 \end{bmatrix} \qquad\qquad \textbf{18}$$

Its inverse would have to be a $2 \times 2$ matrix $\begin{bmatrix} w & x \\ y & z \end{bmatrix}$ such that

$$\begin{bmatrix} 1 & 2 \\ 0 & 0 \end{bmatrix} \begin{bmatrix} w & x \\ y & z \end{bmatrix} = \begin{bmatrix} 1 & 0 \\ 0 & 1 \end{bmatrix} \qquad\qquad \textbf{19}$$

But the $(2,2)$ entry in the product on the left side of system **19** is $0x + 0z$, and that cannot be made equal to 1 no matter what values we assign to x and z. Thus, there is no matrix that can make equation **19** hold; that is, matrix **18**, although square, has no inverse. "Oh well," you say, "matrix **18** has a row of zeros. Surely a square matrix with no row or column of zeros will always have an inverse." Not so. It can be shown, for example, that the matrix

$$\begin{bmatrix} 1 & 2 \\ 3 & 6 \end{bmatrix} \qquad\qquad \textbf{20}$$

See Exercise 30 in this section.

has no inverse. To summarize: non-square matrices do not have inverses. Some square matrices have inverses and some do not, and there appears to be no easy way to tell whether or not a given square matrix has an inverse. (Actually, there is a fairly easy way to tell this for a $2 \times 2$ matrix. But for larger square matrices it can be quite a chore.)

Our problem is: given a square matrix, does it have an inverse and, if it does, how is the inverse found? In some cases, mostly of theoretical interest only, we may want to know only whether a matrix has an inverse, not what the inverse is. There is a method to determine just this, which we discuss in Exercise 49. In the method to be presented here, we begin to calculate the inverse of the matrix without knowing whether or not it has one. If our calculation succeeds, we have the inverse; and it can be shown that, if it fails, the inverse does not exist.

We develop this method by calculating the inverse of matrix **8** above. We seek a $3 \times 3$ matrix [?] such that

$$\begin{bmatrix} 6 & -1 & -5 \\ -7 & 1 & 5 \\ -10 & 2 & 11 \end{bmatrix} \begin{bmatrix} \\ ? \\ \end{bmatrix} = \begin{bmatrix} 1 & 0 & 0 \\ 0 & 1 & 0 \\ 0 & 0 & 1 \end{bmatrix} \qquad \textbf{21}$$

We calculate this unknown matrix one column at a time. Say the first column is $\begin{bmatrix} x_1 \\ x_2 \\ x_3 \end{bmatrix}$. Then matrix **8** times this column must give the first column of the $3 \times 3$ identity matrix in equation **21**:

$$\begin{bmatrix} 6 & -1 & -5 \\ -7 & 1 & 5 \\ -10 & 2 & 11 \end{bmatrix} \begin{bmatrix} x_1 \\ x_2 \\ x_3 \end{bmatrix} = \begin{bmatrix} 1 \\ 0 \\ 0 \end{bmatrix} \qquad \textbf{22}$$

If we multiply out the left hand side of equation **22** we obtain

$$\begin{bmatrix} 6x_1 - x_2 - 5x_3 \\ -7x_1 + x_2 + 5x_3 \\ -10x_1 + 2x_2 + 11x_3 \end{bmatrix} = \begin{bmatrix} 1 \\ 0 \\ 0 \end{bmatrix}$$

In order for these two matrices to be equal, their corresponding entries must be equal; so we obtain the system of equations

$$\begin{bmatrix} 6x_1 - x_2 - 5x_3 = 1 \\ -7x_1 + x_2 + 5x_3 = 0 \\ -10x_1 + 2x_2 + 11x_3 = 0 \end{bmatrix} \qquad \textbf{23}$$

We solve system **23** by Gauss-Jordan reduction:

$$\begin{bmatrix} 6 & -1 & -5 & 1 \\ -7 & 1 & 5 & 0 \\ -10 & 2 & 11 & 0 \end{bmatrix}$$

$$\begin{matrix} \frac{1}{6}R_1 \\ R_2+\frac{7}{6}R_1 \\ R_3+\frac{5}{3}R_1 \end{matrix} \begin{bmatrix} 1 & -\frac{1}{6} & -\frac{5}{6} & \frac{1}{6} \\ 0 & -\frac{1}{6} & -\frac{5}{6} & \frac{7}{6} \\ 0 & \frac{1}{3} & \frac{8}{3} & \frac{5}{3} \end{bmatrix}$$

$$\begin{matrix} R_1-R_2 \\ -6R_2 \\ R_3+2R_2 \end{matrix} \begin{bmatrix} 1 & 0 & 0 & -1 \\ 0 & 1 & 5 & -7 \\ 0 & 0 & 1 & 4 \end{bmatrix} R_2-5R_3 \begin{bmatrix} 1 & 0 & 0 & -1 \\ 0 & 1 & 0 & -27 \\ 0 & 0 & 1 & 4 \end{bmatrix}$$

Hence, $x_1 = -1$, $x_2 = -27$, $x_3 = 4$; so the first column of the inverse matrix is

$$C_1 = \begin{bmatrix} -1 \\ -27 \\ 4 \end{bmatrix} \qquad\qquad \textbf{24}$$

Having found the first column of the inverse, we now proceed in a similar fashion to find the second column. Suppose the second column of the inverse matrix is $\begin{bmatrix} x_1 \\ x_2 \\ x_3 \end{bmatrix}$. Then matrix **8** times this column must give the second column of the identity matrix of equation **21**:

$$\begin{bmatrix} 6 & -1 & -5 \\ -7 & 1 & 5 \\ -10 & 2 & 11 \end{bmatrix} \begin{bmatrix} x_1 \\ x_2 \\ x_3 \end{bmatrix} = \begin{bmatrix} 0 \\ 1 \\ 0 \end{bmatrix} \qquad\qquad \textbf{25}$$

As before we multiply out the left hand side of equation **25**, equate corresponding entries, and obtain a similar system of equations

$$\begin{bmatrix} 6x_1 - x_2 - 5x_3 = 0 \\ -7x_1 + x_2 + 5x_3 = 1 \\ -10x_1 + 2x_2 + 11x_3 = 0 \end{bmatrix} \qquad\qquad \textbf{26}$$

We solve system **26** by Gauss-Jordan reduction:

$$\begin{bmatrix} 6 & -1 & -5 & 0 \\ -7 & 1 & 5 & 1 \\ -10 & 2 & 11 & 0 \end{bmatrix}$$

$$\begin{matrix} \tfrac{1}{6}R_1 \\ R_2+\tfrac{7}{6}R_1 \\ R_3+\tfrac{5}{3}R_1 \end{matrix} \begin{bmatrix} 1 & -\tfrac{1}{6} & -\tfrac{5}{6} & 0 \\ 0 & -\tfrac{1}{6} & -\tfrac{5}{6} & 1 \\ 0 & \tfrac{1}{3} & \tfrac{8}{3} & 0 \end{bmatrix}$$

$$\begin{matrix} R_1-R_2 \\ -6R_2 \\ R_3+2R_2 \end{matrix} \begin{bmatrix} 1 & 0 & 0 & -1 \\ 0 & 1 & 5 & -6 \\ 0 & 0 & 1 & 2 \end{bmatrix} R_2-5R_3 \begin{bmatrix} 1 & 0 & 0 & -1 \\ 0 & 1 & 0 & -16 \\ 0 & 0 & 1 & 2 \end{bmatrix}$$

The second column of the inverse matrix is thus

$$C_2 = \begin{bmatrix} -1 \\ -16 \\ 2 \end{bmatrix} \qquad \textbf{27}$$

Finally, we consider the third column. Suppose the third column of the inverse matrix is $\begin{bmatrix} x_1 \\ x_2 \\ x_3 \end{bmatrix}$. Then, proceeding as before, we must solve

$$\begin{bmatrix} 6 & -1 & -5 \\ -7 & 1 & 5 \\ -10 & 2 & 11 \end{bmatrix}\begin{bmatrix} x_1 \\ x_2 \\ x_3 \end{bmatrix} = \begin{bmatrix} 0 \\ 0 \\ 1 \end{bmatrix} \qquad \textbf{28}$$

$$\begin{bmatrix} 6 & -1 & -5 & 0 \\ -7 & 1 & 5 & 0 \\ -10 & 2 & 11 & 1 \end{bmatrix}$$

$$\begin{matrix} \tfrac{1}{6}R_1 \\ R_2+\tfrac{7}{6}R_1 \\ R_3+\tfrac{5}{3}R_1 \end{matrix} \begin{bmatrix} 1 & -\tfrac{1}{6} & -\tfrac{5}{6} & 0 \\ 0 & -\tfrac{1}{6} & -\tfrac{5}{6} & 0 \\ 0 & \tfrac{1}{3} & \tfrac{8}{3} & 1 \end{bmatrix}$$

$$\begin{matrix} R_1-R_2 \\ -6R_2 \\ R_3+2R_2 \end{matrix} \begin{bmatrix} 1 & 0 & 0 & 0 \\ 0 & 1 & 5 & 0 \\ 0 & 0 & 1 & 1 \end{bmatrix} R_2-5R_3 \begin{bmatrix} 1 & 0 & 0 & 0 \\ 0 & 1 & 0 & -5 \\ 0 & 0 & 1 & 1 \end{bmatrix}$$

The third column of the inverse matrix is thus

$$C_3 = \begin{bmatrix} 0 \\ -5 \\ 1 \end{bmatrix} \qquad \textbf{29}$$

We have computed each column; from equations **24**, **27**, and **29**, the inverse matrix is

$$\begin{bmatrix} -1 & -1 & 0 \\ -27 & -16 & -5 \\ 4 & 2 & 1 \end{bmatrix} \qquad \textbf{30}$$

as was checked in equation **10**.

Now notice this: since the first three columns of the matrices for each of systems **23**, **26**, and **28** is the same matrix, namely matrix **8**, the steps performed in each of the three Gauss-Jordan reductions above were exactly the same. We could have carried out all three Gauss-Jordan reductions at the same time, simply carrying along, in order, the computations with all three columns of the identity matrix of equation **21**, like this:

*This idea has wider application. See Exercises 50 and 51.*

$$\begin{bmatrix} 6 & -1 & -5 & 1 & 0 & 0 \\ -7 & 1 & 5 & 0 & 1 & 0 \\ -10 & 2 & 11 & 0 & 0 & 1 \end{bmatrix}$$

$$\begin{matrix} \frac{1}{6}R_1 \\ R_2 + \frac{7}{6}R_1 \\ R_3 + \frac{5}{3}R_1 \end{matrix} \begin{bmatrix} 1 & -\frac{1}{6} & -\frac{5}{6} & \frac{1}{6} & 0 & 0 \\ 0 & -\frac{1}{6} & -\frac{5}{6} & \frac{7}{6} & 1 & 0 \\ 0 & \frac{1}{3} & \frac{8}{3} & \frac{5}{3} & 0 & 1 \end{bmatrix}$$

$$\begin{matrix} R_1 - R_2 \\ -6R_2 \\ R_3 + 2R_2 \end{matrix} \begin{bmatrix} 1 & 0 & 0 & -1 & -1 & 0 \\ 0 & 1 & 5 & -7 & -6 & 0 \\ 0 & 0 & 1 & 4 & 2 & 1 \end{bmatrix}$$

$$\begin{matrix} \\ R_2 - 5R_3 \\ \\ \end{matrix} \begin{bmatrix} 1 & 0 & 0 & -1 & -1 & 0 \\ 0 & 1 & 0 & -27 & -16 & -5 \\ 0 & 0 & 1 & 4 & 2 & 1 \end{bmatrix}$$

The answer, matrix **30**, appears "all put together" at the end (outlined in dashes).

It can be shown that this method for finding the inverse of a matrix will work for any square matrix that has an inverse. If the method fails, it is either because the given matrix is not square or because it is square but has no inverse. We present the general method in the following flow chart.

**To Find the Inverse**
**of a Matrix,**
**(If It Exists)**

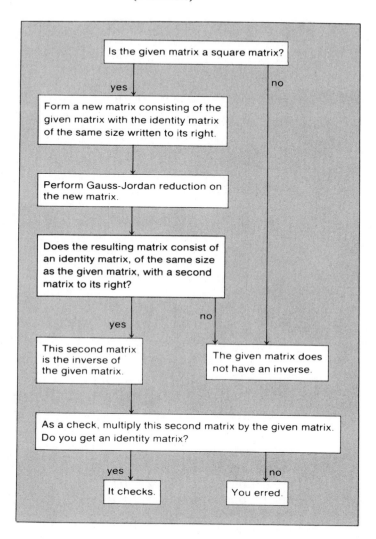

Note: If you do not perform Gauss-Jordan reduction as presented in Section 3 of Chapter 2 but use instead some modification, such as the shortcuts presented in Section 4 of Chapter 2, then add to the third box of this flow chart the statement:

It may also be necessary to switch some rows.

Do not clear any column in the right half of the matrix.

Problem 1   Find the inverse, if it exists, of

$$\begin{bmatrix} 0 & 5 & -7 & 1 \\ -2 & 0 & 0 & 1 \\ 1 & -2 & 3 & -1 \\ 1 & -1 & 1 & 0 \end{bmatrix}$$

Solution

$$\left[\begin{array}{rrrr|rrrr} 0 & 5 & -7 & 1 & 1 & 0 & 0 & 0 \\ -2 & 0 & 0 & 1 & 0 & 1 & 0 & 0 \\ 1 & -2 & 3 & -1 & 0 & 0 & 1 & 0 \\ 1 & -1 & 1 & 0 & 0 & 0 & 0 & 1 \end{array}\right]$$

$$\left[\begin{array}{rrrr|rrrr} -2 & 0 & 0 & 1 & 0 & 1 & 0 & 0 \\ 0 & 5 & -7 & 1 & 1 & 0 & 0 & 0 \\ 1 & -2 & 3 & -1 & 0 & 0 & 1 & 0 \\ 1 & -1 & 1 & 0 & 0 & 0 & 0 & 1 \end{array}\right]$$

$$\left[\begin{array}{rrrr|rrrr} 1 & 0 & 0 & -\frac{1}{2} & 0 & -\frac{1}{2} & 0 & 0 \\ 0 & 5 & -7 & 1 & 1 & 0 & 0 & 0 \\ 0 & -2 & 3 & -\frac{1}{2} & 0 & \frac{1}{2} & 1 & 0 \\ 0 & -1 & 1 & \frac{1}{2} & 0 & \frac{1}{2} & 0 & 1 \end{array}\right]$$

$$\left[\begin{array}{rrrr|rrrr} 1 & 0 & 0 & -\frac{1}{2} & 0 & -\frac{1}{2} & 0 & 0 \\ 0 & 1 & -\frac{7}{5} & \frac{1}{5} & \frac{1}{5} & 0 & 0 & 0 \\ 0 & 0 & \frac{1}{5} & -\frac{1}{10} & \frac{2}{5} & \frac{1}{2} & 1 & 0 \\ 0 & 0 & -\frac{2}{5} & \frac{7}{10} & \frac{1}{5} & \frac{1}{2} & 0 & 1 \end{array}\right]$$

$$\left[\begin{array}{rrrr|rrrr} 1 & 0 & 0 & -\frac{1}{2} & 0 & -\frac{1}{2} & 0 & 0 \\ 0 & 1 & 0 & -\frac{1}{2} & 3 & \frac{7}{2} & 7 & 0 \\ 0 & 0 & 1 & -\frac{1}{2} & 2 & \frac{5}{2} & 5 & 0 \\ 0 & 0 & 0 & \frac{1}{2} & 1 & \frac{3}{2} & 2 & 1 \end{array}\right]$$

$$\left[\begin{array}{rrrr|rrrr} 1 & 0 & 0 & 0 & 1 & 1 & 2 & 1 \\ 0 & 1 & 0 & 0 & 4 & 5 & 9 & 1 \\ 0 & 0 & 1 & 0 & 3 & 4 & 7 & 1 \\ 0 & 0 & 0 & 1 & 2 & 3 & 4 & 2 \end{array}\right]$$

The inverse is

$$\begin{bmatrix} 1 & 1 & 2 & 1 \\ 4 & 5 & 9 & 1 \\ 3 & 4 & 7 & 1 \\ 2 & 3 & 4 & 2 \end{bmatrix}$$

as was checked in equations **13** and **14**.

Problem 2   Find the inverse, if it exists, of

$$\begin{bmatrix} 0 & 1 & 2 & 3 \\ 4 & 7 & 2 & 1 \end{bmatrix}$$

Solution   The matrix is not square, so it has no inverse.

Problem 3   Find the inverse, if it exists, of

$$\begin{bmatrix} -1 & 2 & 4 \\ 3 & -4 & -3 \\ 2 & -2 & 1 \end{bmatrix}$$   **31**

Solution

$$\begin{bmatrix} -1 & 2 & 4 & 1 & 0 & 0 \\ 3 & -4 & -3 & 0 & 1 & 0 \\ 2 & -2 & 1 & 0 & 0 & 1 \end{bmatrix} \begin{bmatrix} 1 & -2 & -4 & -1 & 0 & 0 \\ 0 & 2 & 9 & 3 & 1 & 0 \\ 0 & 2 & 9 & 2 & 0 & 1 \end{bmatrix}$$

$$\begin{bmatrix} 1 & -2 & -4 & -1 & 0 & 0 \\ 0 & 2 & 9 & 3 & 1 & 0 \\ 0 & 0 & 0 & -1 & -1 & 1 \end{bmatrix}$$

The point is: if at any point in the reduction you see that you cannot achieve the identity matrix in the left half, QUIT. This illustrates one advantage the mind has over the computer, or at least we like to think it does.

Halt! It is clear now that we are not going to be able to achieve the 3×3 identity matrix in the left half of this matrix, so we may now say that matrix **31** has no inverse. Perhaps you saw that this was going to happen one step before we did. If so, that's fine; no need to go further. Perhaps, on the other hand, you still do not see what is going to happen. Then you must proceed:

$$\begin{bmatrix} 1 & 0 & 5 & 2 & 1 & 0 \\ 0 & 1 & \frac{9}{2} & \frac{3}{2} & \frac{1}{2} & 0 \\ 0 & 0 & 0 & -1 & -1 & 1 \end{bmatrix} \begin{bmatrix} 1 & 0 & 5 & 0 & -1 & 2 \\ 0 & 1 & \frac{9}{2} & 0 & -1 & \frac{3}{2} \\ 0 & 0 & 0 & 1 & 1 & -1 \end{bmatrix}$$

This is the final result of Gauss-Jordan reduction, from which we conclude that the matrix has no inverse.

For more information on matrix inversion and for a discussion of the related topic of determinants, see the authors' book, *Matrix Methods in Finite Mathematics*.

All of the shortcuts for Gauss-Jordan reduction that were discussed in Section 2.4 may be employed in calculating inverse matrices, with three exceptions: (1) do not clear any column in the right half of the matrix being reduced; (2) rows may have to be switched in order to achieve the identity matrix in the left side; and (3) the cleared columns in the left half must contain 1s. As before we recommend shortcuts only to students who have a thorough understanding of Gauss-Jordan reduction and matrix inversion.

In the following example we use inverse matrices to solve systems of equations.

Appalachian Creations often fills orders for long and short tent stakes. In its Boston warehouse it has 2 types of boxes of tent stakes: type 1 contains 2 dozen short and 1 dozen long stakes; type 2 contains 5 dozen short and 3 dozen long stakes. In filling orders it is easier to ship these boxes than to break them up. For some orders this is possible but for others it seems to be impossible.

Problem 4

How can the order department of AC determine whether or not it is possible to fill a given order with whole boxes, and, if it is, how many of each type are needed to fill the order? Table 1 shows a few of the vast number of incoming orders.

Table 1

| Order number | 51 | 52 | 53 | 54 | 55 | 56 | 57 |
|---|---|---|---|---|---|---|---|
| Short stakes (doz.) | 9 | 5 | 4 | 7 | 98 | 74 | 40 |
| Long stakes (doz.) | 5 | 3 | 2 | 4 | 52 | 30 | 40 |

Solution

Let $x_1$ be the number of type-1 boxes to be shipped and $x_2$ be the number of type-2 boxes to be shipped in filling a given order. A shipment of $x_1$ type-1 boxes and $x_2$ type-2 boxes contains $2x_1 + 5x_2$ dozen short stakes and $x_1 + 3x_2$ dozen long stakes. To fill order number 51, we need to solve the system

$$\begin{bmatrix} 2x_1 + 5x_2 = 9 \\ x_1 + 3x_2 = 5 \end{bmatrix} \qquad \textbf{32}$$

We solve this system by Gauss-Jordan reduction

$$\begin{bmatrix} 2 & 5 & 9 \\ 1 & 3 & 5 \end{bmatrix} \quad \begin{matrix} \frac{1}{2}R_1 \\ R_2 - \frac{1}{2}R_1 \end{matrix} \begin{bmatrix} 1 & \frac{5}{2} & \frac{9}{2} \\ 0 & \frac{1}{2} & \frac{1}{2} \end{bmatrix} \quad \begin{matrix} R_1 - 5R_2 \\ 2R_2 \end{matrix} \begin{bmatrix} 1 & 0 & 2 \\ 0 & 1 & 1 \end{bmatrix}$$

To fill order number 51 we need to use 2 type-1 boxes and 1 type-2 box.

That was easy. But now we have to solve the system for order number 52,

$$\begin{bmatrix} 2x_1 + 5x_2 = 5 \\ x_1 + 3x_2 = 3 \end{bmatrix}$$

then the system for order number 53, and so on. Is there an easier way, that is, a way involving fewer computations than those needed with repeated Gauss-Jordan reductions?

We have to solve many systems of the form

$$\begin{bmatrix} 2x_1 + 5x_2 = a \\ x_1 + 3x_2 = b \end{bmatrix} \qquad \textbf{33}$$

for various orders of a dozen short stakes and b dozen long stakes. Note that it is possible to write system **33** as a single matrix equation

$$\begin{bmatrix} 2 & 5 \\ 1 & 3 \end{bmatrix} \begin{bmatrix} x_1 \\ x_2 \end{bmatrix} = \begin{bmatrix} a \\ b \end{bmatrix} \qquad \textbf{34}$$

To see this, perform the indicated multiplication on the left

$$\begin{bmatrix} 2x_1 + 5x_2 \\ x_1 + 3x_2 \end{bmatrix} = \begin{bmatrix} a \\ b \end{bmatrix}$$

and recall that, for two matrices to be equal, the corresponding entries must be the same; that is,

$$2x_1 + 5x_2 = a$$

and

$$x_1 + 3x_2 = b$$

We now compute the inverse of the matrix $\begin{bmatrix} 2 & 5 \\ 1 & 3 \end{bmatrix}$ that occurs in equation **34**.

$$\begin{bmatrix} 2 & 5 & 1 & 0 \\ 1 & 3 & 0 & 1 \end{bmatrix} \qquad \begin{matrix} \frac{1}{2}R_1 \\ R_2 - \frac{1}{2}R_1 \end{matrix} \begin{bmatrix} 1 & \frac{5}{2} & \frac{1}{2} & 0 \\ 0 & \frac{1}{2} & -\frac{1}{2} & 1 \end{bmatrix}$$

$$\begin{matrix} R_1 - 5R_2 \\ 2R_2 \end{matrix} \begin{bmatrix} 1 & 0 & 3 & -5 \\ 0 & 1 & -1 & 2 \end{bmatrix}$$

**Answer**

$$\begin{bmatrix} 3 & -5 \\ -1 & 2 \end{bmatrix}$$

**Check**

$$\begin{bmatrix} 3 & -5 \\ -1 & 2 \end{bmatrix} \begin{bmatrix} 2 & 5 \\ 1 & 3 \end{bmatrix} = \begin{bmatrix} 1 & 0 \\ 0 & 1 \end{bmatrix}$$

If we multiply both sides of equation **34** by the matrix $\begin{bmatrix} 3 & -5 \\ -1 & 2 \end{bmatrix}$ we obtain

$$\begin{bmatrix} 3 & -5 \\ -1 & 2 \end{bmatrix} \begin{bmatrix} 2 & 5 \\ 1 & 3 \end{bmatrix} \begin{bmatrix} x_1 \\ x_2 \end{bmatrix} = \begin{bmatrix} 3 & -5 \\ -1 & 2 \end{bmatrix} \begin{bmatrix} a \\ b \end{bmatrix}$$

$$\begin{bmatrix} 1 & 0 \\ 0 & 1 \end{bmatrix} \begin{bmatrix} x_1 \\ x_2 \end{bmatrix} = \begin{bmatrix} 3 & -5 \\ -1 & 2 \end{bmatrix} \begin{bmatrix} a \\ b \end{bmatrix}$$

$$\begin{bmatrix} x_1 \\ x_2 \end{bmatrix} = \begin{bmatrix} 3 & -5 \\ -1 & 2 \end{bmatrix} \begin{bmatrix} a \\ b \end{bmatrix} \qquad \textbf{35}$$

We can solve equation **35** for $x_1$ and $x_2$ by substituting particular values for a and b. For example, in order 51 we had $a = 9$ and

$b = 5$. Substituting we obtain

$$\begin{bmatrix} x_1 \\ x_2 \end{bmatrix} = \begin{bmatrix} 3 & -5 \\ -1 & 2 \end{bmatrix} \begin{bmatrix} 9 \\ 5 \end{bmatrix} = \begin{bmatrix} 2 \\ 1 \end{bmatrix}$$

that is, $x_1 = 2$ and $x_2 = 1$ as before.

We may use equation **35** again and again to quickly determine solutions to system **33** for various orders. Then we can see if the orders can be realized, that is, if the numbers $x_1$ and $x_2$ obtained are non-negative. This is obviously a requirement of this problem, since Boston cannot ship a negative number of packages of either type. We may arrange our work as shown in Table 2.

Table 2

| Order # | Order | Result of using equation | Instructions or comments |
|---------|-------|--------------------------|--------------------------|
| 51 | $a = 9$ $b = 5$ | $\begin{bmatrix} x_1 \\ x_2 \end{bmatrix} = \begin{bmatrix} 2 \\ 1 \end{bmatrix}$ | ship 2 type-1 and 1 type-2 |
| 52 | $a = 5$ $b = 3$ | $\begin{bmatrix} x_1 \\ x_2 \end{bmatrix} = \begin{bmatrix} 0 \\ 1 \end{bmatrix}$ | ship 1 type-2 |
| 53 | $a = 4$ $b = 2$ | $\begin{bmatrix} x_1 \\ x_2 \end{bmatrix} = \begin{bmatrix} 2 \\ 0 \end{bmatrix}$ | ship 2 type-1 |
| 54 | $a = 7$ $b = 4$ | $\begin{bmatrix} x_1 \\ x_2 \end{bmatrix} = \begin{bmatrix} 1 \\ 1 \end{bmatrix}$ | ship 1 type-1 and 1 type-2 |
| 55 | $a = 98$ $b = 52$ | $\begin{bmatrix} x_1 \\ x_2 \end{bmatrix} = \begin{bmatrix} 34 \\ 6 \end{bmatrix}$ | ship 34 type-1 and 6 type-2 |
| 56 | $a = 74$ $b = 30$ | $\begin{bmatrix} x_1 \\ x_2 \end{bmatrix} = \begin{bmatrix} 72 \\ -14 \end{bmatrix}$ | cannot be done with whole boxes |
| 57 | $a = 40$ $b = 40$ | $\begin{bmatrix} x_1 \\ x_2 \end{bmatrix} = \begin{bmatrix} -80 \\ 40 \end{bmatrix}$ | cannot be done with whole boxes |

Instructions for this procedure could easily be put on a small computer using the flow chart below.

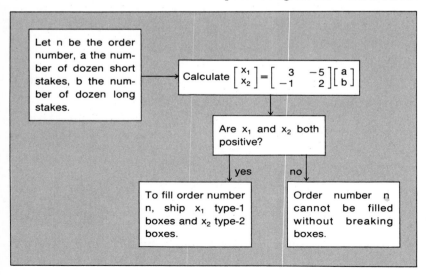

Let n be the order number, a the number of dozen short stakes, b the number of dozen long stakes.

Calculate $\begin{bmatrix} x_1 \\ x_2 \end{bmatrix} = \begin{bmatrix} 3 & -5 \\ -1 & 2 \end{bmatrix} \begin{bmatrix} a \\ b \end{bmatrix}$

Are $x_1$ and $x_2$ both positive?

yes

no

To fill order number n, ship $x_1$ type-1 boxes and $x_2$ type-2 boxes.

Order number n cannot be filled without breaking boxes.

Any system of equations can be converted to a single matrix equation. For examples, the system

$$\begin{bmatrix} 2x_1 + 3x_2 + 7x_3 = 8 \\ 8x_1 - x_2 + 4x_3 = 7 \\ 5x_1 + 2x_2 - 3x_3 = 5 \end{bmatrix}$$

becomes

$$\begin{bmatrix} 2 & 3 & 7 \\ 8 & -1 & 4 \\ 5 & 2 & -3 \end{bmatrix} \begin{bmatrix} x_1 \\ x_2 \\ x_3 \end{bmatrix} = \begin{bmatrix} 8 \\ 7 \\ 5 \end{bmatrix}$$

The system

$$\begin{bmatrix} 3x_1 - 2x_2 + x_3 - x_4 = 5 \\ 4x_1 + x_2 - 7x_3 + 8x_4 = 7 \end{bmatrix}$$

becomes

$$\begin{bmatrix} 3 & -2 & 1 & -1 \\ 4 & 1 & -7 & 8 \end{bmatrix} \begin{bmatrix} x_1 \\ x_2 \\ x_3 \\ x_4 \end{bmatrix} = \begin{bmatrix} 5 \\ 7 \end{bmatrix}$$

and the system

$$\begin{bmatrix} 2x_1 + 3x_2 = 0 \\ x_1 - x_2 = 7 \\ 4x_1 - 3x_2 = -1 \end{bmatrix}$$

becomes

$$\begin{bmatrix} 2 & 3 \\ 1 & -1 \\ 4 & -3 \end{bmatrix} \begin{bmatrix} x_1 \\ x_2 \end{bmatrix} = \begin{bmatrix} 0 \\ 7 \\ -1 \end{bmatrix}$$

The matrix of numbers on the left side of these matrix equations is called the **coefficient matrix** of the corresponding system. It consists of all but the last column of the matrix of the system. The matrix on the right side of these matrix equations is called the **requirement matrix** of the system. It is the last column of the matrix of the system. The column matrix consisting of xs is called the **unknown matrix** of the system.

Capital letter notation is even more suggestive. If we let

$$A = \begin{bmatrix} 3 & 1 & 2 \\ 0 & 1 & 4 \end{bmatrix}$$

$$X = \begin{bmatrix} x_1 \\ x_2 \\ x_3 \end{bmatrix}$$

$$B = \begin{bmatrix} 7 \\ 6 \end{bmatrix}$$

then the equation

$$AX = B$$

is a compact way to write the system

$$\begin{bmatrix} 3 & 1 & 2 \\ 0 & -1 & 4 \end{bmatrix} \begin{bmatrix} x_1 \\ x_2 \\ x_3 \end{bmatrix} = \begin{bmatrix} 7 \\ 6 \end{bmatrix}$$

or

$$\begin{bmatrix} 3x_1 + x_2 + 2x_3 = 7 \\ -x_2 + 4x_3 = 6 \end{bmatrix}$$

Returning to the AC order example, if we let

$$A = \begin{bmatrix} 2 & 5 \\ 1 & 3 \end{bmatrix}$$

$$X = \begin{bmatrix} x_1 \\ x_2 \end{bmatrix}$$

$$B = \begin{bmatrix} a \\ b \end{bmatrix}$$

Then we can represent our system by

$$AX = B \qquad\qquad\qquad \textbf{36}$$

To solve the system we multiplied both sides of this equation by the inverse of A. When we represent this symbolically as follows

$$\frac{1}{A}AX = \frac{1}{A}B$$

$$X = \frac{B}{A}$$

it resembles the process we would use to solve an equation such as $3x = 5$:

$$\tfrac{1}{3}3x = \tfrac{1}{3}5$$

$$x = \tfrac{5}{3}$$

However, there are two important differences. First, before we can apply this method to solve a matrix equation such as **34** we must know that A has an inverse. While every number except zero has an inverse, we know that many matrices do not have inverses. In the first place, only square matrices have inverses. But as we have seen not all square matrices have inverses. Second, even if the matrix A is square and has an inverse, this technique may not be worthwhile. If you happen to know the inverse of A, then this is perhaps the simplest way to solve a system of equations. But

What's worse is that if A is square
and has no inverse it may take a lot of
time to discover this fact.

suppose A is an $n \times n$ matrix whose inverse is not given. Recall that the easiest way to compute the inverse of A is to solve n systems of equations. Thus, unless you plan to solve more than n systems of equations, don't bother to invert A: just solve the systems.

The technique discussed here and above can be generalized to solve any number of systems all having the same coefficient matrix, with no restrictions, provided all the requirement matrices are given in advance. See supplementary exercises 50 through 53, and the paragraph just before them, at the end of this chapter.

In problems such as the multiple order problems above, we are asked to solve many systems of the form

$$AX = B,$$

where the coefficient matrix A is given and the requirement matrix B changes with each order. In these cases it may be worthwhile to compute the inverse of A, provided you have at least n orders.

For the rest of this section we will be concerned with an economic application of inverse matrices.

**Input-Output
Analysis**

Input-output models are an important mathematical tool in modern economics. Their main ingredient is an input-output table, which lists the economic interdependence of various sectors of an economy. For this brief and simplified discussion we will divide the economy into three broad sectors as shown in Table 3.

**Table 3**

This division of the economy was suggested by economist Colin Clark.

| Sector | Examples |
|---|---|
| Extractive | Agriculture, mining, forestry, fisheries |
| Manufacturing | Food processing, mining machinery production, furniture making, boat building |
| Service | Insurance, law, medicine, transportation |

Each sector of the economy uses some of the output of other sectors, as well as some of its own, as its input.

For example, in order to mine one dollar's worth of coal, a company might require 10¢ worth of lumber from the extractive sector, 30¢ worth of mining machinery from the manufacturing sector, and 20¢ worth of insurance from the service sector. In Table 4 we summarize such requirements for a hypothetical economy.

**Table 4
Input (in dollars)
Required to Produce
One Dollar of Output**

| Used by | Extractive | Manufacturing | Services |
|---|---|---|---|
| Obtained from | | | |
| Extractive | .10 | .50 | .10 |
| Manufacturing | .30 | .30 | .20 |
| Services | .20 | .10 | .30 |

Wassily Leontief was awarded the 1973 Nobel prize in economics for his development of the input-output model. Most authors call this model the Leontief model; some, however, require that labor be considered in such models.

Tables have also been compiled for the United States economy in 1958 and 1963 and for many other countries.

Do you really care that printing and publishing spent 1.08 billion dollars on paper and allied products and .77 billion dollars on themselves in 1947? If you want to examine the over 1,000 nonzero entries in his table, consult the cited *Scientific American* article.

The second column of this table indicates, for instance, that in order to produce one dollar's worth of manufactured goods the entire manufacturing sector needs 50¢ worth of raw materials, 30¢ worth of machinery, and 10¢ worth of services. Similarly, the third column lists the needs of the service sector of the economy.

Of course, Table 4 and the other tables in this section do not contain real-life data. We could consider actual input-output tables for the American economy. However, the basic principles would be obscured by unpleasant arithmetic. Actual tables are very difficult to construct. Input-output analysis was first discussed by François Quesnay in 1758. No real progress was made until the 1930s when Leontief and his associates at Harvard University constructed the first input-output tables. Their tables were for the American economy in 1919 and 1929. Leontief then spent five years producing the table for 1939. At that point the Interindustry Economics Division of the Bureau of Labor Statistics became involved. Two years were spent compiling an input-output table for a 500-sector division of the American economy for the year 1947. While this table was never published, Leontief did include a 42-sector version of it in his October, 1951, *Scientific American* article, "Input-Output Economics," pp. 15–21. We presume that the actual entries in this table are not particularly interesting to you unless you happen to be closely involved with the economy.

Table 4 lists all the internal demands on our hypothetical three-sector economy. Most economies will also involve certain external demands. For example, manufacturers will not limit themselves to sales to the three sectors of the economy. They will also export, set some aside in their warehouse inventories, sell to individuals, and so on. These are some of the ways money leaves an economy.

All these external requirements will be called **demands**. For example, suppose our economy of Table 4 is required to produce $1,039,700 worth of extraction, $3,934,000 worth of manufacturing, and $196,700 worth of services beyond what it needs for its own internal functioning. The question we will answer here is, How much should each sector produce to meet these demands? Notice that we have not already answered this question by presenting the figures above. Each sector cannot produce exactly what is demanded—it must produce more. If one sector produces exactly enough to meet an external demand there is noting left for sales to the other sectors, and the economy shuts down.

We will use algebra to solve this problem.

These numbers were obtained from
the first column of Table 4.

Let $x_1 =$ the total output for the extractive sector;
$x_2 =$ the total output for the manufacturing sector;
$x_3 =$ the total output for the service sector.

To produce $x_1$ dollars worth of extracting we need $.1x_1$ dollars worth of extracting, $.3x_1$ dollars worth of manufacturing, and $.2x_1$ dollars worth of services.

For $x_2$ dollars worth of manufacturing we need $.5x_2$ from extracting, $.3x_2$ from manufacturing, and $.1x_2$ from services.

Similarly, services require $.1x_3$ from extracting, $.2x_3$ from manufacturing, and $.3x_3$ from services.

Thus, in order to fill our demands we must produce

$.1x_1 + .5x_2 + .1x_3$ dollars worth of extracting
$.3x_1 + .3x_2 + .2x_3$ dollars worth of manufacturing
and $.2x_1 + .1x_2 + .3x_3$ dollars worth of services

for the economy itself. Beyond this, we must produce \$1,039,700 worth of extracting, \$3,934,000 worth of manufacturing, and \$196,700 worth of services for export.

Thus, the total output is to be

$.1x_1 + .5x_2 + .1x_3 + 1,039,700$ from extraction
$.3x_1 + .3x_2 + .2x_3 + 3,934,000$ from manufacturing
$.2x_1 + .1x_2 + .3x_3 + \ \ 196,700$ from services

Now when we began this discussion we let $x_1, x_2, x_3$ denote these respective outputs. We must therefore solve the system:

$$\begin{bmatrix} x_1 = .1x_1 + .5x_2 + .1x_3 + 1,039,700 \\ x_2 = .3x_1 + .3x_2 + .2x_3 + 3,934,000 \\ x_3 = .2x_1 + .1x_2 + .3x_3 + \ \ 196,700 \end{bmatrix} \qquad 37$$

While we could simply solve this system as it stands, it will be more convenient to use matrix algebra in the solution. For this we let

$$A = \begin{bmatrix} .1 & .5 & .1 \\ .3 & .3 & .2 \\ .2 & .1 & .3 \end{bmatrix}$$

denote the input-output matrix obtained from Table 4;

$$D = \begin{bmatrix} 1,039,700 \\ 3,934,000 \\ 196,700 \end{bmatrix}$$

denote the demand matrix; and

$$X = \begin{bmatrix} x_1 \\ x_2 \\ x_3 \end{bmatrix}$$

denote the final output matrix.

It is easy to check that system **37** can be written as the matrix equation

$$X = AX + D \qquad\qquad \textbf{38}$$

We solve this for X as in ordinary algebra.

$$X - AX = D$$

Here I denotes the identity matrix; so
IX=X.

$$IX - AX = D$$

$$(I - A)X = D$$

$$(I - A)^{-1}(I - A)X = (I - A)^{-1}D$$

$$IX = (I - A)^{-1}D$$

$$X = (I - A)^{-1}D \qquad\qquad \textbf{39}$$

Now if we are given a set of demands D we can determine the final outputs simply by multiplying $(I - A)^{-1}$ by D. In our case we calculate

$$I - A = \begin{bmatrix} 1 & 0 & 0 \\ 0 & 1 & 0 \\ 0 & 0 & 1 \end{bmatrix} - \begin{bmatrix} .1 & .5 & .1 \\ .3 & .3 & .2 \\ .2 & .1 & .3 \end{bmatrix} = \begin{bmatrix} .9 & -.5 & -.1 \\ -.3 & .7 & -.2 \\ -.2 & -.1 & .7 \end{bmatrix}$$

$$(I - A)^{-1} = \begin{bmatrix} .9 & -.5 & -.1 \\ -.3 & .7 & -.2 \\ -.2 & -.1 & .7 \end{bmatrix}^{-1} = \tfrac{10}{281}\begin{bmatrix} 47 & 36 & 17 \\ 25 & 61 & 21 \\ 17 & 19 & 48 \end{bmatrix}$$

$$(I - A)^{-1}D = \tfrac{10}{281}\begin{bmatrix} 47 & 36 & 17 \\ 25 & 61 & 21 \\ 17 & 19 & 48 \end{bmatrix}\begin{bmatrix} 1{,}039{,}700 \\ 3{,}934{,}000 \\ 196{,}700 \end{bmatrix} = \begin{bmatrix} 6{,}898{,}000 \\ 9{,}612{,}000 \\ 3{,}625{,}000 \end{bmatrix}$$

To meet the final demands, this economy must produce

$6,898,000 worth of extraction,
$9,612,000 worth of manufacturing, and
$3,625,000 worth of services.

Problem 5   Suppose the economy of Table 4 is called upon to produce $50,580 of extraction, $14,050 of manufacturing, and $87,110 of services beyond its own needs. How much must each sector produce to meet these demands?

Answer

$$X=(I-A)^{-1}D=\tfrac{10}{281}\begin{bmatrix} 47 & 36 & 17 \\ 25 & 61 & 21 \\ 17 & 19 & 48 \end{bmatrix}\begin{bmatrix} 50,580 \\ 14,050 \\ 87,100 \end{bmatrix}=\begin{bmatrix} 155,293.95 \\ 140,592.53 \\ 188,882.92 \end{bmatrix}$$

The extractive sector must produce about \$155,300; the manufacturing sector must produce about \$140,600; the service sector must produce about \$188,900.

Table 5
(in dollars)

| Used by<br>Obtained from | Extractive | Manufacturing | Services | Demand |
|---|---|---|---|---|
| Extractive | .30 | .70 | .10 | 663 |
| Manufacturing | .40 | .10 | .10 | 897 |
| Services | .10 | .10 | .70 | 507 |

Problem 6

Table 5 is the input-output table for a particular economy. It also gives the demands. What must the total output of the economy be to meet these demands?

Solution

We first calculate $(I-A)^{-1}$.

$$(I-A)^{-1}=\begin{bmatrix} .7 & -.7 & -.1 \\ -.4 & .9 & -.1 \\ -.1 & -.1 & .3 \end{bmatrix}^{-1}=\tfrac{5}{39}\begin{bmatrix} 26 & 22 & 16 \\ 13 & 20 & 11 \\ 13 & 14 & 35 \end{bmatrix}$$

Next we multiply

$$(I-A)^{-1}D=\tfrac{5}{39}\begin{bmatrix} 26 & 22 & 16 \\ 13 & 20 & 11 \\ 13 & 14 & 35 \end{bmatrix}\begin{bmatrix} 663 \\ 897 \\ 507 \end{bmatrix}=\begin{bmatrix} 5,780 \\ 4,120 \\ 4,990 \end{bmatrix}$$

The total outputs must be: extractive, 5,780, manufacturing, 4,120, services, 4,990.

In his book, *The Elements of Input-output Analysis* (New York: Random House, 1966), pp. 40–41, William H. Miernyk indicates the importance of these techniques to the French economy. His comments are equally true for many national economies.

> …the French Planning Commission makes detailed projections of output for the French economy for a specified future period. An input-output model plays an important part in this forecasting procedure. In essence, a detailed forecast of final demand is prepared, and from this, projected levels of interindustry transactions are computed…. The final demand for automobiles is projected, for example, and from the input-output forecast, the French steel industry can determine how an increase in automobile production

will affect its output. The coal industry, in turn, can then see how its production will be affected by the expansion of steel output. The effects of anticipated changes in final demand on each industry can be traced back, through the input-output table, to all other industries.

Consistent forecasting provides an important guide to public policy-makers. But such forecasts are also extremely useful to the management of an individual enterprise. The director of a firm will usually have a pretty good idea of his share of the total market the firm serves. He will also know whether his share of the market is growing, decling, or remaining relatively constant.

**Exercises 6.2**

1. Is $\begin{bmatrix} 3 & 0 & -5 \\ -14 & 1 & 24 \\ -1 & 0 & 2 \end{bmatrix}$ the inverse of $\begin{bmatrix} 2 & 0 & 5 \\ 5 & 1 & 1 \\ 1 & 0 & 3 \end{bmatrix}$? Why or why not?

2. What do you get if you multiply an identity matrix by itself?

Find the inverse, if it exists, of each of the matrices in Exercises 3 through 22.

3. $\begin{bmatrix} 2 & 0 \\ 0 & 3 \end{bmatrix}$   4. $\begin{bmatrix} 0 & 2 \\ 3 & 0 \end{bmatrix}$   5. $\begin{bmatrix} 2 & 4 \\ 0 & 3 \end{bmatrix}$

6. $\begin{bmatrix} 2 & 4 \\ 5 & 3 \end{bmatrix}$   7. $\begin{bmatrix} -2 & 4 \\ -5 & 3 \end{bmatrix}$   8. $\begin{bmatrix} \frac{1}{2} & \frac{1}{4} \\ 5 & 3 \end{bmatrix}$

9. $\begin{bmatrix} -\frac{2}{3} & -\frac{3}{4} \\ \frac{4}{5} & -\frac{3}{7} \end{bmatrix}$   10. $\begin{bmatrix} 2 & 0 & 0 \\ 0 & -3 & 0 \\ 0 & 0 & \frac{4}{5} \end{bmatrix}$

11. $\begin{bmatrix} 1 & 2 & 3 \\ 4 & 5 & 6 \\ 7 & 8 & 9 \end{bmatrix}$   12. $\begin{bmatrix} 1 & 2 & 3 \\ 4 & 5 & 6 \\ 9 & 8 & 7 \end{bmatrix}$

13. $\begin{bmatrix} 1 & 2 & 3 & 4 \\ 5 & 6 & 7 & 8 \end{bmatrix}$   14. $\begin{bmatrix} 5 & 6 & 6 \\ 3 & 3 & 2 \\ 4 & 5 & 5 \end{bmatrix}$

15. $\begin{bmatrix} 3 & -2 & 4 \\ 2 & 1 & 2 \\ 5 & 3 & 5 \end{bmatrix}$   16. $\begin{bmatrix} 3 & 3 & 5 \\ 1 & 6 & 8 \\ 2 & 1 & 2 \end{bmatrix}$

17. $\begin{bmatrix} 4 & 6 & 1 \\ 9 & 8 & 5 \\ 4 & 4 & 2 \end{bmatrix}$   18. $\begin{bmatrix} 2 & 3 & 1 \\ 2 & 7 & 1 \\ 3 & 2 & 1 \end{bmatrix}$

19. $\begin{bmatrix} 1 & 2 & 3 \\ 3 & 1 & 2 \\ 2 & 3 & 1 \end{bmatrix}$  *20. $\begin{bmatrix} -\frac{1}{3} & 0 & \frac{2}{3} \\ 3 & -\frac{1}{2} & 2 \\ \frac{2}{3} & -\frac{3}{4} & 0 \end{bmatrix}$

*21. $\begin{bmatrix} 0 & -3 & 2 & 1 \\ 0 & 2 & 1 & -1 \\ 4 & -2 & 0 & 3 \\ 2 & 0 & 0 & -7 \end{bmatrix}$  *22. $\begin{bmatrix} 2 & 4 & 3 & 2 \\ 3 & 6 & 5 & 2 \\ 2 & 5 & 2 & -3 \\ 4 & 5 & 14 & 14 \end{bmatrix}$

In Exercises 23 through 28, solve the division problem or determine that it has no solution.

23. $\begin{bmatrix} 5 & 2 \\ -1 & 3 \end{bmatrix} \div \begin{bmatrix} 3 & 4 \\ 4 & 5 \end{bmatrix}$

24. $\begin{bmatrix} 3 & 7 \\ 1 & 5 \\ 2 & 9 \end{bmatrix} \div \begin{bmatrix} 1 & 3 \\ 7 & 4 \end{bmatrix}$

25. $\begin{bmatrix} 8 & 2 \\ 1 & 5 \end{bmatrix} \div \begin{bmatrix} 2 & 3 & 7 \\ 1 & 4 & 2 \end{bmatrix}$

26. $\begin{bmatrix} 3 & 4 & 1 \\ 7 & 2 & 8 \\ 9 & 1 & 5 \end{bmatrix} \div \begin{bmatrix} 3 & -2 & 4 \\ 2 & 1 & 2 \\ 5 & 3 & 5 \end{bmatrix}$

27. $\begin{bmatrix} 7 & 2 & 1 \\ -2 & 0 & 3 \\ 4 & 1 & 5 \end{bmatrix} \div \begin{bmatrix} 1 & 2 & 3 \\ 4 & 5 & 6 \\ 7 & 8 & 9 \end{bmatrix}$

28. $\begin{bmatrix} 1 & -3 & 4 & 5 \\ 2 & 2 & 1 & 6 \end{bmatrix} \div \begin{bmatrix} 0 & -3 & 2 & 1 \\ 0 & 2 & 1 & -1 \\ 4 & -2 & 0 & 3 \\ 2 & 0 & 0 & -7 \end{bmatrix}$

*29. PHE's philosophy has always been to stick to what it knows best—the fast-food business. Given its size and volume (sales last year were $3.3 billion), it might be expected to have purchased beef ranches and slaughterhouses. But the managers still prefer to deal with a vast number of suppliers, constantly adjusting their orders to get the best quality-price ratios. Of course, this method of operation involves making a great many decisions about order quantities for many stores from many suppliers. Decisions of this sort often lead to systems of linear equations. One of the matrices that arose recently was the following, having to do with orders from northern Texas for pickles, catsup, and other condiments.

$$\begin{bmatrix} 2 & 3 & 1 & 0 & 1 \\ 1 & 2 & 4 & 1 & 3 \\ 0 & 3 & 0 & 4 & 2 \\ 1 & 0 & 3 & 3 & 0 \\ 0 & 1 & 2 & 0 & 3 \end{bmatrix}$$

Calculate the inverse of this matrix. This problem is starred not because it is difficult but because it is computationally tedious. The current indoor record for hand calculation of this inverse is 30 minutes. Perhaps you can beat this time.

*30. Suppose matrix **20** has an inverse. Then there is a 2×2 matrix $\begin{bmatrix} x & y \\ z & w \end{bmatrix}$ satisfying

$$\begin{bmatrix} 1 & 2 \\ 3 & 6 \end{bmatrix}\begin{bmatrix} x & y \\ z & w \end{bmatrix} = \begin{bmatrix} 1 & 0 \\ 0 & 1 \end{bmatrix} \qquad \dagger$$

(a) What are the $(1,1)$ and $(2,1)$ entries of the product on the left side of equation †?
(b) If equation † is to hold, write the system of equations that would result from (a).
(c) Apply Gauss-Jordan reduction to the system of (b). What happens?
(d) In view of all this, what do you conclude about matrix †?

*31. Calculate the inverse of the matrix

$$\begin{bmatrix} a & b \\ c & d \end{bmatrix}$$

What assumption must you make concerning the numbers a, b, c, and d?

Use the facts that $\begin{bmatrix} 7 & 5 \\ 4 & 3 \end{bmatrix}$ is the inverse of $\begin{bmatrix} 3 & -5 \\ -4 & 7 \end{bmatrix}$, $\frac{1}{18}\begin{bmatrix} 5 & -2 \\ -1 & 4 \end{bmatrix}$ is the inverse of $\begin{bmatrix} 4 & 2 \\ 1 & 5 \end{bmatrix}$, and $\begin{bmatrix} 1 & -1 & 1 \\ -1 & 1 & 0 \\ 0 & -1 & 1 \end{bmatrix}$ is the inverse of $\begin{bmatrix} 1 & 0 & -1 \\ 1 & 1 & -1 \\ 1 & 1 & 0 \end{bmatrix}$ to solve the systems in Exercises 32 through 36.

32. $\begin{bmatrix} 7x_1 + 5x_2 = 1 \\ 4x_1 + 3x_2 = 2 \end{bmatrix}$  33. $\begin{bmatrix} 3x_1 - 5x_2 = -7 \\ -4x_1 + 7x_2 = 20 \end{bmatrix}$

34. $\begin{bmatrix} 4x_1 + 2x_2 = 10 \\ x_1 + 5x_2 = 25 \end{bmatrix}$  35. $\begin{bmatrix} x_1 - x_2 + x_3 = -1 \\ -x_1 + x_2 = 3 \\ -x_2 + x_3 = -5 \end{bmatrix}$

36. $\begin{bmatrix} x_1 - x_2 + x_3 = 2 \\ -x_1 + x_2 = 4 \\ -x_2 + x_3 = 6 \end{bmatrix}$

Solve:

37. (a) $\begin{bmatrix} 2x_1 + 4x_2 + 3x_3 + 2x_4 = 0 \\ 3x_1 + 6x_2 + 5x_3 + 2x_4 = 0 \\ 2x_1 + 5x_2 + 2x_3 - 3x_4 = -1 \\ 4x_1 + 5x_2 + 14x_3 + 14x_4 = 2 \end{bmatrix}$

(b) $\begin{bmatrix} -115x_1 + 145x_2 - 64x_3 - 18x_4 = & 1 \\ 50x_1 - 60x_2 + 26x_3 + 7x_4 = & 0 \\ 5x_1 - 10x_2 + 6x_3 + 2x_4 = & -1 \\ 10x_1 - 10x_2 + 3x_3 + x_4 = & 2 \end{bmatrix}$

Note: the inverse of

$$\begin{bmatrix} 2 & 4 & 3 & 2 \\ 3 & 6 & 5 & 2 \\ 2 & 5 & 2 & -3 \\ 4 & 5 & 14 & 14 \end{bmatrix}$$

is

$$\frac{1}{5}\begin{bmatrix} -115 & 145 & -64 & -18 \\ 50 & -60 & 26 & 7 \\ 5 & -10 & 6 & 2 \\ 10 & -10 & 3 & 1 \end{bmatrix}$$

Solve the system $\begin{bmatrix} x_1 + x_2 + 2x_3 + x_4 = a \\ 4x_1 + 5x_2 + 9x_3 + x_4 = b \\ 3x_1 + 4x_2 + 7x_3 + x_4 = c \\ 2x_1 + 3x_2 + 4x_3 + 2x_4 = d \end{bmatrix}$ for:

$^c$38.  $a = 1$, $b = c = d = 0$

39.  $a = b = 1$, $c = d = 0$

40.  $a = b = c = 1$, $d = 0$

41.  $a = b = c = d = 1$

42.  $a = 0$, $b = c = d = 1$

43.  $a = b = c = 0$, $d = 1$

44.  $a = -19$, $b = 8$, $c = 14$, $d = -12$

45. In the earlier days at AC the two types of boxes of tent stakes (these were wooden stakes) were packed as follows: Type-1 boxes contained 5 pairs of long stakes and 7 pairs of short stakes; type-2 boxes contained 2 pairs of long stakes and 3 of short. Please fill each of the orders in Table 6, except for those that cannot be filled without opening boxes:

Table 6

| Order # | 1 | 2 | 3 | 4 | 5 | 6 | 7 | 8 | 9 |
|---------|---|---|-----|-----|-----|-----|------|---|---|
| Pairs of long | 6 | 7 | 114 | 76 | 137 | 80 | 9815 | 5 | 2 |
| Pairs of short | 9 | 10 | 162 | 106 | 204 | 124 | 14179 | 7 | 3 |

$^c$46. The Acme Candy Company has a large supply of 3 types of boxes of candy left over from last Christmas. Type 1 contains 4 rolls of mints, 4 chocolate bars, and 7 jawbreakers; type II contains 7 rolls of mints and 6 jawbreakers; type III contains 2 rolls of mints, 5 chocolate bars, and 6 jawbreakers. The company is receiving orders for these candies which it would like to fill using these boxes, unopened. For which of the orders in Table 7 can this be done, and how?

Table 7

| Order # | 71 | 72 | 73 | 74 | 75 | 76 | 77 |
|---|---|---|---|---|---|---|---|
| Mints | 45 | 50 | 50 | 40 | 62 | 30 | 450 |
| Chocolates | 80 | 85 | 90 | 70 | 40 | 39 | 800 |
| Jawbreakers | 110 | 115 | 120 | 100 | 80 | 75 | 1,080 |

47. Some of the systems of equations obtained at PHE in connection with order placement have solutions involving fractions, and these solutions do not correspond to reality. One cannot, for example, order $244\frac{15}{43}$ bottles of catsup. The standard PHE policy in cases like this is always to order the next higher whole number; so in this case the order is placed for 245 bottles. On the other hand, a negative value of one of the variables indicates that the region already has an oversupply of that item, and then the policy is, of course, to order no more items. Thus, with these policies, a solution to a given problem such as, say $\begin{bmatrix} x_1 \\ x_2 \\ x_3 \end{bmatrix} = \begin{bmatrix} 49\frac{1}{5} \\ 180 \\ -16\frac{2}{3} \end{bmatrix}$ would be adjusted to the "practical" solution $\begin{bmatrix} x_1 \\ x_2 \\ x_3 \end{bmatrix} = \begin{bmatrix} 50 \\ 180 \\ 0 \end{bmatrix}$. With these policies in mind, give the "practical" solutions to the systems $AX = B$ which arose in connection with supply of various types of hamburger and hotdog buns to several eastern regions, where $A = \begin{bmatrix} 3 & 2 & 4 \\ 7 & 0 & 3 \\ 6 & 4 & 9 \end{bmatrix}$ and where:

(a) $B = \begin{bmatrix} 8 \\ 9 \\ 10 \end{bmatrix}$   (c) $B = \begin{bmatrix} 60 \\ 50 \\ 100 \end{bmatrix}$

(b) $B = \begin{bmatrix} 10 \\ 11 \\ 70 \end{bmatrix}$   (d) $B = \begin{bmatrix} 200 \\ 500 \\ 400 \end{bmatrix}$

48. My cousin claims to be an expert bug exterminator. He tells me that the best insecticide is made from a combination of 3 chemicals: R2D2, C3PO, and RUOK. He wants to test 8 different insecticides with the quantities (in ounces) of each of these chemicals listed in Table 8. His problem is that R2D2, C3PO, and RUOK are not available in pure form. They can only be obtained mixed together in an oil base according to Table 9, where the numbers give ounces per quart. Which combinations can be produced by mixing chemicals A, B, and C, and how many quarts of each chemical should be used in each case?

Table 8

| | a | b | c | d | e | f | g | h |
|---|---|---|---|---|---|---|---|---|
| R2D2 | 14 | 29 | 63 | 148 | 65 | 109 | 21 | 20 |
| C3P0 | 15 | 29 | 61 | 146 | 15 | 120 | 28 | 10 |
| RUOK | 5 | 8 | 15 | 39 | 10 | 142 | 14 | 10 |

Table 9

|            | R2D2 | C3PO | RUOK |
|------------|------|------|------|
| Mixture A  | 7    | 8    | 3    |
| Mixture B  | 3    | 4    | 2    |
| Mixture C  | 4    | 3    | 0    |

49. Use the technique of this section to develop a flow chart to determine whether or not a given matrix has an inverse.

In Exercises 50 and 51 adapt the technique of this section to solve each set of systems in one reduction.

50. $\begin{bmatrix} x_1 + 2x_2 = \phantom{-}2 \\ 2x_1 + 3x_2 = -1 \\ 5x_1 + 9x_2 = \phantom{-}5 \end{bmatrix}$, $\begin{bmatrix} x_1 + 2x_2 = 2 \\ 2x_1 + 3x_2 = 3 \\ 5x_1 + 9x_2 = 7 \end{bmatrix}$

51. $\begin{bmatrix} 2x_1 - x_2 + 3x_3 = 4 \\ 3x_1 + x_2 - \phantom{3}x_3 = 2 \end{bmatrix}$, $\begin{bmatrix} 2x_1 - x_2 + 3x_3 = 0 \\ 3x_1 + x_2 - \phantom{3}x_3 = 4 \end{bmatrix}$, $\begin{bmatrix} 2x_1 - x_2 + 3x_3 = 2 \\ 3x_1 + x_2 - \phantom{3}x_3 = 2 \end{bmatrix}$

Tables 10 through 14 are input-output tables for various economies. In each case determine what the total output of the economy must be to meet the indicated demands.

52.

Table 10
(in dollars)

| Used by<br>Obtained from | Agricultural | Other | Demand |
|--------------------------|--------------|-------|--------|
| Agricultural             | .50          | .20   | 273    |
| Other                    | .30          | .60   | 371    |

53.

Table 11
(in dollars)

| Used by<br>Obtained from | Manufacturing | Other | Demand |
|--------------------------|---------------|-------|--------|
| Manufacturing            | .70           | .60   | 324    |
| Other                    | .20           | .30   | 171    |

54.

Table 12
(in dollars)

| Used by<br>Obtained from | Extractive | Manufacturing | Services | Demand |
|--------------------------|------------|---------------|----------|--------|
| Extractive               | .7         | .2            | .1       | 1,610  |
| Manufacturing            | .1         | .6            | .2       | 2,590  |
| Services                 | .1         | .1            | .5       | 910    |

55.

Table 13
(in dollars)

| Used by<br>Obtained from | Extractive | Manufacturing | Services | Demand |
|--------------------------|------------|---------------|----------|--------|
| Extractive               | .3         | .3            | .3       | 24     |
| Manufacturing            | .3         | .3            | .3       | 11     |
| Services                 | .3         | .3            | .3       | 17     |

56.

Table 14
(in dollars)

| Used by | Extractive | Manufacturing | Services | Demand |
|---|---|---|---|---|
| Obtained from | | | | |
| Extractive | .1 | .7 | 0.0 | 2,924 |
| Manufacturing | .6 | .1 | .1 | 4,816 |
| Services | .2 | .1 | .5 | 1,892 |

57. ACME Secretarial Services, Inc., is a business which does various routine jobs for companies, including itself. The budget director of ACME has determined rough dollar approximations to the various needs of the company. Table 15 indicates the dollar amounts required to produce one dollar's worth of each of the three types of services.

Table 15
(in dollars)

| Used by | Typing | Personnel placement | Copying |
|---|---|---|---|
| Obtained from | | | |
| Typing | .1 | .2 | .1 |
| Personnel placement | .2 | .1 | .1 |
| Copying | .1 | .2 | .2 |

This week the demands are $1,166 worth of typing, $5,830 worth of placement, and $583 worth of copying. How much must each department produce to meet these demands?

58. Soon after I became a billionaire, I quit my job as county commissioner and turned my attention to giving moral support to the community. This was a burdensome task, one which I could not have done without the moral support of my wife and eldest son, who still lives at home. In fact, they joined me in my efforts and, of course, received some of my moral support. The standard unit of moral support is the *turpo*. By definition 1,000 turpos is the amount of moral support required to enable a corrupt public official who has resigned to publicly discuss his life and times. Table 16 gives the number of turpos of support each member of my family needs from the others to provide ten turpos of support.

Table 16
(in turpos)

| Needed by | Me | Wife | Kid |
|---|---|---|---|
| Obtained from | | | |
| Me | 5 | 2 | 1 |
| Wife | 2 | 4 | 8 |
| Kid | 1 | 1 | 0 |

Last week the town's mayor was impeached, the government closed our schools, the crime rate increased, and our local youth club burned down. I figure this place needs 78,400 turpos of support from me, 21,560 from my wife, and 13,720 from my son. How much moral support must we each muster so that my family can meet these demands?

59. The country of Neutralia has a problem. Their only export is
armament, an item in great demand throughout the world. However,
a plethora of civil and guerrilla wars caused by minor parties
threatens to shut down the factories. To prevent this from happening, the government has decided to hire heavily armed security
forces to guard each plant. Naturally, their weapons are made in
Neutralia. Table 17 lists in dollar amounts the approximate value of
the weapons needed to protect the production of each dollar's worth
of each of the various types of weapons.

Table 17
(in dollars)

| To produce<br>They need | Sat. night specials | Automatic rifles | Grenades |
|---|---|---|---|
| Sat. night specials | .3 | .2 | .1 |
| Automatic rifles | .5 | .6 | .4 |
| Grenades | .2 | .4 | .1 |

This week's orders are in $2.82 million worth of Saturday night
specials, $1.23 million of automatic rifles, and $0.87 million of
grenades. How should Neutralia set its production schedule to meet
these demands?

*60. My yard was an airport
With little green men
Who came in a spaceship.
I counted to ten
To see if I dreamed it.
Alas, it was real.
I quivered and gasped
For their voices were shrill.
My life flashed before me
A thousand times over.
But they didn't hurt me.
(I really was sober.)
Their leader stepped forward;
His words were direct.
He spoke just a moment
And was not circumspect:
"Each question needs questions.
Each reason needs rhyme.
All rhymes have good reasons
And questions sometimes.

For each hundred questions
We use thirty rhymes.
We use twenty questions
Ten reasons do fine.

One hundred rhymes use
Ten reasons, ten questions.
That rhymes don't need rhymes
Is our foremost contention.

A hundred good reasons
Need thirty good questions.
Forty good reasons
Ten rhymes—my suggestion.

We cannot go home
Without reason or rhyme.
They'll question us endlessly
Time after time.

Forty-one forty good
Questions are wanted
Eighty-two eighty fine
Reasons are hunted.

Since we are mariners
No one asks us for rhymes
But could you please tell us
How to best use our time?"

I turned to my textbook
And from 6.2
I used a technique
And told them what to do.

Then I heard them exclaim
Ere they flew out of sight,
"Thanks."

**Section 6.3**
**Game Theory**

So far most of the applications described in the text have involved only internal matters at AC. For example, we've used systems of equations to help us fill orders, Bernoulli trials to control material quality, and the simplex method to maximize profits and minimize cost. All these techniques are very important. However, it is also useful to be able to analyze situations involving competition between companies.

In this section we introduce a different kind of model—game theory. Imagine a situation in which two companies are competing for the same market. There are many actions each company could make in an attempt to attract more customers. The effect of such actions will usually depend in part upon the actions of the other company. For example, if Company A decides to improve the quality of its products, sales will probably increase. However, if at the same time Company B decides to lower prices, this decision might more than offset any gains made by Company A. The outcome would depend upon how much the product quality is improved and how far the prices are lowered. In any event, in such situations any benefits Company A manages to obtain are at the expense of Company B. The question for us is: How should each company behave? Game theory can be used to study situations involving such conflicts. The subject was invented by John von Neumann in 1928. He and Oskar Morgenstern subsequently developed the topic extensively in their book, *Theory of Games and Economic Behavior* (Princeton, N.J.: Princeton University Press, 1944).

We are making the assumption that the market is *saturated*, so that no changes by either company can change the size of the market.

This section contains a very brief introduction to game theory. A more detailed treatment may be found in *The Compleat Strategyst* by J. D. Williams (New York: McGraw-Hill, 1966). The latter work presupposes less mathematical background than the present book provides. For this reason its methods of solution are less general than ours. However, the Williams book does provide many interesting and amusing examples.

While most of the real business world is too complex for direct application of the existing theory of games, studying relatively simple games can give some insights into complicated business situations. We will limit our considerations rather severely in that we will consider only games with two players in which one player's gain is always exactly offset by the other player's loss; that is, if one player should win $5, the other player must lose $5. If we agree that "losing" is the same as "winning a negative amount," then, at the end of the game, adding the winnings of one player to the winnings of the other player must always result in zero. For this reason such games are called **two-person zero-sum games.**

This definition of strategy is rather more restrictive than the common one. It is made in order to enable us to construct a mathematical theory of games.

A game involves strategies. A **strategy** is a complete plan of action. It may be as simple as calling heads in a game of flipping coins, or it may include elaborate sequences of moves, each dependent upon all the previous moves in the game. For example, a strategy for the player moving first in checkers would include: (1) a first move, (2) a list of second moves indicating which move to employ depending upon his or her first move and his or her opponent's first move, (3) a list of third moves, and so forth. Once both players have chosen such strategies they may simply hand their decisions over to an intermediary who would actually play the game and then announce the result. The point is that, once the two chosen strategies are made known, the outcome of the game is completely determined. Actually, to list even one strategy for checkers would be a lifetime task. To list them all and then to use the technique of this section to determine an optimal procedure would be beyond the capability of even the largest computer in existence.

We remark that there are computer programs that can play very good games of chess and checkers, but this is a long way from finding an optimal strategy. These programs use more sophisticated techniques than we discuss in this book.

### Example 1

This game is a finite version of the game called Low Number described by David Gale in his book *The Theory of Linear Economic Models* (New York: McGraw-Hill, p. 160). The game was first described by N. S. Mendelsohn, (*American Mathematical Monthly* **53** [1946], 86–88). Our description is general enough to apply to the case in which the players are not limited to a choice among 3 numbers.

Players A and B each secretly write one of the numbers 1, 2, or 3 on a slip of paper. They then show their papers to each other. If the numbers are the same, the game is a draw. Otherwise the player who writes the lower number wins one dollar, unless his or her number is exactly one less than the other player's number. In this case he or she loses 2 dollars. We tabulate these data in Table 18:

Table 18
Amount Player B
Pays Player A

To say "B pays A \$−2" is the same thing as to say "A pays B \$2".

| A writes | B writes | | |
|---|---|---|---|
| | **1** | **2** | **3** |
| 1 | 0 | −2 | 1 |
| 2 | 2 | 0 | −2 |
| 3 | −1 | 2 | 0 |

The matrix associated with this table is called the **payoff matrix**:

$$\begin{bmatrix} 0 & -2 & 1 \\ 2 & 0 & -2 \\ -1 & 2 & 0 \end{bmatrix}$$

The entries in this particular payoff matrix are in dollars. Other units (millions of dollars, points, chips, and so on) are used as required by the game. Every two-person zero-sum game is completely determined by its payoff matrix. We may therefore consider only payoff matrices and not the games from which they arise. The matrix

For this reason such games are called *matrix games*, a term originated by H. Kuhn.

$$\begin{bmatrix} -1 & 2 & 0 & 3 \\ 2 & 1 & 1 & 3 \\ 4 & 2 & -1 & 2 \end{bmatrix}$$

represents a game in which A has three strategies and B has four. If A and B both select strategy 3, for example, then this matrix informs us that B pays A $-1$ dollars, i.e., A pays B \$1. Given any game with relatively few strategies, its matrix can be determined by simply checking the result as A applies each of her strategies against each strategy of B.

We are concerned with two questions. Given a payoff matrix how does one determine (a) the best approach for each player, and (b) the amount each player can expect to win if both play the game optimally? The simplex method can be used to answer both these questions at once. However, some games admit a simpler approach.

**Problem 1**

Players A and B play a game with payoff matrix

$$\begin{bmatrix} 1 & 2 & 4 \\ 4 & 3 & 4 \\ 0 & 1 & 5 \end{bmatrix}$$

How is this game best played? What can each player expect to win?

**Solution**

Since player B wants to pay A as little as possible, he might be tempted to try strategy 1, since it contains the entry 0. However, if he selects strategy 1 and A happens to select strategy 2, then he ends up paying \$4. Rather than take this chance, he decides to give up working for himself and starts working against A. How can he guarantee that, no matter what happens, A will win as little as possible? If he chooses strategy 1, then the worst that can happen is for A to choose strategy 2, in which case B loses \$4. If he chooses strategy 2, then A can win at most \$3 (by selecting strategy 2). Finally, if he chooses strategy 3, the worst that can happen is a loss of \$5. Thus, he selects strategy 2 and minimizes the worst that can happen.

Of course, if for some reason A knows for sure that B will play a certain strategy, then she should abandon the theory developed here and take advantage of the information she has about B.

The situation for A is similar except that she wants to win as much as possible. Again, the greedy temptation to select strategy 3 in hopes of a \$5 win must be avoided. The best bet is to work against B and to select a strategy that results in the maximum loss for B. Strategy 1 would yield a loss for B of at least $1. Strategy 2 would result in a loss of at least $3, and strategy 3 in a loss of at least $0. Thus, A selects strategy 2 to obtain the maximum assured loss for B.

Notice that each player's best strategy involves the $(2, 2)$ entry 3. Thus, the minimum assured win for A in B's best strategy equals the maximum assured loss for B in A's best strategy. When this happens, the game is said to have a **saddle point**. It can be shown that, if a game has a saddle point, then the best plan for each player is to use the same strategy constantly. The most A can hope to win equals the least B can expect to lose. In Problem 1, A and B should both always use strategy 2. Each game will then result in B's paying A $3. The number 3 is called the **value** of the game. It is the amount that A expects to win each time the game is played and the amount she should pay B each time to make the game fair.

Again we remind the reader that throughout this section we are considering only one approach to game theory, namely, *von Neumann's minimax strategies*. This is the most conservative approach, and it is most effective in games that are played repeatedly against a thinking opponent. We are also assuming that a player has no idea which strategy the opponent might pick at any given time. If a game is to be played only once, you may feel inclined to gamble a little bit. If your game is against a nonthinking opponent (for example, prospecting for minerals can be viewed as a game against nature) a different approach might be better. Finally, if you have information about your opponent, you might be able to use it to advantage. For example, if you are A and play the game described in Problem 1 above and you *know* that your opponent B will use strategy 3, then by all means use your strategy 3, not the minimax strategy!

Most games do not have saddle points, however, it is worth applying the simple check shown in the flow chart on the next page before turning to the more difficult technique that follows.

**To Determine
a Saddle Point**

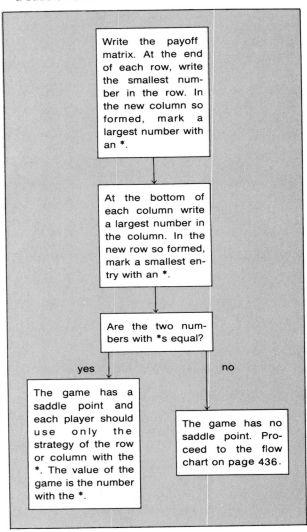

Write the payoff matrix. At the end of each row, write the smallest number in the row. In the new column so formed, mark a largest number with an *.

At the bottom of each column write a largest number in the column. In the new row so formed, mark a smallest entry with an *.

Are the two numbers with *s equal?

yes

no

The game has a saddle point and each player should use only the strategy of the row or column with the *. The value of the game is the number with the *.

The game has no saddle point. Proceed to the flow chart on page 436.

In case of ties there may be several *s at the ends of rows and/or the bottoms of columns. If the starred numbers are equal, then each player may use any one (or even a combination) of the starred strategies.

Problem 2    Use the flow chart to find the saddle point and value (if any) of the following payoff matrices:

(a) $\begin{bmatrix} 4 & -1 & 1 & 0 \\ -2 & -1 & 2 & 0 \\ 3 & 0 & 1 & 1 \\ 5 & -1 & -3 & 1 \end{bmatrix}$    (b) $\begin{bmatrix} 0 & 2 & 3 & 2 & 1 \\ -1 & 1 & -1 & -3 & 4 \\ 3 & 4 & 0 & -2 & 3 \end{bmatrix}$

Solution    (a) The smallest entry in $R_1$ is $-1$. We write a $-1$ to the right of this row and proceed similarly for each of the other rows. The largest entry in $C_1$ is 5. We write 5 below this column and proceed similarly for each of the other columns. Here is the result.

$$\begin{bmatrix} 4 & -1 & 1 & 0 \\ -2 & -1 & 2 & 0 \\ 3 & 0 & 1 & 1 \\ 5 & -1 & -3 & 1 \end{bmatrix} \begin{matrix} -1 \\ -2 \\ 0* \\ -3 \end{matrix}$$
$$\begin{matrix} 5 & 0* & 2 & 1 \end{matrix}$$

The zero in the added column is starred since it is the largest entry. The zero in the new row is starred since it is the smallest entry. Since the starred numbers are equal there is a saddle point. Player A should always use strategy 3 and player B should always use strategy 2. The game is **fair**; that is, its value is zero, so that neither player should expect to gain or lose by playing it.

(b) We proceed as before:

$$\begin{bmatrix} 0 & 2 & 3 & 2 & 1 \\ -1 & 1 & -1 & -3 & 4 \\ 3 & 4 & 0 & -2 & 3 \end{bmatrix} \begin{matrix} 0* \\ -3 \\ -2 \end{matrix}$$
$$\begin{matrix} 3 & 4 & 3 & 2* & 4 \end{matrix}$$

Since the starred numbers are not equal, the game has no saddle point and must be approached by other methods.

**Dominant Strategies**    Before starting to solve a game with no saddle point it is often worth comparing strategies, since it can happen that some strategies are so bad that they should never be used. For example, consider B's first two strategies in the following game:

$$\begin{bmatrix} 7 & 5 & 2 \\ 8 & -3 & 1 \\ -1 & -4 & 3 \end{bmatrix} \qquad \mathbf{1}$$

That is, $7>5$, $8>-3$, and $-1>-4$. See Appendix A if needed.    In every case strategy 1 is worse than strategy 2; that is, each entry in column 1 is larger than the corresponding entry in column 2. We say that strategy 2 **dominates** strategy 1, and we may reduce the payoff matrix by eliminating column 1, since B would never use strategy 1.

$$\begin{bmatrix} 5 & 2 \\ -3 & 1 \\ -4 & 3 \end{bmatrix}$$

Now consider this reduced game from the standpoint of A. Player A would never use strategy 2, since strategy 1 is always better; that is, every entry in row 2 is less than the corresponding entry in row 1. We reduce the game again by eliminating this useless row:

$$\begin{bmatrix} 5 & 2 \\ -4 & 3 \end{bmatrix} \qquad\qquad \mathbf{2}$$

This game cannot be reduced further.

**Example 2**  Player A and player B each write the number 1 or the number 2 on a slip of paper. If the numbers turn out to be the same, B pays A $1. If the numbers turn out to be different, A pays B $1. The payoff matrix is

$$\begin{bmatrix} 1 & -1 \\ -1 & 1 \end{bmatrix}$$

We check for saddle points:

$$\begin{bmatrix} 1 & -1 \\ -1 & 1 \end{bmatrix} \begin{matrix} -1 \\ -1 \end{matrix}$$
$$\begin{matrix} 1 & \phantom{-}1 \end{matrix}$$

and find that there are none. None of the strategies is dominant.

In a game with a saddle point it is best for each player to use the same strategy every time the game is played. In a game without a saddle point such a policy could have disastrous consequences. For example, suppose player B chooses strategy 1 in the game above and decides to stick to it. After a while, player A is likely to notice this and has merely to select strategy 1 to drive B into bankruptcy. Similarly, player A should not employ only one strategy. The best choice for each player is to select a strategy at random. In this way A and B will win equally often (in this example) and neither will experience any gain or loss over the long run. Actually, suppose A decides to follow our advice but B elects to use only strategy 1. Since A will be selecting each strategy at random, she will win half of the time anyway. Thus, in the long run A will not lose anything by using this technique. On the other hand, A can gain considerably if she discovers what B is doing.

The procedure of using each of several strategies a certain percentage of the time is called a **mixed strategy**. In the above example, the mixed strategy for each player would be the same: use the first strategy half the time and use the second strategy half the time. To actually implement such a mixed strategy one might flip a coin: heads would mean choose strategy 1, tails would mean choose strategy 2. It is important that the choice of strategy be left up to chance, since otherwise the risk is run that the other player will discover the pattern and take advantage of it.

In most games the proper mixture of strategies is difficult to determine by just looking at the matrix. It can be shown that the simplex method can be used to determine this mixture, as explained in the flow chart below.

**Problem 3**  Solve the game with payoff matrix **1**.

**Solution**  We first note that the game has no saddle point. Next we eliminate dominated strategies, as explained above, to reduce the game to one with payoff matrix **2**. It is simpler to apply the simplex method to this game than to the original $3 \times 3$ game. The flow chart instructs us to set up the matrix

$$\begin{bmatrix} 5 & 2 & 1 & 0 & 1 \\ -4 & 3 & 0 & 1 & 1 \\ 1 & 1 & 0 & 0 & 0 \end{bmatrix}$$

The simplex method leads to the final matrix

$$\begin{bmatrix} 1 & 0 & \frac{3}{23} & -\frac{2}{23} & \frac{1}{23} \\ 0 & 1 & \frac{4}{23} & \frac{5}{23} & \frac{9}{23} \\ 0 & 0 & -\frac{7}{23} & -\frac{3}{23} & -\frac{10}{23} \end{bmatrix}$$

The ordered pair $\left(\frac{7}{23}, \frac{3}{23}\right)$ is an abbreviation for the solution $x_1 = \frac{7}{23}$, $x_2 = \frac{3}{23}$.

from which we read the minimum solution $\left(\frac{7}{23}, \frac{3}{23}\right)$ and the maximum solution $\left(\frac{1}{23}, \frac{9}{23}\right)$. The sum of the numbers in the first answer is $\frac{10}{23}$. Dividing each number by $\frac{10}{23}$, we obtain the modified minimum solution $\left(\frac{7}{10}, \frac{3}{10}\right)$. Similarly, we obtain the modified maximum solution $\left(\frac{1}{10}, \frac{9}{10}\right)$. Recall that, for A, strategy 2 (that is, $R_2$) was eliminated. Thus, A should use her first strategy $\frac{7}{10}$ of the time, never use her second strategy, and use her third strategy $\frac{3}{10}$ of the time. Recall that for B strategy 1 (that is, $C_1$) was eliminated. Thus, B should never use strategy 1, should use his second strategy $\frac{1}{10}$ of the time, and should use his third strategy $\frac{9}{10}$ of the time. According to the flow chart, the value of the game is $1/\left(\frac{10}{23}\right) = \frac{23}{10}$.

We have read the answer to the dual minimization problem as explained on page 366.

**To Determine a
Best Mixed Strategy**

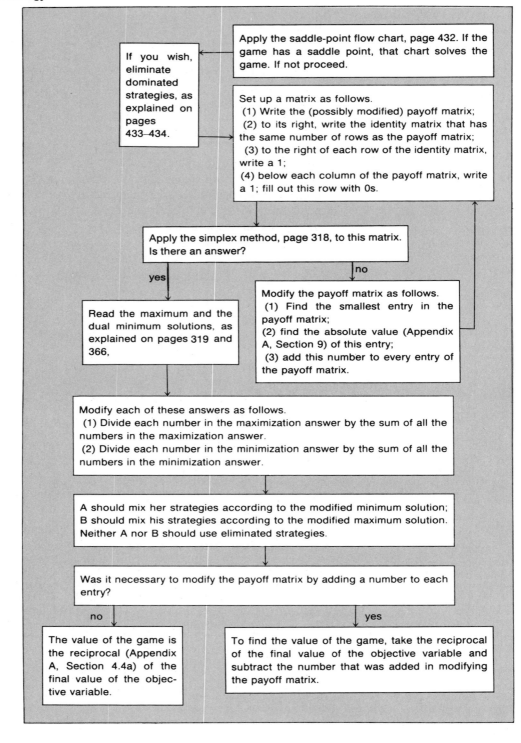

Apply the saddle-point flow chart, page 432. If the game has a saddle point, that chart solves the game. If not proceed.

If you wish, eliminate dominated strategies, as explained on pages 433–434.

Set up a matrix as follows.
 (1) Write the (possibly modified) payoff matrix;
 (2) to its right, write the identity matrix that has the same number of rows as the payoff matrix;
 (3) to the right of each row of the identity matrix, write a 1;
 (4) below each column of the payoff matrix, write a 1; fill out this row with 0s.

Apply the simplex method, page 318, to this matrix. Is there an answer?

yes

no

Read the maximum and the dual minimum solutions, as explained on pages 319 and 366,

Modify the payoff matrix as follows.
 (1) Find the smallest entry in the payoff matrix;
 (2) find the absolute value (Appendix A, Section 9) of this entry;
 (3) add this number to every entry of the payoff matrix.

Modify each of these answers as follows.
 (1) Divide each number in the maximization answer by the sum of all the numbers in the maximization answer.
 (2) Divide each number in the minimization answer by the sum of all the numbers in the minimization answer.

A should mix her strategies according to the modified minimum solution; B should mix his strategies according to the modified maximum solution. Neither A nor B should use eliminated strategies.

Was it necessary to modify the payoff matrix by adding a number to each entry?

no

yes

The value of the game is the reciprocal (Appendix A, Section 4.4a) of the final value of the objective variable.

To find the value of the game, take the reciprocal of the final value of the objective variable and subtract the number that was added in modifying the payoff matrix.

Problem 4    Solve the game

$$\begin{bmatrix} 1 & -1 \\ -1 & 1 \end{bmatrix}$$

Solution    In Example 2, we found that this game had no saddle point or dominant strategies. The matrix to set up for the simplex method is

$$\begin{bmatrix} 1^* & -1 & 1 & 0 & 1 \\ -1 & 1 & 0 & 1 & 1 \\ 1 & 1 & 0 & 0 & 0 \end{bmatrix}$$

If we apply the simplex method to this matrix, the following matrix results:

$$\begin{bmatrix} 1 & -1 & 1 & 0 & 1 \\ 0 & 0 & 1 & 1 & 2 \\ 0 & 2 & -1 & 0 & -1 \end{bmatrix}$$

The second column has a positive last entry, but it has no other positive entries. Thus, the simplex method fails to provide a solution. The smallest entry in the original payoff matrix is $-1$. The flow chart instructs us to add 1, the absolute value of $-1$, to each entry in the payoff matrix and try again. The matrix for the simplex method is

$$\begin{bmatrix} 2 & 0 & 1 & 0 & 1 \\ 0 & 2 & 0 & 1 & 1 \\ 1 & 1 & 0 & 0 & 0 \end{bmatrix}$$

Two operations yield the solution

$$\begin{bmatrix} 1 & 0 & \frac{1}{2} & 0 & \frac{1}{2} \\ 0 & 1 & 0 & \frac{1}{2} & \frac{1}{2} \\ 0 & 0 & -\frac{1}{2} & -\frac{1}{2} & -1 \end{bmatrix}$$

The answer for the minimization problem is

$$\left( \tfrac{1}{2}, \tfrac{1}{2} \right)$$

Since $\frac{1}{2} + \frac{1}{2} = 1$, the required modification does not affect this solution. The answer for the maximization problem is also $(\frac{1}{2}, \frac{1}{2})$. The value of the optimized objective variable is 1. Since we added 1 to the payoff matrix, to find the value of the game we must subtract 1 from the reciprocal of this value: $\frac{1}{1} - 1 = 0$. Thus, each player should use each of the available strategies at random and equally often.

In the following problem we use the notions of Chapters 3 and 4 to extend the theory presented here to a wider class of games. If you have not studied those chapters, you can still benefit from this discussion. In any event, you may simply accept our payoff matrix and proceed from there. The technique we present involves using the payoff matrix to record "expected payoff" rather than the actual payoff. In this way strategies can be combined and the game can be reduced to manageable size.

**Example 3**

This game is also described in Gale's book.

The game 1, 2, 3 is played with 3 cards labeled 1, 2, 3. The "deck" is shuffled and each player is dealt one card. Player A looks at her card and then announces her guess as to which card player B holds. Player B looks at his card, considers player A's guess, and guesses which card A holds. A player who guesses correctly wins $1 from the other player. (An incorrect guess wins nothing. If both are correct, their winnings cancel out.)

Remember B knows his card and would know which other card was not A's.

At first glance it may seem silly for A ever to guess her own card. However, if A never guesses her own card, and if B knows this, then B will guess correctly whenever A guesses wrong, while A will be right only one-half of the time. Thus, A has essentially two strategies—Strategy 1: guess her own card, or Strategy 2: guess a different card. (It really does not matter which.) On the other hand since B plays last it is silly for him to guess his own card. He can use Strategy 1: guess the card A names (or, in case A is correct, guess a different card), or Strategy 2: guess the other card.

Suppose that A uses strategy 1. She will always be wrong. If B now uses strategy 1, he will win $1 and if B uses strategy 2 neither player wins.

Next, suppose that A uses strategy 2 and B uses strategy 1. There are 3 possibilities as outlined in the following tree diagram.

|  |  | Probability | × | Amount A wins | = | Expectation |
|---|---|---|---|---|---|---|
| $\frac{1}{2}$ A is correct $\frac{1}{2}$ B is correct | | $\frac{1}{4}$ | × | 0 | = | 0 |
| $\frac{1}{2}$ B is wrong | | $\frac{1}{4}$ | × | 1 | = | $\frac{1}{4}$ |
| $\frac{1}{2}$ A is wrong $\frac{1}{1}$ B is wrong | | $\frac{1}{2}$ | × | 0 | = | 0 |
| | | Total Expectation | | | = | $\frac{1}{4}$ |

Finally, if both A and B use strategy 2 there are 3 cases.

|  |  | Probability | × | Amount A wins | = | Expectation |
|---|---|---|---|---|---|---|
| $\frac{1}{2}$ A is correct $\frac{1}{2}$ B is correct | | $\frac{1}{4}$ | × | 0 | = | 0 |
| $\frac{1}{2}$ B is wrong | | $\frac{1}{4}$ | × | 1 | = | $\frac{1}{4}$ |
| $\frac{1}{2}$ A is wrong $\frac{1}{1}$ B is correct | | $\frac{1}{2}$ | × | −1 | = | $-\frac{1}{2}$ |
| | | Total Expectation | | | = | $-\frac{1}{4}$ |

The payoff matrix is

$$\begin{bmatrix} -1 & 0 \\ \frac{1}{4} & -\frac{1}{4} \end{bmatrix}$$

We apply the flow chart.

We have added 1 to each entry of the payoff matrix. Recall that if the payoff matrix contains negative entries the simplex method *may* fail to solve the game. It is generally safer to make all the entries positive before applying the simplex method.

$$\begin{bmatrix} 0 & 1 & 1 & 0 & 1 \\ \frac{5}{4}* & \frac{3}{4} & 0 & 1 & 1 \\ 1 & 1 & 0 & 0 & 0 \end{bmatrix}$$

$$\begin{bmatrix} 0 & 1* & 1 & 0 & 1 \\ 1 & \frac{3}{5} & 0 & \frac{4}{5} & \frac{4}{5} \\ 0 & \frac{2}{5} & 0 & -\frac{4}{5} & -\frac{4}{5} \end{bmatrix}$$

$$\begin{bmatrix} 0 & 1 & 1 & 0 & 1 \\ 1 & 0 & -\frac{3}{5} & \frac{4}{5} & \frac{1}{5} \\ 0 & 0 & -\frac{2}{5} & -\frac{4}{5} & -\frac{6}{5} \end{bmatrix}$$

For A the best mixed strategy is to spend $\frac{1}{3}$ of the time with strategy 1 and $\frac{2}{3}$ with strategy 2. For B it is to spend $\frac{5}{6}$ of the time with strategy 1 and $\frac{1}{6}$ of the time with strategy 2. The value of the game is $\frac{1}{6/5} - 1 = \frac{5}{6} - 1 = -\frac{1}{6}$.

In his book, *The Theory of Linear Economic Models*, David Gale interprets A's best mixed strategy as follows: A should name a card at random without looking at the card dealt. In this way she will guess her card $\frac{1}{3}$ of the time as prescribed above. More importantly by doing so she will not transmit any information to B about the card she was dealt.

See *Matrix Methods in Finite Mathematics*, by the present authors.

It can happen that the simplex method results in multiple solutions. In this case, the players will have a whole range of possible mixed strategies to choose from. We shall not discuss this matter in this text.

**Exercises 6.3**  Solve the following six games.

1. $\begin{bmatrix} 1 & 2 \\ 3 & 4 \end{bmatrix}$    2. $\begin{bmatrix} -1 & 3 \\ 2 & -2 \end{bmatrix}$

3. $\begin{bmatrix} -1 & 4 \\ 5 & 2 \end{bmatrix}$    c4. $\begin{bmatrix} 2 & 3 \\ 4 & 4 \end{bmatrix}$

c5. $\begin{bmatrix} -1 & -2 \\ -3 & 1 \end{bmatrix}$    6. $\begin{bmatrix} 3 & 7 \\ 4 & 13 \end{bmatrix}$

<sup>c</sup>7. Player A and player B each write the number 1, 2, or 3 on a slip of paper. If the numbers turn out the same, the game is called a draw. If the numbers are different but their sum is even, B pays A \$2. If the sum is odd, A pays B \$1. How should each player proceed? What amount should B pay A before the game to make the game fair?

Solve the following four games.

8. $\begin{bmatrix} -1 & 2 & 0 & 3 \\ 2 & 1 & 1 & 3 \\ 4 & 2 & -1 & 2 \end{bmatrix}$  9. $\begin{bmatrix} 2 & 1 & 0 \\ 1 & 2 & 2 \\ 0 & 3 & 3 \end{bmatrix}$

10. $\begin{bmatrix} 1 & 1 & 2 & 2 \\ -1 & 2 & 3 & 2 \\ 2 & 0 & 1 & 0 \\ 0 & 3 & 3 & 3 \end{bmatrix}$  <sup>c</sup>11. $\begin{bmatrix} 1 & 3 & -4 & -1 & 1 & 0 \\ 2 & 3 & -3 & 2 & 1 & 2 \\ 4 & 3 & -1 & 3 & 2 & 3 \\ 2 & 1 & 0 & 5 & 4 & 4 \\ 2 & 1 & 4 & 4 & 3 & 5 \\ 5 & 4 & 0 & 4 & 3 & 4 \end{bmatrix}$

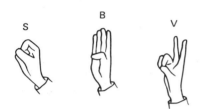

S   B   V

Three-finger Morra is considered in Section 6.6, p. 486.

<sup>c</sup>12. The game of rock, paper, scissors is a two-person zero-sum game often played by children. The players simultaneously display symbols for the above objects usually by signing the letters S, B, or V in the manual alphabet. A player either wins a point or loses a point or ties (if they both display the same symbol). The winner is determined cryptically as follows: "rock breaks scissors, scissors cut paper, paper covers rock." Write the payoff matrix and solve the game.

13. PHE is trying to assess the effects of two types of TV commercials in which they compare their products to those of their arch competitor, MacDougal's (McD). They know that MacDougal's is also considering two types of commercials: the hard sell and the soft sell. The PHE advertising agency estimates that, if PHE and McD both use hard sell, then PHE will get \$6 million of McD business; if they both use soft sell, PHE get \$5 million; if PHE uses hard and McD uses soft, PHE will bet \$3 million; if PHE uses soft and McD uses hard, PHE will get \$2 million. Both types of commercials are in the can (i.e., ready to run) for both companies. How should each company air the commercials, and what will be the result?

14. Morra is a game played by adults. Here we consider a small version, two-finger Morra. The players simultaneously display 1 or 2 fingers and shout their guess as to the total number of fingers to be displayed by both players. If exactly one player is right, he or she wins an amount of money equal to the total number of fingers displayed. Otherwise it is a draw. Write the payoff matrix and solve the game.

15. In Example 1 we described the game of Low Number. The rules still apply if we enlarge the set of numbers.
(a) Solve Low Number for the set $\{1,2,3,4\}$.
(b) Solve Low Number for the set $\{1,2,3,4,5\}$.

*16. Show that if you were to write the payoff matrix for the game of tick tack toe there would be a saddle point.

17. Sam, a ski-slope operator, offers ski lessons to his customers at $5 per person, payable to Sam. Each weekend, he hires some ski instructors, paying each one a flat fee of $400. Each instructor can handle up to 100 people. Sam offers a weekend special: If a customer comes for a lesson, but all instructors are already booked full, Sam pays the customer $1. Sam has observed that if weekend weather at the slope is bad, 200 people will show up for lessons; but if the weather's good, 400 people will come wanting lessons. He will be hiring 2, 3, or 4 instructors, and is, of course, interested in making a profit.

(a) Show that the payoff table for the game pitting Sam against nature is:

| Sam | Nature | |
|---|---|---|
| | Bad Weather | Good Weather |
| Hires 4 instructors | −600 | 400 |
| Hires 3 instructors | −200 | 200 |
| Hires 2 instructors | 200 | 0 |

(Explain the payoff numbers in the table.)

(b) Solve the game of part (a), and describe clearly to Sam (he hasn't had any math) what his strategy whould be and what the value of the game represents in terms of his profit.

## Section 6.4
## Applications
## to Biology

In this connection the documentary film entitled "The Wolf Equation," which has been shown on educational television, is strongly recommended.

Mathematics has been applied to certain problems in biology for nearly a century, but recently some of the techniques of finite mathematics have gained in importance in the effort to understand complex ecosystems more fully. For example, a biologist who is trying to predict the impact of environmental changes on predator-prey relationships may spend many hours at a computer console looking at the predictions of various mathematical models. In this section we briefly examine a few such applications.

**Competition of Species**

Suppose two species of frog, A and B, want to live by the same small pond, which will support only five frogs. Their competition for space may be regarded as a sequence of contests, each resulting in the displacement of one member of one species by one of the other species. We assume that there are always five frogs on the pond and that the competition ends if all frogs of one species leave.

**Problem 1**

Besides the assumptions above, assume that there are now 2 species-A frogs on the pond and that species A has $\frac{2}{3}$ chance of winning each contest. What is the probability that species A will win the competition?

Solution | This is a Markov chain in which the states are the number of species-A frogs on the pond: $0, 1, 2, 3, 4, 5$, and the transition matrix is:

For example, $R_3$ tells us that, if there are 2 As and a contest is held, there is a $\frac{1}{3}$ chance the A population will drop to 1 and a $\frac{2}{3}$ chance it will increase to 3.

$$
\begin{bmatrix}
1 & 0 & 0 & 0 & 0 & 0 \\
\frac{1}{3} & 0 & \frac{2}{3} & 0 & 0 & 0 \\
0 & \frac{1}{3} & 0 & \frac{2}{3} & 0 & 0 \\
0 & 0 & \frac{1}{3} & 0 & \frac{2}{3} & 0 \\
0 & 0 & 0 & \frac{1}{3} & 0 & \frac{2}{3} \\
0 & 0 & 0 & 0 & 0 & 1
\end{bmatrix}
\qquad \mathbf{1}
$$

States 0 and 5 are absorbing states, representing species A losing and winning the competition, respectively. Initially A is in state 2 (that is, row 3). Thus, we are led to determine what fraction of state 2 eventually enters state 5. Applying the flowchart on page 197, we set up the matrix

$$
\begin{bmatrix}
0 & 0 & 0 & 0 & 0 & 0 & 0 \\
\frac{1}{3} & -1 & \frac{2}{3} & 0 & 0 & 0 & 0 \\
0 & \frac{1}{3} & -1 & \frac{2}{3} & 0 & 0 & 0 \\
0 & 0 & \frac{1}{3} & -1 & \frac{2}{3} & 0 & 0 \\
0 & 0 & 0 & \frac{1}{3} & -1 & \frac{2}{3} & 0 \\
0 & 0 & 0 & 0 & 0 & 0 & 0
\end{bmatrix}
\qquad \mathbf{2}
$$

See Exercise 11. | and eventually obtain the limit matrix

$$
\begin{bmatrix}
1 & 0 & 0 & 0 & 0 & 0 \\
\frac{15}{31} & 0 & 0 & 0 & 0 & \frac{16}{31} \\
\frac{7}{31} & 0 & 0 & 0 & 0 & \frac{24}{31} \\
\frac{3}{31} & 0 & 0 & 0 & 0 & \frac{28}{31} \\
\frac{1}{31} & 0 & 0 & 0 & 0 & \frac{30}{31} \\
0 & 0 & 0 & 0 & 0 & 1
\end{bmatrix}
\qquad \mathbf{3}
$$

Multiplying $[0 \quad 0 \quad 1 \quad 0 \quad 0 \quad 0]$ by matrix **3** gives

$$
\begin{bmatrix} \frac{7}{31} & 0 & 0 & 0 & 0 & \frac{24}{31} \end{bmatrix}
$$

Thus, the probability that species A will dominate is $\frac{24}{31} \doteq 0.77$.

Problem 2 | Suppose the pond can hold only 3 frogs and the probability of species A's winning each contest is p. Find the probabilities of A's winning the competition for each possible initial population.

Solution   The transition matrix is

$$\begin{bmatrix} 1 & 0 & 0 & 0 \\ q & 0 & p & 0 \\ 0 & q & 0 & p \\ 0 & 0 & 0 & 1 \end{bmatrix}$$

**4**

where $q = 1 - p$ is the probability that A loses a contest. We are to find the fraction of each state that finally enters the last state. The flow chart yields:

We have omitted rows of all zeros.

$$\begin{bmatrix} q & -1 & p & 0 & 0 \\ 0 & q & -1 & p & 0 \end{bmatrix}$$

$$\begin{bmatrix} -q & 1 & p & 0 & 0 \\ q^2 & 0 & pq-1 & p & 0 \end{bmatrix}$$

We have used the fact that $-1/(qp-1) = 1/(1-pq)$. See Appendix A if necessary.

$$\begin{bmatrix} -q/(1-pq) & 1 & 0 & -p^2/(1-pq) \\ -q^2/(1-pq) & 0 & 1 & -p/(1-pq) \end{bmatrix}$$

The final matrix is

$$\begin{bmatrix} 1 & 0 & 0 & 0 & 0 \\ q/(1-pq) & 1 & 0 & 0 & p^2/(1-pq) \\ q^2/(1-pq) & 0 & 1 & 0 & p/(1-pq) \\ 0 & 0 & 0 & 1 & 1 \end{bmatrix}$$

Thus if no A frogs are present, the chances of eventual dominance are 0 and if 3 are present the chances are 1. This is, of course, obvious. If one A frog is present at the start, the chances of eventual total dominance are $p^2/(1-pq)$, and if two are present the chances are $p/(1-pq)$. (Note that $p/(1-pq)$ is greater than or equal to $p^2/(1-pq)$, since $p \le 1$. If $p = 1$ both of these probabilities become 1 and if $p = 0$ they become 0, which is also as it should be.)

Problem 3   Suppose the pond can hold 4 frogs and each species has the same chance of winning a contest. Find the probabilities of eventual total dominance by A under each possible initial population.

Solution   The transition matrix is

$$\begin{bmatrix} 1 & 0 & 0 & 0 & 0 \\ \frac{1}{2} & 0 & \frac{1}{2} & 0 & 0 \\ 0 & \frac{1}{2} & 0 & \frac{1}{2} & 0 \\ 0 & 0 & \frac{1}{2} & 0 & \frac{1}{2} \\ 0 & 0 & 0 & 0 & 1 \end{bmatrix}$$

**5**

The flowchart gives the final matrix

$$\begin{bmatrix} 1 & 0 & 0 & 0 & 0 \\ \frac{3}{4} & 0 & 0 & 0 & \frac{1}{4} \\ \frac{1}{2} & 0 & 0 & 0 & \frac{1}{2} \\ \frac{1}{4} & 0 & 0 & 0 & \frac{3}{4} \\ 0 & 0 & 0 & 0 & 1 \end{bmatrix} \qquad \textbf{6}$$

Thus, the probability of eventual total dominance by A given an initial population of 0, 1, 2, 3, or 4 is $\frac{0}{4}=0$, $\frac{1}{4}$, $\frac{2}{4}=\frac{1}{2}$, $\frac{3}{4}$, or $\frac{4}{4}=1$, respectively.

See Exercise 19. For large populations the transition matrices for the corresponding problem are a bit cumbersome, although they are not too hard to handle, since each row has at most 3 nonzero entries. Another technique, known as *difference equations*, is easier to apply. We shall not describe this technique here but shall give only the general results. If the pond can hold n frogs, if there are i frogs of species A present initially, and if the probability of species A's winning each contest is p, then the probability that species A will eventually achieve total dominance is

$$\frac{1-(q/p)^i}{1-(q/p)^n}, \text{ where } q=1-p, \qquad \textbf{7}$$

if $p \neq \frac{1}{2}$, and

$$\frac{i}{n}. \qquad \textbf{8}$$

if $p=\frac{1}{2}$. In Problem 1 we had $p=\frac{2}{3}$, $q=\frac{1}{3}$, $i=2$, $n=5$. Then $q/p = (\frac{1}{3})/(\frac{2}{3}) = \frac{1}{2}$, and by formula **7** the answer is $(1-(\frac{1}{2})^2)/(1-(\frac{1}{2})^5)=(\frac{3}{4})/(\frac{31}{32})=\frac{24}{31}$, as we obtained. In Problem 3, $p=\frac{1}{2}$ and $n=4$, and our results agree with formula **8**. The results of Problem 2 do not look like formula **7** with $n=3$, but they are, in fact, the same.

See Exercises 14, 15, 16 and 17.

**Distribution of Genotypes** Suppose our species-A frogs have gained control of a big lake. Hundreds of them live around it. Notice that these frogs come in three colors: some in green, some yellow, and some yellow-green.

In biology the forms that a gene can take are called **alleles**.

A male species-A frog of genotype $C_gC_g$ might be called Mr. Greengenes.

A frog's color is determined at conception by two microscopic particles, one from each parent. The particles are forms of the color-determining **gene** C. This gene has two forms: $C_g$, which causes green pigment to form, and $C_y$, which causes yellow. If a frog receives $C_g$ from each parent it comes out green. If it receives $C_y$ from each parent it comes out yellow. If it receives $C_g$ from one parent and $C_y$ from the other (it doesn't matter which parent contributes which) it comes out yellow-green. Thus, with respect to color, species-A frogs have three possible **genotypes**: $C_gC_g$, $C_gC_y$, $C_yC_y$. We assume that the colors of the frogs have no connection with sex, longevity, or sexual attractiveness (the frogs being colorblind).

**Problem 4**

**Solution**

We are using Equation 4 of Section 3.2 here.

If 20% of the frogs are green and 30% are yellow, what is the probability that a color gene chosen at random is of the form $C_g$? Choose a frog at random and choose one from its pair of color genes at random. Then

$$P(C_g) = P(\text{green} \cap C_g) + P(\text{yellow} \cap C_g) + P(\text{yellow-green} \cap C_g)$$
$$= P(C_g|\text{green})P(\text{green}) + P(C_g|\text{yellow})P(\text{yellow})$$
$$+ P(C_g|\text{yellow-green})P(\text{yellow-green})$$
$$= P(C_g|\text{genotype } C_gC_g)P(\text{green})$$
$$+ P(C_g|C_yC_y)P(\text{yellow}) + P(C_g|C_gC_y)P(\text{yellow-green})$$
$$= (1)(0.2) + (0)(0.3) + (0.5)(1 - 0.2 - 0.3)$$
$$= 0.45.$$

Thus, 45% of the color genes are $C_g$ and 55% are $C_y$.

**Problem 5**

**Solution**

We will use subscripts to denote which generation we're on.

**Careful!**

Assuming random mating, what proportions of each color of frog will surround the pond in later generations?
In the present generation (the zeroth generation), we have by Problem 4, $P_0(C_g) = 0.45$, $P_0(C_y) = 0.55$. Then in the first generation, $P_1(\text{green}) = P(\text{genotype } C_gC_g) = P(C_g \text{ from father} \cap C_g \text{ from mother}) = P_0(C_g)P_0(C_g)$ [since color is independent of sex] = $(0.45)(0.45) = 0.2025$; $P_1(\text{yellow}) = P(C_yC_y) = (0.55)(0.55) = 0.3025$; $P(\text{yellow-green}) = P(C_gC_y) = P((C_g \text{ from father} \cap C_y \text{ from mother}) \cup (C_y \text{ from father} \cap C_g \text{ from mother})) = P_0(C_g)P_0(C_y) + P_0(C_y)P_0(C_g) = 2P_0(C_g)P_0(C_y) = 2(0.45)(0.55) = 0.4950$. As a check we note that these three probabilities add to one.

Now the probabilities of the forms of C in the first generation are calculated as in Problem 4: $P_1(C_g) = P_1(C_g \text{ green})P_1(\text{green}) + P_1(C_g \text{ yellow}) P_1(\text{yellow}) + P_1(C_g \text{ yellow-green}) P_1(\text{yellow-green}) = (1)(0.2025) + (0)(0.3025) + (0.5)(0.4950) = 0.45$; $P_1(C_g) = (0)(0.2025)$

Check: $0.45 + 0.55 = 1$.

$+ (1)(0.3025) + (0.5)(0.4950) = 0.55$. Note: we have $P_1(C_g) = P_0(C_g)$ and $P_1(C_y) = P_0(C_y)$. Thus, in the second generation the calculations will be the same as for the first: $P_2(\text{green}) = P_1(\text{green}) = P_1(\text{green})$, and so on. So in *all later generations* there will be 20.25% green frogs, 30.25% yellow, and 49.5% yellow-green.

The answer to Problem 5 is a case of the following result, discovered independently by Hardy and Weinberg in 1908.

This result is known as the Hardy-Weinberg law.

> If a gene G has two forms $G_1$ and $G_2$, which occur in the proportions p and $q = 1 - p$, respectively, in a population and if these proportions are independent of sex, longevity, and sexual attractiveness, then in each later generation the genotypes $G_1G_1$, $G_1G_2$, $G_2G_2$ occur in the proportions $p^2$, $2pq$, $q^2$, respectively.

The same result holds for a gene that has more than two forms.

Here the numbers $p_1, p_2, \ldots, p_n$ are nonnegative and add to 1.

> If a gene G has n forms $G_1$, $G_2$, ..., $G_n$, which occur in the proportions $p_1$, $p_2, \ldots, p_n$ in a population, with independence as above, then in each later generation the genotypes $G_1G_1$, $G_1G_2, \ldots, G_1G_n$, $G_2G_2$, $G_2G_3, \ldots,$ $G_2G_n, \ldots, G_nG_n$ occur in the proportions $p_1^2, 2p_1p_2, \ldots, 2p_1p_n, p_2^2, 2p_2p_3, \ldots, 2p_2p_n, \ldots, p_n^2$, respectively.

**Problem 6**

The number and structure of toes on our frogs is determined by a gene T that has four forms: $T_1, T_2, T_3, T_4$. The original distribution of genotypes around the pond is: $T_1T_1$, $T_1T_2$, $T_1T_3$, $T_1T_4$, $T_2T_2$, and $T_3T_3$, 6% each; all other genotypes, 16% each. Find the proportions of each genotype in the fifth generation.

**Solution**

See Exercise 25.

(There are ten genotypes and $6 \times 6 + 4 \times 16 = 100\%$, so the distribution makes sense.) In the original population, $p_1 = P_0(T_1) = P(T_1|T_1T_1)P_0(T_1T_1) + P(T_1|T_1T_2)P_0(T_1T_2) + P(T_1|T_1T_3)P_0(T_1T_3) + P(T_1|T_1T_4)P_0(T_1T_4) = (1)(0.06) + (0.5)(0.6) + (0.5)(0.6) + (0.5)(0.6) = 0.15$, $p_2 = P_0(T_2) = 0.6 + (0.5)(0.6 + 0.16 + 0.16) = 0.25$, $p_3 = P_0(T_3) = 0.6 + (0.5)(0.6 + 0.16 + 0.16) = 025$, and $p_4 = P_0(T_4) = 0.16 + (0.5)(0.6 + 0.16) = 0.35$. Then in all later generations, including the fifth,

Check: $0.15 + 0.25 + 0.25 + 0.35 = 1$.

$P(T_1T_1) = (0.15)^2 = 0.0225$, $P(T_2T_2) = P(T_3T_3) = (0.25)^2 = 0.0625$, $P(T_4T_4) = (0.35)^2 = 0.1225$, $P(T_1T_2) = P(T_1T_3) = 2(0.15)(0.25) = 0.075$, $P(T_1T_4) = 2(0.15)(0.35) = 0.105$, $P(T_2T_3) = 2(0.25)(0.25) = 0.125$, and $P(T_2T_4) = P(T_3T_4) = 2(0.25)(0.35) = 0.175$.

Not all types of inherited characteristics satisfy all the hypotheses of the Hardy-Weinberg law. In some cases certain genotypes may have greatly reduced vitality, so that the *fitness* of each genotype must be considered. In some cases certain forms of a gene may only occur in conjunction with a structure that determines sex, so that the genotypes are *sex-linked*. We will treat these cases in the exercises.

**Exercises 6.4**   In Exercises 1 through 10 suppose that species A and B are competing for n spaces as described above, where there are i members of species A present initially and the probability of A's winning a given contest is p. Use the Markov chain technique to find the probability that eventually A (totally) dominates.

1. $n=2$, $i=1$, $p=1/4$.
2. $n=2$, $i=1$, $p=3/4$.
3. $n=3$, $i=2$, $p=1/2$.
4. $n=3$, $i=1$, $p=2/3$.
5. $n=4$, $i=3$, $p=1/10$.
6. $n=4$, $i=1$, $p=1/10$.
7. $n=5$, $i=4$, $p=1/10$.
8. $n=5$, $i=1$, $p=1/10$.
9. $n=6$, $i=1$, $p=1/2$.
10. $n=6$, $i=5$, $p=1/2$.
11. Obtain matrix **3** from matrix **2**.
12. Check your answers to Exercises 2, 4, 6, 8, and 10 by using formulas **7** and **8**.
13. Check your answers to Exercises 1, 3, 5, 7, and 9 by using formulas **7** and **8**.
14. Show that if $p \neq 1/2$ and $q = 1 - p$ then $p^2/(1 - pq) = (1-(q/p))/(1-(q/p)^3)$.
15. Show that if $p \neq 1/2$ and $q = 1 - p$ then $p/(1 - pq) = (1-(q/p)^2)/(1-(q/p)^3)$.
16. Show that if $p=1/2$ and $q=1-p$ then $p^2/(1-pq)=1/3$.
17. Show that if $p=1/2$ and $q=1-p$ then $p/(1-pq)=2/3$.
*18. Carry out the Markov chain calculation for species competition with $n=4$ and p arbitrary, and show that formulas **7** and **8** result.
19. Suppose two species are competing for n positions, as described above. Let $p_i$ be the probability that A eventually dominates, given that i members of species A are initially present.
    (a) Explain why $p_0=0$ and $p_n=1$.
    (b) Show that if i is between 1 and $n-1$ then

This is the difference equation for species competition of the type discussed here.

$$p_i = pp_{i+1} + qp_{i-1}$$

**9**

20. Show that, if $p = q = 1/2$, then $p_i = i/n$ (formula **8**) is a solution of equation **9**.

21. Show that, if $p \neq 1/2$, $q = 1 - p$, then $p_i = (1 - (q/p)^i)(1 - (q/p)^n)$ is a solution of equation **9**.

22. Two equally matched species compete for 10 places. How many places must the first species initially have in order for it to have at least a 90% chance of domination?

23. Suppose a gene A has two forms $A_1$, $A_2$. Assume the genotypes $A_1A_1$, $A_1A_2$, $A_2A_2$ are present in the proportions $a_{11}$, $a_{12}$, $a_{22}$, respectively. Prove that the respective proportions p and q of $A_1$ and $A_2$ are given by

$$p = a_{11} + a_{12}/2 \qquad\qquad \textbf{10}$$

$$q = a_{22} + a_{12}/2 \qquad\qquad \textbf{11}$$

24. Eye color in a certain species of cat is controlled by a gene E with two forms $E_1$, $E_2$. In a certain population of 87 cats 31 are of genotype $E_1E_2$ and 40 are of genotype $E_2E_2$. How many genes of each form are in the population?

25. Prove that, if a gene has n different forms, then there are $C_2^{n+1}$ possible genotypes.

26. Write out the genotypes for a gene having 5 forms.

27. A certain flower has a two-form color gene with genotypes $C_1C_1$ (red), $C_1C_2$ (pink), $C_2C_2$ (white). My garden has 30% red flowers and 45% white flowers. What will the distribution be in the next generation?

28. Another type of flower has a color gene with 3 forms and genotypes $C_1C_1$ (red), $C_1C_2$ (purple), $C_1C_3$ (pink), $C_2C_2$ (dark blue), and $C_2C_3$ (light blue). My garden has 30% red, 30% purple, and 40% light blue flowers. What will the distribution be in the next generation?

Sex-linked genotypes. (This discussion applies to mammals.)

29. Genes are transmitted on two types of structures called **chromosomes**. The types, traditionally denoted X and Y, are determiners of sex; the female has two X chromosomes; the male has one X and one Y. A gene is **sex-linked** if its forms are found only on one type of chromosome. Suppose a gene G has two forms $G_1$, $G_2$, which are only on X chromosomes. Then females have possible genotypes $G_1G_1$, $G_1G_2$, $G_2G_2$, but males have only genotypes $G_1$, $G_2$. Suppose that 30% of the forms of G in the original population of females and 40% in the original population of males are $G_1$. Assuming random mating, find the proportions of each genotype in the first generation.

*30. Under the assumptions of Exercise 29, what percent of females in the second generation are of each genotype?

Genotypes of unequal fitness.

*31. Suppose that a gene G (not sex-linked) has two forms $G_1$, $G_2$ and that the probabilities that an individual of genotype $G_1G_1$, $G_1G_2$, $G_2G_2$ survives to adulthood are, respectively, $s_1$, $s_2$, $s_3$. If initially the forms $G_1$, $G_2$ occur in the respective proportions p, $q = 1 - p$, what are the proportions of the genotypes in the next generation?

**Section 6.5
Maximal Flows
in Networks**

In his 1755 *Dictionary of the English Language*, Samuel Johnson defines a network to be "anything reticulated or decussated at equal distance with interstices between the intersections." For our purposes we will need to modify his formulation. While "reticulated" and "interstices" are pertinent to what we have in mind, "decussated" and "equal distance" are not. With all due respect to Dr. Johnson, when we say **network** we mean a mathematical object consisting of a collection of **vertices** (intersections) connected by **edges** (the reticulation). A few examples should make all this clear.

Example 1

(Pipeweed shipment in The Shire) The governing council of The Shire has placed limits on the number of wagonloads of pipeweed that can travel per season on each of the paved connecting roads between the central towns. Leaf is produced in small quantities around many towns, but the most (and best) comes from around Longbottom. In this network the vertices are the towns, the edges are the paved roads, and numbers on the edges give the restrictions.

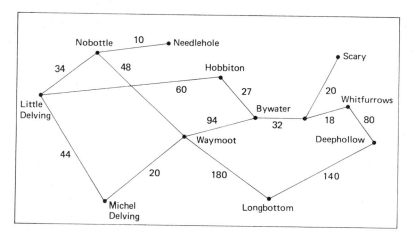

Example 2

(The Telephone Company) When Gulliver returned to England after his voyage to Laputa, he complained that communication between the places he had visited was extremely difficult. Ye Olde Englishe Belle immediately sent representatives to acquire property rights and soon microwave towers dotted all horizons.

The result was the following telephone network. A line (or edge) between two cities (the vertices) indicates that there is a direct telephone connection between them. The numbers on the edges indicate the number of calls that can be carried simultaneously between the connected cities.

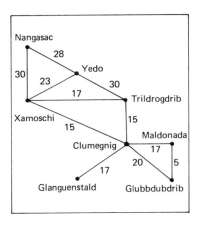

While there are many questions one can ask about any given network, we will limit ourselves to just one: Given two vertices in a network, what is the largest amount which can be shipped between them at one time without exceeding any of the restrictions? For example, in the Shire the residents of Nobottle want as much Longbottom leaf as possible. The direct route can handle some (48 wagonloads), but by routing through Bywater they can get more (75 wagonloads). They want to know if this is the best they can do. Again, all telephone calls from Nangasac to Glubbdubdrib must be routed through other towns. The phone company needs to know how many calls can be transmitted simultaneously because they want to expand their system if it is not large enough to meet the average demand.

If we agree to call the movement of material in a network a **flow**, then we are looking for a maximal (largest) flow. Other applications should come to mind. What is the maximal flow through a network of railways, a system of oil pipelines, a network of power plants? We will even be able to interpret the assignment of persons to jobs as a network flow problem.

This section contains a detailed description of a method, called the Ford-Fulkerson labeling method, for finding the maximal flow through a paticular type of network. There are three restrictions.

(1) Each edge in the network must have a certain carrying capacity. In real-life situations these capacities may be fractional, although by changing units it is possible to avoid fractions altogether. It is also possible to apply the labeling method even if some edges have infinite capacity. All edges of all networks in this text will have finite positive integer capacities.

Send 48 + 27 to Waymoot, 48 to Nobottle, and 27 to Bywater. Then ship this 27 thru Hobbiton and Little Delving to Nobottle.

(2) Each edge must be directed; that is, each edge must have an arrow indicating the direction of flow. No flow can go against the arrow. Although this may seem to be an unreasonable assumption, it is actually not restrictive at all. For example, if an undirected edge with capacity 5 appears in your network:

simply replace it with two directed edges, each with capacity 5;

$$①\ \underset{5}{\overset{5}{\rightleftarrows}}\ ②$$

This does introduce more edges but it really does not change the problem, and it is essential that all edges be given a direction before the Ford-Fulkerson method can be applied.

(3) All material that flows through the network must originate at one single vertex, called the **source**, and end up at one single vertex, called the **sink**. It turns out that this is not really a restriction either. Later in the section we will show how to change a network with many sources and sinks into one with one source and one sink in such a way that the answer will not be changed. We will always call the source ⓢ and the sink ⓣ (for "terminal").

For example, you may not ship more than 10 directly from ⓢ to ②, and you may not ship any items directly from ② to ⓢ.

Below is an example of a directed capacitated network with a single source and a single sink. Our aim is to move as may items from ⓢ to ⓣ as possible without exceeding any edge capacities and without moving against any arrows. For small networks it is often possible to locate a maximal flow by trial and error. However, for large networks a systematic approach adaptable to computers is needed. Beyond that, even if you do find a flow you think is maximal, how can you be *certain* it is maximal? The Ford-Fulkerson labeling method answers both these needs.

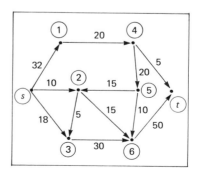

The following flow chart outlines the Ford-Fulkerson labeling method for finding a maximal flow in a directed network. The method is easy to apply but difficult to illustrate in a book. Following the outline we will carefully describe each step and then apply it to the network shown above.

**Outline Flow Chart
for Finding a
Maximal Flow
in a Network**

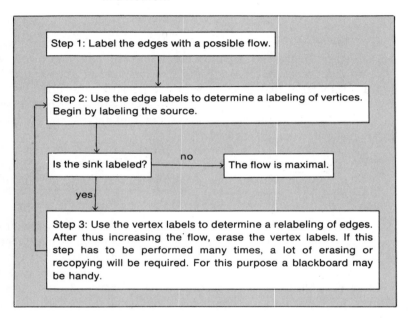

Step 1
Indicate a Possible Flow

This is done by labeling each edge with a number indicating the amount to be shipped along that edge.

Step 2
Label the Vertices

We begin by labeling the source. Proceeding from there, we label other vertices according to the rules set out below. Our aim is to label the sink. However, if the flow is maximal, the labeling rules will tell us to stop before this happens.

Step 3
Increase the Flow

If the sink has been labeled, its label will indicate an amount by which the flow can be increased. The labels on the other vertices indicate how to alter the flow so that it will be increased by that amount. We increase the flow, erase all vertex labels, and return to Step 2.

We now give a detailed explanation of each of these steps, illustrating the entire procedure with Network 1 as we go along.

Otherwise, there will be items left
over along the way. If you can ship 15
items into a vertex but only 10 out, do
not ship 15 in and leave 5 lying
around. They might get ripped off.

This observation can serve as a very
rough check.

The simplex method for standard
maximization problem begins with
zero.

It is necessary to strike a balance between the amount of time you spend
trying to find maximal flow by yourself and the amount of time you
spend using Steps 2 and 3.

When indicating a possible flow there are two rules which must be
followed:

i(i) Do not exceed the capacity of any edge;
(ii) Except for the source and sink, there must be exactly as many
items entering a vertex as leaving it.

It can be shown that, if all edge capacities are given by
integers, then fractions will not appear in the solution or in the
answer. Also, if you follow the two rules given above, there will be
exactly the same number of items leaving the source as entering
the sink. This is guaranteed by rule (ii): everything shipped out
gets through.

If you happen to be a computer or very sleepy, you can
complete Step 1 by simply indicating a flow of zero along each
edge. However, if you are working a problem by hand it will
generally take a very long time for the procedure described in
Steps 2 and 3 to turn a flow of zero into a maximal flow. While the
method we describe is fun to apply, it can get rather tedious. The
best idea is to try to determine a maximal flow immediately by
inspecting the network. If you are lucky and actually do stumble
onto a maximal flow right off, Step 2 will verify this for you rather
quickly. However, in your eagerness to obtain a maximal flow do
not forget the two rules given above.

We will use ordered pairs to label the edges. The first entry
will be the edge capacity; the second entry will denote the flow.
Since the edge capacities are given to us as part of the information
describing the network, the first entries will not change as we
proceed through the solution.

There are always a lot of different ways to follow Step 1. Here
is our initial flow.

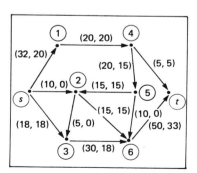

You may be able to see better ways to begin, but do check that we have satisfied rules (i) and (ii). For example, at vertex 4:

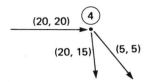

we have 20 coming in and $15+5=20$ going out.

Step 2
Label the Vertices

We now use the edge labels to label the vertices with ordered pairs. The following flow chart outlines the procedure. This chart will help you understand the main idea. However, it does not explain how to label the vertices. We will take care of that aspect in a moment.

**Outline Flow
Chart For
Labeling Vertices**

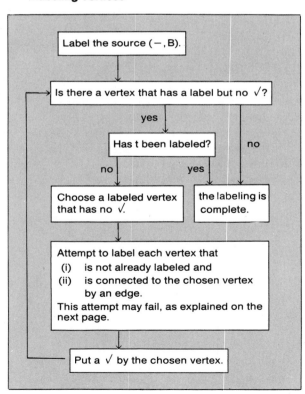

Before we describe how to actually label a given vertex, there
are two matters which deserve clarification.

In this text no number in any network
problem is bigger than 1,000. Thus
for the purpose of this text we could
always label the source $(-, 1,000)$.

1. In the first box in the flow chart we have used the letter B in
   the label for the source. The letter B stands for a number that is
   bigger than any number that occurs in the problem.
2. In the next to last box in the flow chart we have used the word
   "attempt" to indicate that the following rules may not allow
   you to label a vertex. In fact as the flow increases the number
   of vertices which can be labeled will decrease.

We now describe the specifics of the labeling process. There
are two cases.

Case I

The edge is directed out from the labeled vertex.

$(m^+, a)$

⒩   $(b, c)$   ⒫

or

$(m^-, a)$

⒩   $(b, c)$   ⒫

If $b = c$, do not label vertex p.
If $b > c$, label vertex p

$(n^+, d)$

where d is the smaller of the numbers $b - c$ and a.

Problem 1    Label vertex ⑨ in each of the following cases:

(a)   $(2^+, 4)$
      ⑧  $(5, 2)$  ⑨

(b)   $(3^-, 2)$
      ⑦  $(5, 1)$  ⑨

(c)   $(2^+, 3)$
      ⑥  $(5, 5)$  ⑨

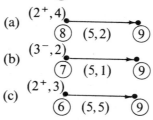

Solution    (a) According to the label on the edge, it has capacity 5 of which 2
            are being used. Although there are 4 items at vertex ⑧, we can
            ship only $3 = 5 - 2$ more of them to ⑨. In order to indicate
            their origin, we label vertex ⑨:

$(8^+, 3)$

The label means: we can bring

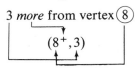

to vertex $\textcircled{9}$.

(b) There is room for $4 = 5 - 1$ more on the edge from $\textcircled{7}$ to $\textcircled{9}$, but the label on vertex $\textcircled{7}$ tells us we have only 2 available for shipment. In this case vertex $\textcircled{9}$ is labeled

$$(7^+, 2)$$

(c) The label on the edge from $\textcircled{6}$ to $\textcircled{9}$ indicates that this edge is completely filled. We cannot ship anymore from $\textcircled{6}$ to $\textcircled{9}$ than is already being shipped. Therefore, we do not label vertex $\textcircled{9}$.

**Case II**

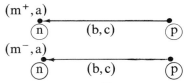

The edge is directed in toward the labeled vertex.

If $c = 0$, do not label vertex $\textcircled{p}$.
If $c > 0$, label vertex $\textcircled{p}$

$$(n^-, d)$$

where d is the smaller of the numbers c and a.

**Problem 2** Label vertex $\textcircled{9}$ in each of the following cases:

(a) $(2^+, 3)$    $\textcircled{8}$   $(6, 0)$   $\textcircled{9}$

(b) $(3^-, 4)$    $\textcircled{8}$   $(6, 1)$   $\textcircled{9}$

(c) $(1^+, 2)$    $\textcircled{8}$   $(6, 3)$   $\textcircled{9}$

**Solution**

There might be edges in the network which go from $\textcircled{8}$ to $\textcircled{9}$. We would label vertex $\textcircled{9}$ as directed by Case I.

The labeling process begins at the source. We began at the source and labeled vertices until we got out to vertex $\textcircled{8}$. Now we want to label vertex $\textcircled{9}$. The arrow indicates that it is impossible to use this edge to ship anything from vertex $\textcircled{8}$ directly to vertex $\textcircled{9}$. The edge is "backwards." The best we can do is to ship fewer items from $\textcircled{9}$ to $\textcircled{8}$.

(a) In this case, we are not shipping anything along this edge. We certainly do not want to change that. Vertex ⑨ remains unlabeled.

(b) In this case, 1 unit is "going backwards." We want to subtract and reroute it. The label for vertex ⑨ is $(8^-, 1)$. This label means:

Ship 1 item *less* from vertex ⑨ to vertex ⑧.

$$(8^-, 1)$$

(c) In this case we would like to reroute all 3 items on the edge. However, we have only 2 items at ⑧. Thus, we can only reschedule 2 of the 3 items. Vertex ⑨ is labeled

$$(8^-, 2).$$

For our purposes we will rarely consider networks with more than one edge between any two vertices. Nevertheless, here is an extreme example to help you understand what to do if you need to label a network with more than one edge between a given pair of vertices.

Problem 3    Label vertex ⑨.

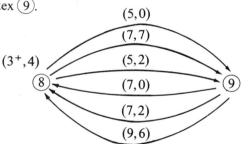

Solution    We can label vertex ⑨ in many ways. There are four edges which could be used:

We are counting edges from top down.

| Edge | Label for 9 |
|------|-------------|
| 1    | $(8^+, 4)$  |
| 3    | $(8^+, 3)$  |
| 5    | $(8^-, 2)$  |
| 6    | $(8^-, 4)$  |

Mathematically it does not matter which label we use. Practically, we should use either $(8^+, 4)$ or $(8^-, 4)$ if we want to have fewer steps in the solution of the problem.

If it is possible to label a vertex you must do so. Do not simply look at the second edge and say ⑨ cannot be labeled.

Once a vertex is labeled, this label remains until all the labels are erased after the flow is increased.

We illustrate Step 2 for our particular network. In general, there will be a lot of different choices for unchecked vertices, and so there will be a lot of different ways to implement Step 2. In our case, however, there are two ways to label the vertices. Here is one.

This is because the flow we have indicated in Step 1 is nearly maximal.

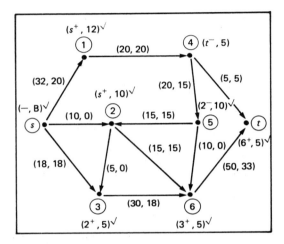

The full sequence of steps used in obtaining this labeling is as follows.

1. label Ⓢ $(-, B)$
2. label ① $(s^+, 12)$
3. label ② $(s^+, 10)$
4. ③ cannot yet be labeled.
5. check off Ⓢ
6. choose ① (② could have been chosen instead)
7. ④ cannot be labeled
8. check off ①
9. choose ② (no other choice at this point)
10. label ③ $(2^+, 5)$
11. label ⑤ $(2^-, 10)$
12. check off ②
13. choose ③
14. label ⑥ $(3^+, 5)$
15. check off ③
16. choose ⑥
17. ⑤ is labeled
18. label ⓣ $(6^+, 5)$
19. check off ⑥

20. choose ⓣ
21. label ④ (t⁻,5)
22. check off ⓣ
23. choose ④
24. ⑤ is labeled
25. check off ④
26. choose ⑤
27. check off ⑤
28. The labeling is complete.

**Step 3**
**Increase the Flow**

If the flow is maximal it is impossible to ship more material through the network. However, there may be many different routes by which this maximal amount may be shipped. For this reason we say *a* maximal flow instead of *the* maximal flow.

If the sink has not been labeled in Step 2, the flow is a maximal flow. Otherwise it is possible to increase the flow by the amount indicated by the second coordinate of the sink label. In our labeling above, for example, ⓣ is labeled $(6^+, 5)$, so the flow can be increased by 5. From now on we look only at the first coordinate of the vertex label. *We begin by examining the sink label and proceed systematically back to the source.* There are two cases.

**Case I**

A vertex is labeled

$$ⓐ^{(b^+, c)} \checkmark$$

Increase the flow along the edge between ⓑ and ⓐ by the amount indicated in the sink label. Now examine vertex ⓑ.

If there is more than one edge between a and b you must, of course, use the edge that you originally used in getting the label.

**Case II**

A vertex is labeled

$$ⓐ^{(b^-, c)} \checkmark$$

Decrease the flow along the edge between ⓑ and ⓐ by the amount indicated in the sink label. Now examine vertex ⓑ.

*In both cases, the number c is ignored.*

Here are the steps involved in our particular example.

1. The sink is labeled $(6^+, 5)$. The flow can be increased by 5. In particular we increase the flow from ⑥ to ⓣ from 33 to 38. Now examine vertex ⑥.
2. At vertex ⑥ the label $(3^+, 5)$ tells us to increase the flow from vertex ③ to vertex ⑥ by 5. We increase the flow from 18 to 23 and go to vertex ③.
3. At vertex ③ we find a label with a $2^+$ in it. We increase the flow from ② to ③ by 5 and go to vertex ②.
4. At vertex ② we find the label $(s^+, 10)$. We increase the flow from ⓢ to ② by 5 (*not by* 10). Since we have reached the source we erase all vertex labels and return to Step 2.

If we make all these changes we obtain the new edge labeling:

Changed labels are underlined here for clarity. (They usually are not.)

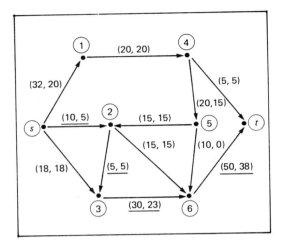

It can be shown that, if you alter the flow according to the rules in Step 3, it will still satisfy the conditions in Step 1. Notice that some of the vertex labels were not used (for example vertex ④) and that the flow on most of the edges did not change.

Thus, in the 28 steps described above in the first labeling of vertices, we should have stopped after Step 18.

Having actually applied Step 3 to a particular example, you should now notice that there is no need to label and check all the vertices. You need only label vertices until you reach the sink. In the network below we didn't bother to label vertices ③ and ④ or check vertices ⑤, ⑥, or ⓣ.

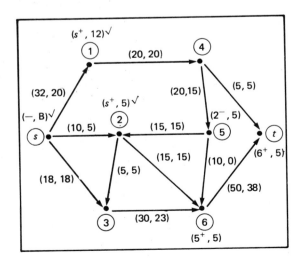

We are now ready for Step 3 again.

1. Increase the flow from ⑥ to ⓣ by 5.
2. Increase the flow from ⑤ to ⑥ by 5.
3. *Decrease* the flow from ② to ⑤ by 5.
4. Increase the flow from ⓢ to ② by 5.

In the following network we not only indicate the new flow but we also give the new vertex labels.

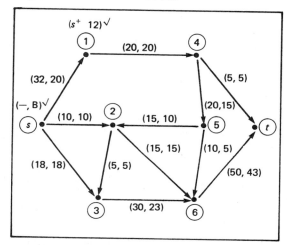

Since the Rules in Step 2 will not allow us to label any vertices except ⓢ and ① the flow of 48 units is maximal.

**The Minimal Cut**  A **cut** in a network is any edge blockade which completely cuts off the flow from ⓢ to ⓣ. The **cut capacity** is the total capacity of all edges involved in the cut. Here are three examples with our network.

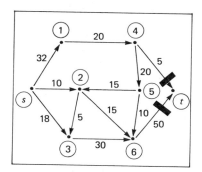

This cut has capacity $50 + 5 = 55$.

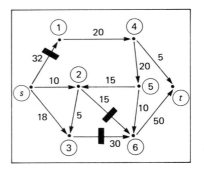

In this case we are blocking $32 + 15 + 30 = 77$ units.

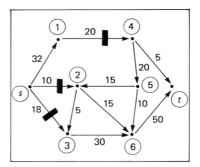

Now we have completely stopped the flow by blocking $20 + 10 + 18 = 48$ units.

There is a rather close relationship between cuts and flows. In the first place, a cut completely blocks the flow. It follows that each item in the flow must pass some cut barricade. Thus, no flow can exceed any cut capacity. In our case, since we know that it is possible to ship 48 items through our network, we see that it is impossible to find a cut with a smaller capacity. Similarly, since we have found a cut with capacity 48 we know that the flow of 48 is maximal.

In general, in any network if you can find a flow and a cut with the same capacity then the flow is maximal and the cut is minimal. It is easy to use the Ford-Fulkerson labeling technique to find a minimal cut.

Need we point out the importance of this material to those engaged in sabotage, and hence also to those engaged in countersabotage?

It is possible to formulate a network flow problem as a standard maximization linear programming problem. If you do that, then this comment amounts to the dual variable check.

**How to Find a Minimal Cut**

Edges from vertices in U to vertices in L must not be included.

(1) Use Step 2 to label as many vertices as possible.
(2) Form two sets: L = the set of labeled vertices; U = the set of unlabeled vertices.
(3) The minimal cut consists of all edges in the network which go *from* a vertex in L *to* a vertex in U.

In our case

$$L = \{(s),(1)\}$$

$$U = \{(2),(3),(4),(5),(6),(t)\}$$

and a minimal cut consists of the edges from $(s)$ to $(2)$, $(s)$ to $(3)$, and $(1)$ to $(4)$ as indicated in the third example above.

**Multiple Sources and Sinks**

It is easy to handle a network with more than one source or sink. Suppose we are given a network which begins and ends as follows.

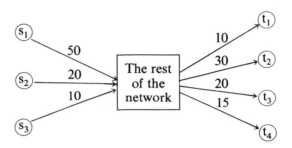

Simply enlarge the network.

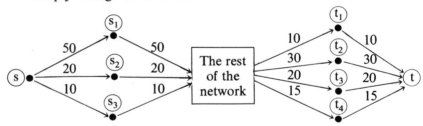

This converts the original network into a network with exactly one source and one sink. We solve the problem exactly as before and then erase $(s)$, $(t)$, and the edges we added.

**The Assignment Problem**

Actually, 100 jobs were created and 120 people were interviewed. We cannot illustrate the solution of a problem of that size in this text. Such problems must be solved by computers.

In an attempt to ease unemployment, the management at AC created 10 new jobs. They advertised widely and finally interviewed 12 applicants. The interviewers determined which jobs each applicant could do. The following chart shows the results of the interviews. AC wants to hire as many qualified people as possible. However, since some jobs can be done by very few applicants, it is not even clear that all 10 positions can be filled. Even less clear is the relevance of maximal flow in networks to this problem.

We use the technique of this section as follows. Create a network with 12 sources (one for each applicant) and 10 sinks (one for each job). Insert an edge with capacity 1 directed from each applicant to each job he or she can do. Now the network problem is to ship as many individuals to as many jobs as possible. To guarantee that no job is filled by more than one applicant we add a sink to the network and connect each job to the sink by an edge with capacity one. To guarantee that no applicant gets assigned to more than one job we add a source to the network and connect this source to each applicant by an edge with capacity one.

| Job <br> Applicant | I | II | III | IV | V | VI | VII | VIII | IX | X |
|---|---|---|---|---|---|---|---|---|---|---|
| A | × |   | × |   |   | × | × |   |   |   |
| B |   | × |   |   | × |   |   |   |   | × |
| C |   |   |   | × |   | × |   |   |   |   |
| D | × |   |   |   |   |   |   |   |   | × |
| E |   | × |   | × |   |   |   |   |   |   |
| F | × | × |   |   |   |   |   |   |   | × |
| G | × | × |   |   | × |   |   |   |   |   |
| H | × |   | × |   |   | × |   |   |   |   |
| I |   |   |   |   |   |   |   | × | × |   |
| J | × |   |   |   |   |   |   | × |   | × |
| K |   |   |   | × |   |   | × |   |   |   |
| L | × |   |   |   |   |   |   | × |   |   |

We draw the complete network as follows. We have omitted all the labels and all the arrows.

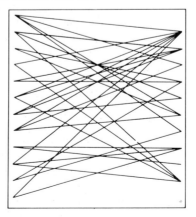

This network is a hopeless jumble, especially in the middle where all the lines cross. Imagine how much worse it would be if we inserted all the arrows and labels we needed to solve the problem. In order to handle this problem more easily we split the network into two pieces as shown in the next chart. Each "middle"

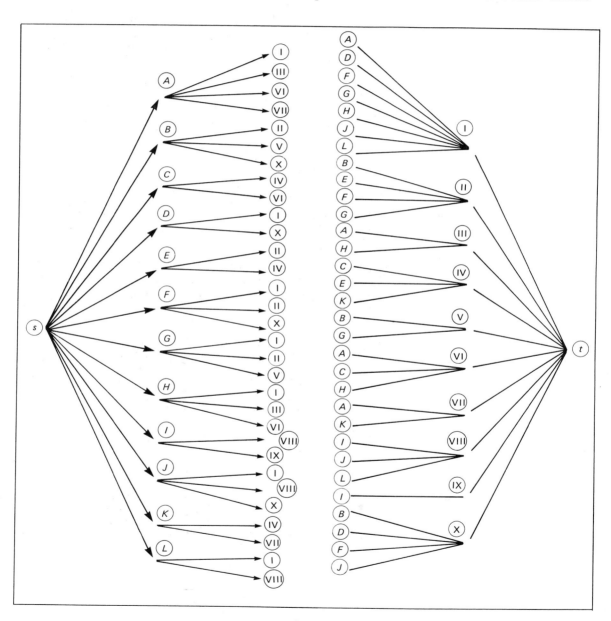

edge appears twice. For example, the edges labeled

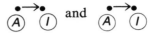

are really the same edge. We will apply the labeling technique as usual keeping in mind the duplication of edges. To simplify matters we will not indicate any edge capacities (they are all 1), a flow of zero, nor any arrows on the right side.

We begin by arbitrarily assigning individuals to jobs:

> A gets I
> B gets II
> C gets IV
> D gets X
> E is left out
> F is left out
> G gets V
> H gets VI
> I gets VIII
> J is left out
> K gets VII
> L is left out

These job assignments are indicated by the flow shown on the following chart. On the same chart we have indicated just enough vertex labels to get from the source to the sink. The labels were inserted in this order:

| Vertex | Label | Implication |
|--------|-------|-------------|
| (s) | $(-, B)$ | |
| (E) | $(s^+, 1)$ | E is unemployed. |
| (IV) | $(E^+, 1)$ | E can do job IV. |
| (C) | $(IV^-, 1)$ | Should C be taken off job IV? |
| (VI) | $(C^+, 1)$ | C can also do job VI. |
| (H) | $(VI^-, 1)$ | Should H be taken off job VI? |
| (III) | $(H^+, 1)$ | H can also do job III. |
| (t) | $(III^+, 1)$ | Job III is unfilled. |

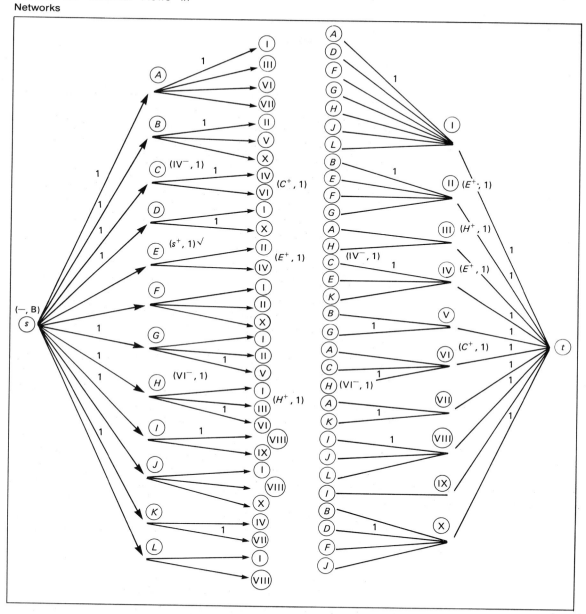

Thus, we put H on job III and take her off job VI. We put C on
job VI and take him off job IV. Finally, we put E on job IV. The
result is shown on the following chart.

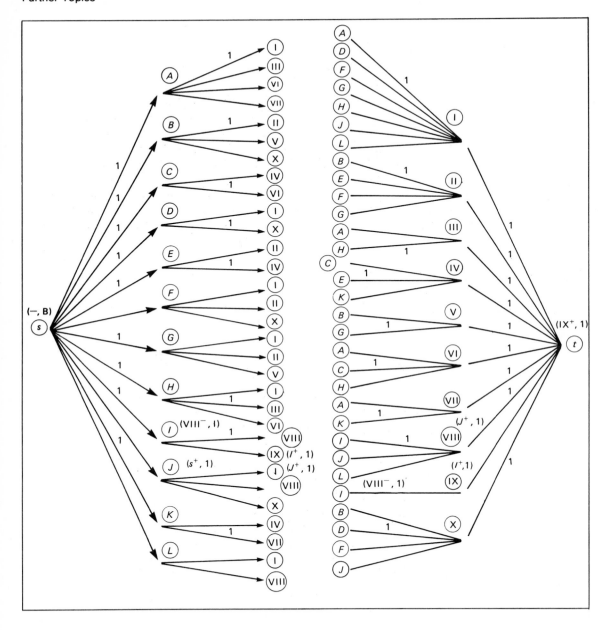

Again we have indicated only enough labels to show how to increase the flow. Now the labels tell us to let J do job VIII and let I do job IX.

Had some of the jobs been unfilled,
we would have not been able to skip
this step anyway.

Since all the jobs are filled, this flow must be maximal.
However, as further practice in the labeling technique we label
vertices once again.

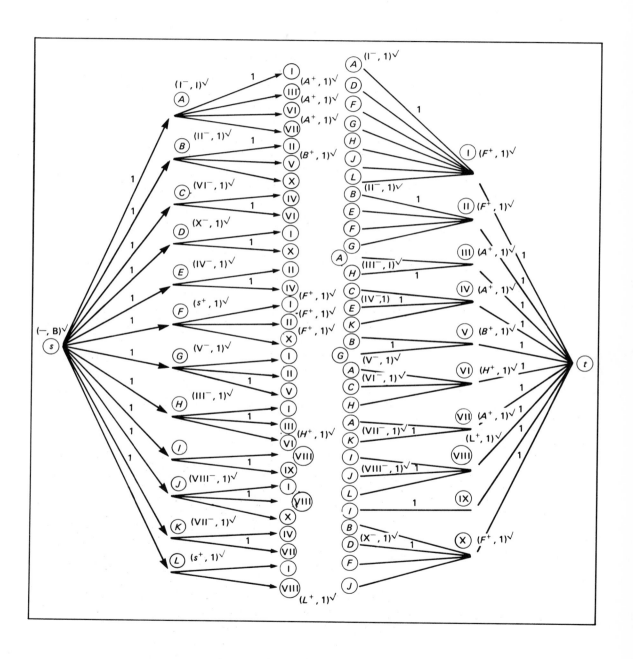

The answer:

> A gets job I
> B get job II
> C gets job VI
> D gets job X
> E gets job IV
> F is still unemployed
> G gets job V
> H gets job III
> I gets job IX
> J gets job VIII
> K gets job VII
> L is still unemployed

Although this flow is maximal, there may be other ways to assign the jobs. For examples, let L do job I and lay off A, let C do job I and A do job IV, and so on.

In real-life situations there are often other factors which must be considered in order to obtain useful answers. For example, we have already noted that there may be many ways to ship the same maximal amount through a network. If there are costs associated with each of these different flows, then a company will want to know which maximal flow is cheapest. A related problem known as the transshipment problem asks to determine the minimal cost of filling certain orders at some vertices from supplies at other vertices, where the edges have unlimited capacities but differing per-unit shipping costs, which are proportional to the amount sent along the edge. A special case of the transshipment problem is the transportation problem in which the total transportation cost from several factories to several stores is to be minimized. For another variation, suppose you not only want to fill jobs, but you want to fill them with the best qualified people available. Say an aptitude test has been given. The task is now to find an assignment that not only fills as many jobs as possible but also fills them is such a way as to maximize the total of the workers' aptitude scores. Other variations will occur to the interested reader.

In Exercise 11, Section 5.5, you are asked to use the simplex method to solve a transportation problem. For another way to handle the transportation problem see *Matrix Methods in Finite Mathematics*, by Althoen and Bumcrot, Chapter 4.

It is theoretically possible to apply the simplex method of Chapter 5 directly to a mathematical formulation of any of these problems. Unfortunately, the mathematical formulation of even very small network flow problems leads to extremely large systems of inequalities. There are more efficient ways to approach all these problems. One such method is an extension of the Ford-Fulkerson labeling method, but we will not discuss this here.

See Exercise 10.

**Exercises 6.5**
See Example 1.

1. What is the maximal number of wagonloads of pipeweed that can be legally transported from Longbottom to Nobottle in one season?

See Example 2.

2. What is the maximal number of calls that can be made from Nangasac to Glubbdubdrib simultaneously?

In Exercises 3 through 8 find the maximal flow and minimal cut for the given network.

3.

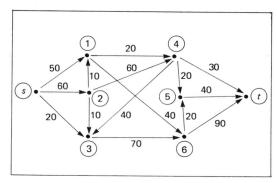

4.

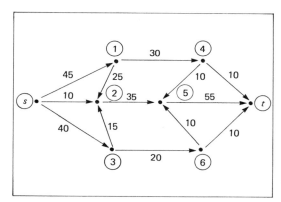

5.

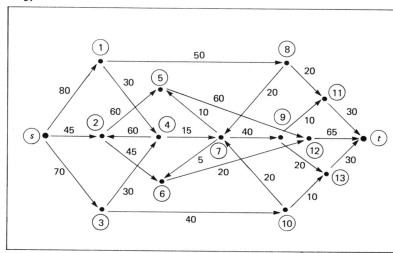

6.

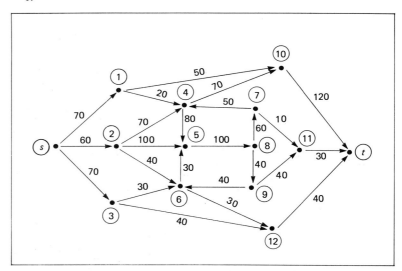

7.

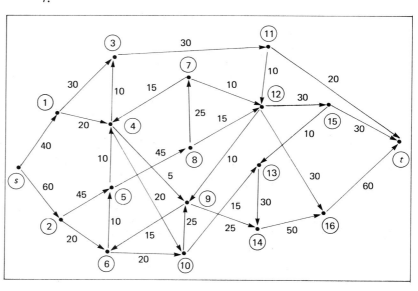

8.

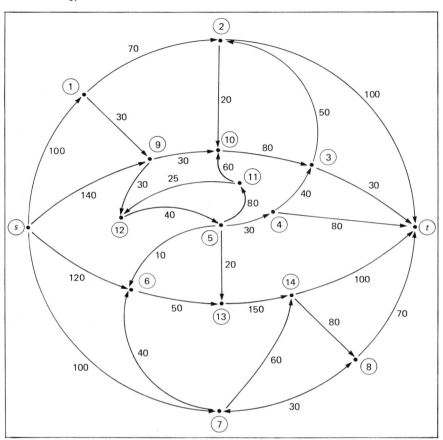

9. (a) The following network represents an oil pipeline system. What is a maximal flow for the network?

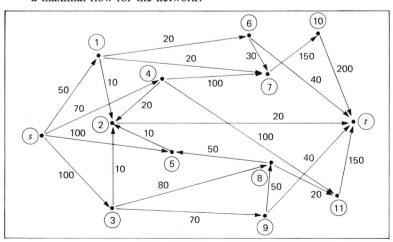

(b) The owners of the pipeline system intend to build a pipeline between vertices ④ and ⑤. Which direction should it go and what should be its capacity?

*10. Use the simplex method to find a maximal flow through the following network.

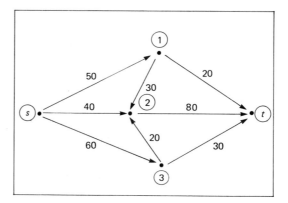

In Exercises 11 and 12 lettered applicants are interviewed for numbered jobs. The ×s in the chart indicate which jobs each applicant can do. Please assign as many applicants to jobs as possible.

11.

|   | 1 | 2 | 3 | 4 | 5 | 6 | 7 | 8 | 9 | 10 |
|---|---|---|---|---|---|---|---|---|---|---|
| A | × |   | × |   |   |   | × | × | × |   |
| B |   | × |   |   |   | × |   |   |   |   |
| C |   | × |   | × |   |   |   |   |   |   |
| D |   |   |   | × |   |   |   |   |   | × |
| E | × |   |   |   |   | × |   |   |   | × |
| F |   | × |   |   | × |   |   |   | × |   |
| G | × |   | × |   |   |   | × |   |   |   |
| H |   |   |   |   |   |   |   | × | × |   |
| I |   | × |   |   |   | × |   |   |   |   |
| J |   | × |   |   |   |   |   |   |   | × |

12.

| | 1 | 2 | 3 | 4 | 5 | 6 | 7 | 8 | 9 | 10 | 11 | 12 |
|---|---|---|---|---|---|---|---|---|---|---|---|---|
| A | | | | | | | × | | × | | | |
| B | | | | | | | | | | | × | × |
| C | × | | | | | | | | × | | | |
| D | | | | × | | | | | × | | | |
| E | | | | | × | | × | | | | | |
| F | | | | × | × | | | × | | | | × |
| G | | | | | | × | × | | | × | | × |
| H | × | × | | | | × | | × | | | | |
| I | | × | | × | × | | | | | | | |
| J | | | × | | | | | | × | | | |
| K | | | | | | | × | | | × | × | |
| L | | | × | | | × | | | | | | |

## Section 6.6 Computers, Hand Calculators, and Finite Mathematics

In this book we have presented and explained a number of applications of finite mathematics. Although the majority of our examples have had a business flavor, the same techniques that you have now learned have equally direct applications to economics, natural sciences, social sciences, and to other areas of mathematics. If we have seemed preoccupied with techniques it is because we feel that the only way to actually learn this kind of mathematics, with its applications and limitations, is through practical experience.

Once these methods are understood, computers can often be used as computational aids. In fact, most business applications involve problems so large that hand computation is out of the question. However, it must be kept in mind that a computer will not usually help you understand or interpret your problem. Before you submit a problem to a computer, you must have the problem properly formulated—and you must be sure that the mathematical expressions are actually relevant to the real-world situations being modeled. Furthermore, you must have some feeling for the answer. This is especially important because machines will use only the data you actually give them, not the data you intended to supply. It is easy to introduce errors into the input data. Whether these are merely typographical errors or actual errors of formulation, the machine will uselessly crank out an answer anyway. The only way to use a computer effectively is to understand the techniques it employs.

Many computations we have performed can be made less laborious with the help of a simple hand calculator. Suppose you had spent twenty dollars or less for a simple calculator and you were faced with the classical birthday problem. After the necessary analysis (done with your *head*, not the calculator), you would have to calculate $\frac{365}{365}$, $\frac{365 \cdot 364}{365 \cdot 365}$, $\frac{365 \cdot 364 \cdot 363}{365 \cdot 365 \cdot 365}$, and so on until you reach the first number that is less than $\frac{1}{2}$. Take a piece of paper. On your calculator punch $365 \div 365 \times$; read 1. Make a mark on the paper. Punch $364 \div 365 \times$; read 0.997. Make another mark. Punch $363 \div 365 \times$; read 0.992. Make another mark. Continue. After you punch $344 \div 365 \times$, you read 0.524 and then make the 22nd mark. You then punch $343 \div 365 \times$ and read 0.493. Since this is the first result less than $\frac{1}{2} = 0.5$, you conclude that you need 23 people to make it a "good bet" that at least two have the same birthday.

Exercise 15, Section 1.4.

We assume your calculator has at least four-decimal-place accuracy, which we round to three. If you only have two-place accuracy you may miss the correct answer of 23 (see below) by one or two, due to round-off error.

If your calculator had a memory, you could begin by punching 365 STO. Then each time 365 is needed you would punch RCL instead of 365, with only $\frac{1}{3}$ of the effort!

**Problem 1** Use your calculator to find $C_5^{14}$. (See p. 32.)

**Solution** Punch $14 \div 5 \times 13 \div 4 \times 12 \div 3 \times 11 \div 2 \times 10 =$ . Read 2,002.

If you've spent a little more money your calculator may have a $\Sigma$ (sigma) key for cumulative addition. With that you can fairly easily find any entry desired in the product of two matrices.

**Problem 2** Use your calculator (with $\Sigma$ key) to find (a) the $(2, 3)$ entry and (b) the $(3, 4)$ entry of

$$\begin{bmatrix} 2 & 1 & 4 \\ 3 & 2 & 5 \\ -4 & 7 & -7 \end{bmatrix} \begin{bmatrix} 6 & 8 & 4 & 2 \\ 5 & 1 & 7 & -3 \\ 2 & 1 & 4 & -5 \end{bmatrix}$$

**Solution**

$+/-$ is a single key.

(a) Punch $3 \times 4 = \Sigma 2 \times 7 = \Sigma 5 \times 4 = \Sigma RCL$. Read 46.

(b) Punch $4 +/- \times 2 = \Sigma 7 \times 3 +/- = \Sigma 7 +/- \times 5 +/- = \Sigma RCL$. Read 6.

See Exercise 3.

It gets a bit cumbersome to do Gauss-Jordan reduction with a calculator, but it can save time *if* the coefficients are terrible things like $-17.68$. Here is a simple example.

**Problem 3** Solve $\begin{bmatrix} -3x_1 + 4x_2 = -5 \\ 7x_1 - 6x_2 = 8 \end{bmatrix}$, first by hand and then with your calculator.

Solution

By hand:

$$
\begin{bmatrix} -3 & 4 & -5 \\ 7 & -6 & 8 \end{bmatrix}
\begin{matrix} -\frac{1}{3}R_1 \\ R_2+\frac{7}{3}R_1 \end{matrix}
\begin{bmatrix} 1 & -\frac{4}{3} & \frac{5}{3} \\ 0 & \frac{10}{3} & -\frac{11}{3} \end{bmatrix}
$$

$$
\begin{matrix} R_1+\frac{2}{5}R_2 \\ \frac{3}{10}R_2 \end{matrix}
\begin{bmatrix} 1 & 0 & \frac{1}{5} \\ 0 & 1 & -\frac{11}{10} \end{bmatrix}
$$

By calculator:

**Start with a blank $2 \times 3$ matrix. "Write $(1,1)1$," for example, means "write 1 at address $(1,1)$".**

Write $(1,1)1$; write $(2,1)0$. Punch $4 \div 3 +/- =$
Read, and write $(1,2) -1.33$
Punch $5 +/- \div 3 +/- =$
Read, and write $(1,3)1.67$
Punch $7 \div 3 = \text{STO} \times 4 - 6 =$
Read, and write $(2,2)\ 3.33$
Punch $5 +/- \times \text{RCL} + 8 =$
Read, and write $(2,3) -3.67$

$$
\begin{bmatrix} 1 & -1.33 & 1.67 \\ 0 & 3.33 & -3.67 \end{bmatrix}
$$

**Make another blank matrix.**

Write $(1,2)0$; write $(2,2)1$
Punch $1.33 \div 3.33 \times 3.67 +/- + 1.67 =$
Read, and write $(1,3)0.20$
Punch $3.67 +/- \div 3.33 =$
Read, and write $(2,3) -1.10$

$$
\begin{bmatrix} 1 & 0 & 0.20 \\ 0 & 1 & -1.10 \end{bmatrix}
$$

**Notice that we were lucky in that the round-off errors generated by the *incorrect* assumptions $\frac{1}{3} = .33$ and $\frac{2}{3} = .67$ canceled out to give the correct answer. This will not always happen.**

in agreement with the hand calculation.

**With a very sophisticated hand calculator you can postpone your trip to the computer, but probably not forever.**

In order to deal effectively with problems involving matrices of any size, a machine must possess a memory with hundreds (better, thousands) of positions. Also, the machine must be capable of performing a whole sequence of operations of arithmetic and copying of numbers, with no human involvement after the initial stage. Thus, we must put down the hand calculator and go to the terminal or keypunch for a full-size computer.

**Not to be confused with linear programming!**

The body of techniques for feeding instructions and data into a computer is known as **computer programming**. Since it is very tedious to communicate directly with a computer, a number of "languages" have been developed in which a few instructions of a kind more easily understood by the human user are "translated" by the computer into a long sequence of "machine language" instructions, which it can then execute. For example, in one language the instruction

INVA

preceded by the appropriate instructions to read the matrix A and by the entries of A themselves and followed by the appropriate writing instructions, will result in $A^{-1}$ being typed out on the terminal (or printed out on the printer) in a few seconds. Similarly, matrices can be added, subtracted, multiplied, and transposed by simple instructions.

If $A^{-1}$ does not exist, a notation to that effect will be made.

It should be clear now that anyone familiar with an appropriate "language" and with any of the computational techniques described in this book will be able to program a computer to carry out that technique. Perhaps the most complicated, as well as the most important technique we have presented is the simplex method, of Chapter 5, for solving problems in linear programming. For the rest of this section we shall discuss a computer program that has been written to solve such problems and that can be used with no knowledge of computer programming.

Since we do not assume familiarity with computers, we shall confine our further discussion of computer programming to Exercise 6.

The particular computer program we will discuss is called LPS (Linear Programming System). It was developed by IBM (International Business Machines) for business use. We will relate LPS only to the types of problems that we have already treated. LPS itself is tremendously sophisticated and allows many variations. Our discussion will be vague and limited to an explanation of the computer output that follows. If you have LPS at your disposal, you might be able to learn the particulars by consulting the appropriate IBM manuals.

The first task is to get the data into the machine. Cards are punched giving each *nonzero* entry of the constraint and objective matrices. An unspecified entry is interpreted by the machine as zero. Next, the bound matrix is punched into cards. For this the zeros must be punched as well. To these cards are joined the title card, a card specifying the bound matrix, and a few other instruction cards, including the cards that call up the massive LPS program from storage. Next, a computer operator feeds the cards into the card reader, waits a few minutes, and hands you the output. This includes a listing of the input data, for checking.

Finally, you must read and interpret the answer. Let us see how each of these steps is implemented in a few particular examples.

Maximize $z = x_1 - x_2$ subject to $x_1 \geq 0$, $x_2 \geq 0$, $x_3 \geq 0$ and

$$y_1 = x_1 - 2x_2 \qquad \leq 2$$
$$y_2 = 2x_1 - 3x_2 - x_3 \leq 6$$
$$y_3 = x_1 - 3x_2 + x_3 \leq 1$$

This is Problem 3, p. 322.

Note the minor changes. We have given the names $y_1$, $y_2$, and $y_3$ to the left sides of the constraints and have denoted the objective variable by z instead of y.

First we punch the constraint matrix. LPS requires us to mention columns before rows. We begin with $x_1$. This variable has the coefficient 1 in the z row, 1 in the $y_1$ row, 2 in the $y_2$ row, and 1 in the $y_3$ row. We punch four cards as follows:

The X is in card column 5; the Z is in card column 15 and the . (decimal point) is in card column 30.

```
X1   Z    1.0
X1   Y1   1.0
X1   Y2   2.0
X1   Y3   1.0
```

Next, we turn to $x_2$ and punch the following four cards:

```
X2   Z    -1.0
X2   Y1   -2.0
X2   Y2   -3.0
X2   Y3   -3.0
```

We could also punch
```
X3   Z    0
X3   Y1   0
```
but, as we said, we don't have to.

Finally, we do $x_3$. Since we do not have to include cards where the coefficients are zero, we merely punch

```
X3   Y2   -1.0
X3   Y3   1.0
```

Unless you specify otherwise, LPS assumes that $x_1 \geq 0, x_2 \geq 0$, and $x_3 \geq 0$. However, we must tell it that $y_1$ is bounded above by 2, $y_2$ by 6, and $y_3$ by 1. Furthermore, z is not bounded; it is *free*. The possible specifications are

LB for a $\geq$        (lower bound)
UB for a $\leq$        (upper bound)
FX for an $=$        (fixed variable)
FR for no bound(free variable)

Even though you must use these specifications in your input, the computer will use the abbreviations

LO for LB and UP for UB

This is a peculiarity of the LPS program and not of computer programs in general.

in one place, while in another place it uses LL to indicate that a variable attains its lower bound and UL to indicate that a variable attains its upper bound in the answer.

Apart from all this, LPS requires that you give the bounds a name. We decided to use the word "bound." Here are the cards:

The F is in card column 2; the B of BOUND is in card column 5; the Z is in card column 15; the decimal point is in card column 30.

```
FR   BOUND   Z
UB   BOUND   Y1   2.0
UB   BOUND   Y2   6.0
UB   BOUND   Y3   1.0
```

After these cards, we insert a few machine instruction cards. The printed output begins by listing our input.

| NAME | | LP1 | |
|------|---|-----|---|
| COLUMNS | | | |
| X1 | Z | 1.000000 |
| X1 | Y1 | 1.000000 |
| X1 | Y2 | 2.000000 |
| X1 | Y3 | 1.000000 |
| X2 | Z | −1.000000 |
| X2 | Y1 | −2.000000 |
| X2 | Y2 | −3.000000 |
| X2 | Y3 | −3.000000 |
| X3 | Y2 | −1.000000 |
| X3 | Y3 | 1.000000 |
| BOUNDS | | | |
| FR BOUNDS | Z | |
| UP BOUND | Y1 | 2.000000 |
| UP BOUND | Y2 | 6.000000 |
| UP BOUND | Y3 | 1.000000 |
| ENDATA | | | |

Next follow some data about the solution process. These data will tell us if the objective variable was optimized and, if not, whether it was because the feasible region was unbounded or nonexistent, that is, empty.

| LPSOLUTION ITERATION NUMBER | VALUE OF 'Z | NUMBER 'INFEAS | SUM OF INFEAS |
|---|---|---|---|
| 0 | 0.000 | 0 | 0.000 |

SOLUTION UNBOUNDED
ERROR BELOW TOLERANCE          0.000000

Finally, we obtain more detailed information about the answer.

LP1

| VARIABLE | TYPE | ENTRIES | SOLUTION ACTIVITY | UPPER BOUND | LOWER BOUND |
|---|---|---|---|---|---|
| X1 | B* | 4 | 4.001 | *899000.000 | 0.000 |
| Z | B* | 0 | 3.000 | *899000.000 | *899000.000 |
| Y1 | UL | 0 | 2.000 | 2.000 | 0.000 |
| Y2 | B* | 0 | 5.000 | 6.000 | 0.000 |
| Y3 | UL | 0 | 1.000 | 1.000 | 0.000 |
| X2 | B* | 4 | 1.001 | *899000.000 | 0.000 |
| X3 | LL | 2 | 0.000 | *899000.000 | 0.000 |

VARIABLE CAUSES UNBOUNDED SOLUTION

See Exercise 7.
Example 2

We will say more about reading this part of the output later. For the moment, we simply note that the computer found the problem to be unbounded—as you will observe, if you solve this problem by hand.

Our next example yields a more interesting answer.

This is Problem 7, pp. 350–351.

Maximize $z = 3x_1 + 6x_2 + 8x_3 + 4x_4$ subject to $x_1 \geq 0$, $x_2 \geq 0$, $x_3 \geq 0$, $x_4 \geq 0$ and

$$
\begin{aligned}
y_1 &= 3x_1 + 2x_2 + x_3 + 4x_4 \leq 8 \\
y_2 &= 2x_1 + 2x_2 + 4x_3 \qquad \leq 6 \\
y_3 &= \qquad 4x_2 + 3x_3 + 4x_4 \leq 10 \\
y_4 &= 4x_1 + 4x_2 + 2x_3 + 2x_4 \leq 9
\end{aligned}
$$

The cards are punched, the operator feeds them into the machine, and the following information is printed out.

| NAME | LP2 | |
|---|---|---|
| COLUMNS | | |
| X1 | Z | 3.000000 |
| X1 | Y1 | 3.000000 |
| X1 | Y2 | 2.000000 |
| X1 | Y4 | 4.000000 |
| X2 | Z | 6.000000 |
| X2 | Y1 | 2.000000 |
| X2 | Y2 | 2.000000 |
| X2 | Y3 | 4.000000 |
| X2 | Y4 | 4.000000 |
| X3 | Z | 8.000000 |
| X3 | Y1 | 1.000000 |
| X3 | Y2 | 4.000000 |
| X3 | Y3 | 3.000000 |
| X3 | Y4 | 2.000000 |
| X4 | Z | 4.000000 |
| X4 | Y1 | 4.000000 |
| X4 | Y3 | 4.000000 |
| X4 | Y4 | 2.000000 |
| BOUNDS | | |
| FR BOUND | Z | |
| UP BOUND | Y1 | 8.000000 |
| UP BOUND | Y2 | 6.000000 |
| UP BOUND | Y3 | 10.000000 |
| UP BOUND | Y4 | 9.000000 |
| ENDATA | | |

| LPSOLUTION | | | |
|---|---|---|---|
| ITERATION NUMBER | VALUE OF 'Z | NUMBER 'INFEAS | SUM OF INFEAS |
| 0 | 0.000 | 0 | 0.000 |
| 3 | 17.626 | 0 | 0.000 |

SOLUTION OPTIMUM
ERROR BELOW TOLERANCE   0.000000

LP2

| VARIABLE | TYPE | ENTRIES | SOLUTION ACTIVITY | UPPER BOUND | LOWER BOUND |
|----------|------|---------|-------------------|-------------|-------------|
| X1 | B* | 4 | 0.251 | *899000.000 | 0.000 |
| Z | B* | 0 | 17.626 | *899000.000 | *899000.000 |
| Y1 | UL | 0 | 8.000 | 8.000 | 0.000 |
| Y2 | UL | 0 | 6.000 | 6.000 | 0.000 |
| Y4 | B* | 0 | 6.688 | 9.000 | 0.000 |
| X2 | LL | 5 | 0.000 | *899000.000 | 0.000 |
| Y3 | UL | 0 | 10.000 | 10.000 | 0.000 |
| X3 | B* | 5 | 1.376 | *899000.000 | 0.000 |
| X4 | B* | 4 | 1.469 | *899000.000 | 0.000 |

See Exercise 8. After checking our input, we read that 3 *iterations* (or clearings of columns) were required to achieve the solution $z = 17.626$, which is optimal. The actual answer is 17.625, but the machine works with decimal arithmetic and hence there is often a slight round-off error.

The last nine lines contain the answer. We will interpret each of these lines.

Line 1   This line refers to $x_1$. We see that it is bounded (the B*) and are told that it occurred in 4 constraints (counting z). Under the heading SOLUTION ACTIVITY we find its value, .251, in the final answer. (Our hand calculations yielded .25.) Next we see the number *899000.000. This is a puzzling and unexpected number, and besides, though we find it under the heading UPPER BOUND, we did not specify an upper bound for $x_1$. The explanation is simple: under upper bound and lower bound are listed our specifications. If you do not specify an upper bound, the program tries to insert infinity. But the machine prints *899000.000. Thus, all this number indicates is that no upper bound was specified. Under the heading LOWER BOUND, we find 0.000. This is just as we wished.

Line 2   Here we see that z, the objective variable, is bounded, occurs in no constraints, and has the value 17.626 in the final answer. The last columns indicate that neither an upper nor a lower bound was specified for z.

Line 3   $y_1$ achieves its upper bound, occurs in no constraints (it *is* a constraint), and takes on the value 8.000. Its upper bound was specified to be 8.000, and no lower bound was indicated, although the machine supplies the harmless lower bound zero.

Line 4   $y_2$ achieves its upper bound, occurs in no constraints, and takes on the value 6.000 with bounds as indicated.

Line 5    $y_4$ is bounded, occurs in no constraints, takes on the value 6.688, and has bounds as indicated. (We obtained 6.6875 by hand computation.)

Line 6    $x_2$ achieves its lower bound, occurs in five constraints (including the objective variable), takes on the value 0, and was unbounded above but bounded below by 0.

Line 7    $y_3$ achieves its upper bound, 10.

Line 8    $x_3$ is bounded and has the value 1.376. (We obtained 1.375 by hand computation.)

Line 9    $x_4$ is bounded and has the value 1.469. (We obtained 1.46875 by hand computation.)

Summary

$$x_1 = .251$$
$$x_2 = 0.000$$
$$x_3 = 1.376$$
$$x_4 = 1.469$$

Constraints 1, 2, and 4 are met exactly, while constraint 3 is not met but has slack of $9.000 - 6.688 = 2.312$.

The value of the objective variable is 17.626.

Example 3    Minimize $z = 3x_1 + 9x_2 + 12x_3 + 7x_4 + 9x_5$ subject to $x_1 \geq 0$, $x_2 \geq 0$,
This is Problem 2, p. 352.    $x_3 \geq 0$, $x_4 \geq 0$, $x_5 \geq 0$, and

$$y_1 = x_1 + 2x_2 + 3x_3 + x_4 + 2x_5 \geq 3$$
$$y_2 = 2x_1 + x_2 + x_4 + 3x_5 \geq 2$$
$$y_3 = \tfrac{1}{2}x_1 + 2x_2 + 2x_3 + 3x_4 + 2x_5 \geq 2$$

The punched cards are fed in and the following is printed out.

| NAME | LP3 | |
|------|-----|--|
| COLUMNS | | |
| X1 | Z | 3.000000 |
| X1 | Y1 | 1.000000 |
| X1 | Y2 | 2.000000 |
| X1 | Y3 | 0.500000 |
| X2 | Z | 9.000000 |
| X2 | Y1 | 2.000000 |
| X2 | Y2 | 1.000000 |
| X2 | Y3 | 2.000000 |
| X3 | Z | 12.000000 |
| X3 | Y1 | 3.000000 |
| X3 | Y3 | 2.000000 |
| X4 | Z | 7.000000 |
| X4 | Y1 | 1.000000 |
| X4 | Y2 | 1.000000 |
| X4 | Y3 | 3.000000 |

| | | |
|---|---|---|
| X5 | Z | 9.000000 |
| X5 | Y1 | 2.000000 |
| X5 | Y2 | 3.000000 |
| X5 | Y3 | 2.000000 |

BOUNDS

| | | |
|---|---|---|
| FR BOUND | Z | |
| LO BOUND | Y1 | 3.000000 |
| LO BOUND | Y2 | 2.000000 |
| LO BOUND | Y3 | 2.000000 |

ENDATA

LP SOLUTION

| ITERATION NUMBER | VALUE OF 'Z | NUMBER 'INFEAS | SUM OF INFEAS |
|---|---|---|---|
| 0 | 0.000 | 3 | 4.221 |
| 2 | 9.800 | 0 | 0.000 |

SOLUTION OPTIMUM
ERROR BELOW TOLERANCE   0.000000
LP3

| VARIABLE | TYPE | ENTRIES | SOLUTION ACTIVITY | UPPER BOUND | LOWER BOUND |
|---|---|---|---|---|---|
| X1 | B* | 4 | 2.801 | *899000.000 | 0.000 |
| Z | B* | 0 | 9.800 | *899000.000 | *899000.000 |
| Y1 | LL | 0 | 3.000 | *899000.000 | 3.000 |
| Y2 | B* | 0 | 5.801 | *899000.000 | 2.000 |
| Y3 | LL | 0 | 2.000 | *899000.000 | 2.000 |
| X2 | LL | 4 | 0.000 | *899000.000 | 0.000 |
| X3 | LL | 3 | 0.000 | *899000.000 | 0.000 |
| X4 | B* | 4 | 0.200 | *899000.000 | 0.000 |
| X5 | LL | 4 | 0.000 | *899000.000 | 0.000 |

We see that two iterations were required to find the minimal value of z. The answer is $z = 9.8$, $x_1 = 2.801$, $x_2 = 0$, $x_3 = 0$, $x_4 = .200$, and $x_5 = 0$. Allowing for small round-off errors, this agrees with the hand-done solution.

See Exercise 9.

**Example 4**   Maximize $z = 3.12x_1 + 6.8x_2 + 7.43x_3 + 4.01x_4$ subject to $x_1 \geq 0$, $x_2 \geq 0$, $x_3 \geq 0$, $x_4 \geq 0$, and

$$y_1 = 2.91x_1 + 2.44x_2 + .87x_3 + 4.34x_4 \leq 8.29$$
$$y_2 = 1.78x_1 + 2.19x_2 + 4.00x_3 \qquad \leq 5.98$$
$$y_3 = \qquad 4.28x_2 + 2.60x_3 + 3.92x_4 \leq 9.84$$
$$y_4 = 4.60x_1 + 3.60x_2 + 2.10x_3 + 1.80x_4 \leq 9.20$$

| NAME | LP4 | |
|------|-----|---|
| COLUMNS | | |
| X1 | Z | 3.120000 |
| X1 | Y1 | 2.910000 |
| X1 | Y2 | 1.780000 |
| X1 | Y4 | 4.600000 |
| X2 | Z | 6.800000 |
| X2 | Y1 | 2.440000 |
| X2 | Y2 | 2.190000 |
| X2 | Y4 | 3.600000 |
| X2 | Y3 | 4.280000 |
| X3 | Z | 7.430000 |
| X3 | Y1 | 0.870000 |
| X3 | Y2 | 4.000000 |
| X3 | Y4 | 2.100000 |
| X3 | Y3 | 2.600000 |
| X4 | Z | 4.010000 |
| X4 | Y1 | 4.340000 |
| X4 | Y4 | 1.800000 |
| X4 | Y3 | 3.920000 |

Note that some of these data are out of order. The computer doesn't mind.

| BOUNDS | | |
|--------|---|---|
| FR BOUND | Z | |
| UP BOUND | Y1 | 8.290000 |
| UP BOUND | Y2 | 5.980000 |
| UP BOUND | Y4 | 9.200000 |
| UP BOUND | Y3 | 9.840000 |

ENDATA

LP SOLUTION

| ITERATION NUMBER | VALUE OF 'Z | NUMBER 'INFEAS | SUM OF INFEAS |
|------------------|-------------|----------------|---------------|
| 0 | 0.000 | 0 | 0.000 |
| 4 | 17.448 | 0 | 0.000 |

SOLUTION OPTIMUM
ERROR BELOW TOLERANCE   0.000000

LP4

| VARIABLE | ENTRIES TYPE | | SOLUTION ACTIVITY | UPPER BOUND | LOWER BOUND |
|----------|------|---|----------|-------------|-------------|
| X1 | B* | 4 | 0.475 | *899000.000 | 0.000 |
| Z | B* | 0 | 17.448 | *899000.000 | *899000.000 |
| Y1 | UL | 0 | 8.290 | 8.290 | 0.000 |
| Y2 | UL | 0 | 5.980 | 5.980 | 0.000 |
| Y4 | UL | 0 | 9.200 | 9.200 | 0.000 |
| X2 | B* | 5 | 1.174 | *899000.000 | 0.000 |
| Y3 | UL | 0 | 9.840 | 9.840 | 0.000 |
| X3 | B* | 5 | 0.642 | *899000.000 | 0.000 |
| X4 | B* | 4 | 0.804 | *899000.000 | 0.000 |

This problem is a slight modification of Example 2. Notice that the answer is also only slightly different. Do not think that what happened in this example always happens, however. Consider the following problems.

**Problem 4**   Maximize $y = 5.001x_1 + 100.01x_2$ subject to $x_1 \geq 0$, $x_2 \geq 0$, and $x_1 + 20x_2 \leq 20$.

**Solution**   The region of feasibility is a triangle with corner points

$$(0,0), (0,1), \text{ and } (20,0).$$

The answer is $x_1 = 20$, $x_2 = 0$, $y = 100.02$.

**Problem 5**   Maximize $y = 5.001x_1 + 100.03x_2$ subject to $x_1 \geq 0$, $x_2 \geq 0$, and $x_1 + 20x_2 \leq 20$.

**Solution**   The region of feasibility is the same as in Problem 1. The answer is $x_1 = 0$, $x_2 = 1$, $y = 100.03$.

The only difference between these problems is a change of 0.02 in one of the objective coefficients, but values of $x_1$ and $x_2$ in the answers have changed by 20 and 1, respectively. One important aspect of linear programming is called *sensitivity analysis*. It is concerned with estimating the effect of slight modifications of a problem on the answer. We shall not further discuss this aspect here.

**Example 5**

See Exercise 14, p. 440.

We now turn our attention to more practical matters. The game Morra is a game that is actually played by adults. While it is a simple game, it is not easy to play because it is played very fast—usually in a noisy bar. To simplify matters, we will discuss and solve a version of three-finger Morra.

In this game, each player shouts a number and extends one, two, or three fingers. The players shout and extend fingers simultaneously. If exactly one player happens to shout a number equal to the total of fingers extended by both players, then he or she wins that number of dollars. If both or neither guess correctly, the round is a draw. For example, if A extends 1 finger and shouts 2 while B extends 1 finger and shouts 3, A wins $2. Clearly, it is silly to extend 3 fingers and shout 2 or 3. When we eliminate all bad moves, there are nine strategies left. We will indicate a strategy by two numbers. The first number indicates the number of fingers extended, and the second number indicates the number shouted. It is easily checked that the payoff matrix for this game is:

$$
A \quad
\begin{array}{c}
\\
12 \\
13 \\
14 \\
23 \\
24 \\
\\
\\
\\
36
\end{array}
\begin{array}{ccccccccc}
1\,2 & 1\,3 & 1\,4 & 2\,3 & 2\,4 & 2\,5 & 3\,4 & 3\,5 & 3\,6 \\
\left[\begin{array}{rrrrrrrrr}
0 & 2 & 2 & -3 & 0 & 0 & -4 & 0 & 0 \\
-2 & 0 & 0 & 0 & 3 & 3 & -4 & 0 & 0 \\
-2 & 0 & 0 & -3 & 0 & 0 & 0 & 4 & 4 \\
3 & 0 & 3 & 0 & -4 & 0 & 0 & -5 & 0 \\
0 & -3 & 0 & 4 & 0 & 4 & 0 & -5 & 0 \\
0 & -3 & 0 & 0 & -4 & 0 & 5 & 0 & 5 \\
4 & 4 & 0 & 0 & 0 & -5 & 0 & 0 & -6 \\
0 & 0 & -4 & 5 & 5 & 0 & 0 & 0 & -6 \\
0 & 0 & -4 & 0 & 0 & -5 & 6 & 6 & 0
\end{array}\right]
\end{array}
$$

From the description we see that the game is symmetric, i.e., neither player has an advantage. Thus A and B will have the same mixed strategies. We proceed to solve this game by applying the simplex method to the associated maximization problem. Since there are nine variables and nine constraints, we elect to use a computer!

See Section 6.3.

See the Flow Chart, p. 436.

When the matrix has negative entries, the simplex method may fail to work. Just in case, we decide to add 6 to each entry to get a matrix with nonnegative entries. While the failure of the simplex method would have been no disaster, it would have meant repunching the data. Here is the result.

NAME            MORRA

COLUMNS

| | | |
|---|---|---|
| X1 | Z | 1.000000 |
| X1 | Y1 | 6.000000 |
| X1 | Y2 | 4.000000 |
| X1 | Y3 | 4.000000 |
| X1 | Y4 | 9.000000 |
| X1 | Y5 | 6.000000 |
| X1 | Y6 | 6.000000 |
| X1 | Y7 | 10.000000 |
| X1 | Y8 | 6.000000 |
| X1 | Y9 | 6.000000 |
| X2 | Z | 1.000000 |
| X2 | Y1 | 8.000000 |
| X2 | Y2 | 6.000000 |
| X2 | Y3 | 6.000000 |
| X2 | Y4 | 6.000000 |
| X2 | Y5 | 3.000000 |
| X2 | Y6 | 3.000000 |
| X2 | Y7 | 10.000000 |

| | | |
|---|---|---|
| X2 | Y8 | 6.000000 |
| X2 | Y9 | 6.000000 |
| X3 | Z | 1.000000 |
| X3 | Y1 | 8.000000 |
| X3 | Y2 | 6.000000 |
| X3 | Y3 | 6.000000 |
| X3 | Y4 | 9.000000 |
| X3 | Y5 | 6.000000 |
| X3 | Y6 | 6.000000 |
| X3 | Y7 | 6.000000 |
| X3 | Y8 | 2.000000 |
| X3 | Y9 | 2.000000 |
| X4 | Z | 1.000000 |
| X4 | Y1 | 3.000000 |
| X4 | Y2 | 6.000000 |
| X4 | Y3 | 3.000000 |
| X4 | Y4 | 6.000000 |
| X4 | Y5 | 10.000000 |
| X4 | Y6 | 6.000000 |
| X4 | Y7 | 6.000000 |
| X4 | Y8 | 11.000000 |
| X4 | Y9 | 6.000000 |
| X5 | Z | 1.000000 |
| X5 | Y1 | 6.000000 |
| X5 | Y2 | 9.000000 |
| X5 | Y3 | 6.000000 |
| X5 | Y4 | 2.000000 |
| X5 | Y5 | 6.000000 |
| X5 | Y6 | 2.000000 |
| X5 | Y7 | 6.000000 |
| X5 | Y8 | 11.000000 |
| X5 | Y9 | 6.000000 |
| X6 | Z | 1.000000 |
| X6 | Y1 | 6.000000 |
| X6 | Y2 | 9.000000 |
| X6 | Y3 | 6.000000 |
| X6 | Y4 | 6.000000 |
| X6 | Y5 | 10.000000 |
| X6 | Y6 | 6.000000 |
| X6 | Y7 | 1.000000 |
| X6 | Y8 | 6.000000 |
| X6 | Y9 | 1.000000 |
| X7 | Z | 1.000000 |
| X7 | Y1 | 2.000000 |
| X7 | Y2 | 2.000000 |
| X7 | Y3 | 6.000000 |
| X7 | Y4 | 6.000000 |
| X7 | Y5 | 6.000000 |
| X7 | Y6 | 11.000000 |
| X7 | Y7 | 6.000000 |
| X7 | Y8 | 6.000000 |
| X7 | Y9 | 12.000000 |
| X8 | Z | 1.000000 |

| | | |
|---|---|---|
| X8 | Y1 | 6.000000 |
| X8 | Y2 | 6.000000 |
| X8 | Y3 | 10.000000 |
| X8 | Y4 | 1.000000 |
| X8 | Y5 | 1.000000 |
| X8 | Y6 | 6.000000 |
| X8 | Y7 | 6.000000 |
| X8 | Y8 | 6.000000 |
| X8 | Y9 | 12.000000 |
| X9 | Z | 1.000000 |
| X9 | Y1 | 6.000000 |
| X9 | Y2 | 6.000000 |
| X9 | Y3 | 10.000000 |
| X9 | Y4 | 6.000000 |
| X9 | Y5 | 6.000000 |
| X9 | Y6 | 11.000000 |
| X9 | Y7 | 0.000000 |
| X9 | Y8 | 0.000000 |
| X9 | Y9 | 6.000000 |

We wasted time punching a couple of zero entries. LPS doesn't mind.

BOUNDS

| | | |
|---|---|---|
| FR BOUND | Z | |
| UP BOUND | Y1 | 1.000000 |
| UP BOUND | Y2 | 1.000000 |
| UP BOUND | Y3 | 1.000000 |
| UP BOUND | Y4 | 1.000000 |
| UP BOUND | Y5 | 1.000000 |
| UP BOUND | Y6 | 1.000000 |
| UP BOUND | Y7 | 1.000000 |
| UP BOUND | Y8 | 1.000000 |
| UP BOUND | Y9 | 1.000000 |

ENDATA

LP SOLUTION

| ITERATION NUMBER | VALUE OF 'Z | NUMBER 'INFEAS | SUM OF INFEAS |
|---|---|---|---|
| 0 | 0.000 | 0 | 0.000 |
| 6 | 0.167 | 0 | 0.000 |

SOLUTION OPTIMUM
ERROR BELOW TOLERANCE  0.000000

MORRA

| VARIABLES | ENTRIES TYPE | | SOLUTION ACTIVITY | UPPER BOUND | LOWER BOUND |
|---|---|---|---|---|---|
| X1 | LL | 10 | 0.000 | *899000.000 | 0.000 |
| Z | B* | 0 | 0.167 | *899000.000 | *899000.000 |
| Y1 | B* | 0 | 0.973 | 1.000 | 0.000 |
| | | | | | |
| Y2 | UL | 0 | 1.000 | 1.000 | 0.000 |
| Y3 | UL | 0 | 1.000 | 1.000 | 0.000 |
| Y4 | B* | 0 | 0.987 | 1.000 | 0.000 |

| Y5 | UL | 0 | 1.000 | 1.000 | 0.000 |
|----|----|---|-------|-------|-------|
| Y6 | B* | 0 | 0.987 | 1.000 | 0.000 |
| Y7 | UL | 0 | 1.000 | 1.000 | 0.000 |
| Y8 | UL | 0 | 1.000 | 1.000 | 0.000 |
| Y9 | B* | 0 | 0.973 | 1.000 | 0.000 |
| X2 | LL | 10 | 0.000 | *899000.000 | 0.000 |
| X3 | B* | 10 | 0.070 | *899000.000 | 0.000 |
| X4 | LL | 10 | 0.000 | *899000.000 | 0.000 |
| X5 | B* | 10 | 0.056 | *899000.000 | 0.000 |
| X6 | B* | 10 | 0.000 | *899000.000 | 0.000 |
| X7 | B* | 10 | 0.042 | *899000.000 | 0.000 |
| X8 | B* | 10 | 0.000 | *899000.000 | 0.000 |
| X9 | LL | 10 | 0.000 | *899000.000 | 0.000 |

We read from this the answer

$$z = .167 \doteq \tfrac{1}{6}$$

$$x_3 = .070$$

$$x_5 = .056$$

$$x_7 = .042$$

with all other variables zero.

Since we added 6 to the matrix, the value of the game is the reciprocal of $z \doteq \tfrac{1}{6}$ minus 6, that is, about zero. This was to be expected since neither player had any advantage. The best mixed strategy is, then

$$1 \ 4 : \tfrac{3}{12}$$

$$2 \ 4 : \tfrac{1}{3}$$

$$3 \ 4 : \tfrac{1}{4}$$

all others 0.

### Exercises 6.6

There are 669 Martian days in a Martian year.

1. Solve the birthday problem for Martians.

2. Use a hand calculator to find the $(2,3)$ entry of

$$\begin{bmatrix} -1 & 2 & -1 & 2 & 1 \\ 4 & -2 & 3 & -3 & 9 \\ 6 & 2 & 5 & 1 & 0 \end{bmatrix} \begin{bmatrix} 0 & 2 & 6 & 3 \\ 0 & 1 & 5 & 1 \\ 1 & 1 & -4 & 0 \\ 2 & 2 & -7 & 4 \\ 1 & 1 & -8 & 7 \end{bmatrix}$$

3. Use a hand calculator to find

$$\begin{bmatrix} -17.68 & -17.68 \\ -17.68 & -17.68 \end{bmatrix}^3$$

4. Use a hand calculator to find

$$\begin{bmatrix} 19 & 20 \\ -21 & -22 \end{bmatrix} \begin{bmatrix} -23 & 24 \\ -25 & 26 \end{bmatrix}$$

5. Use a hand calculator to solve

$$\begin{bmatrix} -6.81x_1 + 3.21x_2 = & 25.8084 \\ 4.13x_1 - 7.77x_2 = & -22.8144 \end{bmatrix}$$

In writing these computer programs, the flow charts in this book may prove helpful.

6. Program a computer to:
   (a) multiply any given $3 \times 4$ matrix by any given number,
   (b) multiply any given $1 \times 5$ matrix by any given $5 \times 1$ matrix,
   (c) add any two matrixes or, if they cannot be added, print "they cannot be added,"
   (d) multiply any given $4 \times 5$ matrix by any given $5 \times 6$ matrix,
   (e) multiply any given matrix by any given matrix, or print "they cannot be multiplied in the order given,"
   (f) print out higher and higher powers of a given square matrix, in the format "power number ____ is[   ]", up to the 10th power,
   (g) solve the birthday problem for any given number of days and any required "good bet" probability, with the answer in the format, "if the 'year' has ____ days, then the number of individuals needed to make the probability of a repeated birthday at least ____ is ____",
   (h) do Gauss-Jordan reduction on any matrix,
   (i) find the inverse of any matrix, or print that it has none,
   (j) find the long-range effect of any given regular Markov chain, or print "this chain is not regular."

7. Verify by hand the result of Example 1.
8. Verify by hand the result of Example 2.
9. Verify by hand the result of Example 3.
10. Use a hand calculator to apply the dual variable check to Example 4.

Another big computer problem appears in the supplementary exercises below.

$^{c}$11. When my friend told the board of directors of the Vertigo Knolls Mountaineering Club that I had just completed a course in linear programming with this book, they invited me to their next board meeting. The chairperson asked me in and then explained their problem as follows:

"Each year we've been having an outing for executives from the big three sporting-goods manufacturers, Appalachian Creations, Adirondack Knapsacks, and Pocono Productions. We've hoped this would induce them to donate equipment. However, in the past the executives haven't been very happy. Here are the most frequent complaints:

(1) the tents were old;

(2) some executives weren't provided with a tent manufactured by their own company;

(3) there were too many off-brand tents on the site.

(4) Our camp manager even complained that there wasn't enough room in his big truck to take all the tents to the site in one trip.

"The board has decided to buy all new tents. Here is a list of the best tents available (Table 19).

Table 19

| Tent number | Manufacturer | Size | | Cost ($) |
| --- | --- | --- | --- | --- |
| | | No. of persons | Cubic In. (packed) | |
| 1 | AC | 2 | 804 | 70 |
| 2 | AC | 2 | 616 | 105 |
| 3 | AC | 2 | 565 | 100 |
| 4 | AC | 2 | 565 | 80 |
| 5 | AK | 2 | 565 | 70 |
| 6 | AK | 2 | 650 | 98 |
| 7 | AK | 3 | 285 | 150 |
| 8 | AK | 2 | 678 | 125 |
| 9 | AK | 1 | 275 | 35 |
| 10 | PP | 2 | 427 | 110 |
| 11 | PP | 2 | 553 | 150 |
| 12 | PP | 3 | 554 | 142 |
| 13 | PP | 6 | 1428 | 195 |
| 14 | PP | 2 | 396 | 100 |
| 15 | PP | 2 | 565 | 125 |
| 16 | MA | 2 | 565 | 165 |
| 17 | TA | 2 | 285 | 43 |
| 18 | CB | 2 | 906 | 142 |
| 19 | DB | 3 | 1011 | 159 |

"I'm expecting 17 campers from AC, 15 from AK, 13 from PP, and 40 from the club. We only have 15 cubic feet of truck space. How can we meet our requirements at minimal cost?"

**Supplementary Exercises**

Since you may not have covered every section in this chapter, these exercises are presented in the order of the sections. Thus, the first exercises are about poker and the last involve a calculator or computer. By glancing at an exercise you should be able to tell whether or not you have the knowledge to attempt it.

1. *(a) What is the probability in straight poker that a man is holding four of a kind, given that he is holding at least three of a kind?

*There are two interpretations of this problem. Give two answers!*

   (b) A woman holding a straight poker hand remarks that she has less than a full house, but more than two pair. What are the odds she has a straight?

2. When Alan was dealt the ace of diamonds, hearts, and clubs, the king of clubs, and the king of hearts, he knew that he had the best

full house possible in that game. After the early betting everyone dropped out except Janet and him.

(a) Use the partition of poker into the standard hands (p. 390) to find the probability that Janet has a better hand.

*(b) Did you use the information provided by Alan's cards in answering part (a)? If not, your answer is slightly wrong. Now find a more nearly exact answer.

3. A woman holding a straight poker hand remarks, truthfully, that she is holding three of a kind "and maybe better."
   (a) What is the probability that she has a full house?
   (b) What is the probability that she just has three of a kind?

4. What is the probability that the letters in a starting set in Scrabble® Brand Crossword Game can be arranged to spell GREGORY?

Remember a blank can be anything. Alan was so excited when he actually got this starting set that he lost his turn by trying to use a proper name.

Exercises 5 through 7 describe hands in five-card poker. What is the probability of each hand?

5. Three black and 2 red cards.
6. At least 4 face cards.
7. No aces.

8. A five-card poker hand is dealt. Which of the following pairs of events are independent?
   (a) "full house," "three of a kind"
   (b) "straight," "flush"
   (c) "full house," "two pair or better"

9. In poker which pairs of the following events are disjoint? The hand contains a pair, the hand contains 2 pair, the hand contains three of a kind, four of a kind, flush, straight?

*10. Suppose p and q are positive integers that are both divisible by the positive integer n. Show that odds of p to q for A are the same as odds of $\frac{p}{n}$ to $\frac{q}{n}$ for A.

11. If the odds against my winning the silver cup are 19 to 5, what is the probability that I will win it?

12. If the odds for my winning the gold medal are 5 to 91, what is the probability that I won't win it?

13. If the probability that you will inherit \$3,141,592.65 is exactly $\frac{4}{71,697}$, what are the odds against your inheriting that amount?

In each of Exercises 14 through 31, find the inverse matrix, if it exists.

14. $\begin{bmatrix} 1 & 2 \\ 3 & 4 \end{bmatrix}$    15. $\begin{bmatrix} 99 & 100 \\ 101 & 102 \end{bmatrix}$

16. $\begin{bmatrix} \frac{1}{3} & -\frac{1}{4} \\ \frac{2}{5} & -\frac{3}{7} \end{bmatrix}$    17. $\begin{bmatrix} \frac{8}{9} & \frac{9}{8} \\ -\frac{9}{8} & -\frac{8}{9} \end{bmatrix}$

18. $\begin{bmatrix} 7 & 3 & 2 \\ 2 & 1 & 1 \\ 3 & 7 & 2 \end{bmatrix}$　　　　19. $\begin{bmatrix} -2 & -3 & 1 \\ 5 & 5 & 4 \\ 4 & 3 & 7 \end{bmatrix}$

20. $\begin{bmatrix} 5 & 4 & 3 \\ 7 & 5 & 6 \\ 7 & 8 & -3 \end{bmatrix}$　　　　21. $\begin{bmatrix} 2 & 3 & 1 \\ 2 & 7 & 1 \\ 3 & 2 & 1 \end{bmatrix}$

22. $\begin{bmatrix} 1 & 2 & 3 \\ 3 & 1 & 2 \\ 2 & 3 & 1 \end{bmatrix}$　　　　23. $\begin{bmatrix} 1 & 3 & 1 \\ 2 & 8 & 3 \\ 2 & 4 & 1 \end{bmatrix}$

24. $\begin{bmatrix} 1 & 2 & 1 \\ 2 & 3 & 3 \\ 2 & 3 & 4 \end{bmatrix}$　　　　25. $\begin{bmatrix} 3 & 4 & -1 \\ -2 & -1 & -3 \\ 2 & 2 & 1 \end{bmatrix}$

26. $\begin{bmatrix} 4 & 6 & 1 \\ 9 & 8 & 5 \\ 4 & 4 & 2 \end{bmatrix}$　　　　*27. $\begin{bmatrix} -1 & -5 & 0 \\ -4 & -6 & 5 \\ 4 & 8 & 3 \end{bmatrix}$

*28. $\begin{bmatrix} 5 & 5 & 9 \\ 2 & -5 & -2 \\ 6 & 2 & 4 \end{bmatrix}$　　　　*29. $\begin{bmatrix} 4 & 5 & 7 \\ 6 & 9 & 3 \\ 6 & 6 & -7 \end{bmatrix}$

*30. $\begin{bmatrix} -2 & 1 & 9 \\ -6 & -3 & 2 \\ 1 & -8 & 4 \end{bmatrix}$　　　　31. $\begin{bmatrix} 4 & 3 & 2 & 4 \\ 1 & 1 & 2 & 3 \\ 2 & 2 & 5 & 6 \\ 2 & 2 & 6 & 7 \end{bmatrix}$

In each of Exercises 32 through 37 solve the equation for the matrix X.

32. $\begin{bmatrix} 2 & 1 & 3 \\ 3 & -6 & -4 \\ 5 & 2 & 7 \end{bmatrix} X + \begin{bmatrix} -1 & 7 \\ 2 & 4 \\ 3 & 6 \end{bmatrix} = \begin{bmatrix} 2 & -1 \\ 4 & 2 \\ 7 & 0 \end{bmatrix}$

c33. $\begin{bmatrix} -1 & 1 \\ 1 & -1 \end{bmatrix} X + \begin{bmatrix} 3 & 2 & 0 \\ -1 & 2 & 4 \end{bmatrix} = \begin{bmatrix} 3 & 2 & 1 \\ 4 & 2 & 5 \end{bmatrix}$

34. $\begin{bmatrix} 1 & 0 \\ 2 & 1 \end{bmatrix} X + \begin{bmatrix} 3 \\ 4 \end{bmatrix} = \begin{bmatrix} 2 & -1 \\ 7 & 4 \end{bmatrix}$

c35. $X \begin{bmatrix} -1 & 1 \\ 1 & -1 \end{bmatrix} + \begin{bmatrix} 3 & 2 & 0 \\ -1 & 2 & 4 \end{bmatrix} = \begin{bmatrix} 3 & 2 & 1 \\ 4 & 2 & 5 \end{bmatrix}$

36. $\begin{bmatrix} 1 & 0 \\ 0 & 1 \end{bmatrix} X + X \begin{bmatrix} 1 & 0 \\ 0 & 1 \end{bmatrix} = \begin{bmatrix} 1 & 0 \\ 0 & 1 \end{bmatrix}$

c37. $X \begin{bmatrix} -2 & -3 & 1 \\ 5 & 5 & 4 \\ 4 & 3 & 7 \end{bmatrix} - \begin{bmatrix} 4 & 5 & 0 \\ 2 & 0 & 1 \\ -3 & -2 & 3 \end{bmatrix} = \begin{bmatrix} 8 & -1 & 0 \\ 0 & 2 & 1 \\ 0 & 3 & 0 \end{bmatrix}$

In Exercises 38 and 39 use the fact that

$$\begin{bmatrix} 1 & 1 & 2 & 1 \\ 4 & 5 & 9 & 1 \\ 3 & 4 & 7 & 1 \\ 2 & 3 & 4 & 2 \end{bmatrix}^{-1} = \begin{bmatrix} 0 & 5 & -7 & 1 \\ -2 & 0 & 0 & 1 \\ 1 & -2 & 3 & -1 \\ 1 & -1 & 1 & 0 \end{bmatrix}$$

to solve the system.

38. $\begin{bmatrix} & 5x_2 - 7x_3 + x_4 = & 0 \\ -2x_1 & + x_4 = -1 \\ x_1 - 2x_2 + 3x_3 - x_4 = -2 \\ x_1 - x_2 + x_3 & = -3 \end{bmatrix}$

39. $\begin{bmatrix} x_1 + x_2 + 2x_3 + x_4 = \frac{1}{2} \\ 4x_1 + 5x_2 + 9x_3 + x_4 = -\frac{2}{3} \\ 3x_1 + 4x_2 + 7x_3 + x_4 = \frac{3}{4} \\ 2x_1 + 3x_2 + 4x_3 + 2x_4 = -\frac{7}{8} \end{bmatrix}$

In Exercises 40 and 41, use the fact that

$$\begin{bmatrix} 1 & 3 & 3 & 2 & 1 \\ 1 & 4 & 3 & 3 & -1 \\ 1 & 3 & 4 & 1 & 1 \\ 1 & 1 & 1 & 1 & -1 \\ 1 & -2 & -1 & 2 & 2 \end{bmatrix}^{-1} = \frac{1}{15}\begin{bmatrix} 30 & -20 & -15 & 25 & -5 \\ 30 & -11 & -18 & 7 & -8 \\ -30 & 12 & 21 & -9 & 6 \\ -15 & 12 & 6 & -9 & 6 \\ 15 & -7 & -6 & -1 & -1 \end{bmatrix}$$

to solve the system.

40. $\begin{bmatrix} x_1 + 3x_2 + 3x_3 + 2x_4 + x_5 = -2 \\ x_1 + 4x_2 + 3x_3 + 3x_4 - x_5 = 3 \\ x_1 + 3x_2 + 4x_3 + x_4 + x_5 = -1 \\ x_1 + x_2 + x_3 + x_4 - x_5 = 2 \\ x_1 - 2x_2 - x_3 + 2x_4 + 2x_5 = 4 \end{bmatrix}$

41. $\begin{bmatrix} 30x_1 - 20x_2 - 15x_3 + 25x_4 - 5x_5 = -2 \\ 30x_1 - 11x_2 - 18x_3 + 7x_4 - 8x_5 = 3 \\ -30x_1 + 12x_2 + 21x_3 - 9x_4 + 6x_5 = -1 \\ -15x_1 + 12x_2 + 6x_3 - 9x_4 + 6x_5 = 2 \\ 15x_1 - 7x_2 - 6x_3 - x_4 - x_5 = 4 \end{bmatrix}$

42. Which of the following matrices are inverses of which?

$$A = \begin{bmatrix} \frac{2}{3} & 5 \\ \frac{3}{25} & \frac{6}{5} \end{bmatrix}, \qquad B = \begin{bmatrix} \frac{10}{3} & -25 \\ -\frac{3}{5} & 6 \end{bmatrix},$$

$$C = \begin{bmatrix} 0 & -\frac{2}{3} \\ -\frac{3}{2} & 0 \end{bmatrix}, \qquad D = \begin{bmatrix} 6 & -25 \\ -\frac{3}{5} & \frac{10}{3} \end{bmatrix}$$

43. Write the third equation in the system $AX = B$, where

$$A = \begin{bmatrix} 9 & 10 & 11 & 12 \\ 13 & 14 & 15 & 16 \\ 17 & 18 & 19 & 20 \\ 21 & 22 & 23 & 24 \end{bmatrix} \text{ and } B = \begin{bmatrix} 21 \\ 22 \\ 23 \\ 24 \end{bmatrix}.$$

*44. Find a matrix [?] such that

$$\begin{bmatrix} 0 & 2 & -1 \\ 1 & 2 & 0 \\ -1 & 0 & -2 \end{bmatrix} \begin{bmatrix} ? \end{bmatrix} \begin{bmatrix} 0 & 2 & -1 \\ 1 & 2 & 0 \\ -1 & 0 & -2 \end{bmatrix} = \begin{bmatrix} 1 & 1 & 1 \\ 1 & 1 & 2 \\ 1 & 2 & 2 \end{bmatrix}$$

*45. Find a $3 \times 5$ matrix [?] such that

$$\begin{bmatrix} -2 & 2 & 1 \\ 1 & -\frac{1}{2} & -\frac{1}{2} \\ 1 & -1 & -1 \end{bmatrix} \begin{bmatrix} ? \end{bmatrix} = \begin{bmatrix} 1 & 2 & -1 & 0 & 2 \\ 2 & 0 & 1 & -2 & 0 \\ 0 & -1 & -1 & 2 & 1 \end{bmatrix}.$$

*46. Let $A = [2 \ -3 \ 4], B = \begin{bmatrix} \frac{3}{2} \\ \frac{2}{3} \\ -\frac{8}{5} \end{bmatrix}$. Write out the system $BAX = B$.

The tabulations in Exercises 47, 48, and 49 are input-output tables for various economics. In each exercise determine what the total output of the economy must be to meet the indicated demand.

47.

(in dollars)

| Used by | Services | Other | Demand |
|---|---|---|---|
| **Obtained from** | | | |
| Services | .1 | .3 | 525 |
| Other | .2 | .1 | 225 |

<sup>C</sup>48.

(in dollars)

| Used by | Extractive | Manufacturing | Services | Demand |
|---|---|---|---|---|
| **Obtained from** | | | | |
| Extractive | .3 | .4 | .1 | 4,590 |
| Manufacturing | .5 | .3 | .2 | 1,785 |
| Services | .1 | .2 | .3 | 2,805 |

49.

(in dollars)

| Used by | A | B | C | D | Demand |
|---|---|---|---|---|---|
| **Obtained from** | | | | | |
| A | .7 | .2 | .3 | 0 | 2,322 |
| B | .1 | .3 | .2 | .2 | 1,548 |
| C | 0 | .1 | .1 | .3 | 3,096 |
| D | .1 | .1 | 0 | .4 | 774 |

Another, more general method for efficiently solving by hand several systems of linear equations, each with the same coefficient matrix, is illustrated by the solution of the following systems.

$$\begin{bmatrix} 2x_1 + 3x_2 - x_3 = 4 \\ 3x_1 - x_2 + x_3 = 5 \end{bmatrix} \qquad \textbf{a}$$

$$\begin{bmatrix} 2x_1 + 3x_2 - x_3 = -1 \\ 3x_1 - x_2 + x_3 = 0 \end{bmatrix} \qquad \textbf{b}$$

$$\begin{bmatrix} 2 & 3 & -1 & 4 & -1 \\ 3 & -1 & 1 & 5 & 0 \end{bmatrix} \begin{bmatrix} 2 & 3 & -1 & 4 & -1 \\ 1 & -4 & 2 & 1 & 1 \end{bmatrix}$$

$$\begin{bmatrix} 0 & 11 & -5 & 2 & -3 \\ 1 & -4 & 2 & 1 & 1 \end{bmatrix} \begin{bmatrix} 0 & 1 & -\frac{5}{11} & \frac{2}{11} & -\frac{3}{11} \\ 1 & 0 & \frac{2}{11} & \frac{19}{11} & -\frac{1}{11} \end{bmatrix}$$

**Answers** **a:** $x_1 = \frac{19}{11} - \frac{2}{11}x_3$, $x_2 = \frac{2}{11} + \frac{5}{11}x_3$, $x_3$ free, **b:** $x_1 = \frac{3}{11} - \frac{2}{11}x_3$, $x_2 = -\frac{3}{11} + \frac{2}{11}x_3$, $x_3$ free.

Use this technique to solve the systems in Exercises 50 through 53.

50.

$$\begin{bmatrix} x_1 - x_2 + x_3 = 4 \\ 2x_1 + x_2 + 2x_3 = 5 \end{bmatrix}, \begin{bmatrix} x_1 - x_2 + x_3 = -1 \\ 2x_1 + x_2 + 2x_3 = 0 \end{bmatrix}$$

51.

$$\begin{bmatrix} x_1 + 2x_2 = -2 \\ 3x_1 + 4x_2 = -1 \end{bmatrix}, \begin{bmatrix} x_1 + 2x_2 = 0 \\ 3x_1 + 4x_2 = 1 \end{bmatrix}, \begin{bmatrix} x_1 + 2x_2 = 2 \\ 3x_1 + 4x_2 = 3 \end{bmatrix}$$

52.

$$\begin{bmatrix} x_1 - 3x_2 = 5 \\ -2x_1 + 6x_2 = 0 \end{bmatrix}, \begin{bmatrix} x_1 - 3x_2 = 4 \\ -2x_1 + 6x_2 = 0 \end{bmatrix}, \begin{bmatrix} x_1 - 3x_2 = 0 \\ -2x_1 + 6x_2 = 0 \end{bmatrix}$$

53.

$$\begin{bmatrix} x_1 + x_2 - x_3 = 2 \\ x_1 - x_2 - x_3 = 3 \\ 3x_1 - x_2 - 3x_3 = 8 \end{bmatrix}, \begin{bmatrix} x_1 + x_2 - x_3 = 3 \\ x_1 - x_2 - x_3 = -1 \\ 3x_1 - x_2 - 3x_3 = 0 \end{bmatrix}$$

54. Solve the game $\begin{bmatrix} 4 & 2 \\ 1 & 3 \end{bmatrix}$.

55. Solve the game $\begin{bmatrix} 1 & -1 & 0 \\ -1 & 0 & 1 \\ 1 & 1 & -1 \end{bmatrix}$.

56. A and B each write the number 1, 2, 3, or 4 on a slip of paper. If the absolute value of the difference of the numbers written is less than 2, then B pays A $10. Otherwise, A pays B $5. How should each player proceed? Should one of the players pay something to the other to make the game fair? How much?

57. Find the value of the game with payoff matrix $\begin{bmatrix} 1 & -1 & -2 \\ -1 & 1 & 1 \\ 2 & -1 & x \end{bmatrix}$ where $x \geq -1$.

58. Solve the game $\begin{bmatrix} -1 & 2 \\ 2 & -1 \\ 1 & 0 \end{bmatrix}$.

59. A and B play tick-tack-toe on a $3 \times 3$ matrix. A move such as $A(1, 3)$ means A places X at address $(1, 3)$; move $B(2, 1)$ means B placed O at address $(2, 1)$. Assuming the first two moves are $A(2, 2)$, $B(1, 2)$, write a complete winning strategy for A.

60. You toss a die and I flip a dime and a quarter. If I get 2 heads, I win 4 times the amount on your die. If I get 2 tails I lose 3 times the amount on your die. Otherwise I lose 3 or the amount on your die, whichever is smaller.
    (a) Write the $6 \times 4$ payoff matrix for this game.
    (b) A second game is the same as the game above except "win" is replaced by "lose," "lose" by "win," and "smaller" by "larger." Write the $6 \times 4$ payoff matrix for this game.
    (c) Find a matrix A which when added to the matrix of part (a) gives the matrix of part (b).
    (d) Describe a game whose payoff matrix is **A**.

61. An environment can support 20 ducks, which are of two species: A and Z. Whenever one duck of species A meets one of species Z, the probability that Z flies away and a duck of species A flies in from outside is $\frac{4}{5}$. If this does not happen, then an A flies away and a new Z flies in. If there are now 5 species-A ducks in the environment, what is the probability that there will eventually be no species-A ducks there?

62. Suppose a gene G has 4 forms $G_1$, $G_2$, $G_3$, $G_4$, which are now present in equal proportions in a population of shrews. Assuming random mating, what proportion of the shrews in the ninth generation will have genotype $G_1 G_4$?

A genotype is **homozygous** if the two forms that make it up are the same; otherwise the genotype is **heterozygous**.

63. Suppose a gene G has n forms $G_1, G_2, \ldots, G_n$, which are initially present in equal proportions in a certain population. Show that in all later generations there are $n - 1$ times as many heterozygotes as homozygotes, assuming random mating.

In Exercises 64 and 65 lettered people apply for numbered jobs. After they are interviewed it is determined that they qualified for jobs as indicated in the following charts. Please assign as many people to jobs as possible.

c64.

| | 1 | 2 | 3 | 4 | 5 | 6 | 7 | 8 | 9 |
|---|---|---|---|---|---|---|---|---|---|
| A | × | × | | × | | | × | | |
| B | | | | × | | | | | |
| C | | | × | | × | × | | × | |
| D | × | × | × | | | | | | × |
| E | | | | | | | | × | × |
| F | | | × | | | × | × | | |
| G | | | | | × | | × | × | |
| H | | × | | | | × | | | |

65.

| | 1 | 2 | 3 | 4 | 5 | 6 | 7 | 8 | 9 | 10 | 11 |
|---|---|---|---|---|---|---|---|---|---|---|---|
| A | | × | | × | | × | | | | | × |
| B | × | | | × | | × | | × | | | |
| C | | | × | | × | | × | | | × | |
| D | | × | | | | | | | × | | |
| E | × | | | × | | × | | × | | | |
| F | | | × | | × | | × | | | × | |
| G | × | | | × | | | | | | | |
| H | × | | | × | | × | | × | | | |
| I | | × | | | | | | × | | | |
| J | | | | × | | × | | | | | |
| K | | × | | | | | | | × | | × |

Find maximal flows and minimal cuts for the networks given in Exercises 66, 67, and 68.

c66.

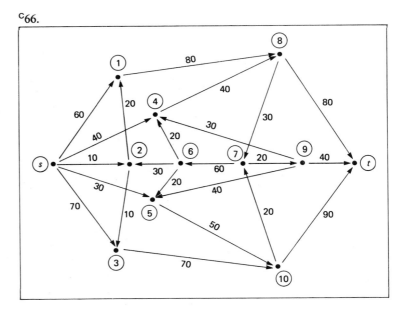

67.

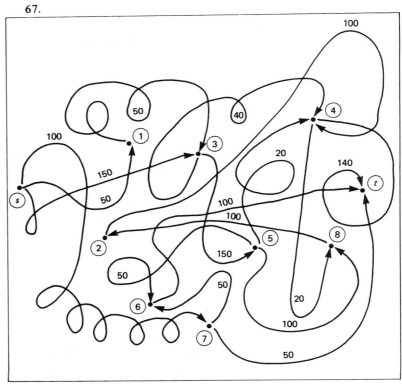

<sup>c</sup>68.

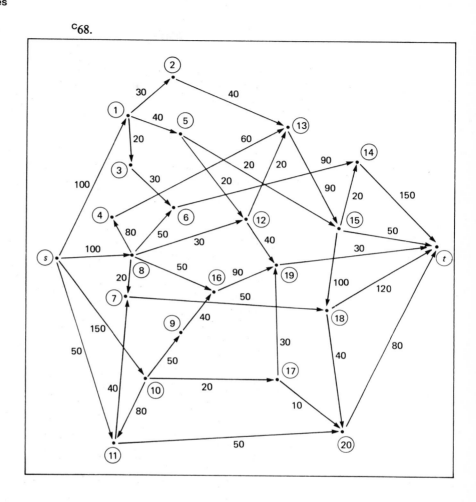

69. PHE store number 4173 in Ft. Scott, Kansas, has materials on hand as listed in Table 20. From these materials they make food items, which are sold for the profits listed in Table 21. Some of these items are assembled into special package meals, though they are also sold separately. The components and profits for the package meals are shown in Table 22. The store must sell at least 70 dogfeasts, exactly 22 fishfeasts, and at least 20 lbs. of potatoes; and they must use up all their hamburger patties. Maximize profit.

Table 20

| Materials | Quantity |
|---|---|
| Hamburger patties | 342 |
| Cheese slices | 194 |
| Potatoes | 35 lbs. (16 oz. in a lb.) |
| Cola syrup | 26 qts. (32 oz. in a qt.) |
| Short wieners | 244 |
| Long wieners | 110 |
| Hamburger buns | 284 |
| Superburger buns | 178 |
| Short hotdog buns | 244 |
| Long hotdog buns | 130 |
| Fish patties | 180 |

Table 21

| Item | Materials | Profit (cents) |
|---|---|---|
| Hamburger | 1 hamburger, 1 hamburger bun | 7 |
| Cheeseburger | 1 ham., 1 cheese slice, 1 ham. bun | 10 |
| Superburger | 2 ham., 1 cheese sl., 1 sup. bun | 17 |
| Small fires | 3 oz. potato | 6 |
| Large fries | 5 oz. potato | 8 |
| Hot dog | 1 short wiener, 1 short h. d. bun | 9 |
| Foot-long hot dog | 1 long wiener, 1 long h. d. bun | 11 |
| Fishburger | 1 fish patty, 1 sup. bun | 14 |
| Small cola | 0.4 oz. cola syrup | 10 |
| Medium cola | 0.6 oz. cola syrup | 15 |
| Large cola | 0.8 oz. cola syrup | 20 |

Table 22

| Package meal | Components | Profit (cents) |
|---|---|---|
| Burger snack | hamburger, small cola | 19 |
| Burger meal | cheeseburger, sm. fries, med. cola | 35 |
| Burgerfeast | superburger, lg. fries, lg. cola | 52 |
| Dogfeast | ft.-long hot dog, lg. fries, lg. cola | 35 |
| Fishfeast | fishburger, lg. fries, lg. cola | 42 |

70. Write a computer program for the solution of an arbitrary problem in input-output analysis using the Leontief model. Test it on Exercises 47, 48, and 49 above.

# Appendix A
# Review
# of
# Arithmetic
# and
# Algebra

For a general review of these topics, see Martin Zuckerman, *Intermediate Algebra: A Straightforward Approach* (New York: Norton, 1976).

This appendix should not be considered as a general review of these subjects, since it covers only those topics required in this book. The appendix concludes with exercises, which can be used as a test of your preparedness.

**Section 1**
**Use of**
**Parentheses**

An expression such as $13-4\times 2$ is interpreted as $13-(4\times 2)=13-8=5$; *not* as $(13-4)\times 2=9\times 2=18$. If we had meant the latter expression we would have had to employ parentheses: $(13-4)\times 2$. The former expression, $13-4\times 2$, will always be interpreted as $13-(4\times 2)$ whether or not the parentheses were inserted. In general in an expression in arithmetic, we always do the multiplications and divisions before the additions and subtractions unless there are parentheses to indicate otherwise. A few examples:

$$4\div 2+3\times 3-2=2+9-2=9;$$
$$6\div(2+1)+(4-2)\div 2-6\div 2+1+4\div 2-2$$
$$=6\div 3+2\div 2-3+1+2-2=2+1-3+1+2-2=1;$$
$$(1+2+3-4)\div(5+6-10)=2\div 1=2$$

**Section 2**
**Other Notations**

The product $3\times 4$ is also written $3\cdot 4$ and $(3)(4)$. Thus, $3\times 4=3\cdot 4=(3)(4)=12$. If one or more of the numbers in the product is denoted by a letter, such as $3\times a$, the notation $3a$ is used. Thus, $3\times a=3\cdot a=(3)(a)=3a$; $7\times x_1=7x_1$.

The quotient $6\div 2$ is also written $6/2$ and $\frac{6}{2}$ Thus, $6\div 2=\frac{6}{2}=6/2=3$.

A special notation for addition (mixed fraction notation) will be explained below.

**Section 2a**
**Exponents**

Exponents are used to denote repeated multiplication. In an expression such as

$$3^5$$

the number 3 is called the **base** and the number five is called the **exponent** or **power**. The exponent tells how many times the base appears in the product with itself. For example,

$$2^3 = \overbrace{2 \times 2 \times 2}^{3 \text{ times}} = 8$$

$$4^4 = \overbrace{4 \times 4 \times 4 \times 4}^{4 \text{ times}} = 256$$

$$6^1 = \overbrace{6}^{1 \text{ time}}$$

$$3^5 = 3 \times 3 \times 3 \times 3 \times 3 = 243$$

Some powers have special names: the exponent 2 is called the **square**, and the exponent 3 is called the **cube**. It is convenient to *define* the zero power of any number (except 0) to be 1. Thus,

$$2^0 = 1$$
$$1^0 = 1$$
$$6^0 = 1$$

$0^0$ is undefined.

**Section 3**
**Zero**

The laws for combining zero with any number a are:

$$a + 0 = a$$
$$a - 0 = a$$
$$a0 = 0$$
$$a \div 0 \text{ and } a/0 \text{ are undefined}$$
$$0 + a = a$$
$$0 - a = -a$$
$$0a = 0$$
$$0 \div a = \frac{0}{a} = 0$$

Examples:

$$3+0=3$$
$$4-0=4$$
$$4 \cdot 0=0$$
$$7 \div 0 \text{ and } \tfrac{7}{0} \text{ are undefined}$$
$$0+8=8$$
$$0-8=-8$$
$$(0)(8)=0$$
$$\tfrac{0}{10}=0$$

### Section 4
### Fractions

In the fraction $\frac{3}{4}$ the number 3 is called the **numerator** and the number 4 is called the **denominator**. From Section 3 we see that a fraction must not have denominator zero. Any whole number may be written as a fraction with denominator one: $7=\frac{7}{1}$, $3=\frac{3}{1}$, $-4=-\frac{4}{1}$.

#### 4.1  Cancellation

Fractions can often be simplified by dividing their numerator and denominator by the same number. For example: $\frac{6}{9}=\frac{\cancel{3}\cdot 2}{\cancel{3}\cdot 3}=\frac{2}{3}$, $\frac{77}{154}=\frac{\cancel{11}\cdot 7}{\cancel{11}\cdot 14}=\frac{7}{14}=\frac{\cancel{7}\cdot 1}{\cancel{7}\cdot 2}=\frac{1}{2}$. It is usually a good idea to cancel, when possible, to make the denominator of a fraction as small as possible. It is not serious if you fail to notice a tricky cancellation, such as $\frac{3,813}{1,763}=\frac{\cancel{41}\cdot 93}{\cancel{41}\cdot 43}=\frac{93}{43}$.

#### 4.2  Mixed Fraction Form

In some cases fractions with a larger numerator than denominator, such as $\frac{18}{7}$, are better written in **mixed form**: $\frac{18}{7}=2\frac{4}{7}$. Here it must be kept in mind that $2\frac{4}{7}$ means $2+\frac{4}{7}$ and *not* $2\times\frac{4}{7}$. Another example, involving cancellation: $\frac{18}{12}=1\frac{6}{12}=1\frac{1}{2}$; another solution: $\frac{18}{12}=\frac{3}{2}=1\frac{1}{2}$.

#### 4.3  Multiplication of Fractions

To multiply fractions, multiply numerator and denominators, respectively, after cancellation where possible. Examples:

$$\frac{2}{3}\cdot\frac{5}{4}=\frac{2}{3}\cdot\frac{5}{\cancel{4}_2}=\frac{5}{6}; \qquad \frac{4}{9}\cdot\frac{15}{14}=\frac{\cancel{4}^2}{\cancel{9}_3}\cdot\frac{\cancel{15}^5}{\cancel{14}_7}=\frac{10}{21};$$

$$\frac{9}{4}\cdot\frac{14}{15}=\frac{\cancel{9}^3}{\cancel{4}_2}\cdot\frac{\cancel{14}^7}{\cancel{15}_5}=\frac{21}{10}=2\frac{1}{10}; \qquad \frac{1}{4}\cdot\frac{4}{2}\cdot\frac{6}{8}=\frac{\cancel{1}^1\cdot\cancel{4}^2\cdot\cancel{6}^1}{\cancel{4}_1\cdot\cancel{2}_1\cdot\cancel{8}_4}=\frac{2}{8}=\frac{1}{4}$$

**4.3a  Exponents and Fractions**

We use exponents to denote repeated multiplication of fractions as well as integers. For example,

$$\left(\tfrac{2}{3}\right)^4 = \tfrac{2}{3} \times \tfrac{2}{3} \times \tfrac{2}{3} \times \tfrac{2}{3} = \tfrac{2^4}{3^4} = \tfrac{16}{81}$$

$$\left(\tfrac{3}{4}\right)^3 = \tfrac{3}{4} \times \tfrac{3}{4} \times \tfrac{3}{4} = \tfrac{3^3}{4^3} = \tfrac{27}{64}$$

$$\left(\tfrac{1}{2}\right)^1 = \tfrac{1^1}{2^1} = \tfrac{1}{2}$$

$$\left(\tfrac{7}{8}\right)^0 = \tfrac{7^0}{8^0} = \tfrac{1}{1} = 1$$

Note that to raise a fraction to a given power we simply raise the numerator and denominator to the given power. As with integers, the 0 power of any fraction (except 0) is 1.

**4.4  Division of Fractions**

To divide one fraction by another, invert the divisor and multiply, as in 4.3. Examples:

$$\frac{\tfrac{2}{3}}{\tfrac{4}{3}} = \tfrac{2}{3} \cdot \tfrac{3}{4} = \tfrac{1}{2}; \quad \frac{4}{\tfrac{2}{5}} = \tfrac{4}{1} \cdot \tfrac{5}{2} = 10;$$

$$2\tfrac{3}{4} \div 3\tfrac{1}{2} = \left(\tfrac{11}{4}\right) \div \left(\tfrac{7}{2}\right) = \left(\tfrac{11}{4}\right)\left(\tfrac{2}{7}\right) = \tfrac{11}{14};$$

$$3\tfrac{1}{2} \div 2\tfrac{3}{4} = \left(\tfrac{7}{2}\right) \div \left(\tfrac{11}{4}\right) = \left(\tfrac{7}{2}\right)\left(\tfrac{4}{11}\right) = \tfrac{14}{11} = 1\tfrac{3}{11};$$

$$\frac{\tfrac{8}{7}}{6} = \tfrac{8}{7} \cdot \tfrac{1}{6} = \tfrac{4}{21}$$

**4.4a  Cross Multiplication**

The easiest way to tell if two fractions are equal is by cross multiplication. For example:

(a) $\tfrac{2}{3} = \tfrac{12}{18}$, since $2 \times 18 = 3 \times 12 = 36$, the fractions are equal: $\tfrac{2}{3} = \tfrac{12}{18}$
(b) $\tfrac{5}{8} \neq \tfrac{16}{25}$, since $5 \cdot 25 \neq 8 \cdot 15$, the fractions are *not* equal: $\tfrac{5}{8} \neq \tfrac{16}{25}$.

See Section 5 of this appendix for treatment of minus sign.

The **reciprocal** of a nonzero number is defined to be 1 divided by that number. For example, the reciprocal of 3 is $\tfrac{1}{3}$; the reciprocal of $-3$ is $\tfrac{1}{-3} = -\tfrac{1}{3}$; the reciprocal of $\tfrac{4}{5}$ if $1/(\tfrac{4}{5}) = \tfrac{5}{4}$; the reciprocal of $-\tfrac{2}{3}$ is $1/(-\tfrac{2}{3}) = \tfrac{3}{-2} = -1\tfrac{1}{2}$. The number 0 has no reciprocal since, if we had $\tfrac{1}{0} = x$, we would have $1 = 0 \cdot x = 0$, which is absurd. Thus, "$\tfrac{1}{0}$" is left undefined.

Note however that $\tfrac{0}{1}$ *is* defined, and in fact $\tfrac{0}{1} = 0$.

The reciprocal of a nonzero number is also called the **multiplicative inverse** of that number. The reciprocal of 3 is also written $3^{-1}$, read "3 inverse." Thus, $3^{-1} = \tfrac{1}{3}$, $(-3)^{-1} = -\tfrac{1}{3}$, $(\tfrac{4}{5})^{-1} = \tfrac{5}{4}$, $(-\tfrac{2}{3})^{-1} = -\tfrac{3}{2}$. Since 0 has no reciprocal, $0^{-1}$ is undefined.

**4.5 Common Denominators**

For purposes of addition, subtraction, and comparison it is convenient to write fractions with the same (common) denominators. For example, $\frac{1}{4}$ and $\frac{1}{6}$ can be written with common denominator 24: $\frac{1}{4} = \frac{6}{24}$, $\frac{1}{6} = \frac{4}{24}$. Actually, these fractions could be written with common denominator 12: $\frac{1}{4} = \frac{3}{12}$, $\frac{1}{6} = \frac{2}{12}$. Here, the number 12 is the smallest integer that can serve as a common denominator; it is the **least common denominator** for $\frac{1}{4}$ and $\frac{1}{6}$. It is easy to find a common denominator for a collection of fractions: multiply together all of the different denominators. Usually the common denominator found in this way is not the least one. Finding that takes a bit more practice. Examples: the least common denominator of $\frac{2}{9}, \frac{4}{15}, \frac{5}{3}$ is 45: $\frac{2}{9} = \frac{10}{45}, \frac{4}{15} = \frac{12}{45}, \frac{5}{3} = \frac{75}{45}$; the least common denominator of $\frac{8}{5}, \frac{7}{4}, \frac{11}{6}, \frac{5}{2}$ is 60: $\frac{8}{5} = \frac{96}{60}, \frac{7}{4} = \frac{105}{60}, \frac{11}{6} = \frac{110}{60}, \frac{5}{2} = \frac{150}{60}$.

**4.6 Addition and Subtraction of Fractions**

To add or subtract fractions: (1) Find a common denominator for the fractions; (2) add or subtract, as required, the numerators of the fractions written with the common denominator; (3) put the result of step 2 over the common denominator; (4) cancel if possible. Examples: $\frac{1}{2} + \frac{2}{3} - \frac{3}{4} = \frac{6}{12} + \frac{8}{12} - \frac{9}{12} = \frac{6+8-9}{12} = \frac{5}{12}$; $\frac{4}{15} + \frac{3}{5} - \frac{1}{15} = \frac{4}{15} + \frac{9}{15} - \frac{1}{15} = \frac{12}{15} = \frac{4}{5}$.

**4.7 Applications**

(a) How many minutes are in $\frac{7}{8}$ of an hour? Answer:

$$\left(\frac{7}{8}\right)(60) = \frac{7}{\underset{2}{8}} \cdot \frac{\overset{15}{60}}{1} = \frac{105}{2} = 52\frac{1}{2} \text{ minutes.}$$

(b) What fraction of an hour is 52 minutes? Answer: $\frac{52}{60} = \frac{13}{15}$ of an hour.

(c) A factory can make $\frac{4}{5}$ of one computer in a 40-hour work week. If the work week is increased to 50 hours, how many computers can they make? Answer: $\left(\frac{4}{5}\right)\left(\frac{50}{40}\right) = 1$ computer.

**4.8 Square root**

See Section 8 for the definition of positive.

Given any positive whole number or fraction we define its **square root** to be the positive number whose square is the given number.

$$\sqrt{16} = 4 \text{ since } 4^2 = 16$$
$$\sqrt{625} = 25 \text{ since } 25^2 = 625$$
$$\sqrt{\tfrac{1}{4}} = \tfrac{1}{2} \text{ since } \left(\tfrac{1}{2}\right)^2 = \tfrac{1}{4}$$
$$\sqrt{\tfrac{16}{25}} = \tfrac{4}{5} \text{ since } \left(\tfrac{4}{5}\right)^2 = \tfrac{16}{25}$$
$$\sqrt{0} = 0 \text{ since } 0^2 = 0$$
$$\sqrt{1} = 1 \text{ since } 1^2 = 1$$

Some square roots do not "come out even."

$$\sqrt{11} \doteq 3.317$$

$$\sqrt{\tfrac{3}{5}} \doteq .7746$$

$$\sqrt{128} \doteq 11.314$$

These square roots are most easily determined by use of tables of square roots or pocket calculators. See Table 1, p. 514.

There are several quick methods of determining square root by hand. Unfortunately, these methods have descriptions that this margin is too narrow to contain.

**Section 5**
**Plus and Minus**

The sign $+$ is omitted whenever possible. For example, we write $+18$ simply as 18, and $+8+9$ as $8+9$. The rules connecting plus and minus signs are as follows, with examples in brackets:

$$+-a = -a \qquad [+-6 = -6]$$
$$--+a = -a \qquad [-+5 = -5]$$
$$--a = +a \qquad [--4 = 4]$$
$$(-a)(b) = -(ab) \qquad [(-\tfrac{2}{3})(\tfrac{3}{4}) = -((\tfrac{2}{3})(\tfrac{3}{4})) = -\tfrac{1}{2}]$$
$$a(-b) = -(ab) \qquad [4(-\tfrac{5}{6}) = -((\tfrac{4}{1})(\tfrac{5}{6})) = -\tfrac{10}{3}]$$
$$(-a)(-b) = ab \qquad [(-\tfrac{2}{3})(-\tfrac{3}{4}) = (\tfrac{2}{3})(\tfrac{3}{4}) = \tfrac{1}{2}]$$
$$(-a)/b = -a/b \qquad [\tfrac{(-4)}{6} = -(\tfrac{4}{6}) = -\tfrac{2}{3}]$$
$$a/(-b) = -a/b \qquad [(\tfrac{2}{5})/(-\tfrac{3}{4}) = -((\tfrac{2}{5})/(\tfrac{3}{4})) = -((\tfrac{2}{5})/(\tfrac{4}{3})) = -\tfrac{8}{15}]$$
$$(-a)/(-b) = a/b \qquad [(-\tfrac{4}{5})/(-\tfrac{2}{15}) = (\tfrac{4}{5})/(\tfrac{2}{15}) = (\tfrac{4}{5})(\tfrac{15}{2}) = 6]$$
$$a+-b = a-b \qquad [6+-4 = 6-4 = 2]$$
$$-a+b = b-a \qquad [-7+12 = 12-7 = 5]$$
$$a-+b = a-b \qquad [\tfrac{2}{3}-+\tfrac{1}{2} = \tfrac{2}{3}-\tfrac{1}{2} = \tfrac{4}{6}-\tfrac{3}{6} = \tfrac{1}{6}]$$
$$-a+b = -(a-b) \qquad [-9+4 = -(9-4) = -5]$$
$$a-b = -(b-a) \qquad [4-7 = -(7-4) = -3]$$
$$-a-b = -(a+b) \qquad [-\tfrac{1}{2}-\tfrac{1}{3} = -(\tfrac{1}{2}+\tfrac{1}{3}) = -\tfrac{5}{6}]$$
$$-a--b = -a+b \qquad [-7--8 = -7+8 = 1]$$

**Section 6**
**The Distributive Law**

This law can sometimes make calculations easier. It says: if $a, b, c$ are any numbers, then $ab + ac = a(b+c)$. For example: it looks hard to calculate $(\tfrac{3}{4})(\tfrac{4}{7}) - (\tfrac{3}{4})(\tfrac{6}{7})$, but: $(\tfrac{3}{4})(\tfrac{4}{7} - \tfrac{6}{7}) = (\tfrac{3}{4})(-\tfrac{2}{7}) = -\tfrac{3}{14}$.

**Section 7**
**Decimals and**
**Percent**

One-place decimals are tenths, two-place decimals are hundredths, three-place decimals are thousandths, and so on. For example: $0.3 = \tfrac{3}{10}$, $0.4 = \tfrac{4}{10} = \tfrac{2}{5}$; $6.3 = \tfrac{63}{10} = 6\tfrac{3}{10}$; $-7.2 = -\tfrac{72}{10} = -7\tfrac{2}{10} = -7\tfrac{1}{5}$;

$-0.07 = -\frac{7}{100}$;  $0.25 = \frac{25}{100} = \frac{1}{4}$;  $-3.62 = -\frac{362}{100} = -3\frac{31}{50}$;  $0.215 = \frac{215}{1,000}$ $= \frac{43}{200}$.

To convert a fraction to a decimal, use long division to divide the denominator into the numerator. For example: $\frac{7}{10} = 0.7$; $\frac{4}{5} = \frac{8}{10}$ $= 0.8$; $9\frac{1}{2} = 9\frac{5}{10} = 9.5$; $7\frac{6}{25} = 7\frac{24}{100} = 7.24$; $-\frac{151}{250} = -0.604$. The long division in the last example above is:

$$
\begin{array}{r}
0.604 \\
250\overline{)151.000} \\
150.0 \\
\hline
1.000 \\
1.000 \\
\hline
\end{array}
$$

For some fractions, conversion to decimals can only be done approximately. For example: $\frac{1}{3} \doteq 0.333$, $\frac{2}{3} \doteq 0.667$; $\frac{1}{7} \doteq 0.143$.

To convert a fraction of a whole to a percent, write it as a decimal and multiply by 100; that is, move the decimal point two places to the right. For example: $\frac{7}{10} = 0.7 = 70\%$; $\frac{71}{200} = 0.355 = 35.5\%$.

The symbol $\doteq$ indicates that the number on the right is a decimal approximation of the number on the left, rounded off to the number of places given.

**Problem 1**  If an 8-hour day is cut by 3 hours, what percent of the day is left?

**Answer**  $(8-3)/8 = \frac{5}{8} = 0.625 = 62.5\%$.

**Section 8
Less Than and
Greater Than**

The following table summarizes these symbols.

Table 1

| Symbol | Read | Examples |
|---|---|---|
| < | is less than | $3 < 5, -2 < 0, -5 < -3$ |
| > | is greater than | $7 > 2, 6 > -2, -8 > -9$ |
| ≤ | is less than or equal to | $6 \leq 7, 6 \leq 6, -3 \leq -3$ |
| ≥ | is greater than or equal to | $9 \geq 8, -7 \geq -7, -7 \geq -8$ |

Note that, for two numbers a and b, saying that $a \leq b$ is the same as saying $b \geq a$. For example, the statement $7 \leq \frac{21}{3}$ can also be written $\frac{21}{3} \geq 7$; the statement $-9 \geq -11$ can also be written as $-11 \leq -9$.

Here are a few other phrases which arise in connection with inequalities.

(1) at least. Example: "the die shows at least 3" means "the die shows a 3, 4, 5, or 6." At least usually has the same meaning as $>$.

(2) at most. Example: "the die shows at most 3" means "the die shows a 1, 2, or 3." At most usually has the same meaning as $\leq$ .

(3) no more than. Example: "He will pay no more than 25¢" means "he will pay 0¢ or 25¢ or any amount in between." No more than and at most are interchangeable.

(4) no less than. Example: "He will accept no less than 25¢" means "he will accept 25¢ or more." No less than and at least are interchangeable.

A number x is said to be **positive** if $x > 0$; x is **negative** if $x < 0$; x is **non-negative** if $x \geq 0$. The number zero is neither positive nor negative, but it is non-negative.

If two fractions are close together in value, it may be hard to tell which is larger. To do so, write them with a common denominator.

**Problem 2**   Which is larger, $\frac{12}{29}$ or $\frac{5}{12}$?

**Solution**   $\frac{12}{29} = \frac{144}{12\cdot29}$, $\frac{5}{12} = \frac{145}{12\cdot29}$; hence $\frac{5}{12}$ is larger. (Note: there is no need to multiply out $12\cdot29$.)

It is possible to "add" inequalities. For example

$$
\begin{array}{ll}
\begin{array}{r} 2 \leq 5 \\ 3 \leq 8 \\ \hline 5 \leq 13 \end{array} &
\begin{array}{r} -2 \leq 10 \\ -7 \leq -5 \\ \hline -9 \leq 5 \end{array}
\end{array}
$$

In general if $a, b, c, d$ are numbers, $a \leq b$, and $c \leq d$, then $a + c \leq b + d$.   This result extends to any finite number of inequalities.   For example, if $a \leq b$, $c \leq d$, $e \leq f$, and $g \leq h$, then $a + c + e + g \leq b + d + f + h$.

**Section 9**
**Absolute Value**

The *absolute value* of a number is the distance from the number to 0 on the coordinate line. This distance is always non-negative. For example, the absolute value of $-6$ is 6, since $-6$ is six units from the origin, 0, on the coordinate line (p. 55). The absolute value of 6 is also 6. Thus, 6 and $-6$ have the same absolute value.

The absolute value of a number x is written $|x|$. Thus, the above results may be written

$$|-6| = |6| = 6$$

The absolute value of zero is zero; the absolute value of any positive number is positive; and the absolute value of any negative number is also positive. We express this as follows:

$$|0| = 0$$

$$\text{If } a \neq 0, \text{ then } |a| > 0$$

### Section 10
### Working with
### Inequalities

The same number may be added to both sides on an inequality. Suppose we know that $x_2 - \frac{2}{3} \geq 3\frac{1}{3}$. Then we may add $\frac{2}{3}$ to both sides to obtain $x_2 - \frac{2}{3} + \frac{2}{3} \geq 3\frac{1}{3} + \frac{2}{3}$, that is, $x_2 \geq 4$.

The same number may be subtracted from both sides of an inequality. Suppose we are given that $x_3 + 6 \leq 14$. Then we may conclude that $x_3 + 6 - 6 \leq 14 - 6$; that is, $x_3 \leq 8$.

If both sides of an inequality are multiplied by the same *positive* number, then the inequality sign stays the same. Suppose $\frac{2}{3}x_1 \geq -\frac{7}{3}$. Then we may multiply both sides by the positive number 3 to obtain $3 \cdot (\frac{2}{3})x_1 \geq 3 \cdot (-\frac{7}{3})$, that is, $2x_1 \geq -7$.

If both sides of an inequality are multiplied by the same *negative* number, then the inequality sign is reversed; that is, $\leq$ becomes $\geq$ and $\geq$ becomes $\leq$. Suppose we multiply both sides of the inequality $\frac{2}{3}x_1 \geq -\frac{7}{3}$ by the negative number $-3$. Then we must change $\geq$ to $\leq$: $-3 \cdot (\frac{2}{3})x_1 \leq -3 \cdot (-\frac{7}{3})$; that is, $-2x_1 \leq 7$.

This last law, that multiplication by a negative number reverses inequalities, is most frequently used in this text for the negative number $-1$. Multiplication by $-1$ changes all $+$ signs to $-$ signs, all $-$ signs to $+$ signs, the $\leq$ sign to $\geq$, and the $\geq$ sign to $\leq$. However it does leave the $=$ sign unchanged.

### Problem 3

Rewrite the inequality $3x_1 - x_2 + 4 \leq 2x_2 - x_3 + 1$ as a standard format upper bound constraint, that is, with all xs on the left, a $\leq$, and a number on the right.

### First Solution

Subtract $2x_2$ from both sides: $3x_1 - x_2 + 4 - 2x_2 \leq 2x_2 - x_3 + 1 - 2x_2$; that is, $3x_1 - 3x_2 + 4 \leq -x_3 + 1$. Now add $x_3$ to both sides: $3x_1 - 3x_2 + 4 + x_3 \leq -x_3 + 1 + x_3$; that is, $3x_1 - 3x_2 + x_3 + 4 \leq 1$. Finally, subtract 4 from both sides: $3x_1 - 3x_2 + x_3 \leq -3$.

### Fancy Solution

Add $-2x_2 + x_3 - 4$ to both sides: $3x_1 - 3x_2 + x_3 \leq -3$.

**Section 11**
**Finding Unknown**
**Numbers**

We need to be able to solve only rather simple problems of this type, such as the following.

**Problem 4**   What number should be added to $\frac{7}{5}$ to yield $\frac{3}{4}$?

**Solution**   Call the unknown number x. We want to have $\frac{7}{5}+x=\frac{3}{4}$. Then
$$x=\frac{3}{4}-\frac{7}{5}=-(\frac{7}{5}-\frac{3}{4})=-(\frac{28}{20}-\frac{15}{20})=-\frac{13}{20}.$$

**Check**   $\frac{7}{5}+-\frac{13}{20}=\frac{28}{20}-\frac{13}{20}=\frac{15}{20}=\frac{3}{4}\ \sqrt{.}$

**Problem 5**   What number should be multiplied by $-\frac{3}{2}$ to yield $\frac{4}{5}$?

**Solution**   We want $x(-\frac{3}{2})=\frac{4}{5}$. Then $x=(\frac{4}{5})\div(-\frac{3}{2})=-(\frac{4}{5})(\frac{2}{3})=-\frac{8}{15}.$

**Check**
$$(-\tfrac{8}{15})(-\tfrac{3}{2})=\frac{\overset{4}{\cancel{8}}}{\underset{5}{\cancel{15}}}\cdot\frac{\overset{1}{\cancel{3}}}{\underset{1}{\cancel{2}}}=\frac{4}{5}\ \sqrt{.}$$

**Problem 6**   What number should be multiplied by $\frac{7}{8}$ so that when the result is added to $-\frac{3}{2}$ the sum is zero?

**Solution**   We want $-\frac{3}{2}+x(\frac{7}{8})=0$. Then $x(\frac{7}{8})=\frac{3}{2}$. Then $x=(\frac{3}{2})\div(\frac{7}{8})=(\frac{3}{2})(\frac{8}{7})$
$=\frac{12}{7}=1\frac{5}{7}$. Check: $(\frac{12}{7})(\frac{7}{8})+-\frac{3}{2}=\frac{12}{8}-\frac{3}{2}=\frac{3}{2}-\frac{3}{2}=0\ \sqrt{.}$

**Exercises**

1. Calculate the indicated power.
   (a) $3^3$                    (f) $6^0$
   (b) $4^5$                    (g) $2^5$
   (c) $(\frac{1}{2})^3$         (h) $7^2$
   (d) $1^0$                    (i) $(\frac{2}{3})^4$
   (e) $(\frac{3}{4})^3$         (j) $(\frac{17}{19})^0$

2. Write each of the following in the form $\frac{m}{n}$, where m and n are integers, $n>0$, and n is as small as possible. Write $\frac{m}{1}$ simply as m.
   (a) $2\times2$               (e) $(-\frac{8}{3})-(-\frac{9}{20})$
   (b) $(-2)(-3)$               (f) $-\frac{3}{4}+\frac{5}{12}$
   (c) $6--3+2(4-3)$           (g) $-(\frac{17}{8}-\frac{2}{12})$
   (d) $(-\frac{2}{3})(\frac{9}{20})$

3. Write the answers to parts e and g of Exercise 2 in mixed fraction form.

4. Find:
   (a) $6^{-1}$                 (e) $(\frac{3}{5})^{-1}$
   (b) $(-8)^{-1}$              (f) $(-\frac{5}{6})^{-1}$
   (c) $-8^{-1}$                (g) $((\frac{3}{4})^{-1})^{-1}$
   (d) $(\frac{2}{3})^{-1}$

5. Find the least common denominator for $\frac{5}{6}$ and $-\frac{7}{9}$.

6. Convert to decimals:
   (a) $-7\frac{4}{25}$      (b) $-(-3.21-\frac{15}{4})$

7. By what percent do you increase a 40-hour work week when you change it to a 45-hour week?

8. (a) Which is larger, $\frac{13}{24}$ or $\frac{7}{13}$?
   (b) Which is smaller (that is, most negative), $-\frac{13}{24}$ or $-\frac{7}{13}$?

9. Consider the integers between 1 and 10 (including 1 and 10). To which integers do the following phrases refer?
   (a) The number is less than 5.
   (b) The number is at most 7.
   (c) The number is no more than 9.
   (d) The number is greater than 2.
   (e) The number is less than or equal 4.
   (f) The number is no less than 8.
   (g) The number is greater than or equal 6.
   (h) The number is at least 3.

10. Find the absolute values of $-\frac{3}{4}$, $-70$, $8-12$, $8-8$, $--3$, and $12-8$.

11. Rewrite the inequality $-4x_1+3-2x_2+x_4 \geq -5x_1-2x_2-2x_3-4+3x_4$ as a standard format upper bound constraint, that is, as a $\leq$ inequality with all the xs on the left and a number on the right.

12. What number should be multiplied by $-\frac{7}{2}$ so that when the result is added to $\frac{6}{5}$ the final result is zero?

# Appendix B
# Tables

Table I.
Square Roots To find the square root of a given 3-digit number, first locate the first two digits in the column on the left. The desired square root is in this row under the column headed by the third digit. For example, from row 37, column 8 we read

$$\sqrt{378} \doteq 19.442$$

This table may be applied to other numbers by use of the following simple formulas.

| Formula | Example |
|---|---|
| $\sqrt{n} = 100\sqrt{\frac{n}{10,000}}$ | $\sqrt{8,630,000} = 100\sqrt{863} \doteq 2937.7$ |
| $\sqrt{n} = 10\sqrt{\frac{n}{100}}$ | $\sqrt{17,800} = 10\sqrt{178} \doteq 133.42$ |
| $\sqrt{n} = \frac{1}{10}\sqrt{100n}$ | $\sqrt{.57} = \frac{1}{10}\sqrt{.57} \doteq .7550$ |
| $\sqrt{n} = \frac{1}{100}\sqrt{10,000n}$ | $\sqrt{.068} = \frac{1}{100}\sqrt{680} \doteq .26077$ |

Nearly all the numbers in this table and the following table are approximations. However, in Table I, numbers that end with 3 zeros beyond the decimal point are exact.

| | 0 | 1 | 2 | 3 | 4 | 5 | 6 | 7 | 8 | 9 |
|---|---|---|---|---|---|---|---|---|---|---|
| 00 | 0.000 | 1.000 | 1.414 | 1.732 | 2.000 | 2.236 | 2.449 | 2.646 | 2.828 | 3.000 |
| 01 | 3.162 | 3.317 | 3.464 | 3.606 | 3.742 | 3.873 | 4.000 | 4.123 | 4.243 | 4.359 |
| 02 | 4.472 | 4.583 | 4.690 | 4.796 | 4.899 | 5.000 | 5.099 | 5.196 | 5.292 | 5.385 |
| 03 | 5.477 | 5.568 | 5.657 | 5.745 | 5.831 | 5.916 | 6.000 | 6.083 | 6.164 | 6.245 |
| 04 | 6.325 | 6.403 | 6.481 | 6.557 | 6.633 | 6.708 | 6.782 | 6.856 | 6.928 | 7.000 |
| 05 | 7.071 | 7.141 | 7.211 | 7.280 | 7.348 | 7.416 | 7.483 | 7.550 | 7.616 | 7.681 |
| 06 | 7.746 | 7.810 | 7.874 | 7.937 | 8.000 | 8.062 | 8.124 | 8.185 | 8.246 | 8.307 |
| 07 | 8.367 | 8.426 | 8.485 | 8.544 | 8.602 | 8.660 | 8.718 | 8.775 | 8.832 | 8.888 |
| 08 | 8.944 | 9.000 | 9.055 | 9.110 | 9.165 | 9.220 | 9.274 | 9.327 | 9.381 | 9.434 |
| 09 | 9.487 | 9.539 | 9.592 | 9.644 | 9.695 | 9.747 | 9.798 | 9.849 | 9.899 | 9.950 |
| 10 | 10.000 | 10.050 | 10.100 | 10.149 | 10.198 | 10.247 | 10.296 | 10.344 | 10.392 | 10.440 |
| 11 | 10.488 | 10.536 | 10.583 | 10.630 | 10.677 | 10.724 | 10.770 | 10.817 | 10.863 | 10.909 |
| 12 | 10.954 | 11.000 | 11.045 | 11.091 | 11.136 | 11.180 | 11.225 | 11.269 | 11.314 | 11.358 |
| 13 | 11.402 | 11.446 | 11.489 | 11.533 | 11.576 | 11.619 | 11.662 | 11.705 | 11.747 | 11.790 |
| 14 | 11.832 | 11.874 | 11.916 | 11.958 | 12.000 | 12.042 | 12.083 | 12.124 | 12.166 | 12.207 |
| 15 | 12.247 | 12.288 | 12.329 | 12.369 | 12.410 | 12.450 | 12.490 | 12.530 | 12.570 | 12.610 |

|     | 0 | 1 | 2 | 3 | 4 | 5 | 6 | 7 | 8 | 9 |
|-----|-------|-------|-------|-------|-------|-------|-------|-------|-------|-------|
| 16 | 12.649 | 12.689 | 12.728 | 12.767 | 12.806 | 12.845 | 12.884 | 12.923 | 12.961 | 13.000 |
| 17 | 13.038 | 13.077 | 13.115 | 13.153 | 13.191 | 13.229 | 13.267 | 13.304 | 13.342 | 13.379 |
| 18 | 13.416 | 13.454 | 13.491 | 13.528 | 13.565 | 13.601 | 13.638 | 13.675 | 13.711 | 13.748 |
| 19 | 13.784 | 13.820 | 13.856 | 13.892 | 13.928 | 13.964 | 14.000 | 14.036 | 14.071 | 14.107 |
| 20 | 14.142 | 14.177 | 14.213 | 14.248 | 14.283 | 14.318 | 14.353 | 14.387 | 14.422 | 14.457 |
| 21 | 14.491 | 14.526 | 14.560 | 14.595 | 14.629 | 14.663 | 14.697 | 14.731 | 14.765 | 14.799 |
| 22 | 14.832 | 14.866 | 14.900 | 14.933 | 14.967 | 15.000 | 15.033 | 15.067 | 15.100 | 15.133 |
| 23 | 15.166 | 15.199 | 15.232 | 15.264 | 15.297 | 15.330 | 15.362 | 15.395 | 15.427 | 15.460 |
| 24 | 15.492 | 15.524 | 15.556 | 15.588 | 15.621 | 15.652 | 15.684 | 15.716 | 15.748 | 15.780 |
| 25 | 15.811 | 15.843 | 15.875 | 15.906 | 15.937 | 15.969 | 16.000 | 16.031 | 16.062 | 16.093 |
| 26 | 16.125 | 16.155 | 16.186 | 16.217 | 16.248 | 16.279 | 16.310 | 16.340 | 16.371 | 16.401 |
| 27 | 16.432 | 16.462 | 16.492 | 16.523 | 16.553 | 16.583 | 16.613 | 16.643 | 16.673 | 16.703 |
| 28 | 16.733 | 16.763 | 16.793 | 16.823 | 16.852 | 16.882 | 16.912 | 16.941 | 16.971 | 17.000 |
| 29 | 17.029 | 17.059 | 17.088 | 17.117 | 17.146 | 17.176 | 17.205 | 17.234 | 17.263 | 17.292 |
| 30 | 17.321 | 17.349 | 13.378 | 17.407 | 17.436 | 17.464 | 17.493 | 17.521 | 17.550 | 17.578 |
| 31 | 17.607 | 17.635 | 17.664 | 17.692 | 17.720 | 17.748 | 17.776 | 17.804 | 17.833 | 17.861 |
| 32 | 17.889 | 17.916 | 17.944 | 17.972 | 18.000 | 18.028 | 18.055 | 18.083 | 18.111 | 18.138 |
| 33 | 18.166 | 18.193 | 18.221 | 18.248 | 18.276 | 18.303 | 18.330 | 18.358 | 18.385 | 18.412 |
| 34 | 18.439 | 18.466 | 18.493 | 18.520 | 18.547 | 18.574 | 18.601 | 18.628 | 18.655 | 18.682 |
| 35 | 18.708 | 18.735 | 18.762 | 18.788 | 18.815 | 18.841 | 18.868 | 18.894 | 18.921 | 18.947 |
| 36 | 18.974 | 19.000 | 19.026 | 19.053 | 19.079 | 19.105 | 19.131 | 19.157 | 19.183 | 19.209 |
| 37 | 19.235 | 19.261 | 19.287 | 19.313 | 19.339 | 19.365 | 19.391 | 19.416 | 19.442 | 19.468 |
| 38 | 19.494 | 19.519 | 19.545 | 19.570 | 19.596 | 19.621 | 19.647 | 19.672 | 19.698 | 19.723 |
| 39 | 19.748 | 19.774 | 19.799 | 19.824 | 19.849 | 19.875 | 19.900 | 19.925 | 19.950 | 19.975 |
| 40 | 20.000 | 20.025 | 20.050 | 20.075 | 20.100 | 20.125 | 20.149 | 20.174 | 20.199 | 20.224 |
| 41 | 20.248 | 20.273 | 20.298 | 20.322 | 20.347 | 20.372 | 20.396 | 20.421 | 20.445 | 20.469 |
| 42 | 20.494 | 20.518 | 20.543 | 20.567 | 20.591 | 20.616 | 20.640 | 20.664 | 20.688 | 20.712 |
| 43 | 20.736 | 20.761 | 20.785 | 20.809 | 20.833 | 20.857 | 20.881 | 20.905 | 20.928 | 20.952 |
| 44 | 20.976 | 21.000 | 21.024 | 21.048 | 21.071 | 21.095 | 21.119 | 21.142 | 21.166 | 21.190 |
| 45 | 21.213 | 21.237 | 21.260 | 21.284 | 21.307 | 21.331 | 21.354 | 21.378 | 21.401 | 21.424 |
| 46 | 21.448 | 21.471 | 21.494 | 21.517 | 21.541 | 21.564 | 21.587 | 21.610 | 21.633 | 21.656 |
| 47 | 21.679 | 21.703 | 21.726 | 21.749 | 21.772 | 21.794 | 21.817 | 21.840 | 21.863 | 21.886 |
| 48 | 21.909 | 21.932 | 21.955 | 21.977 | 22.000 | 22.023 | 22.045 | 22.068 | 22.091 | 22.113 |
| 49 | 22.136 | 22.159 | 22.181 | 22.204 | 22.226 | 22.249 | 22.271 | 22.294 | 22.316 | 22.338 |
| 50 | 22.361 | 22.383 | 22.405 | 22.428 | 22.450 | 22.472 | 22.494 | 22.517 | 22.539 | 22.561 |
| 51 | 22.583 | 22.605 | 22.627 | 22.650 | 22.672 | 22.694 | 22.716 | 22.738 | 22.760 | 22.782 |
| 52 | 22.804 | 22.825 | 22.847 | 22.869 | 22.891 | 22.913 | 22.935 | 22.956 | 22.978 | 23.000 |
| 53 | 23.022 | 23.043 | 23.065 | 23.087 | 23.108 | 23.130 | 23.152 | 23.173 | 23.195 | 23.216 |
| 54 | 23.238 | 23.259 | 23.281 | 23.302 | 23.324 | 23.345 | 23.367 | 23.388 | 23.409 | 23.431 |
| 55 | 23.452 | 23.473 | 23.495 | 23.516 | 23.537 | 23.558 | 23.580 | 23.601 | 23.622 | 23.643 |
| 56 | 23.664 | 23.685 | 23.707 | 23.728 | 23.749 | 23.770 | 23.791 | 23.812 | 23.833 | 23.854 |
| 57 | 23.875 | 23.896 | 23.917 | 23.937 | 23.958 | 23.979 | 24.000 | 24.021 | 24.042 | 24.062 |
| 58 | 24.083 | 24.104 | 24.125 | 24.145 | 24.166 | 24.187 | 24.207 | 24.228 | 24.249 | 24.269 |
| 59 | 24.290 | 24.310 | 24.331 | 24.352 | 24.372 | 24.393 | 24.413 | 24.434 | 24.454 | 24.474 |
| 60 | 24.495 | 24.515 | 24.536 | 24.556 | 24.576 | 24.597 | 24.617 | 24.637 | 24.658 | 24.678 |
| 61 | 24.698 | 24.718 | 24.739 | 24.759 | 24.779 | 24.799 | 24.819 | 24.839 | 24.860 | 24.880 |
| 62 | 24.890 | 24.920 | 24.940 | 24.960 | 24.980 | 25.000 | 25.020 | 25.040 | 25.060 | 25.080 |
| 63 | 25.100 | 25.120 | 25.140 | 25.160 | 25.180 | 25.200 | 25.219 | 25.239 | 25.259 | 25.278 |
| 64 | 25.298 | 25.318 | 25.338 | 25.357 | 25.377 | 25.397 | 25.417 | 25.436 | 25.456 | 25.475 |
| 65 | 25.495 | 25.515 | 25.534 | 25.554 | 25.573 | 25.593 | 25.613 | 25.632 | 25.652 | 25.671 |
| 66 | 25.690 | 25.710 | 25.729 | 25.749 | 25.768 | 25.788 | 25.807 | 25.826 | 25.846 | 25.865 |
| 67 | 25.884 | 25.904 | 25.923 | 25.942 | 25.962 | 25.981 | 26.000 | 26.019 | 26.038 | 26.058 |

|    | 0 | 1 | 2 | 3 | 4 | 5 | 6 | 7 | 8 | 9 |
|----|---|---|---|---|---|---|---|---|---|---|
| 68 | 26.077 | 26.096 | 26.115 | 26.134 | 26.153 | 26.173 | 26.192 | 26.211 | 26.230 | 26.249 |
| 69 | 26.268 | 26.287 | 26.306 | 26.325 | 26.344 | 26.363 | 26.382 | 26.401 | 26.420 | 26.439 |
| 70 | 26.458 | 26.476 | 26.495 | 26.514 | 26.533 | 26.552 | 26.571 | 26.589 | 26.608 | 26.627 |
| 71 | 26.646 | 26.665 | 26.683 | 26.702 | 26.721 | 26.739 | 26.758 | 26.777 | 26.796 | 26.814 |
| 72 | 26.833 | 26.851 | 26.870 | 26.889 | 26.907 | 26.926 | 26.944 | 26.963 | 26.981 | 27.000 |
| 73 | 27.019 | 27.037 | 27.056 | 27.074 | 27.092 | 27.111 | 27.129 | 27.148 | 27.166 | 27.185 |
| 74 | 27.203 | 27.221 | 27.240 | 27.258 | 27.276 | 27.295 | 27.313 | 27.331 | 27.350 | 27.368 |
| 75 | 27.386 | 27.404 | 27.423 | 27.441 | 27.459 | 27.477 | 27.495 | 27.514 | 27.532 | 27.550 |
| 76 | 27.568 | 27.586 | 27.604 | 27.622 | 27.641 | 27.659 | 27.677 | 27.695 | 27.713 | 27.731 |
| 77 | 27.749 | 27.767 | 27.785 | 27.803 | 27.821 | 27.839 | 27.857 | 27.875 | 27.893 | 27.911 |
| 78 | 27.928 | 27.946 | 27.964 | 27.982 | 28.000 | 28.018 | 28.036 | 28.054 | 28.071 | 28.089 |
| 79 | 28.107 | 28.125 | 28.142 | 28.160 | 28.178 | 28.196 | 28.213 | 28.213 | 28.249 | 28.267 |
| 80 | 28.284 | 28.302 | 28.320 | 28.337 | 28.355 | 28.373 | 28.390 | 28.408 | 28.425 | 28.443 |
| 81 | 28.461 | 28.478 | 28.496 | 28.513 | 28.531 | 28.548 | 28.566 | 28.583 | 28.601 | 28.618 |
| 82 | 28.636 | 28.653 | 28.671 | 28.688 | 28.705 | 28.723 | 28.740 | 28.758 | 28.775 | 28.792 |
| 83 | 28.810 | 28.827 | 28.844 | 28.862 | 28.879 | 28.896 | 28.914 | 28.931 | 28.948 | 28.966 |
| 84 | 28.983 | 29.000 | 29.017 | 29.034 | 29.052 | 29.069 | 29.086 | 29.103 | 29.120 | 29.138 |
| 85 | 29.155 | 29.172 | 29.189 | 29.206 | 29.223 | 29.240 | 29.257 | 29.275 | 29.292 | 29.309 |
| 86 | 29.326 | 29.343 | 29.360 | 29.377 | 29.394 | 29.411 | 29.428 | 29.445 | 29.462 | 29.479 |
| 87 | 29.496 | 29.513 | 29.530 | 29.547 | 29.563 | 29.580 | 29.597 | 29.614 | 29.631 | 29.648 |
| 88 | 29.665 | 29.682 | 29.698 | 29.715 | 29.732 | 29.749 | 29.766 | 29.783 | 29.799 | 29.816 |
| 89 | 29.833 | 29.850 | 29.866 | 29.883 | 29.900 | 29.917 | 29.933 | 29.950 | 29.967 | 29.983 |
| 90 | 30.000 | 30.017 | 30.033 | 30.050 | 30.067 | 30.083 | 30.100 | 30.116 | 30.133 | 30.150 |
| 91 | 30.166 | 30.183 | 30.199 | 30.216 | 30.232 | 30.249 | 30.265 | 30.282 | 30.299 | 30.315 |
| 92 | 30.332 | 30.348 | 30.364 | 30.381 | 30.397 | 30.414 | 30.430 | 30.447 | 30.463 | 30.480 |
| 93 | 30.496 | 30.512 | 30.529 | 30.545 | 30.561 | 30.578 | 30.594 | 30.610 | 30.627 | 30.643 |
| 94 | 30.659 | 30.676 | 30.692 | 30.708 | 30.725 | 30.741 | 30.757 | 30.773 | 30.790 | 30.806 |
| 95 | 30.822 | 30.838 | 30.855 | 30.871 | 30.887 | 30.903 | 30.919 | 30.935 | 30.952 | 30.968 |
| 96 | 30.984 | 31.000 | 31.016 | 31.032 | 31.048 | 31.064 | 31.081 | 31.097 | 31.113 | 31.129 |
| 97 | 31.145 | 31.161 | 31.177 | 31.193 | 31.209 | 31.225 | 31.241 | 31.257 | 31.273 | 31.289 |
| 98 | 31.305 | 31.321 | 31.337 | 31.353 | 31.369 | 31.385 | 31.401 | 31.417 | 31.432 | 31.448 |
| 99 | 31.464 | 31.480 | 31.496 | 31.512 | 31.528 | 31.544 | 31.560 | 31.575 | 31.591 | 31.607 |

**Table II**
**Area under the Normal Curve from 0 to z.**

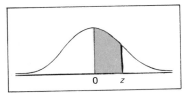

| z | .0 | .1 | .2 | .3 | .4 | .5 | .6 | .7 | .8 | .9 |
|---|----|----|----|----|----|----|----|----|----|----|
| 0 | .000 | .040 | .080 | .118 | .155 | .192 | .226 | .258 | .288 | .316 |
| 1 | .341 | .364 | .385 | .403 | .419 | .433 | .445 | .455 | .464 | .471 |
| 2 | .477 | .482 | .486 | .489 | .492 | .494 | .495 | .497 | .497 | .498 |
| 3 | .499 | .499 | .499 | .500 | .500 | .500 | .500 | .500 | .500 | .500 |

Table III
Area under the
Normal Curve
beyond z.

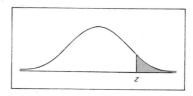

| z | .0 | .1 | .2 | .3 | .4 | .5 | .6 | .7 | .8 | .9 |
|---|----|----|----|----|----|----|----|----|----|----|
| 0 | .500 | .460 | .421 | .382 | .345 | .309 | .274 | .242 | .212 | .184 |
| 1 | .159 | .136 | .115 | .097 | .081 | .067 | .055 | .045 | .036 | .029 |
| 2 | .023 | .018 | .014 | .011 | .008 | .006 | .005 | .004 | .003 | .002 |
| 3 | .001 | .001 | .001 | .001 | .000 | .000 | .000 | .000 | .000 | .000 |

Table IV
Poisson Probabilities
$m^k/(e^m P_k^k)$
Part A:
$m \le 4.0$

| m\k | 0 | 1 | 2 | 3 | 4 | 5 | 6 | 7 | 8 | 9 | 10 | 11 | 12 |
|-----|---|---|---|---|---|---|---|---|---|---|----|----|----|
| .1 | .905 | .091 | .005 | .000 | .000 | .000 | .000 | .000 | .000 | .000 | .000 | .000 | .000 |
| .2 | .819 | .164 | .016 | .001 | .000 | .000 | .000 | .000 | .000 | .000 | .000 | .000 | .000 |
| .3 | .741 | .222 | .033 | .003 | .000 | .000 | .000 | .000 | .000 | .000 | .000 | .000 | .000 |
| .4 | .670 | .268 | .054 | .007 | .001 | .000 | .000 | .000 | .000 | .000 | .000 | .000 | .000 |
| .5 | .607 | .303 | .076 | .013 | .002 | .000 | .000 | .000 | .000 | .000 | .000 | .000 | .000 |
| 1.0 | .368 | .368 | .184 | .061 | .015 | .003 | .001 | .000 | .000 | .000 | .000 | .000 | .000 |
| 1.5 | .223 | .335 | .251 | .126 | .047 | .014 | .004 | .001 | .000 | .000 | .000 | .000 | .000 |
| 2.0 | .135 | .271 | .271 | .180 | .090 | .036 | .012 | .003 | .001 | .000 | .000 | .000 | .000 |
| 3.0 | .050 | .149 | .224 | .224 | .168 | .101 | .050 | .022 | .008 | .003 | .001 | .000 | .000 |
| 4.0 | .018 | .073 | .147 | .195 | .195 | .156 | .104 | .060 | .030 | .013 | .005 | .002 | .001 |

Part B:
$m \ge 5.0$;
$0 \le k \le 12$

| m\k | 0 | 1 | 2 | 3 | 4 | 5 | 6 | 7 | 8 | 9 | 10 | 11 | 12 |
|-----|---|---|---|---|---|---|---|---|---|---|----|----|----|
| 5.0 | .007 | .034 | .084 | .140 | .176 | .176 | .146 | .104 | .065 | .036 | .018 | .008 | .003 |
| 6.0 | .003 | .015 | .045 | .089 | .134 | .161 | .161 | .138 | .103 | .069 | .041 | .023 | .011 |
| 7.0 | .001 | .006 | .022 | .052 | .091 | .128 | .149 | .149 | .130 | .101 | .071 | .045 | .026 |
| 8.0 | .000 | .003 | .011 | .029 | .057 | .092 | .122 | .140 | .140 | .124 | .099 | .072 | .048 |
| 9.0 | .000 | .001 | .005 | .015 | .034 | .061 | .091 | .117 | .132 | .132 | .119 | .097 | .073 |
| 10.0 | .000 | .001 | .002 | .008 | .019 | .038 | .063 | .090 | .113 | .125 | .125 | .114 | .095 |

Part C:
$m \ge 5.0$;
$13 \le k \le 22$

| m\k | 13 | 14 | 15 | 16 | 17 | 18 | 19 | 20 | 21 | 22 |
|-----|----|----|----|----|----|----|----|----|----|----|
| 5.0 | .001 | .001 | .000 | .000 | .000 | .000 | .000 | .000 | .000 | .000 |
| 6.0 | .005 | .002 | .001 | .000 | .000 | .000 | .000 | .000 | .000 | .000 |
| 7.0 | .014 | .007 | .003 | .001 | .001 | .000 | .000 | .000 | .000 | .000 |
| 8.0 | .030 | .017 | .009 | .005 | .002 | .001 | .000 | .000 | .000 | .000 |
| 9.0 | .050 | .032 | .019 | .011 | .006 | .003 | .001 | .001 | .000 | .000 |
| 10.0 | .073 | .052 | .035 | .022 | .013 | .007 | .004 | .002 | .001 | .000 |

# Appendix C
# Answers to
# Odd-numbered and
# Starred Exercises,
# with Selected
# Comments and Solutions

Section 1.1
page 6

1. (a) $\frac{1}{2}$  (b) $\frac{1}{2}$ ("Tails down" is the same as "heads up".)  (c) 1 (This event is certain.)  (d) $\frac{1}{2}$ ("Heads down and tails up" is just a redundant way to say "tails up.")  (e) $\frac{1}{2}$ (another redundancy)  (f) 0 (This event is impossible.)

3. (a) $\frac{1}{6}$  (b) $\frac{2}{6} = \frac{1}{3}$  (c) $\frac{3}{6} = \frac{1}{2}$  (d) $\frac{5}{6}$

5. (a) $65 \cdot 20 + 115 \cdot 40 = 5900$ boxes  (b) $65 \cdot 20 \cdot 12 + 115 \cdot 40 \cdot 8 = 52,400$ buns.

7. (a) $26 \cdot 26 = 676$  (b) $26 \cdot 25 = 650$

   (c) If the letters can be the same, there are $24 \cdot 24 = 576$ different plates. If the letters must be different, there are $24 \cdot 23 = 552$ different plates.

   (d) There are exactly 2 different license plates with the letters O and I: OI and IO. If O and I cannot occur in the same plate, these 2 must be subtracted from the previous counts. Thus, there are 674 plates if the letters may be the same and 648 if the letters must be different.

   (e) If the letters may be the same, there are $2 \cdot 2 = 4$, namely OO, OI, IO, and II. If the letters must be different, there are $2 \cdot 1 = 2$, namely OI and IO.

9. $52 \cdot 52 \cdot 52 \cdot 52 = 7,311,616$  11. $\frac{5,350}{21,000,000} = \frac{107}{420,000} \doteq 0.00025$.

13. No. There are at most $9 \cdot 5 = 45$ departments.

Section 1.2
page 14

1. $\{ \heartsuit, \diamondsuit, \clubsuit, \spadesuit \}$

3. (a) {both heads, both tails, one heads and one tails} (We don't distinguish the coins.)  (b) {(nickel is heads, dime is heads), (nickel heads, dime tails), (NT, DH), (NT, DT)}

5. Surely $S = \{10, 11, 12, \ldots, 400\}$ is *a* sample space. In order to write *the* sample space, we would need to know what is meant by the term "man" and then know the weights of all of them.

7. $S = \{0, 10, 20, 30, 40, 50, 60, 70, 80, 90, 100, e\}$

9. The red die comes up 4.

11. The total number of spots up is 7.

13. $S = \{A \text{ and } B, A \text{ and } C, B \text{ and } C, A \text{ only}, B \text{ only}, C \text{ only}, \text{ no one}\}$
15. Same as 13.
17. Use ordered pairs (sales, personnel) and let N stand for "none of Alan, Betty, Carl."
$S = \{(A, B), (C, B), (N, B), (B, A), (B, C), (B, N)\}$
19. $S = \{a, b, x\}$. Events are: $\varnothing$, $\{a\}$, $\{b\}$, $\{x\}$, $\{a, b\}$, $\{a, x\}$, $\{b, x\}$, $S$.
21. (a) yes   (b) no   (c) no   (d) yes
22. (a) yes   (b) no   (c) no
23. (a) $\{2, 3, 5, 6, 7, 9, 10, 11\}$   (b) $\{3, 6, 9, 12\}$
    (c) $\{2, 3, 4, 5, 6, 7, 8, 10, 11\}$   (d) $\{9, 12\}$
25. If there is an even number of $\sim$s, the event is A; otherwise, the event is $\sim$A
27. (a) $(A \cap B) \cup (A \cap C)$   (b) $(A \cup B) \cap (A \cup C)$   (c) The elements of $A \cap (B \cup C)$ are those in A that are in B or C, that is, those that are in both A and B together with those that are in both A and C. Hence (a). The elements of $A \cup (B \cap C)$ are those that are in A or in both B and C, that is, those that are in A or B and also in A or C. Hence (b).
29. (a) w is $\sim(A \cup B)$, x is $A \cap \sim B$, y is $B \cap \sim A$, z is $A \cap B$   (b) A is x with z, B is y with z, $A \cup B$ is x with y with z   (c) Let $\bar{w}, \bar{x}, \bar{y}, \bar{z}$ be, respectively, the number of elements in w, x, y, z. We are told $\bar{w} + \bar{x} + \bar{y} + \bar{z} = 30$, $\bar{x} = \bar{y} = 7$, $\bar{w} = 4$. Then $\bar{z} = 12$.   (d) Now let $\bar{w}, \bar{x}, \bar{y}, \bar{z}$ be, respectively, the percentage of elements of S in w, x, y, z. Then $\bar{y} = 0.1$; that is, y has 10%.   (e) $\bar{x} = 0\%$; so A is a subset of B.
31. 16 regions. This is Venn's solution. (See *Symbolic Logic* by Lewis Carroll [New York: Dover, 1958], p. 175.) There are other solutions (all with 16 regions).

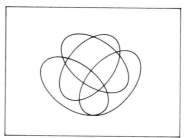

33. Let A denote the set of mature trees, B the set of healthy trees, and C the set of pine trees. The Venn diagram (Figure 2, page 17) with known percentages is:

$\sim A \cap \sim B \cap \sim C$:   $s = 35$
$A \cap \sim B \cap C$:   $z = 20$
$A \cap \sim B \cap \sim C$:   $w = 10$
$A \cap B \cap \sim C$:   $x = 10$
$A \cap B \cap C$:   $y = 10$
$\sim A \cap \sim B \cap C$:   $v = 5$
$\sim A \cap B \cap \sim C$:   $u = 5$
_____
95

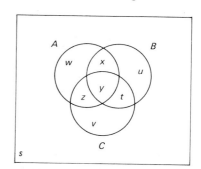

Hence $y = 5$; that is, 5% or 500 of the trees are healthy, immature pines.
35. 8, 16, 32, $2^n$

1. Not a distribution, since $P(a) + P(b) + P(c) + P(d) \neq 1$.
3. Not a distribution, since $P(d) < 0$.     5. $P(V) = 0$.
7. Mark each face with a different letter, chosen from the first six of the alphabet.
9. Mark two faces 1, two faces 2, and two faces 3.
11. Mark four faces u, one face v, and one face w.
13. $0.161 + 0.170 + 0.165 + 0.163 + P(5) + P(6) = 1$,   $0.659 + P(5) + P(6) = 1$,   $P(5) + P(6) = 0.341$, so $P(5) = P(6) = 0.1705$.
15. $E = \emptyset$ is the only event disjoint from S.
17. $P(A \cap B) = 0.4359 + 0.4359 - 0.7727 = 0.0991$.
19. $P(A \cap B) = 0$, $P(A \cup B) = \frac{8}{10} = \frac{4}{5}$.
21. Let B denote the set of customers who buy burgers and F the set of customers who buy fries. $P(F) = 1 - P(\sim F) = 1 - 0.3 = 0.7$. P(burger or fries) $= P(B \cup F) = P(B) + P(F) - P(B \cap F) = 0.65 + 0.7 - 0.59 = 0.76$, so 760,000 buy a burger or fries (or both). Since $P(B \cap F) = 0.59$, 590,000 buy a burger and fries; hence $760,000 - 590,000 = 170,000$ buy a burger or fries but not both.
22. (a) anything in $\sim A \cap B$ is in $\sim A$ and hence not in A.
    (b) everything in A is in B; everything in B that is not in A is in $\sim A \cap B$.
    (c) $P(A) \leq P(A) + P(\sim A \cap B) = P(A \cup (\sim A \cap B)) = P(B)$.
    (d) A is a subset of S so if we let $B = S$ we obtain $P(A) \leq P(S) = 1$.
23. (a) $P(A \cap B) = \frac{1}{3} + \frac{1}{2} - \frac{2}{3} = \frac{1}{6}$,   $P(\sim A) = 1 - \frac{1}{3} = \frac{2}{3}$,   $P(\sim B) = 1 - \frac{1}{2} = \frac{1}{2}$,   $P(\sim(A \cup B)) = 1 - \frac{2}{3} = \frac{1}{3}$,   $P(\sim(A \cap B)) = 1 - \frac{1}{6} = \frac{5}{6}$. (b) $P(\sim A \cup \sim B) + P(\sim A \cap \sim B) = P(\sim(A \cap B)) + P(\sim(A \cup B)) = \frac{5}{6} + \frac{1}{3} = \frac{7}{6}$   and   $P(\sim A) + P(\sim B) = \frac{2}{3} + \frac{1}{2} = \frac{7}{6}$.

1. 0.112     3. 0.012     5. 0.9     7. 0.048     9. 0.166
11. (a) $P(S) = \overbrace{p + p + \ldots + p} = np$. (b) $P(S) = np$, so $np = 1$, $p = 1/n$.
$\qquad\qquad\quad$ np's
13. (a) $26 \cdot 26 \cdot 26 = 17{,}576$. (b) $P_3^{26} = 15{,}600$. (c) $21 \cdot 21 \cdot 21 = 9{,}261$. (d) $5 \cdot 5 \cdot 5 = 125$.
    (e) $P_3^{24} = 12{,}144$. (f) $26 \cdot 26 \cdot 26 - 21 \cdot 21 \cdot 21 = 8{,}315$. (g) $21 \cdot 21 \cdot 21 + 3(5 \cdot 21 \cdot 21) = 15{,}876$. (h) $3(26 \cdot 25) = 1{,}950$. (i) $C_3^{26} = 2{,}600$. (Choose the letters, then alphabetize them.) (j) $C_3^{26} + 2C_2^{26} + C_1^{26} = 3{,}276$.
15. (a) $1 - \frac{365}{365} \cdot \frac{364}{365} \cdot \frac{363}{365} \cdot \frac{362}{365} \cdot \frac{361}{365} \doteq 0.027$.
    (b) 23, if a "good bet" means probability greater than $\frac{1}{2}$.
    (c) $1 - \frac{365 \cdot 364 \ldots 330}{365 \cdot 365 \ldots 365} \doteq 0.832$
    (d) 70. $1 - \frac{365 \cdot 364 \ldots 296}{365 \cdot 365 \ldots 365} \doteq 0.9992$; 69 won't do.
17. (a) 4,096, if any choice can be made. 60 if the meal is one salad, one potato, one drink. (b) 16.

1. $\frac{8}{26}$     3. $\frac{7}{13}$     5. 0     7. 1     9. $\frac{1}{9}$     11. $\frac{4}{15}$
13. The answer cannot be determined from information given.
15. (a) 0  (b) 1  (c) 1
17. (a) dependent  (b) dependent  (c) dependent  (d) dependent
    (e) dependent
19. No
20. (a) $B = (A \cap B) \cup (\sim A \cap B)$, and $A \cap B$ and $\sim A \cap B$ are disjoint. Hence $P(B) = P(A \cap B) + P(\sim A \cap B)$, so $P(\sim A \cap B) = P(B) - P(A \cap B) = P(B) - P(A)P(B) = (1 - P(A))P(B) = P(\sim A)P(B)$. Thus, $\sim A$ and B are independent.
    (b) By (a) $\sim A$ and B are independent. Then by (a) $\sim A$ and $\sim B$ are independent.
21. $P(\sim A \cap \sim B) = \frac{6}{35}$, $P(A \cap \sim B) = \frac{9}{35}$, $P(\sim A \cap B) = \frac{8}{35}$.
23. 0.58     25. 0.70

1. (a) 10,000,000,000  (b) 1,800,000,000  (c) 1,296,000,000
2. {(face, H), (face, T), (not, 1), (not, 2), (not, 3), (not, 4), (not, 5), (not, 6)}
3. {(face, H), (not, 2), (not, 4), (not, 6)}
4. (a) $A \cup \sim B$  (b) $\sim(A \cap B)$  (c) $\sim\sim\sim A = \sim A$
5. (a) 1/12  (b) 1/4
6. $P(e) = \frac{1}{20}$, $P(A) = \frac{37}{60}$, $P(\sim A) = \frac{23}{60}$.  7. $\frac{3}{4}$
8. $P(A \cup B) = P(A) + P(B) - P(A)P(B)$, $\frac{3}{4} = \frac{1}{3} + P(B) - \frac{1}{3}P(B)$, $P(B) = \frac{5}{8}$.
9. $\frac{5}{13}$
10. {1, 2, 3} and {1, 3, 4, 5}, for instance.

1. $\frac{1}{2}P_{11}^{11} = 19,958,400$; there are two t's  3. 96  5. $P_4^4 P_3^3 P_6^6 P_8^8 = 4,180,377,600$
7. (a) {1, 2, 6}, {1, 3, 4}, {2, 3, 5}, {4, 5, 6}  (b) No, it's impossible.
9. Write the fractions with a common denominator (in the example the denominator is 2,520 and the fractions are $\frac{945}{2,540}$; $\frac{720}{2,540}$; $\frac{504}{2,540}$; $\frac{280}{2,540}$). Use a different-colored ball for each fraction and put the numerator number of balls into the urn.
11. (a) $P(A \cup B \cup C) = P(A) + P(B \cup C) - P((A \cap B) \cup (A \cap C)) = P(A) + P(B) + P(C) - P(B \cap C) - [P(A \cap B) + P(A \cap C) - P(A \cap B \cap C)] = P(A) + P(B) + P(C) - P(A \cap B) - P(A \cap C) - P(B \cap C) + P(A \cap B \cap C)$
    (b) $P(A \cup B \cup C \cup D) = P(A) + P(B) + P(C) + P(D) - P(A \cap B) - P(A \cap C) - P(A \cap D) - P(B \cap C) - P(B \cap D) - P(A \cap D) + P(A \cap B \cap C) + P(A \cap B \cap D) + P(A \cap C \cap D) + P(B \cap C \cap D) - P(A \cap B \cap C \cap D)$
    (c) $P(A_1 \cup A_2 \cup \ldots \cup A_n) = $ the sum of P of the intersection of each odd number of events minus the sum of P of the intersection of each even number of events.
    (d) $P(A_1 \cap A_2 \cap \ldots \cap A_n) = $ the sum of P of the union of each odd number of events minus the sum of the union of each even number of events.
13. $P(A|B \cap C)P(B|C)P(C) = \dfrac{P(A \cap B \cap C)}{P(B \cap C)} \dfrac{P(B \cap C)}{P(C)} P(C) = P(A \cap B \cap C)$.
15. $\frac{3}{4}$   17. $\frac{1}{2}$   19. (a) $2^7$  (b) 99  (c) 61
20. (c) $\frac{1}{2}P_n^n$ clasp necklaces. $\frac{1}{2}P_{n-1}^{n-1}$ nonclasp necklaces.
21. Imagine the two As are different. Then the number of different plates in $P_4^4 = 4 \cdot 3 \cdot 2 \cdot 1 = 24$. But the As are not different; if the As in a given plate were switched, we would have the same plate. Thus, we have "counted" each plate twice, and there are actually $\frac{24}{2} = 12$ plates.
22. If all the letters were different there would be $P_{11}^{11}$ rearrangements. In a given rearrangement, the 4 Ss could be switched in any of $P_4^4$ ways, and for each arrangement, the 4 Is could be switched in $P_4^4$ ways and the 2 Ps could be switched in $P_2^2$ ways without changing the rearrangement. Thus, each rearrangement was "counted" $P_4^4 \cdot P_4^4 \cdot P_2^2$ times, and the number of different rearrangements is

$$\frac{P_{11}^{11}}{P_4^4 \cdot P_4^4 \cdot P_2^2} = \frac{11 \cdot 10 \cdot \overset{3}{\cancel{9}} \cdot \cancel{8} \cdot 7 \cdot \cancel{6} \cdot 5 \cdot \cancel{4} \cdot 3 \cdot \cancel{2} \cdot 1}{\cancel{4} \cdot \cancel{3} \cdot \cancel{2} \cdot 1 \cdot \cancel{4} \cdot \cancel{3} \cdot \cancel{2} \cdot 1 \cdot \cancel{2} \cdot 1} = 11 \cdot 10 \cdot 3 \cdot 7 \cdot 5 \cdot 3 = 34,650$$

23. (a) 2  (b) 3  (c) 6  (d) 12  (e) 1,680  (f) 3,024
24. Let A be the event "prefers AC parkas" and let B be the event "prefers AC sleeping bags." The survey has measured P(A) as 0.62, P(B) as 0.84, and $P(A \cap B)$ as 0.46, all within errors of at most 0.03. If the errors have indeed been this carefully controlled, then P(A) is between 0.59 and 0.65, P(B) is between 0.81 and 0.87, and $P(A \cap B)$ is

between 0.43 and 0.49. It follows that P(A)P(B) is between $(0.59)(0.81) = 0.4779$ and $(0.65)(0.87) = 0.5655$. Thus, it could be that A and B are independent, since the true value of $P(A \cap B)$ could equal the true value of P(A)P(B) without exceeding the 0.03 maximum error. (For example, we could have $P(A \cap B) = P(A)P(B) = 0.4800$.)

25. 17,081
27. (a) 256  (b)17,208  (c) there are $3 \cdot 512 \cdot 23 = 35,328$ meals. It will take nearly 97 years to eat every possible meal.
29. (a) $A \cup B = A \cap B = A$  (b) $A = B$.

1. (a)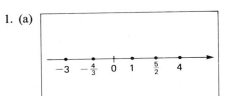

1. (b)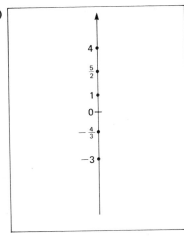

3. $(-2,3), (3,3), (3,8), (-2,8)$
4. $(-45\sqrt{2}, 45\sqrt{2})$ or $(45\sqrt{2}, -45\sqrt{2})$, depending on whether second base is on the positive or the negative 2-axis. (This problem requires use of the Pythagorean theorem.)

5.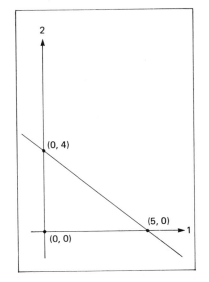

7.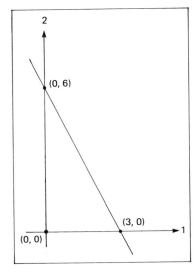

9.

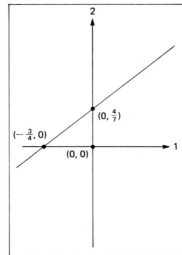

11.

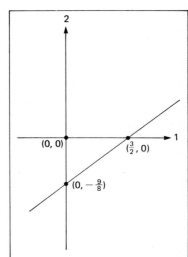

13.

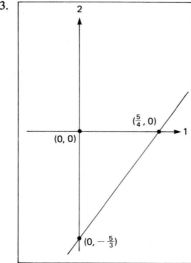

15.

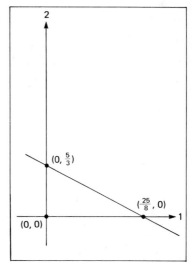

17.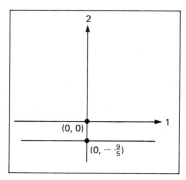

19.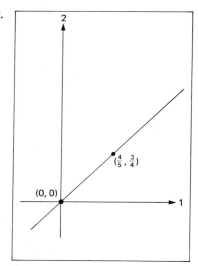

21. The graph is the 1-axis.
23. (a) $2\frac{3}{4}$ inches  (b) $1\frac{3}{4}$ inches
    (c) For $x_1 = 80$, $x_2 = .5$. However, such a value for $x_1$ is not included in the graph and it is not proper to so extrapolate. In fact, essentially no insulation is required for sleeping at $80°F$, so that the answer $x_2 = .5$ is incorrect.
    (d) Similarly, for $x_1 = -80$, the formula predicts that $x_2 = 4\frac{1}{2}$. However, again we have no reason to suppose that this answer is correct.
25. There are infinitely many correct answers to this problem. Here are two:
    (i) $(0, 30)$, $(40, 0)$, $(\frac{120}{7}, \frac{120}{7})$, $(2, \frac{57}{2})$
    (ii) $(\frac{116}{3}, 1)$, $(\frac{112}{3}, 2)$, $(36, 3)$, $(\frac{104}{3}, 4)$
26. (a) $(x_1, -x_2)$  (b) $(-x_1, x_2)$  (c) $(-x_1, -x_2)$
    (d) same as (c)  (e) $(x_2, x_1)$
27. Sale of $x_1$ hamburgers gives a profit of $15x_1$ cents $= 0.15x_1$ dollars, hence a net profit of $0.15x_1 - 105$ dollars. Thus, the relation is $x_2 = 0.15x_1 - 105$, which we rewrite as $0.15x_1 - x_2 = 105$. Using the flow chart on page 60, we see that the graph of this linear equation is the line through the points $(\frac{105}{0.15}, 0)$ and $(0, \frac{105}{-1})$, that is, the points $(700, 0)$ and $(0, -105)$. It will be convenient to mark off the 1-axis and 2-axis in units of 100. This graph is mathematically correct but quite unsatisfactory in a sales

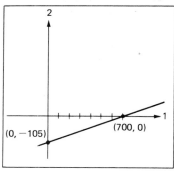

presentation for the following reasons: (1) the negative values of $x_1$ are meaningless, (2) the terms $x_1$, $x_2$, 1-axis, 2-axis, will not be understood by the managers, (3) the negative values of $x_2$ may not be understood by the managers, (4) the graph rises too slowly to excite the managers about selling burgers. We therefore make the following changes in the presentation, resulting in a new presentation: (1) eliminate that part of the graph to the left of the 2-axis; (2) call the axes "burgers sold" and "profit"; (3) call the negative 2-axis "loss"; (4) mark the 1-axis in units of 1,000.

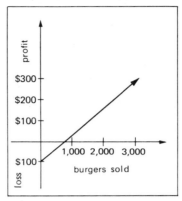

29. $(0, 3)$      31. $(-3, -2)$

32. If we allow both a and b to be zero in the general equation for a line, we obtain the equation

$$0x_1 + 0x_2 = b$$

If b is not zero, then this equation has no solution since zero times any number is zero. In this case the graph is not a line. It contains no points; that is, it is empty. If b is zero, then every pair of numbers is a solution so the graph is the entire plane, which is also not a line.

Section 2.2
page 75

1. $\begin{bmatrix} 1 & 2 & 3 \\ 3 & 8 & 13 \end{bmatrix} \begin{matrix} \\ R_2-3R_1 \end{matrix} \begin{bmatrix} 1 & 2 & 3 \\ 0 & 2 & 4 \end{bmatrix} \begin{matrix} R_1-R_2 \\ \end{matrix} \begin{bmatrix} 1 & 0 & -1 \\ 0 & 2 & 4 \end{bmatrix} \frac{1}{2}R_2 \begin{bmatrix} 1 & 0 & -1 \\ 0 & 1 & 2 \end{bmatrix}$

Answer: $(-1, 2)$. Check: $\begin{bmatrix} -1+ & 4= & 3 \\ -3+ & 16= & 13 \end{bmatrix} \begin{matrix} \checkmark \\ \checkmark \end{matrix}$

3. $\begin{bmatrix} 0 & 3 & 16 \\ 1 & -6 & 0 \end{bmatrix} \begin{matrix} R_2 \\ R_1 \end{matrix} \begin{bmatrix} 1 & -6 & 0 \\ 0 & 3 & 16 \end{bmatrix} \begin{matrix} R_1+2R_2 \\ \end{matrix} \begin{bmatrix} 1 & 0 & 32 \\ 0 & 3 & 16 \end{bmatrix} \frac{1}{3}R_2 \begin{bmatrix} 1 & 0 & 32 \\ 0 & 1 & \frac{16}{3} \end{bmatrix}$

Answer: $(32, \frac{16}{3})$. Check: $\begin{bmatrix} 0+16=16 \\ 32-32= 0 \end{bmatrix} \begin{matrix} \checkmark \\ \checkmark \end{matrix}$

5. $\begin{bmatrix} 4 & -1 & 2 \\ -20 & 5 & -1 \end{bmatrix} \begin{matrix} \\ R_2+5R_1 \end{matrix} \begin{bmatrix} 4 & -1 & 2 \\ 0 & 0 & 9 \end{bmatrix} \frac{1}{4}R_1 \begin{bmatrix} 1 & -\frac{1}{4} & \frac{1}{2} \\ 0 & 0 & 9 \end{bmatrix}$

Answer: no solution; the lines are parallel.

7. $\begin{bmatrix} -2 & 1 & 3 \\ 4 & -2 & -6 \end{bmatrix} \begin{matrix} \\ R_2+2R_1 \end{matrix} \begin{bmatrix} -2 & 1 & 3 \\ 0 & 0 & 0 \end{bmatrix} -\frac{1}{2}R_1 \begin{bmatrix} 1 & -\frac{1}{2} & -\frac{3}{2} \\ 0 & 0 & 0 \end{bmatrix}$

Answer: $(-\frac{3}{2}+\frac{1}{2}x_2, x_2)$ where $x_2$ may be any number. The lines are identical.

Check: $\begin{bmatrix} -2\left(-\frac{3}{2}+\frac{1}{2}x_2\right)+ x_2= 3- x_2+ x_2= 3 \\ 4\left(-\frac{3}{2}+\frac{1}{2}x_2\right)-2x_2= -6+2x_2-2x_2= -6 \end{bmatrix} \begin{matrix} \checkmark \\ \checkmark \end{matrix}$

9. $(\frac{22}{5}, \frac{48}{5})$     11. $(-\frac{6}{7}, -\frac{1}{7})$     13. There is no solution; the lines are parallel.

15. $(\frac{27}{50}, -\frac{32}{25})$

17. $(0, x_2)$ where $x_2$ may be any number. The lines are identical     19. $(\frac{3}{2}, \frac{3}{2})$

21. The "crossover point" was found by solving $\begin{bmatrix} 0.15x_1 - x_2 = 105 \\ x_1 - 3x_2 = 1500 \end{bmatrix}$, where the first

equation came from the solution of Exercise 27, Section 2.1. The summary presentation to the 894 managers is: "As long as you sell at least 2,155 burgers a day you
will be beating the average Midwestern store, even if they sell as many burgers as
you do."

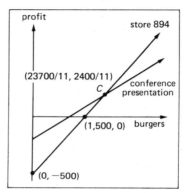

22. (a) Operate Springfield for one day and Waterbury for 2 days.
    (b) Do not operate Springfield at all and operate Waterbury for 3 days.
    (c) Operate Springfield for $\frac{2}{3}$ of one day and Waterbury for 4 days.
    (d) Impossible, since the value for $x_1$ in the solution of the system is negative.

23.

| Dearborn | 4 | 3 | 2 | 1 | 0 |
|----------|---|---|---|---|---|
| Oshkosh | 0 | 2 | 4 | 6 | 8 |

| Oshkosh | 8 | 7 | 6 | 5 | 4 | 3 | 2 | 1 | 0 |
|---------|---|-----|---|-----|---|-----|---|-----|---|
| Dearborn | 0 | 0.5 | 1 | 1.5 | 2 | 2.5 | 3 | 3.5 | 4 |

24. Let $x_1, x_2, x_3$, respectively, be the number of packets of types 1, 2, and 3 used to
    make an expedition packet. Then

$$\begin{bmatrix} 3x_1 + 4x_2 + 2x_3 = 86 \\ 2x_1 + x_2 + 5x_3 = 88 \\ 3x_1 + 3x_2 + 3x_3 = 90 \end{bmatrix}$$

25. Let $x_1, x_2, x_3, x_4$, be, respectively, the number of hamburgers, superburgers, fishfeasts,
    and root beers in an order. We are asked to find all solutions (at least all meaningful
    solutions) of the system

$$\begin{bmatrix} 30x_1 + 40x_2 + 100x_3 + 25x_4 = 350 \\ 40x_1 + 60x_2 + 140x_3 + 30x_4 = 480 \\ 50x_1 + 70x_2 + 170x_3 + 35x_4 = 570 \end{bmatrix}$$

1. $x_1 = x_2 = x_3 = 1$     3. $x_1 = -1, x_2 = 2, x_3 = -2$     5. $(132, 460, -716)$, that is, $x_1 = 132$, $x_2 = 460$, $x_3 = -716$.

7. $(-1, 3, 1)$     9. $x_1 = x_2 = x_3 = 0$     11. $x_1 = 1$, $x_2 = 2$, $x_3 = 3$

13. $(-5, 0, 15)$     15. $(-14, -7, 43)$     17. $x_1 = \frac{52}{58}$, $x_2 = \frac{177}{58}$, $x_3 = -\frac{16}{58}$

19. $x_1 = \frac{604}{477}$, $x_2 = \frac{110}{477}$, $x_3 = \frac{546}{477}$

21. $(x_3, x_3, x_3)$; that is, $x_1 = x_3$, $x_2 = x_3$, and $x_3$ is free. For example, $(1, 1, 1)$, $(2, 2, 2)$, $(-\frac{1}{3}, -\frac{1}{3}, -\frac{1}{3})$ are solutions.

23. $(\frac{53}{16}, \frac{41}{16}, \frac{3}{16})$

25. $x_1 = (91 - 25x_4)/31$, $x_2 = (22 - 35x_4)/31$, $x_3 = (39 + 7x_4)/31$, $x_4$ is free.

27. $(5, -3, 4, 5, 4)$

29. (a) Run Springfield 6 hours, 40 minutes; close Danbury; run Mystic 5 hours.
    (b) Close Springfield; run Danbury and Mystic 5 hours each.

31. No. The system has no solution.

32. The mistake occurs in the second matrix, which should read

$$\begin{bmatrix} 1 & \frac{4}{3} & 0 & -\frac{1}{3} \\ 0 & 2 & 3 & 1 \\ 0 & \frac{8}{3} & 4 & \frac{4}{3} \end{bmatrix} \begin{matrix} R_1 - \frac{2}{3}R_2 \\ \\ R_3 - \frac{4}{3}R_2 \end{matrix} \begin{bmatrix} 1 & 0 & -2 & -1 \\ 0 & 2 & 3 & 1 \\ 0 & 0 & 0 & 0 \end{bmatrix}$$

The correct answer is $x_1 = 2x_3 - 1$, $x_2 = \frac{1}{2}(1 - 3x_3)$. I found the particular solution corresponding to $x_3 = \frac{2}{3}$. While such mistakes are possible, they are rare. Unfortunately, these kinds of errors are impossible to detect since the answer one obtains does, in fact, check. I was lucky enough to have given this problem on an exam so the students caught the error.

33. 6 odes, 2 cantos, 5 epics, 13 poems, 4 pages.

35. 8 bedrooms, 7 game rooms, 5 reading rooms, 7 parlors.

37. 6 Lite, 8 Jiffy, 10 He. I'll make $4 \cdot 2 + 2 \cdot 3 = \$14$.

39. None

40. Let $x_1 = $ Lefty's take, $x_2 = $ Spike's take, $x_3 = $ Jimmy's take, and $a = $ the total stolen. Then $x_1 + x_2 + x_3 = a$, $x_3 = 2(x_1 + x_2)$, and $x_1 = x_3 - x_2 - 10{,}000$. The system to solve is

$$\begin{bmatrix} x_1 + x_2 + x_3 = & a \\ 2x_1 + 2x_2 - x_3 = & 0 \\ -x_1 - x_2 + x_3 = & 10{,}000 \end{bmatrix}$$

Trying to solve this, we obtain

$$\begin{bmatrix} 1 & 1 & 1 & a \\ 2 & 2 & -1 & 0 \\ -1 & -1 & 1 & 10{,}000 \end{bmatrix} \begin{bmatrix} 1 & 1 & 1 & a \\ 0 & 0 & -3 & -2a \\ 0 & 0 & 2 & 10{,}000 + a \end{bmatrix}$$

$$\begin{bmatrix} 1 & 1 & 1 & a \\ 0 & 0 & 1 & 2a/3 \\ 0 & 0 & 1 & (10{,}000 + a)/2 \end{bmatrix}$$

This system will be inconsistent unless the last two rows give the same value to $x_3$; that is, we must have $x_3 = 2a/3 = (10{,}000 + a)/2$ or $4a = 30{,}000 + 3a$ or $a = 30{,}000$. Thus, $x_3 = 20{,}000$ and $x_1 + x_2 = 10{,}000$. Since Lefty got $\$1{,}000$ more than Spike, $x_1 = \$5{,}500$, $x_2 = \$4{,}500$.

41. No solution.     43. $(2, x_2, 3, 2)$

45. $x_1 = 2 - 3x_3$, $x_2 = 3 - 2x_5$, $x_3$ is free, $x_4 = 4$, $x_5$ is free.

47. $(2 - x_3, \frac{1}{3}(-6 + 2x_3), x_3, 3)$

49. $x_1 = 1 - 2x_3$, $x_2 = 2 - x_3$, $x_3$ is free, $x_4 = -2$, $x_5 = 2$     51. $\frac{5}{11}$

53. Let $x_1 = P(a)$, $x_2 = P(b)$, $x_3 = P(c)$, $x_4 = P(d)$. Then we are given $x_1 + x_2 = \frac{4}{7}$, $x_2 + x_3 = \frac{1}{2}$, $x_3 + x_4 = \frac{3}{7}$. Also, since we are determining a probability distribution, $x_1 + x_2 + x_3 + x_4 = 1$. When we solve this system, we obtain the answer: $x_1 = \frac{1}{2} - x_4$, $x_2 = \frac{1}{14} + x_4$, $x_3 = \frac{3}{7} - x_4$ where $x_4$ is free. Of course, each variable must be between zero and 1. So $0 \le x_4 \le 1$. But, $0 \le x_1 \le 1$ or $0 \le \frac{1}{2} - x_4 \le 1$, $-\frac{1}{2} \le -x_4 \le \frac{1}{2}$, $-\frac{1}{2} \le x_4 \le \frac{1}{2}$. Similarly $-\frac{1}{14} \le x_4 \le \frac{13}{14}$, $-\frac{4}{7} \le x_4 \le \frac{3}{7}$. Since $x_4$ must satisfy all these conditions, we simply enforce the most stringent requirements. Then $x_1 = \frac{1}{2} - x_4$, $x_2 = \frac{1}{14} + x_4$, $x_3 = \frac{3}{7} - x_4$, where $x_4$ is any number such that $0 \le x_4 \le \frac{3}{7}$.

**Section 2.4
page 101**

1. The answer to the given system is $x_1 = 28$, $x_2 = \frac{85}{2}$, $x_3 = -23$, $x_4 = -44$. If we permit ourselves to use all 10 digits $0, 1, \ldots, 9$ as entries in the matrix for a system of the size given in Problem 1, then, by the principle of multiplication in counting, there are $10^{20}$ possible problems to work.

3. For example, in Problem 2 we might begin with

$$\begin{bmatrix} 3 & -8 & 3 & -8 \\ -1 & 2 & -1 & 2 \\ 7 & -6 & 2 & -9 \\ -8 & 2 & 0 & 7 \end{bmatrix}$$

decide on an answer such as $x_1 = 0$, $x_2 = -2$, $x_3 = 1$, $x_4 = 2$, substitute:

$$\begin{bmatrix} 3(0) - 8(-2) + 3(1) - 8(2) = & 3 \\ -1(0) + 2(-2) - 1(1) + 2(2) = & -1 \\ 7(0) - 6(-2) + 2(1) - 9(2) = & -4 \\ -8(0) + 2(-2) - 0(1) + 7(2) = & 10 \end{bmatrix}$$

and then solve the system

$$\begin{bmatrix} 3x_1 - 8x_2 + 3x_3 - 8x_4 = & 3 \\ -x_1 + 2x_2 - x_3 + 2x_4 = & -1 \\ 7x_1 - 6x_2 + 2x_3 - 9x_4 = & -4 \\ -8x_1 + 2x_2 & x_3 + 7x_4 = & 10 \end{bmatrix}$$

5. The system is inconsistent; there is no solution.

7. $P(a) = \frac{2}{7}$, $P(b) = \frac{1}{7}$, $P(c) = \frac{1}{7}$, $P(d) = \frac{2}{7}$, $P(e) = \frac{1}{7}$. $P(a, d, e) = \frac{2}{7} + \frac{2}{7} + \frac{1}{7} = \frac{5}{7}$.

**Section 2.5
page 106**

1. $x_1 = \frac{21}{5} - x_3$, $x_2 = \frac{1}{5}$, $x_3$ is free. The planes intersect in a line. Since $x_2 = \frac{1}{5}$, the line of intersection lies in a plane parallel to the 1-3 plane and $\frac{1}{5}$ units to the right of it.

3. $x_1 = (3 - 3x_3)/-2$, $x_2 = (\frac{9}{2} - \frac{9}{2}x_3)/-2$, $x_3$ free. The planes intersect in a line.

5. No solution. The planes have no point in common.

7. All four planes meet at the point $(\frac{1}{7}, -\frac{4}{7}, \frac{2}{7})$.

9. The equations of Section 2.5 represent planes in space—that is, 2-dimensional spaces in a 3-dimensional space. By analogy, the system of Exercise 25 in Section 2.3 represents three 3-dimensional spaces in a 4-dimensional "space"—whatever that is. Since the solution to this system contains one free variable, it must represent a single line in 4-dimensional space. So the three 3-dimensional spaces intersect in a

1-dimensional "space," namely a line. This is analogous to Figure 9, in which three 2-dimensional "spaces" (planes) intersect in a 0-dimensional "space" (a point), but in the present case all of the dimensions are one higher, which makes things more difficult to visualize.

**Section 2.6**
**page 128**

1. $\begin{bmatrix} -2 & 0 & 6 \\ 4 & 8 & 14 \\ 6 & 16 & 10 \end{bmatrix}$　　3. $\begin{bmatrix} 1 & 0 & -2 & 3 \\ 4 & 2 & -3 & 1 \\ 1 & -1 & 0 & 2 \end{bmatrix}$　　5. $\begin{bmatrix} 4 & -6 & 5 \\ 0 & 3 & -8 \end{bmatrix}$

7. (a) 365V　(b) 366V (leap year!)　(c) 3,653V (3 leap years)

9. $\begin{bmatrix} 3 & 4 \\ 5 & 6 \end{bmatrix}$

**Available Output**
**Table for**
**November**

11.

| Item | Factory | | |
|------|---------|---|---|
| | Danbury | Springfield | Rutland |
| Light sleeping bags | 90 | 90 | 72 |
| Heavy sleeping bags | 18 | 18 | 0 |
| Down jackets | 36 | 36 | 0 |
| Two-person tents | 126 | 198 | 0 |
| Four-person tents | 0 | 288 | 72 |

13. $\begin{bmatrix} 1 & 7 \\ 2 & 5 \end{bmatrix}$　　15. $\begin{bmatrix} 2 \\ 1 \\ 2 \end{bmatrix}$

17. They cannot be subtracted.

19. $\begin{bmatrix} 0 \\ 0 \end{bmatrix}$ A matrix consisting entirely of zeros is called a **zero matrix**. In this case we have the $2 \times 1$ zero matrix.

21. $\begin{bmatrix} 11 & -13 & 24 \\ 13 & 5 & 26 \\ 12 & 22 & 8 \end{bmatrix}$　　23. $\begin{bmatrix} -\frac{5}{6} & 4 \\ -\frac{7}{6} & \frac{7}{3} \end{bmatrix}$

25. While the first two matrices can be combined, the last matrix cannot be combined with the results, since it has a different size from the other two. Thus, the problem has no solution.

26. $\begin{bmatrix} 5 & -1 & 1 \\ 4 & 3 & -2 \end{bmatrix}$　　27. $\begin{bmatrix} 4 \\ 0 \\ 1 \end{bmatrix}$

28. (b) $5U + 7V = W$　(c) $W = F - 2U$

29. (a) $J + A + S$　(b) $\begin{bmatrix} 115 & 95 & 195 & 205 \\ 155 & 75 & 180 & 185 \\ 105 & 155 & 185 & 140 \end{bmatrix}$

(c) $T = F - O$　(d) $\begin{bmatrix} 80 & 65 & 120 & 125 \\ 95 & 35 & 90 & 90 \\ 80 & 85 & 130 & 95 \end{bmatrix}$

31. $\begin{bmatrix} 2x_1 \ x_2 + x_3 = 8 \\ -3x_1 + x_2 - 4x_3 = -25 \end{bmatrix}$　　33. $\begin{bmatrix} 3 & 2 & -1 \\ 1 & -2 & 3 \\ 4 & -1 & 2 \end{bmatrix} \begin{bmatrix} x_1 \\ x_2 \\ x_3 \end{bmatrix} = \begin{bmatrix} -2 \\ 12 \\ 11 \end{bmatrix}$

35. 47　　37. 6

39. $3\times5$. Notice that, if you multiply a matrix by a square matrix, the answer is the same size as the original matrix.

41. They cannot be multiplied.

43. Not enough information is given in the problem. They could have been a $5\times2$ and a $2\times7$ or a $5\times4$ and a $4\times7$ or infinitely many other sizes.

45. $\begin{bmatrix} 11 \\ 9 \end{bmatrix}$    47. $\begin{bmatrix} 7 & 10 \\ 10 & 8 \end{bmatrix}$    49. $\begin{bmatrix} 2 & 1 \\ 1 & 1 \end{bmatrix}$

50. $\begin{bmatrix} 1 & 1 \\ 1 & 2 \end{bmatrix}$ Compare this problem with Problem 49. Notice that, even with rather simple matrices, the order of multiplication matters.

51. $\begin{bmatrix} 13 & 5 \\ 10 & 3 \end{bmatrix}$

52. $\begin{bmatrix} 13 & 5 \\ 10 & 3 \end{bmatrix}$ Compare this problem with Problem 51. Notice that sometimes (very rarely) the order of multiplication does not matter.

53. $\begin{bmatrix} 3 & -1 & 5 \\ 2 & 4 & -2 \end{bmatrix}$    55. $\begin{bmatrix} 1 & 0 \\ 0 & 1 \end{bmatrix}$    57. $\begin{bmatrix} 0 & -8 & 8 & 5 \\ 5 & 11 & -1 & 0 \end{bmatrix}$

58. $\begin{bmatrix} -26 & -3 \\ 22 & 36 \end{bmatrix}$    59. $\begin{bmatrix} 14 & 5 \\ 0 & 0 \\ -6 & 6 \end{bmatrix}$    60. $\begin{bmatrix} -26 & -3 \\ 22 & 36 \end{bmatrix}$

In Exercises 57, 58, 59, 60 you are verifying that the product

$$\left( \begin{bmatrix} -1 & 1 & 2 \\ 2 & -2 & 1 \end{bmatrix} \begin{bmatrix} 3 & 4 & 0 & -2 \\ 1 & -2 & 2 & -1 \\ 1 & -1 & 3 & 2 \end{bmatrix} \right) \begin{bmatrix} 2 & 3 \\ 1 & 2 \\ -1 & 1 \\ -2 & 1 \end{bmatrix}$$

is the same as the product

$$\begin{bmatrix} -1 & 1 & 2 \\ 2 & -2 & 1 \end{bmatrix} \left( \begin{bmatrix} 3 & 4 & 0 & -2 \\ 1 & -2 & 2 & -1 \\ 1 & -1 & 3 & 2 \end{bmatrix} \begin{bmatrix} 2 & 3 \\ 1 & 2 \\ -1 & 1 \\ -2 & 1 \end{bmatrix} \right)$$

It can be shown that, if there are three matrices to be multiplied, it does not matter which multiplication is done first. The same is true for numbers. For example $(2\times3)\times4=2\times(3\times4)$. The fact that the placement of parentheses in a product of three matrices is unimportant is called the **associative law of matrix multiplication**.

61. $[-1]$    62. $\begin{bmatrix} 6 & 3 & -3 & 9 \\ -2 & -1 & 1 & -3 \\ 4 & 2 & -2 & 6 \\ -2 & -1 & 1 & -3 \end{bmatrix}$

Again, we remark that the order in which two matrices are written down usually affects the product. Multiplication of numbers is **commutative**. For example, $3\times4=4\times3$. Multiplication of matrices is *not* commutative. Compare Exercises 49 and 50. Here the answers are the same size. In Exercises 61 and 62 the answers are not even the same size. In Exercise 59 the matrices cannot be multiplied in the other order.

63. $\begin{bmatrix} 0 & 1 & 0 \\ 0 & 0 & 1 \\ 1 & 0 & 0 \end{bmatrix}$    65. $\begin{bmatrix} 1 & 0 & 0 \\ 0 & -1 & 0 \\ 0 & 0 & 1 \end{bmatrix}$

67., 68., 69., 70. $\begin{bmatrix} 2 & 1 & 3 \\ 3 & 2 & 1 \\ 1 & 2 & 3 \end{bmatrix}$ (same answer!)

71. The answer is the $3\times 3$ matrix with every entry zero. An important fact about the multiplication of numbers is that if a and b are numbers and $a\times b=0$ then either a or b (or possibly both a and b) is zero. Apparently, the product of two matrices can be zero even though neither matrix is the zero matrix.

73. $\begin{bmatrix} 0 & 4 & -4 \\ 0 & 8 & -8 \\ 0 & 5 & -5 \end{bmatrix}$    75. $\begin{bmatrix} 0 & 0 & 0 \\ 0 & 0 & 0 \\ 0 & 0 & 0 \end{bmatrix}$

77. $\begin{bmatrix} 32 & 41 & 76 \\ 194 & 38 & 49 \\ 25 & 86 & 97 \end{bmatrix}$ Of course, we are multiplying this matrix by the $3\times 3$ identity matrix.

78. The problem should read

$$\begin{bmatrix} 1 & -1 & 2 \\ 3 & 1 & 4 \\ 2 & 0 & 1 \end{bmatrix}\begin{bmatrix} 1 & 2 & 3 \\ 4 & 1 & 2 \\ 1 & 3 & 6 \end{bmatrix} = \begin{bmatrix} -1 & 7 & 13 \\ 11 & 19 & 35 \\ 3 & 7 & 12 \end{bmatrix}$$

79. $\begin{bmatrix} 1 & 0 & 0 & 0 & 0 & 0 \\ 0 & 1 & 0 & 0 & 0 & 0 \\ 0 & 0 & 1 & 0 & 0 & 0 \\ 0 & 0 & 0 & 1 & 0 & 0 \\ 0 & 0 & 0 & 0 & 1 & 0 \\ 0 & 0 & 0 & 0 & 0 & 1 \end{bmatrix}$

81. Itself      83. QC (or $(J+A+S)C$)

85. To obtain the total amount that each store paid each factory, the associated matrices were multiplied,

$$\begin{bmatrix} 100 & 120 & 80 & 100 & 250 \\ 120 & 150 & 90 & 80 & 200 \\ 150 & 200 & 100 & 90 & 200 \end{bmatrix}\begin{bmatrix} 50 & 50 & 50 \\ 30 & 40 & 30 \\ 60 & 80 & 60 \\ 40 & 50 & 0 \\ 0 & 40 & 30 \end{bmatrix} = \begin{bmatrix} 17{,}400 & 31{,}200 & 20{,}900 \\ 19{,}100 & 31{,}200 & 21{,}900 \\ 23{,}100 & 36{,}000 & 25{,}500 \end{bmatrix}$$

| Amount Each Store Paid Each Factory | Store | Factory | | |
|---|---|---|---|---|
| | | Danbury | Springfield | Rutland |
| | Hartford | $17,400 | $31,200 | $20,900 |
| | Providence | $19,100 | $31,200 | $21,900 |
| | Barre | $23,100 | $36,000 | $25,500 |

1. (a) There are four possible work schedules (see Table 1).

|  | I | II | III | IV |
|---|---|---|---|---|
| Me | 7 | 7 | 7 | 7 |
| Jane | 0 | 1 | 2 | 3 |
| Bill | 6 | 6 | 6 | 6 |
| Fred | 3 | 2 | 1 | 0 |

(b) There is only one possibility (Table 2).

Table 2
(in days)

|  | I |
|---|---|
| Me | 6 |
| Jane | 4 |
| Bill | 6 |
| Fred | 2 |

(c) Again, there are four possibilities (Table 3).

Table 3
(in days)

|  | I | II | III | IV |
|---|---|---|---|---|
| Me | 5 | 5 | 5 | 5 |
| Jane | 4 | 5 | 6 | 7 |
| Bill | 3 | 3 | 3 | 3 |
| Fred | 3 | 2 | 1 | 0 |

(d) Now there are three possible schedules (Table 4).

Table 4
(in days)

|  | I | II | III |
|---|---|---|---|
| Me | $3\frac{1}{2}$ | $3\frac{1}{2}$ | $3\frac{1}{2}$ |
| Jane | 0 | 1 | 2 |
| Bill | $3\frac{1}{4}$ | $3\frac{1}{4}$ | $3\frac{1}{4}$ |
| Fred | $2\frac{1}{4}$ | $1\frac{1}{4}$ | $\frac{1}{4}$ |

2.

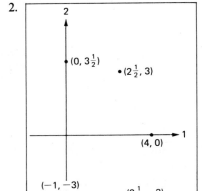

3. (a)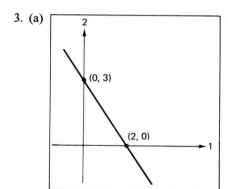

(b)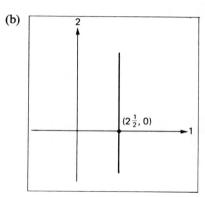

(c)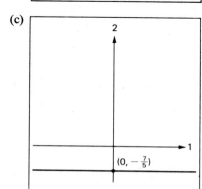

(d)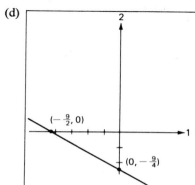

(e)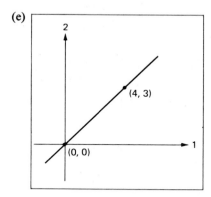

4. (a) $(2,3)$   (b) There is no solution.   (c) $x_1 = \frac{7}{2} - \frac{1}{2}x_2$, $x_2$ is free.
   (d) $x_1 = \frac{590}{77}$, $x_2 = \frac{192}{77}$   (e) There is no solution.   (f) $(2-x_2, x_2, 1)$
   (g) $(\frac{12}{5}, -\frac{3}{5}, -\frac{1}{5})$   (h) $x_1 = -2, x_2 = 1, x_3 = 3$
   (i) $x_1 = \frac{3}{2} - \frac{3}{2}x_4$, $x_2 = \frac{1}{4} + \frac{3}{4}x_4$, $x_3 = \frac{5}{2} + \frac{3}{2}x_4$, $x_4$ is free.   (j) $(38, 29, 83, 47)$

5. (a) $\begin{bmatrix} -2 & \frac{19}{12} & -\frac{1}{5} \end{bmatrix}$   (b) not defined   (c) $\begin{bmatrix} -2 & \frac{4}{3} \\ 4 & -\frac{1}{6} \end{bmatrix}$

(d) $\begin{bmatrix} -\frac{73}{60} \\ \frac{107}{60} \end{bmatrix}$ (e) $\begin{bmatrix} 1 & -2 & 3 \\ -1 & 5 & -6 \\ 7 & -8 & 9 \end{bmatrix}$ (f) $\begin{bmatrix} 0 & 0 \\ 0 & 0 \end{bmatrix}$

(g) $\begin{bmatrix} -4 & -12 \\ 12 & 4 \end{bmatrix}$ (h) $\begin{bmatrix} 1 & 2 \\ 3 & 4 \end{bmatrix}$ (i) not defined

(j) $\begin{bmatrix} 0 & -11 \\ -3 & 7 \\ 16 & -6 \\ -15 & 6 \end{bmatrix}$

Supplementary
Exercises.
page 139

1.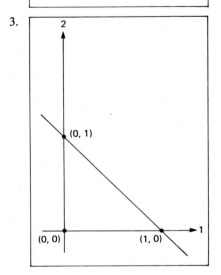

2.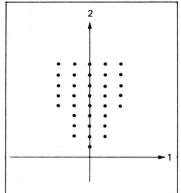

3.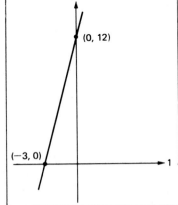

5.

7.

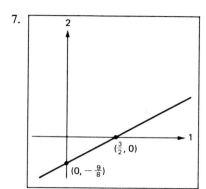

9.

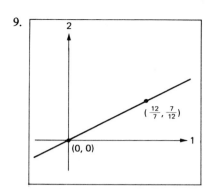

11.

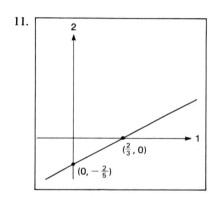

13. $(2,3)$     15. $(\frac{8}{10}, -\frac{9}{10})$

17. $(\frac{1}{3}(4x_2 - 9), x_2)$ The lines are identical.

19. $(7,3)$     21. $(0,5)$     23. $(1,-1,2)$     25. $(1,2,1)$     27. $(-2,3,1)$

29. $(-4+2x_3, -1+x_3, x_3)$     31. $(2-x_2, x_2, 1)$     33. $(-2,1,3)$     35. $(2,1,2)$

37. $(-\frac{14}{3}, \frac{47}{6}, \frac{1}{3})$     39. $(2,3)$     41. $(0,2,-1,1)$     43. $(6-2x_4, \frac{3}{2}, -2+2x_4, x_4)$

45. $(\frac{3}{2} - 5x_4, 4+8x_4, \frac{5}{2} - 20x_4, x_4)$     47. No solution     49. $(-1,0,4,-\frac{1}{3})$

51. $(\frac{3}{2} - \frac{3}{2}x_4, \frac{1}{4} + \frac{3}{4}x_4, \frac{5}{2} + \frac{3}{2}x_4, x_4)$     53. $(11,2,-10,-4)$

54. Let $x_1, x_2, x_3$ be the number of senior execs, juniors, and workers, respectively. Then $x_2 = 5x_1$, $x_3 = 50x_2$, $1{,}000x_1 + 500x_2 + 200x_3 = 107{,}000$, so we solve

$$\begin{bmatrix} 10x_1 + 5x_2 + 2x_3 = 1{,}070 \\ 5x_1 - x_2 = 0 \\ 50x_2 - x_3 = 0 \end{bmatrix} \text{to obtain} \begin{bmatrix} 2 \\ 10 \\ 500 \end{bmatrix}$$

55. 2 As, 3 Bs, 10 Cs, 9 Ds, 8 Fs, (Despite the tremendous thought that went into my grading policy, the college fired me for incompetency.)

57. Blantyria: 6 new to old     59. Galadriel     61. Maine: 375
    Iwalam: 2 old to new                           Utah: 743
    Neofrom: 3 new to old                          Iowa: 291
    Concordia: 4 old to new

62. Here is one way:

$$\begin{bmatrix} 0 & 1 & 2 \\ 3 & 1 & 0 \\ 1 & 2 & 3 \end{bmatrix} \underset{R_3+R_1}{\phantom{x}} \begin{bmatrix} 0 & 1 & 2 \\ 3 & 1 & 0 \\ 1 & 3 & 5 \end{bmatrix} \overset{R_1-R_3}{\phantom{x}} \begin{bmatrix} -1 & -2 & -3 \\ 3 & 1 & 0 \\ 1 & 3 & 5 \end{bmatrix}$$

$$\underset{R_3+R_1}{\phantom{x}} \begin{bmatrix} -1 & -2 & -3 \\ 3 & 1 & 0 \\ 0 & 1 & 2 \end{bmatrix} \overset{-R_1}{\phantom{x}} \begin{bmatrix} 1 & 2 & 3 \\ 3 & 1 & 0 \\ 0 & 1 & 2 \end{bmatrix}$$

63. (a) $-x_1+x_2=1$ (b) $x_1-3x_2=-25$ (c) $3x_1+4x_2=0$ (d) $4x_1-3x_2=0$ (e) $x_2=0$
(f) $-3x_1+2x_2=12$

65. $4\times7$

67.

$$\begin{bmatrix} 2 & 3 & -1 \\ 4 & 1 & 6 \\ 0 & 2 & 5 \end{bmatrix}^2 = \begin{bmatrix} 2 & 3 & -1 \\ 4 & 1 & 6 \\ 0 & 2 & 5 \end{bmatrix}\begin{bmatrix} 2 & 3 & -1 \\ 4 & 1 & 6 \\ 0 & 2 & 5 \end{bmatrix} = \begin{bmatrix} 16 & 7 & 11 \\ 12 & 25 & 32 \\ 8 & 12 & 37 \end{bmatrix}$$

69. $x=\frac{1}{2}$

71. (a) and (b) Each entry is multiplied by 7.
(c) The first row is multiplied by 7.
(d) The first column is multiplied by 7.
(e) Its first and second rows are interchanged.
(f) It becomes a matrix with $C_1$ the same as $C_2$ in the original matrix, $C_2$ the same as $C_3$, $C_3$ the same as $C_4$, and $C_4$ the same as $2C_1$.

73. (a) The $162\times1$ matrix with all entries equal to 1.
(b) The $1\times25$ matrix with all entries equal to 1.

74. (b) The amount motel 4 would have made on June 15 if it had the same rates as motel 5.

75. To increase each entry in N by 25% I would multiply N by $1+.25=1\frac{1}{4}=\frac{5}{4}$. To decrease each entry in M by 20% I multiply M by $1-.20=1-\frac{1}{5}=\frac{4}{5}$. I should compute

$$\left(\tfrac{5}{4}N\right)\left(\tfrac{4}{5}M\right).$$

It can be shown that

$$\left(\tfrac{5}{4}N\right)\left(\tfrac{4}{5}M\right)=\left(\tfrac{5}{4}\times\tfrac{4}{5}\right)NM=NM.$$

Therefore, I simply tell them the old product.

76. $x_1=\begin{bmatrix} 1 & 2 \\ 2 & 3 \end{bmatrix}$, $x_2=\begin{bmatrix} 1 & -1 \\ 2 & 0 \end{bmatrix}$

77. $$\begin{bmatrix} 18 \\ -\frac{3}{2} \\ 0 \end{bmatrix} \quad \begin{bmatrix} -6 & -9 & 12 \\ -\frac{3}{2} & 0 & -6 \\ -15 & 21 & -54 \end{bmatrix}$$
$$\begin{bmatrix} 9 \\ -6 \end{bmatrix} \quad \begin{bmatrix} 3 & 0 & -\frac{21}{8} \\ \frac{9}{4} & -\frac{15}{8} & 57 \end{bmatrix}$$

79. (a) $$\begin{bmatrix} 1 & 0 & -1 \\ 2 & 1 & 2 \end{bmatrix} \begin{bmatrix} 2 \\ 2 \end{bmatrix}$$
$$\begin{bmatrix} 0 & 0 & 1 \\ 0 & 0 & 0 \\ 0 & 2 & 1 \end{bmatrix} \begin{bmatrix} 1 \\ 0 \\ 3 \end{bmatrix}$$
$$\begin{bmatrix} 1 & 2 & 2 \\ 0 & 1 & 1 \\ 0 & 2 & 4 \end{bmatrix} \begin{bmatrix} 5 \\ 3 \\ 4 \end{bmatrix}$$

(b) $$\begin{bmatrix} 1 & 0 & -1 & 2 \\ 2 & 1 & 2 & 2 \\ 0 & 0 & 1 & 1 \\ 0 & 0 & 0 & 0 \\ 0 & 2 & 1 & 3 \\ 1 & 2 & 2 & 5 \\ 0 & 1 & 1 & 3 \\ 0 & 1 & 4 & 4 \end{bmatrix}$$

81. $x_1 = 2$, $x_2 = -1$, $x_3 = 4$, $x_4 = 1$
82. $x_1 = 2 + x_4$, $x_2 = 2x_4$, $x_3 = x_4 - 1$, $x_4$ free
83. $x_1 = 2x_3 - x_4 + 1$, $x_2 = 3x_3 + 2x_4 - 2$, $x_3$ and $x_4$ free
84. $x_1 = 2x_2 + x_3 - x_4 + 3$, $x_2$, $x_3$, and $x_4$ free
85. $x_1 = 3$, $x_2 = 1 - x_4$, $x_3 = 2 + 2x_4$, $x_4$ free
86. $x_1 = x_2 + x_4 - 1$, $x_3 = 4$, $x_2$ and $x_4$ free
87. $x_1 = 2$, $x_2 = 1 + x_4$, $x_3 = 1$, $x_4$ free
88. Inconsistent
89. (a) 5,040  (b) 5,040  (c) 5,040  (d) 0
91. (a) $[\frac{1}{6} \quad \frac{1}{6} \quad \frac{1}{6} \quad \frac{1}{6} \quad \frac{1}{6} \quad \frac{1}{6}]$  (b) $[\frac{1}{6} \quad \frac{1}{6} \quad \frac{1}{6} \quad \frac{1}{6} \quad \frac{1}{6} \quad \frac{1}{6}]$  (c) $[0 \quad 0 \quad 0 \quad 0 \quad 0 \quad 0]$
   (d) $[0 \quad 0 \quad 0 \quad 0 \quad \frac{1}{6} \quad \frac{1}{6}]$  (e) $[0 \quad \frac{1}{3} \quad 0 \quad \frac{1}{3} \quad 0 \quad \frac{1}{3}]$  (f) $[1 \quad 1 \quad 1 \quad 1 \quad 1 \quad 1]$
   (g) $[\frac{1}{6} \quad \frac{1}{6} \quad \frac{1}{6} \quad \frac{1}{6} \quad \frac{1}{6} \quad \frac{1}{6}]$  (h) $[\frac{1}{6} \quad \frac{1}{3} \quad \frac{1}{6} \quad 0 \quad \frac{2}{3} \quad 0]$
92. (f) 162
   (g) We, the authors of this text, cannot. Therefore for us, the answer is no.
93. Either I swim 5 days and bicycle 1 day, or else I swim 3, jog 1, and bicycle 2.
95. (a) 6.     (b) $x_2 = 0$
              $x_1 + x_2 = 1$     (c) $\dfrac{n(n-1)}{2}$
              $2x_1 + x_2 = 2$
              $x_1 + 2x_2 = 2$
              $x_1 + x_2 = 2$
              $x_1 = 0$

Section 3.1     1.
page 152

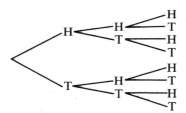

3.

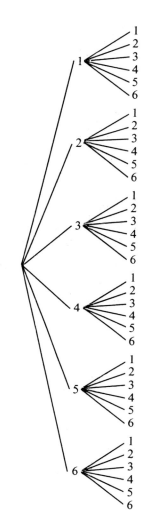

5.

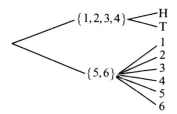

7.

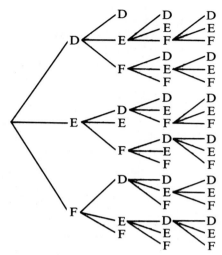

9. The diagram is the same as the tree in Exercise 7 with D, E, F replaced (in any order) with J, B, T.

11.

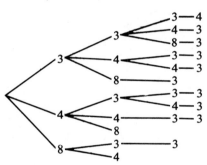

13.

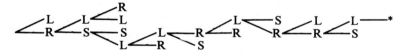

15. Call the players A and B, and also let A mean A wins the point, B mean B wins the point, and D mean deuce. If the game lasts 8 points, the score at the end of the eight

point must be D. Each such D then continues $D\begin{cases}A\begin{cases}A\\B\end{cases}\\B\begin{cases}D\\B\end{cases}\end{cases}$, and the chart goes on

forever.

Section 3.2
page 167

1. This is a partition.   3. This is not a partition, since Boston and Massachusetts are not disjoint.

5. This is not a partition, since it does not include all of U.S.

7. $A_1 \cup A_2 \cup A_3 \cup A_4 = S$, $A_1 \cap A_2 = A_1 \cap A_3 = A_1 \cap A_4 = A_2 \cap A_3 = A_2 \cap A_4 = A_3 \cap A_4 = \emptyset$.

9. This is a partition.   11. This is a partition.

13. $A_1 = \{2, 12\}$, $A_2 = \{3, 11\}$, $A_3 = \{4, 10\}$, $A_4 = \{5, 9\}$, $A_5 = \{6, 8\}$, $A_6 = \{7\}$.

15. $\emptyset, A_2, \emptyset, A_4, \emptyset, A_6$, or simply $A_2, A_4, A_6$. $P(B) = \frac{1}{2}$ and $P(A_2) + P(A_4) + P(A_6) = \frac{4}{36} + \frac{8}{36} + \frac{6}{36} = \frac{1}{2}$.

17. $\emptyset, \emptyset, \{10\}, \{5\}, \emptyset, \emptyset$, or simply $\{10\}, \{5\}$.

19. $\frac{3}{700}$   21. 0.195   23. $\frac{75}{392}$

25. $P(4, 2)/[P(1, 5) + P(2, 4) + P(3, 3) + P(4, 2)] = \frac{1}{3}$.

27. There is not enough information given to determine an answer.

Section 3.3
page 182

1. The initial-state matrix is $[\frac{1}{3} \quad \frac{2}{3}]$ and the transition matrix is $\begin{bmatrix} \frac{1}{2} & \frac{1}{2} \\ 0 & 1 \end{bmatrix}$. After 6 weeks, $\frac{1}{192}$ of the salespeople are being sent to town A and $\frac{191}{192}$ are being sent to town B.

3. We have 84,500; they have 43,500.   5. $\frac{17}{40}$.

6. The initial state is $[2 \quad 1]$; the transition for (1) is

$$\begin{bmatrix} \frac{2}{3} & \frac{1}{3} \\ \frac{1}{4} & \frac{3}{4} \end{bmatrix} = \frac{1}{12}\begin{bmatrix} 8 & 4 \\ 3 & 9 \end{bmatrix};$$

the transition for (2) is

$$\begin{bmatrix} \frac{1}{2} & \frac{1}{2} \\ \frac{3}{4} & \frac{1}{4} \end{bmatrix} = \frac{1}{4}\begin{bmatrix} 2 & 2 \\ 3 & 1 \end{bmatrix}.$$

(a)

$$[2 \quad 1]\begin{bmatrix} \frac{2}{3} & \frac{1}{3} \\ \frac{1}{4} & \frac{3}{4} \end{bmatrix}\begin{bmatrix} \frac{1}{2} & \frac{1}{2} \\ \frac{3}{4} & \frac{1}{4} \end{bmatrix}\begin{bmatrix} \frac{2}{3} & \frac{1}{3} \\ \frac{1}{4} & \frac{3}{4} \end{bmatrix}\begin{bmatrix} \frac{1}{2} & \frac{1}{2} \\ \frac{3}{4} & \frac{1}{4} \end{bmatrix}$$

$$= \left(\frac{1}{48}\right)^2[2 \quad 1]\left(\begin{bmatrix} 8 & 4 \\ 3 & 9 \end{bmatrix}\begin{bmatrix} 2 & 2 \\ 3 & 1 \end{bmatrix}\right)^2 = \left(\frac{1}{48}\right)^2[2 \quad 1]\begin{bmatrix} 28 & 20 \\ 33 & 15 \end{bmatrix}^2$$

$$= \left(\frac{1}{48}\right)^2[2 \quad 1]\begin{bmatrix} 1444 & 860 \\ 1419 & 885 \end{bmatrix} = \begin{bmatrix} \frac{4307}{48^2} & \frac{2605}{48^2} \end{bmatrix}$$

(b)

$$[2 \quad 1]\begin{bmatrix} \frac{1}{2} & \frac{1}{2} \\ \frac{3}{4} & \frac{1}{4} \end{bmatrix}\begin{bmatrix} \frac{2}{3} & \frac{1}{3} \\ \frac{1}{4} & \frac{3}{4} \end{bmatrix}\begin{bmatrix} \frac{1}{2} & \frac{1}{2} \\ \frac{3}{4} & \frac{1}{3} \end{bmatrix}\begin{bmatrix} \frac{2}{3} & \frac{1}{3} \\ \frac{1}{3} & \frac{3}{4} \end{bmatrix}$$

$$= \left(\frac{1}{48}\right)^2[2 \quad 1]\begin{bmatrix} 1186 & 1118 \\ 1161 & 1143 \end{bmatrix} = \begin{bmatrix} \frac{3533}{48^2} & \frac{3863}{48^2} \end{bmatrix}$$

(c)

$$[2 \quad 1]\begin{bmatrix} \frac{2}{3} & \frac{1}{3} \\ \frac{1}{4} & \frac{3}{4} \end{bmatrix}^2\begin{bmatrix} \frac{1}{2} & \frac{1}{2} \\ \frac{3}{4} & \frac{1}{4} \end{bmatrix}^2 = \left(\frac{1}{48}\right)^2[2 \quad 1]\begin{bmatrix} 1372 & 932 \\ 1347 & 957 \end{bmatrix}$$

$$= \begin{bmatrix} \frac{4091}{48^2} & \frac{2821}{48^2} \end{bmatrix}$$

The sale is a disaster. The result of each scheme is that PHE will have less than twice as many customers as McD. In fact, scheme b would actually result in McD's being larger than PHE! If one of these schemes must be tried, scheme a would do the least damage; it would reduce PHE's customer advantage from 2 to 1 to $\frac{4307}{2605}$ to 1, that is, about 1.65 to 1.

7. $\frac{341}{1536}$

1.
$$\begin{bmatrix} \frac{2}{3} & 0 & \frac{1}{3} \\ \frac{1}{2} & 0 & \frac{1}{2} \\ 0 & 1 & 0 \end{bmatrix}^4 = \begin{bmatrix} \frac{68}{162} & \frac{51}{162} & \frac{43}{162} \\ \frac{43}{108} & \frac{39}{108} & \frac{26}{108} \\ \frac{17}{36} & \frac{6}{36} & \frac{13}{36} \end{bmatrix} = \begin{bmatrix} .4196 & .3149 & .2655 \\ .3981 & .3611 & .2408 \\ .4721 & .1667 & .3612 \end{bmatrix}$$

The theoretical long-range distribution is

$$\begin{bmatrix} \frac{3}{7} & \frac{2}{7} & \frac{2}{7} \end{bmatrix} = [.4288 \quad .2856 \quad .2856]$$

$$\begin{bmatrix} 1 & 0 & 0 & 0 \\ 0 & 1 & 0 & 0 \\ 0 & \frac{1}{2} & \frac{1}{4} & \frac{1}{4} \\ 0 & 0 & 0 & 1 \end{bmatrix}^4 = \begin{bmatrix} 1 & 0 & 0 & 0 \\ 0 & 1 & 0 & 0 \\ 0 & \frac{85}{128} & \frac{1}{256} & \frac{85}{256} \\ 0 & 0 & 0 & 1 \end{bmatrix} \doteq \begin{bmatrix} 1 & 0 & 0 & 0 \\ 0 & 1 & 0 & 0 \\ 0 & .6641 & .0039 & .3320 \\ 0 & 0 & 0 & 1 \end{bmatrix}$$

The theoretical limit matrix is

$$\begin{bmatrix} 1 & 0 & 0 & 0 \\ 0 & 1 & 0 & 0 \\ 0 & \frac{2}{3} & 0 & \frac{1}{3} \\ 0 & 0 & 0 & 1 \end{bmatrix} \doteq \begin{bmatrix} 1 & 0 & 0 & 0 \\ 0 & 1 & 0 & 0 \\ 0 & .6667 & 0 & .3333 \\ 0 & 0 & 0 & 1 \end{bmatrix}$$

2. Since the second power of the matrix has no zero entries, it is regular. The system to be solved is
$$\begin{bmatrix} -\frac{2}{3} & \frac{1}{4} & 0 & 0 \\ \frac{1}{3} & -\frac{1}{2} & 1 & 0 \\ \frac{1}{3} & \frac{1}{4} & -1 & 0 \\ 1 & 1 & 1 & 1 \end{bmatrix}.$$ The result is $\begin{bmatrix} \frac{3}{14} & \frac{8}{14} & \frac{3}{14} \end{bmatrix}$.

3. To compute the limit matrix we must solve the system

$$\begin{bmatrix} 0 & 0 & 0 & 0 & 0 & 0 \\ \frac{1}{4} & -1 & \frac{1}{2} & \frac{1}{4} & 0 & 0 \\ 0 & 0 & 0 & 0 & 0 & 0 \\ 0 & 0 & 0 & 0 & 0 & 0 \\ 0 & \frac{1}{3} & \frac{1}{3} & 0 & -\frac{2}{3} & 0 \end{bmatrix}$$

We eliminate the rows consisting entirely of zeros and solve for $x_2$ and $x_5$ (since states 2 and 5 are nonabsorbing states) in terms of $x_1$, $x_3$, and $x_4$ (since states 1, 3 and 4 are absorbing states):

$$\begin{bmatrix} \frac{1}{4} & -1 & \frac{1}{2} & \frac{1}{4} & 0 & 0 \\ 0 & \frac{1}{3} & \frac{1}{3} & 0 & -\frac{2}{3} & 0 \end{bmatrix} \begin{bmatrix} -\frac{1}{4} & 1 & -\frac{1}{2} & -\frac{1}{4} & 0 & 0 \\ \frac{1}{12} & 0 & \frac{1}{2} & \frac{1}{12} & -\frac{2}{3} & 0 \end{bmatrix}$$

$$\begin{bmatrix} -\frac{1}{4} & 1 & -\frac{1}{2} & -\frac{1}{4} & 0 & 0 \\ -\frac{1}{8} & 0 & -\frac{3}{4} & -\frac{1}{8} & 1 & 0 \end{bmatrix}$$

We see that

$$x_2 = \tfrac{1}{4}x_1 + \tfrac{1}{2}x_3 + \tfrac{1}{4}x_4$$

$$x_5 = \tfrac{1}{8}x_1 + \tfrac{3}{4}x_3 + \tfrac{1}{8}x_4$$

The limit matrix is therefore

$$\begin{bmatrix} 1 & 0 & 0 & 0 & 0 \\ \tfrac{1}{4} & 0 & \tfrac{1}{2} & \tfrac{1}{4} & 0 \\ 0 & 0 & 1 & 0 & 0 \\ 0 & 0 & 0 & 1 & 0 \\ \tfrac{1}{8} & 0 & \tfrac{3}{4} & \tfrac{1}{8} & 0 \end{bmatrix}$$

Check:

$$\begin{bmatrix} 1 & 0 & 0 & 0 & 0 \\ \tfrac{1}{4} & 0 & \tfrac{1}{2} & \tfrac{1}{4} & 0 \\ 0 & 0 & 1 & 0 & 0 \\ 0 & 0 & 0 & 1 & 0 \\ 0 & \tfrac{1}{3} & \tfrac{1}{3} & 0 & \tfrac{1}{3} \end{bmatrix} \begin{bmatrix} 1 & 0 & 0 & 0 & 0 \\ \tfrac{1}{4} & 0 & \tfrac{1}{2} & \tfrac{1}{4} & 0 \\ 0 & 0 & 1 & 0 & 0 \\ 0 & 0 & 0 & 1 & 0 \\ \tfrac{1}{8} & 0 & \tfrac{3}{4} & \tfrac{1}{8} & 0 \end{bmatrix} = \begin{bmatrix} 1 & 0 & 0 & 0 & 0 \\ \tfrac{1}{4} & 0 & \tfrac{1}{2} & \tfrac{1}{4} & 0 \\ 0 & 0 & 1 & 0 & 0 \\ 0 & 0 & 0 & 1 & 0 \\ \tfrac{1}{8} & 0 & \tfrac{3}{4} & \tfrac{1}{8} & 0 \end{bmatrix}$$

To compute the long-range distribution we simply multiply

$$\begin{bmatrix} \tfrac{1}{10} & \tfrac{1}{5} & \tfrac{3}{10} & \tfrac{3}{10} & \tfrac{1}{10} \end{bmatrix} \begin{bmatrix} 1 & 0 & 0 & 0 & 0 \\ \tfrac{1}{4} & 0 & \tfrac{1}{2} & \tfrac{1}{4} & 0 \\ 0 & 0 & 1 & 0 & 0 \\ 0 & 0 & 0 & 1 & 0 \\ \tfrac{1}{8} & 0 & \tfrac{3}{4} & \tfrac{1}{8} & 0 \end{bmatrix} = \begin{bmatrix} \tfrac{13}{80} & 0 & \tfrac{38}{80} & \tfrac{29}{80} & 0 \end{bmatrix}$$

4. In the long run the probability that the AAT machine is not broken down is $\tfrac{7}{9}$, while the probability that the IIT machine is not broken down is $\tfrac{12}{17}$. Since $\tfrac{12}{17} < \tfrac{7}{9}$, AC should buy from AAT.

5. Everything is absorbed by state four.

7. $[0 \quad \tfrac{9}{32} \quad 0 \quad \tfrac{13}{24} \quad \tfrac{17}{96} \quad 0]$      9. $[\tfrac{7}{22} \quad \tfrac{14}{22} \quad \tfrac{1}{22}]$

11. $[0 \quad 101 \quad 0 \quad 52 \quad 0]$

12. While we did not treat this case, note that $\tfrac{1}{4}$ of the distribution will remain in the isolated absorbing state 1. The rest of the distribution will be acted on by the

regular transistion matrix $\begin{bmatrix} \tfrac{1}{3} & \tfrac{1}{3} & \tfrac{1}{3} \\ \tfrac{1}{4} & \tfrac{1}{2} & \tfrac{1}{4} \\ 0 & 1 & 0 \end{bmatrix}$. The long-range distribution for this

matrix was found to be $[\tfrac{3}{14} \quad \tfrac{8}{14} \quad \tfrac{3}{14}]$ in Exercise 2. Thus, $\tfrac{3}{4}$ of the initial distribution is distributed among states 2, 3, and 4 in this way. The final result is $\left[\begin{array}{cccc} \frac{1}{4} & \frac{9}{56} & \frac{24}{56} & \frac{9}{56} \end{array}\right]$.

13. The transition matrix $\begin{bmatrix} \frac{1}{6} & \frac{1}{2} & \frac{1}{3} \\ \frac{5}{6} & \frac{1}{6} & 0 \\ \frac{1}{5} & \frac{3}{5} & \frac{1}{5} \end{bmatrix}$ is regular. The flow chart on page 189 gives

the final distribution $\left[\begin{array}{ccc} \frac{60}{139} & \frac{54}{139} & \frac{25}{139} \end{array}\right]$, which checks. Multiplying these fractions by $1{,}251 = 139 \cdot 9$ customers gives in the long run: 540 customers for store 1; 486 for store 2; and 225 for store 3.

15. The farmers have $\frac{42}{89}$ of the wealth, the clothiers have $\frac{25}{89}$, and the carpenters have $\frac{22}{89}$.

**Section 3.5**
**page 221**

1.    3.    5. A→B→   6. A→C→

7. $\begin{bmatrix} 0 & 0 & 1 \\ 1 & 0 & 0 \\ 0 & 1 & 0 \end{bmatrix}$   9. $\begin{bmatrix} 0 & \frac{1}{3} & 0 & 0 & \frac{1}{3} & \frac{1}{3} & 0 \\ 0 & 0 & 0 & 0 & 0 & 0 & 1 \\ 0 & 0 & 0 & 1 & 0 & 0 & 0 \\ 0 & 0 & 1 & 0 & 0 & 0 & 0 \\ 0 & 0 & 0 & 0 & 0 & 0 & 1 \\ 0 & 0 & 0 & 0 & 0 & 0 & 1 \\ 1 & 0 & 0 & 0 & 0 & 0 & 0 \end{bmatrix}$

11. Regular   13. Periodic
15. [138  207  720  800  320  0  575]
17. A:       0
    B:   183,897
    C:   636,064
    D:   367,794
    E:   141,372
    F:   238,524
    G:   157,080
    H:   238,524
    I:       0
    J:       0
    K:    26,271
    L:    65,450
18. The transition matrix as it currently stands is

$$\begin{array}{c} B \\ G_1 \\ G_2 \\ P_1 \\ P_2 \end{array} \begin{bmatrix} 0 & \frac{1}{3} & \frac{2}{3} & 0 & 0 \\ 0 & 0 & 0 & \frac{1}{2} & \frac{1}{2} \\ 0 & 0 & 0 & \frac{1}{3} & \frac{2}{3} \\ 1 & 0 & 0 & 0 & 0 \\ 1 & 0 & 0 & 0 & 0 \end{bmatrix}$$

Scheme 1 would change this to

$$\begin{bmatrix} 0 & \frac{1}{3} & \frac{2}{3} & 0 & 0 \\ \frac{1}{2} & 0 & 0 & 0 & \frac{1}{2} \\ 0 & 0 & 0 & \frac{1}{3} & \frac{2}{3} \\ 1 & 0 & 0 & 0 & 0 \\ 1 & 0 & 0 & 0 & 0 \end{bmatrix}$$

This is a regular Markov chain with final distribution

$$\begin{bmatrix} \frac{18}{51} & \frac{6}{51} & \frac{12}{51} & \frac{4}{51} & \frac{11}{51} \end{bmatrix}.$$

No matter how things start out, I will eventually have about $\frac{6}{51}$ of the market under this scheme.

Scheme 2 changes the original transition matrix to

$$\begin{bmatrix} 0 & \frac{1}{3} & \frac{2}{3} & 0 & 0 \\ \frac{1}{4} & 0 & 0 & \frac{1}{2} & \frac{1}{4} \\ 0 & 0 & 0 & \frac{1}{3} & \frac{2}{3} \\ 1 & 0 & 0 & 0 & 0 \\ 1 & 0 & 0 & 0 & 0 \end{bmatrix}$$

This, too, is a regular Markov chain. Here the final distribution is

$$\begin{bmatrix} \frac{36}{105} & \frac{12}{105} & \frac{24}{105} & \frac{14}{105} & \frac{19}{105} \end{bmatrix}$$

with $\frac{4}{35}$ of the market eventually at my station. Therefore, I should use Scheme 1. In fact, this will increase my average weekly business from 153 customers to 243 customers.

Chapter 3
Review Exercises
page 226

1. (a) $\frac{73}{480}$  (b) $\frac{7}{64}$  (c) $\frac{13}{96}$
2. (a) not a partition  (b) not a partition  (c) a partition
3. $\frac{30}{77} \doteq 39\%$  4. $\frac{10}{19} = 53\%$  5. three months

6. $\begin{bmatrix} \frac{2}{9} & \frac{3}{9} & \frac{4}{9} \\ \frac{2}{9} & \frac{3}{9} & \frac{4}{9} \\ \frac{2}{9} & \frac{3}{9} & \frac{4}{9} \end{bmatrix}$; $[\frac{2}{9} \quad \frac{3}{9} \quad \frac{4}{9}]$  7. (a) see p. 184  (b) False, see p. 185

8. $\begin{bmatrix} 1 & 0 & 0 & 0 \\ 0 & 1 & 0 & 0 \\ 0 & \frac{4}{5} & 0 & \frac{1}{5} \\ 0 & 0 & 0 & 0 \end{bmatrix}$; $[\frac{1}{6} \quad \frac{3}{5} \quad 0 \quad \frac{7}{30}]$

9. $[\frac{3}{7} \quad \frac{1}{10} \quad \frac{5}{14} \quad \frac{2}{35} \quad \frac{3}{70}]$    10. $[0 \quad \frac{4}{15} \quad \frac{1}{5} \quad \frac{32}{105} \quad \frac{24}{105}]$

**Chapter 3**
**Supplementary**
**Exercises**
**page 228**

1. $\{\{r,w,b\}\}$, $\{\{r,w\},\{b\}\}$, $\{\{r,b\},\{w\}\}$, $\{\{b,w\},\{r\}\}$, $\{\{r\},\{w\},\{b\}\}$, (neglecting $\emptyset$).

3. $\frac{377}{512}$

5. (a) $\frac{19}{64}$  (b) $\frac{1}{2}$  (c) $\frac{7}{32}$

7. $[129 \quad 0 \quad 87 \quad 0 \quad 127]$

9. (a) states 3 and 6  (b) no

11. A will control $\frac{16}{33}$, B $\frac{9}{33}$, C $\frac{8}{33}$

13. $\frac{2}{5}$

14. P(friend was on 8:00 bus or 8:30 bus) $= \frac{13}{16}$; ask away.

15. (a) $\frac{1}{81}$  (b) $\frac{1}{20}$  (c) 0

17. (a) $\frac{1,808}{2,187}$  (b) $\frac{85}{150}$  (c) insufficient information

**Section 4.1**
**page 247**

1. This is not a random variable, since the clerk did not assign a number.

3. This is a random variable.

5.
| H1 | H2 | H3 | H4 | H5 | H6 | T1 | T2 | T3 | T4 | T5 | T6 |
|----|----|----|----|----|----|----|----|----|----|----|----|
| 1  | 1  | 1  | 1  | 1  | 1  | −1 | −1 | −1 | −1 | −1 | −1 |

7.
| H1 | H2 | H3 | H4 | H5 | H6 | T1 | T2 | T3 | T4 | T5 | T6 |
|----|----|----|----|----|----|----|----|----|----|----|----|
| 0  | 2  | 0  | 2  | 0  | 2  | −2 | 0  | −2 | 0  | −2 | 0  |

8.
| H1 | H2 | H3 | H4 | H5 | H6 | T1 | T2 | T3 | T4 | T5 | T6 |
|----|----|----|----|----|----|----|----|----|----|----|----|
| 2  | 3  | −4 | 5  | 6  | −9 | 3  | 4  | −3 | 6  | 7  | −8 |

9. (a) $\frac{1}{12}$,  (b) $\frac{1}{6}$  (c) $\frac{1}{3}$  (d) 1  (e) 0

11. (a) $\frac{1}{6}$,  (b) $\frac{1}{4}$  (c) $\frac{1}{3}$  (d) 1  (e) 0

13.

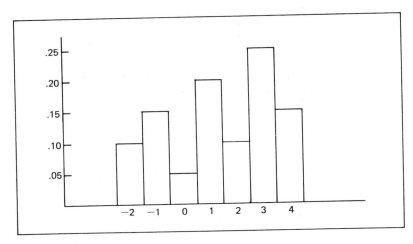

15. (a)  (b) is the shaded part.

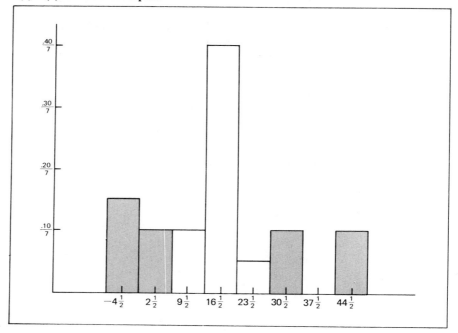

17. (a) We guess they're independent.  (b) We're wrong. For we have example
$P(X_1 = 3 \cap X_2 = 3) = P((1,1)) = \frac{1}{36}$, but $P(X_1 = 3)P(X_2 = 3) = (\frac{2}{36})(\frac{2}{36})$.

Section 4.2
page 255

1. 3  3. $-\frac{8}{525}$  5. $\frac{20}{3}$  7. $\frac{625}{9}$  9. 2.73
11. 1 km = 0.62 mi., so the answer should be $E(0.62X) = 0.62E(X) = (.62)(16.78) \doteq 10.40$.
13. $E(X_1) = 7$,  $E(X_2) = \frac{35}{18}$,  $E(X_3) = \frac{49}{4}$,  $E(X_4) = \frac{7}{2}$
15. $\frac{35}{4}$  17. No
19. $X_2 \le X_1$,  $X_4 \le X_1$,  $X_2 \le X_3$,  $X_4 \le X_3$. (and $X_1 \le X_1$, $X_2 \le X_2$, $X_3 \le X_3$, $X_4 \le X_4$.)
20. Let $a_1, a_2, \ldots, a_n$ be the numbers assigned, let m be their minimum, and let M be
their maximum. Then $\min X = m \cdot 1 = m(P(X = a_1) + \ldots + P(X = a_n)) = mP(X = a_1) + \ldots + mP(X = a_n) \le a_1 P(X = a_1) + \ldots + a_n P(X = a_n) \le MP(X = a_1) + \ldots + MP(X = a_n) = M(P(X = a_1) + \ldots + P(X = a_n)) = M \cdot 1 = \max X$; that is, $\min X \le E(X) \le \max X$.
21. 0.76. Not much.

Section 4.3
page 262

1. m = 5, v = $\frac{13}{3}$, s $\doteq$ 2.08  3. m = $-\frac{6}{43} \doteq -0.14$, v $\doteq$ 1.89, s $\doteq$ 1.37
5. m = 3, v = 6, s = $\sqrt{6}$
6. Different data may have the same mean and variance.
7. $E(X - m) = E(X) - E(m) = m - m = 0$  9. m = $\frac{14}{5}$, median = 3
11. m = $\frac{9}{50}$, median = $\frac{2}{3}$. There is no fixed relation between mean and median.
13. True for {1,2}; false for {1,2,3}
15. True for {1,2}; false for {1,2,2,3,4}  17. True for {1,2}; false for {1,2,3}
19. True. The median is such a number.
21. (a) Let m = E(X). Then $v = E((X - m)^2) = E(X^2 - 2mX + m^2) = E(X^2) - 2mE(X) + m^2 = E(X^2) - 2m^2 + m^2 = E(X^2) - m^2 = E(X^2) - (E(X))^2$.

(b) The mean of the square minus the square of the mean equals the variance.

(c) $E(X) = 0.25$, $v = \frac{83}{16} = 5.1875$, $E(X^2) = 5.25$, $E(X^2) - (E(X))^2 = 5.1875$

23. (Mean = First Moment = 221.3) Second moment $\doteq 315.4$, third $\doteq -1,046.6$, fourth $\doteq$ 186,293.8

**Section 4.4**
**page 272**

1. No; six trials are specified, but not necessarily carried out.

3. Yes   5. Approx. 0.008   7. Approx. 0.94   9. $\frac{1}{2}$   11. 0   13. 3

15.

| 0 | 1 | 2 | 3 | 4 | 5 | 6 | 7 |
|------|------|------|------|------|------|------|------|
| .008 | .055 | .164 | .273 | .273 | .164 | .055 | .008 |

17. $(\frac{1}{2})^7 = \frac{1}{128}$

19. We seek the smallest n such that $1 - (\frac{10}{13})^n \geq .9$. $n = 9$

20. (a) $\frac{21}{128}$   (b) $\frac{1}{3}$   (c) $\frac{28}{67}$   21. $\frac{64}{81}$

**Section 4.5**
**page 286**

1. $x^8 + 8x^7y + 28x^6y^2 + 56x^5y^3 + 70x^4y^4 + 56x^3y^5 + 28x^2y^6 + 8xy^7 + y^8$.

3. $C_7^{12}x^7y^5 = 792x^7y^5$.   5. $m = \frac{5}{2}$, $v = \frac{15}{8}$, $s \doteq 1.37$.   7. $m = 702$, $v \doteq 209$, $s \doteq 14.5$.

9. (a) 7.3   (b) 2   (c) $-4$   (d) 3.5   (e) 0.75

11.

| k | 0 | 2 | 3 |
|----------|------|------|------|
| binomial | .063 | .375 | .250 |
| normal | .061 | .384 | .241 |

13.

| k | 0 | 5 | 10 |
|----------|------|------|------|
| binomial | .349 | .001 | .000 |
| normal | .253 | .000 | .000 |

15.

| k | 0 | 2 | 4 | 8 |
|----------|------|------|------|------|
| binomial | .012 | .137 | .218 | .022 |
| normal | .017 | .131 | .236 | .023 |

17. 0.159   19. 0.000   21. 0.977   23. 618   25. 0.682   27. 0.193   29. 14400

31. Assume a normal distribution with $m = 22$, $s = 4$. Then P (more than 27 visits) = P(z $\geq 1.4$) = 0.081, so the number is $0.081 \times 200$ million = 16,200,000.

33. 21.8%.

**Section 4.6**
**page 291**

1. 0.030   3. $0.268 + 0.054 = 0.322$   5. $1 - 0.007 = 0.993$

7. $0.041 + 0.023 + 0.011 + 0.005 + 0.002 + 0.001 = 0.083$

9. $m = \frac{45}{9} = 5$, $P(k = 0) = 0.007$, about one in 143.

**Chapter 4**
**Review Exercises**
**page 293**

1. Choose a girl and note her weight range. Then X assigns to each girl the middle number of her weight range.

2.

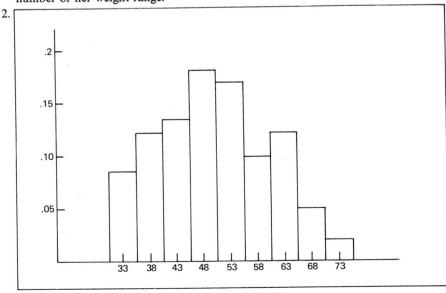

3. (a) $\frac{52}{82} = \frac{26}{41} \doteq 0.63$    (b) $1 - \frac{25}{82} = \frac{57}{82} \doteq 0.70$
   (c) $\frac{6}{82} = \frac{3}{41} \doteq 0.07$.

4. 50 pounds. (Here there would be false accuracy in giving decimals.)

5. $v = 107$, $s = 10.4$.

6. Let $X_1$ be the correct random variable. Then $.9X_1 = X$ and $E(.9X_1) = E(X) = 50$. Then $.9E(X_1) = 50$, so the correct mean is $E(X_1) = \frac{50}{.9} \doteq 56$ lbs.

7.

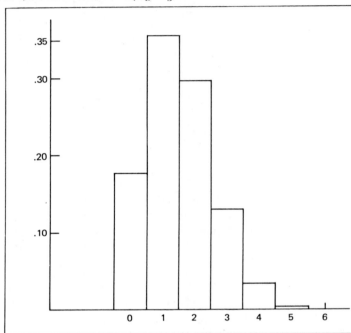

The last bar on this histogram is too short to be seen.

8. $m = 2500$, $s \doteq 35.4$. $P(2,439.5 \le k \le 2,470.5) = P((2,439.5 - 2,500)/35.4 \le z \le (2,470.5 - 2,500)/35.4) = P(-1.7 \le z \le -0.8) = 0.455 - 0.288 = 0.167$.

9. $P(k \ge 149.5) = P(z \ge 2.3) = 0.011$; 1.1%.

10. $P(1 \le k \le 4) = 0.335 + 0.251 + 0.126 + 0.047 = 0.759$, by Table 4, Part A.

Chapter 4
Supplementary
Exercises
page 293

1. 854 years, 2 months.

3. (a) Choose a camping store at random; $X_1 = $ gross on packs, $E(X_1) = 940$; $X_2 = $ gross on bags, $E(X_2) = 2,280$; $X_3 = $ gross on stoves, $E(X_3) = 1,485$; $X_4 = $ gross on gear, $E(X_4) = 960$; $X_5 = $ gross on tents, $E(X_5) = 8,880$.
   (b) $E((1.1)X_1)$, $E((1.1)(1.15)X_2)$, $E((1.1)(.95)X_3)$, $E((1.1)(1.15)X_4)$, $E((1.1)(1.15)X_5)$.
   (c) 1,034; 2,884.20; 1,551.83; 1,214.40; 11,233.20 (bucks).

5. $m(aX + bY) = E(aX + bY) = E(aX) + E(bY) = aE(X) + bE(Y) = am(X) + bm(Y)$.

7. $m(X) = c$, $s(X) = 0$.

8. Recall that $s(X) = \sqrt{E((X-m)^2)}$ , where $m = m(X) = E(X)$. Then

$$(s(X+Y))^2 = E((X-m(X))^2) + E((Y-m(Y))^2) + 2E((X-m(X))(Y-m(Y)))$$

$$= s(X)^2 + s(Y)^2 + 2[E(XY) - m(X)E(Y) - m(Y)E(X) + m(X)m(Y)].$$

Since X and Y are independent, we have by equation 6 of Section 4.2, $m(XY) = E(XY) = E(X)E(Y) = m(X)m(Y)$. Then the quantity in square brackets is $m(X)m(Y) - m(X)m(Y) - m(Y)m(X) + m(X)m(Y) = 0$; so the result holds.

9. The random variables $X_1$, $X_2$ and $X_1 + X_2$ are given by the following tabulations.

| x | $P(X_1 = x)$ | $P(X_2 = x)$ | $P(X_1 + X_2 = x)$ |
|---|---|---|---|
| 5 | $\frac{1}{3}$ | $\frac{3}{5}$ | 0 |
| 10 | $\frac{2}{3}$ | $\frac{2}{5}$ | $\frac{1}{5}$ |
| 15 | 0 | 0 | $\frac{8}{15}$ |
| 20 | 0 | 0 | $\frac{4}{15}$ |

$E(X_1) = (\frac{1}{3})5 + (\frac{2}{3})10 = \frac{25}{3}$

$E(X_2) = (\frac{3}{5})5 + (\frac{2}{5})10 = 7$

$E(X_1 + X_2) = (\frac{1}{5})10 + (\frac{8}{15})15 + (\frac{4}{15})20 = \frac{46}{3}$

$v(X_1) = (\frac{1}{3})(5 - \frac{25}{3})^2 + (\frac{2}{3})(10 - \frac{25}{3})^2 = \frac{50}{9}$

$v(X_2) = (\frac{3}{5})(5-7)^2 + (\frac{2}{5})(10-7)^2 = 6$

$v(X_1 + X_2) = \frac{1}{5}(10 - \frac{46}{3})^2 + \frac{8}{15}(15 - \frac{46}{3})^2 + \frac{4}{15}(20 - \frac{46}{3})^2 = \frac{104}{9}$

$v(X_1) + v(X_2) = \frac{50}{9} + 6 = \frac{104}{9} = v(X_1 + X_2)$ (since $s^2 = v$).

11. We want $P(k \le 2) = C_0^5(1-p)^5 + C_1^5p(1-p)^4 + C_2^5p^2(1-p)^3 = (1-p)^3(6p^2 + 3p + 1) \ge .90$. $p \le 0.24$.

13. $m = np = \frac{7}{4}$. $0 \cdot C_0^7(\frac{1}{4})^0(\frac{3}{4})^7 + \cdots + 7C_7^7(\frac{1}{4})^7(\frac{3}{4})^0 = \frac{7}{4}$.

14. (a) $(1 - \frac{1}{2})^{n-1}(\frac{1}{2}) = (\frac{1}{2})^n$ (b) They are each $\frac{1}{2}$. (c) They are infinite. (This curious result is called the **St. Petersburg paradox**.)

15. (a) $C_n^n + C_{n-1}^n + \cdots + C_1^n + C_0^n = C_n^n(1)^n(1)^0 + C_{n-1}^n(1)^{n-1}(1)^1 + \cdots + C_1^n(1)^1(1)^{n-1} + C_0^n(1)^0(1)^n = (1+1)^n = 2^n$.

(b) First count: Look at each element and either put it in the subset or not. There are n choices, each with 2 possible results, for $2^n$ subsets.

Second count: There are $C_r^n$ subsets of r objects for each r from 0 to n; so the total number of subsets is $C_0^n + C_1^n + \cdots + C_n^n$.

17. Yes

19. $P(A \cup B \cup C) = P(A) + P(B) + P(C) - P(A \cap B) - P(A \cap C) - P(B \cap C) + P(A \cap B \cap C) = .12 + .35 + .27 - (.12)(.35) - (.12)(.27) - (.35)(.27) + (.12)(.27) + (.12)(.35)(.27) \doteq .58$, so the probability is $1 - .58 = .42$.

21. (a) independent (b) independent (c) independent (d) dependent

22. (c) The only probabilities for events in the throw of a die are 0, $\frac{1}{6}$, $\frac{1}{3}$, $\frac{1}{2}$, $\frac{2}{3}$, $\frac{5}{6}$, and 1. If events A, B, C are independent and not certain, then their probabilities must be in the set $\{\frac{1}{6}, \frac{1}{3}, \frac{1}{2}, \frac{2}{3}, \frac{5}{6}\}$. But the only products of numbers in this set that are in this set are $(\frac{1}{3})(\frac{1}{2}) = \frac{1}{6}$ and $(\frac{1}{2})(\frac{2}{3}) = \frac{1}{3}$; so the required equations for independence cannot all be satisfied.

1.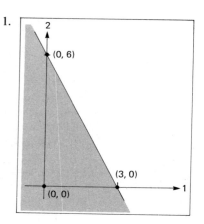

3.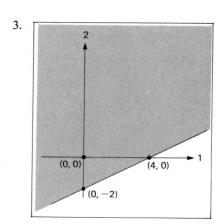

5.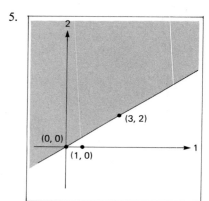

7.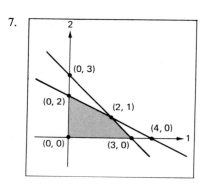

9.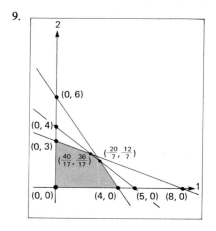

11.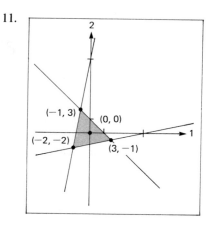

13. The region is empty.

15. (a) $x_1 = \frac{5}{3}$, $x_2 = \frac{4}{3}$, $y = 7\frac{1}{3}$   (b) $x_1 = 5$, $x_2 = 0$, $y = 5$   (c) $x_1 = 0$, $x_2 = 3$, $y = 3$

17. (a) $x_1=2$, $x_2=1$, $y=7$  (b) $x_1=\frac{1}{3}$, $x_2=\frac{8}{3}$, $y=6\frac{1}{3}$  (c) $x_1=4$, $x_2=0$, $y=4$
    (d) $x_1=0$, $x_2=4$, $y=4$
18. Note that the first and third constraints impose no further restriction on the problem than is already imposed by the second constraint.
19. (a) Maximum $x_1=3$, $x_2=-1$, $y=7$; minimum $x_1=-1$, $x_2=3$, $y=-5$
    (b) Maximum $x_1=-1$, $x_2=3$, $y=9$; minimum $x_1=-2$, $x_2=-2$, $y=-14$
    (c) Maximum $x_1=3$, $x_2=-1$, $y=3$; minimum $x_1=-2$, $x_2=-2$, $y=-2$
    (d) Maximum $x_1=-1$, $x_2=3$, $y=3$; minimum $x_1=-2$, $x_2=-2$, $y=-2$
21. Since the region is empty, there are no feasible and therefore no optimal solutions.
23. $x_1=\frac{6}{5}$, $x_2=\frac{6}{5}$, $y=\frac{12}{5}$.
25. The region is unbounded. There is no minimum value for y. In fact, y can be made as small as we please by suitably choosing feasible solutions.
27. (a) Maximum: $x_1=6$, $x_2=5$, $y=41$; minimum: $x_1=1$, $x_2=6$, $y=12$
    (b) Maximum: $x_1=1$, $x_2=6$, $y=43$; minimum: $x_1=4$, $x_2=2$, $y=18$

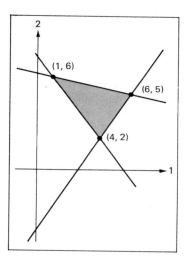

29. The region of feasibility is empty, so there are no answers.
31. Maximum: $x_1=2$, $x_2=2$, $y=4$. Minimum: $x_1=-2$, $x_2=-2$, $y=-4$. The region of feasibility is a square.
33. (a) Operate Springfield for 7 days and Waterbury for 2 days to exactly fill the orders at a minimum cost of $1,080.
    (b) Operate Springfield for 1 day and Waterbury for 2 days to exactly fill the orders at a minimum cost of $360.
    (c) Do not operate Springfield. Operate Waterbury for $\frac{1}{4}$ of a day. The minimum cost will be $30. There will be one pair of booties left over.
    (d) Do not operate Waterbury. Operate Springfield for $\frac{5}{6}$ of a day. The minimum cost will be $100. There will be two jackets left over.
34. One dollar.

35. (a)

| | For one cheeseburger | For one superburger | Total available | Units |
|---|---|---|---|---|
| Meat | 5 | 7 | 350 | ounces |
| Cheese | 0.7 | 0.6 | 42 | ounces |
| Time | 3 | 11 | 330 | minutes |
| Profit | 10 | 40 | | cents |

Let $x_1 =$ the number of cheeseburgers to be made; let $x_2 =$ the number of superburgers to be made. Maximize $y = 10x_1 + 40x_2$ subject to $x_1 \geq 0$, $x_2 \geq 0$, $5x_1 + 7x_2 \leq 350$, $0.7x_1 + 0.6x_2 \leq 42$, $3x_1 + 11x_2 \leq 330$.

The second constraint can be freed of decimals by multiplying through by 10 to obtain $7x_1 + 6x_2 \leq 420$. (See Appendix A, Section 10, if needed.) The numbers can be made more manageable by the following changes of units: Count burgers by tens; that is, let $x_1 =$ the number of tens of cheeseburgers, and so on. (Thus, $x_1 = 15.3$ would mean 153 cheeseburgers, for example.) The profit then becomes $y = 100x_1 + 400x_2$ cents, or $x_1 + 4x_2$ dollars, so measure profit in dollars. Then the problem becomes: maximize $y = x_1 + 4x_2$ subject to $x_1 \geq 0$, $x_2 \geq 0$, $5x_1 + 7x_2 \leq 35$, $7x_1 + 6x_2 \leq 42$, $3x_1 + 11x_2 \leq 33$.

(b) Make no cheeseburgers and 30 superburgers for a profit of \$12.

(c) There will be 140 ounces of meat and 24 ounces of cheese left over, but all the available preparation time will be used up.

36. The region of feasibility is the line segment from $\left(\frac{7}{10}, \frac{27}{10}\right)$ to $\left(\frac{3}{2}, \frac{7}{2}\right)$ as indicated in the figure. These points are the corner points of the region. The maximum occurs at the point $\left(\frac{3}{2}, \frac{7}{2}\right)$. Thus, the answer is $x_1 = \frac{3}{2}$, $x_2 = \frac{7}{2}$, $y = 11\frac{1}{2}$.

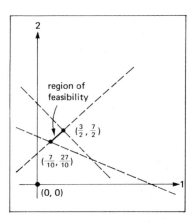

1. $x_1 = 2$, $x_2 = 1$, $y = 10$.     3. $x_1 = \frac{4}{3}$, $x_2 = \frac{2}{3}$, $y = \frac{14}{3}$

5. The second constraint does not satisfy Condition 2. Therefore, the geometric method must be used. The answer is $x_1 = \frac{5}{3}$, $x_2 = \frac{8}{3}$, $y = 6$.

7. It is not necessary to clear any columns to solve this problem. The answer $x_1 = 0$,

$x_2 = 0$, $y = 0$ is read from the first matrix:

$$\begin{bmatrix} -1 & 1 & 1 & 0 & 2 \\ 1 & 1 & 0 & 1 & 2 \\ -2 & -3 & 0 & 0 & 0 \end{bmatrix}$$

9. There are feasible solutions, but the objective variable is unbounded so there is no maximum.

11. $x_1 = 4$, $x_2 = 3$, $y = 10$.     13. $x_1 = 3$, $x_2 = 4$, $y = 17$.

15. The problem does not satisfy Condition 1. The second and third constraints do not satisfy Condition 3. The geometric method yields the answer $x_1 = -3$, $x_2 = 6$, $y = 9$.

17. $x_1 = 2$, $x_2 = 2$, $x_3 = 0$, $y = 56$.

19. $x_1 = 5$, $x_2 = 0$, $x_3 = 3$, $y = 53$.

21. The objective variable is unbounded.

23. $x_1 = 1$, $x_2 = 0$, $x_3 = 2$, $x_4 = 0$, $y = 14$.

25. $x_1 = \frac{2}{3}$, $x_2 = 0$, $x_3 = 0$, $x_4 = \frac{11}{18}$, $y = \frac{31}{6}$.

27. $x_1 = x_2 = x_3 = x_4 = y = 0$. Compare Exercise 7 above.

29. $x_1 = 0$, $x_2 = \frac{1}{10}$, $x_3 = \frac{23}{5}$, $y = 28\frac{2}{5}$.

31. $x_1 = 1$, $x_2 = 0$, $x_3 = 2$, $x_4 = 0$, $x_5 = 4$, $y = 7$. (Another answer is $x_1 = 1$, $x_2 = 0$, $x_3 = 2$, $x_4 = 1$, $x_5 = 3$.)

33. (a) 5

(b) The smallest such problem has as many constraints as nonzero variables. Of course, it must have at least as many variables as there are nonzero variables in the answer.

35. A fishfeast consisting of $x_1$ servings of fish, $x_2$ of fries, and $x_3$ of slaw would weigh $y = 3x_1 + 3x_2 + 3x_3$ ounces. We are to maximize $y = 3x_1 + 3x_2 + 3x_3$ subject to $x_1 \geq 0$, $x_2 \geq 0$, $x_3 \geq 0$, $21x_1 + 18x_2 + 14x_3 \leq 126$. The corners of the region of feasibility are $(0,0,0)$, $(6,0,0)$, $(0,7,0)$, and $(0,0,9)$. The values of $y$ at these corners are 0, 18, 21, and 27, respectively. Thus, the solution is $x_1 = x_2 = 0$, $x_3 = 9$, $y = 27$, which is patently absurd: serve no fish or fries and 27 ounces of slaw!

37. $x_1 = x_2 = x_3 = 0$, $x_4 = 6$, $y = 24$.

Section 5.3
page 334

1. Suppose, say, the bottom entry in $C_1$ is positive but all other entries in $C_1$ are less than or equal to zero. This means that in each constraint the coefficient of $x_1$ is less than or equal to zero. Then as $x_1$ gets bigger the left side of each constraint will get smaller or stay the same, and so the constraints will all continue to hold no matter how large $x_1$ gets. But, since the coefficient of $x_1$ in the expression for $y$ is positive, the value of $y$ will get larger and larger as $x_1$ does. In other words, $y$ is unbounded, so there is no maximum value of $y$. The argument is essentially the same if some other column instead of $C_1$ is involved.

3. The problem: Maximize $y = x_1 + 4x_2$ subject to $x_1 \geq 0$, $x_2 \geq 0$, and $5x_1 + 7x_2 \leq 35$, $7x_1 + 6x_2 \leq 42$, $3x_1 + 11x_2 \leq 33$.

We need three slack variables $x_3$, $x_4$, and $x_5$ to convert this system of inequalities to the system of equations:

$$\begin{bmatrix} 5x_1 + 7x_2 + x_3 & & = 35 \\ 7x_1 + 6x_2 & + x_4 & = 42 \\ 3x_1 + 11x_2 & + x_5 & = 33 \\ x_1 + 4x_2 & & = y \end{bmatrix}$$

In the formula for the objective variable $y = x_1 + 4x_2$ we see that an increase in either $x_1$ or $x_2$ will cause y to increase. Many people like to increase the variable that causes y to increase the most. It is easy to construct problems in which this is the worst possible approach. Thus, we do not give that advice in the text. Nevertheless, for this problem that is very good advice: increase $x_2$.

Having said all that, we will increase $x_1$ instead. This leads to a more interesting and involved solution. (If you increase $x_2$ you are done in one step.) Question: How much can we increase $x_1$? To see this we let $x_2 = 0$ and solve the three equalities for the other variables:

$$x_3 = 35 - 5x_1$$
$$x_4 = 42 - 7x_1$$
$$x_5 = 33 - 3x_1$$

The second equality is the most restrictive; it says we cannot increase $x_1$ past 6. So we increase $x_1$ to 6 in the second equation and then use this equation to eliminate $x_1$ from the other equations:

$$\begin{bmatrix} \frac{19}{7}x_2 + x_3 - \frac{5}{7}x_4 & = 5 \\ x_1 + \frac{6}{7}x_2 & + \frac{1}{7}x_4 & = 6 \\ \frac{59}{7}x_2 & - \frac{3}{7}x_4 + x_5 = 15 \\ \frac{22}{7}x_2 & - \frac{1}{7}x_4 & = y - 6 \end{bmatrix}$$

We are now at the corner where $x_1 = 3$, $x_2 = 0$, $x_3 = 5$, $x_4 = 0$, and $x_5 = 0$. Here the profit is given by

$$y = \frac{22}{7}x_2 - \frac{1}{7}x_4 + 6.$$

We can increase y by increasing $x_2$ and holding $x_4 = 0$. To see how much we can increase $x_2$, we solve the above system for the other variables:

$$x_3 = 5 - \frac{19}{7}x_2$$
$$x_1 = 6 - \frac{6}{7}x_2$$
$$x_5 = 15 - \frac{59}{7}x_2$$

Since each of the variables $x_1$, $x_3$, and $x_2$ must always be greater than zero, we may not increase $x_2$ indefinitely. In fact, as we increase $x_2$, $x_3$ hits zero first when $x_2 = \frac{105}{59}$, so we must stop there. We set $x_2 = \frac{105}{59}$ in the first equation and then use Gauss-Jordan reduction to eliminate $x_2$ from the other equations:

$$\begin{bmatrix} x_3 - \frac{34}{59}x_4 - \frac{19}{59}x_5 = \frac{10}{59} \\ x_1 & + \frac{11}{59}x_4 - \frac{6}{59}x_5 = \frac{264}{59} \\ x_2 & - \frac{3}{59}x_4 + \frac{7}{59}x_5 = \frac{105}{59} \\ & \frac{1}{59}x_4 - \frac{22}{59}x_5 = y - \frac{684}{59} \end{bmatrix}$$

Now we have $x_1 = \frac{264}{59}$, $x_2 = \frac{105}{59}$, $x_3 = \frac{10}{59}$, and $x_4 = x_5 = 0$. In the formula for y:

$$y = \frac{1}{59}x_4 - \frac{22}{59}x_5 + \frac{684}{59}$$

we see that we should increase $x_4$ and set $x_5=0$. If we solve as before we discover:

$$x_3 = \tfrac{10}{59} + \tfrac{34}{59}x_4$$

$$x_1 = \tfrac{264}{59} - \tfrac{11}{59}x_4$$

$$x_2 = \tfrac{105}{59} + \tfrac{3}{59}x_4$$

The only limitation is expressed by the second equation. We increase $x_4$ to 24 (and thus decrease $x_1$ to 0). The effect on the other variables is determined as before:

$$\begin{bmatrix} \tfrac{34}{11}x_1 & +x_3 & -\tfrac{7}{11}x_5 = 14 \\ \tfrac{59}{11}x_1 & +x_4 - \tfrac{6}{11}x_5 = 24 \\ \tfrac{3}{11}x_1 + x_2 & +x_5 = 3 \\ -\tfrac{1}{11}x_1 & -\tfrac{4}{11}x_5 = y - 12 \end{bmatrix}$$

We now find that $x_1=0$, $x_2=3$, $x_3=14$, $x_4=24$, $x_5=0$, and $y=12$. From the expression for $y$:

$$y = 12 - \tfrac{1}{11}x_1 - \tfrac{4}{11}x_5$$

we see that we cannot increase $y$. The maximum occurs where $x_1$ and $x_5$ are as small as possible, that is, zero. Thus, the answer is $x_1=0$, $x_2=3$, $y=12$.

Again, if we had started this whole problem by increasing $x_2$, we would have arrived at this solution at once.

**Section 5.4**
**page 347**

1. (a) $x_1 - 2x_2 \le 4$  (b) $-3x_1 - x_2 + 4x_3 + x_4 \le 2$  (c) $-2x_1 + x_2 + x_3 + 2x_4 - x_5 \le 7$
   (d) $x_1 + 3x_2 - 5x_3 \le 2$  (e) $x_1 - 2x_2 - x_3 \le -13$
3. $x_1 = x_2 = 1$, $y=5$      5. $x_1 = 6$, $x_2 = 5$, $y=41$      7. $x_1 = \tfrac{105}{22}$, $x_2 = \tfrac{9}{22}$, $y = \tfrac{162}{11}$
9. The region of feasibility is empty; there is no feasible and, therefore, no optimal solution.
11. The region is unbounded. There are feasible, but no optimal, solutions.
12. While we have not explicitly assumed that $x_1 \ge 0$, $x_2 \ge 0$, this fact is implied by the constraints. To solve this problem, rewrite the constraints as the four constraints $1 \le x_1$, $x_1 \le 2$, $1 \le x_2$, $x_2 \le 2$.
13. $x_1 = \tfrac{6}{7}$, $x_2 = \tfrac{16}{7}$, $x_3 = 0$, $y = \tfrac{120}{7}$
15. $x_1 = 0$, $x_2 = 0$, $x_3 = \tfrac{11}{2}$, $y = 33$.
17. The region is empty. There are no feasible and therefore no optimal solutions.
19. There are feasible solutions but no optimal solutions. The objective variable is unbounded. It can be made as large as we wish.
21. $x_1 = \tfrac{5}{3}$, $x_2 = \tfrac{4}{3}$, $y = 7\tfrac{1}{3}$.      23. $x_1 = x_2 = \tfrac{1}{2}$, $y = 5$.      25. $x_1 = \tfrac{1}{3}$, $x_2 = \tfrac{8}{3}$, $y = 8\tfrac{2}{3}$.
27. $x_1 = 7$, $x_2 = 2$, $y = 312$. The region of feasibility consists of a single point.
29. The region is unbounded. There is no minimum value for $y$. In fact, $y$ can be made as small as we please by suitably choosing feasible solutions.
31. $x_1 = 0$, $x_2 = 6$, $x_3 = 1$, $y = 53$.      33. $x_1 = 0$, $x_2 = \tfrac{1}{3}$, $x_3 = \tfrac{7}{3}$, $y = \tfrac{67}{3}$.
35. $x_1 = \tfrac{10}{3}$, $x_2 = \tfrac{82}{15}$, $x_3 = \tfrac{26}{5}$, $x_4 = 0$, $y = \tfrac{234}{5}$.      36. Compare Exercise 12.
37. $x_1 = 1$, $x_2 = 2$, $y = 7$.      39. $x_1 = 1$, $x_2 = 2$, $y = 1$.      41. $x_1 = \tfrac{7}{10}$, $x_2 = \tfrac{27}{10}$, $y = \tfrac{15}{2}$.
43. $x_1 = \tfrac{10}{11}$, $x_2 = \tfrac{28}{11}$, $x_3 = x_4 = 0$, $y = \tfrac{142}{11}$.      45. No feasible solution.

**Section 5.5**
**page 356**

1. Mix 4 grams of I with 2 grams of II to obtain a pellet with $46\tfrac{2}{3}$ calories.
3. Produce 10 trucks, 3 beach balls, and 3 music boxes at a profit of $38.

4. Minimize $y = x_1 + x_2$ subject to $x_1 \geq 0$, $x_2 \geq 0$, $3x_1 + 2x_2 \geq 6$, $x_1 + 7x_2 \geq 7$, $2x_1 + 3x_2 \geq 6$. Answer: $x_1 = x_2 = \frac{6}{5}$; hire each firm for 6 hrs.

5. Operate method 1 for 2 hours, 40 minutes; method 2 for 1 hour, 20 minutes; and method 3 for 1 hour, 20 minutes. There will be no overproduction. The total cost will be $72.

7. Let $x_1$, $x_2$, $x_3$ be the number of ladlesful of uncooked strawberries, uncooked apples, and cooked peaches, respectively, in one serving. The cost of the serving is $y = 4x_1 + 3x_2 + 5x_3$ dimes. The constraint on salt is $2x_1 + 3x_3 \geq 4$; the constraint on weight is $x_1 + 2x_2 + 3x_3 \geq 3$; the constraint on volume is $3x_1 + 2x_3 \geq x_2 + 5$; that is, $3x_1 - x_2 + 2x_3 \geq 5$.

$$\begin{bmatrix} -2 & 0 & -3 & 1 & 0 & 0 & -4 \\ -1^* & -2 & -3 & 0 & 1 & 0 & -3 \\ -3 & 1 & -2 & 0 & 0 & 1 & -5 \\ -4 & -3 & -5 & 0 & 0 & 0 & 0 \end{bmatrix} \begin{bmatrix} 0 & 4 & 3 & 1 & -2 & 0 & 2 \\ 1 & 2 & 3 & 0 & -1 & 0 & 3 \\ 0 & 7 & 7^* & 0 & -3 & 1 & 4 \\ 0 & 5 & 7 & 0 & -4 & 0 & 12 \end{bmatrix}$$

$$\begin{bmatrix} 0 & 1 & 0 & 1 & -\frac{5}{7} & -\frac{3}{7} & \frac{2}{7} \\ 1 & -1 & 0 & 0 & \frac{2}{7} & -\frac{3}{7} & \frac{9}{7} \\ 0 & 7 & 7 & 0 & -3 & 1 & 4 \\ 0 & -2 & 0 & 0 & -1 & -1 & 8 \end{bmatrix}$$

$x_1 = \frac{9}{7}$, $x_2 = 0$, $x_3 = \frac{4}{7}$, $y = 8$.

Answer: Use no apples. Mix 9 parts strawberries (before cooking) with 4 parts peaches. One serving will cost 80¢

9. Let $x_1$ = the number of Basic houses, $x_2$ = the number of Deluxe house, and $x_3$ = the number of garages built. The builder's requirements are

(i) $x_3 \leq x_1 + x_2$
(ii) $100x_1 + 160x_2 + 20x_3 \leq 900$
(iii) $1{,}000x_1 + 2{,}000x_2 + 500x_3 \geq 10{,}000$ and he wants to maximize $y = x_1 + x_2$. Changing units, we can formulate this problem:

Maximize $y = x_1 + x_2$ subject to $x_1 \geq 0$, $x_2 \geq 0$, $x_3 \geq 0$, and $-x_1 - x_2 + x_3 \leq 0$, $10x_1 + 16x_2 + 2x_3 \leq 90$, $-2x_1 - 4x_2 - x_3 \leq -20$. The answer is: Make $8\frac{1}{3}$ Basic houses, no Deluxe houses, and $3\frac{1}{3}$ garages.

While the builder can actually implement this solution by partially finishing the last project, he wants to complete all projects begun during the month. Therefore, he decides to build 8 Basic houses and 4 garages.

11. Ship 30 pounds from Secaucus to Winesburg, 10 pounds from Secaucus to the Ozarks, nothing from Gary to Winesburg, and 40 pounds from Gary to the Ozarks. The total cost will be $270.

13. Let $x_1$ denote the number of ounces of beef, $x_2$ the number of ounces of chicken, and $x_3$ the number of ounces of pork consumed per week. We are to Minimize $y = 17x_1 + 22x_2 + 18x_3$ subject to $x_1 \geq 0$, $x_2 \geq 0$, $x_3 \geq 0$, and $3x_1 + \frac{1}{2}x_2 + x_3 \geq 70$, $7x_1 + 9x_2 + 8x_3 \geq 224$, $27x_1 + 21x_2 + 24x_3 \leq 864$. the answer is $x_1 = 19\frac{13}{17}$, $x_2 = 0$, $x_3 = 10\frac{12}{17}$. Thus, I should eat $19\frac{13}{17}$ ounces of beef, no ounces of chicken, and $10\frac{12}{17}$ ounces of pork per week.

15. Let $x_1$ be the number of beef cattle, $x_2$ the number of pigs, $x_3$ the number of chickens and $x_4$ the number of acres of sweet corn. The animals will require $3x_1 + x_2 + \frac{1}{2}x_3$ acres. Thus the first constraint is

$$3x_1 + x_2 + \frac{1}{2}x_3 + x_4 = 40.$$

Notice that $x_4$ is like a slack variable—although it does contribute to the profit

$$y = 100x_1 + 50x_2 + 27x_3 + 30x_4$$

The second constraint concerns meat production

$$80x_1 + 30x_2 \geq 450$$

The last constraint involves her limited time. Recall that the animals need $3x_1 + x_2 + \frac{1}{2}x_3$ acres. This acreage will require $50(3x_1 + x_2 + \frac{1}{2}x_3) = 150x_1 + 50x_2 + 25x_3$ hours of time. We must require that

$$150x_1 + 50x_2 + 25x_3 + 75x_4 \leq 700.$$

Our problem:

Maximize $y = 100x_1 + 50x_2 + 27x_3 + 30x_4$, subject to $x_1 \geq 0$, $x_2 \geq 0$, $x_3 \geq 0$, $x_4 \geq 0$ and $80x_1 + 30x_2 \geq 450$, $3x_1 + x_2 + \frac{1}{2}x_3 + x_4 = 40$, $150x_1 + 50x_2 + 25x_3 + 75x_4 \leq 700$. Before we set up the first matrix, we divide these conditions by $\frac{1}{2}$, 10, and 5, respectively.

$$\begin{bmatrix} 6 & 2 & 1^* & 2 & 0 & 0 & 0 & 80 \\ -8 & -3 & 0 & 0 & 1 & 0 & 0 & -45 \\ 30 & 10 & 5 & 15 & 0 & 0 & 1 & 140 \\ 100 & 50 & 27 & 30 & 0 & 0 & 0 & 0 \end{bmatrix}$$

$$\begin{bmatrix} 6 & 2 & 1 & 2 & 0 & 0 & 0 & 80 \\ -8 & -3 & 0 & 0 & 1 & 0 & 0 & -45 \\ 0 & 0 & 0 & 5 & 0 & 0 & 1 & -360 \\ -62 & -4 & 0 & -24 & 0 & 0 & 0 & -2,160 \end{bmatrix}$$

The third row of this matrix indicates that there is no feasible solution. Either the farmer must rethink her requirements, or the author has to devise a more sensible set of data.

**Section 5.6**
**page 374**

1. Minimize $y = 2x_1 + 4x_2$ subject to $x_1 \geq 0, x_2 \geq 0$, $x_1 + x_2 \geq 2, x_1 + 4x_2 \geq 3$.
3. Maximize $y = 12x_1 + 16x_2 + 6x_3$ subject to $x_1 \geq 0$, $x_2 \geq 0$, $x_3 \geq 0$, $2x_1 + x_2 + 2x_3 \leq 6$, $3x_1 + 8x_2 + 5x_3 \leq 22$, $2x_1 + 2x_2 + 3x_3 \leq 12$.
5. Minimize $y = -2x_1 - 2x_2$ subject to $x_1 \geq 0$, $x_2 \geq 0$, $2x_1 - x_2 \geq 3$, $-x_1 + 2x_2 \geq -2$.
7. The answer to the given maximization problem is $x_1 = \frac{5}{3}$, $x_2 = \frac{8}{3}$, $y = 6$. This answer is feasible since $-\frac{5}{3} + \frac{8}{3} = 1 \leq 1$, $\frac{5}{3} + \frac{8}{3} = \frac{13}{3} \geq 2$, $\frac{20}{3} - \frac{8}{3} = 4 \leq 4$; also $y = \frac{10}{3} + \frac{8}{3} = \frac{18}{3} = 6$.
   The answer to the dual minimization problem is $x_1 = 2$, $x_2 = 0$, $x_3 = 1$, $y = 6$. This answer is feasible since $-2 - 0 + 4 = 2 \geq 2$, $2 - 0 - 1 = 1 \geq 1$; also $y = 2 - 0 + 4 = 6$.
9. The answer to the given minimization problem is $x_1 = \frac{1}{2}$, $x_2 = \frac{4}{3}$, $x_3 = 0$, $y = \frac{31}{6}$. This answer is feasible since $1 + 4 + 0 = 5 \geq 5$, $\frac{1}{2} + 4 + 0 = 4\frac{1}{2} \geq 4$, $\frac{3}{2} + \frac{8}{3} + 0 = \frac{25}{6} \geq 2$, $3 + 0 + 0 = 3 \geq 3$; also $y = \frac{5}{2} + \frac{8}{3} + 0 = \frac{31}{6}$.
   The answer to the dual maximization problem is $x_1 = \frac{2}{3}$, $x_2 = 0$, $x_3 = 0$, $x_4 = \frac{11}{18}$, $y = \frac{31}{6}$. This answer is feasible since $\frac{4}{3} + 0 + 0 + \frac{11}{6} = 5 \leq 5$, $2 + 0 + 0 + 0 = 2 \leq 2$, $\frac{8}{3} + 0 + 0 + \frac{11}{6} = \frac{27}{6} \leq 6$; also $y = \frac{10}{3} + 0 + 0 + \frac{11}{6} = \frac{31}{6}$.
11. Problem 1: Maximize $y = 3x_1 + 4x_2$ subject to $5x_1 - x_2 \geq -8$, $x_1 - 5x_2 \leq 8$, $x_1 + x_2 \leq 2$.

Solution:

$$\begin{bmatrix} -5 & 5 & 1 & -1 & 1 & 0 & 0 & 8 \\ 1 & -1 & -5 & 5 & 0 & 1 & 0 & 8 \\ 1 & -1 & 1^* & -1 & 0 & 0 & 1 & 2 \\ 3 & -3 & 4 & -4 & 0 & 0 & 0 & 0 \end{bmatrix}$$

$$\begin{bmatrix} -6 & 6^* & 0 & 0 & 1 & 0 & -1 & 6 \\ 6 & -6 & 0 & 0 & 0 & 1 & 5 & 18 \\ 1 & -1 & 1 & -1 & 0 & 0 & 1 & 2 \\ -1 & 1 & 0 & 0 & 0 & 0 & -4 & -8 \end{bmatrix}$$

$$\begin{array}{cccc} x_{1p} & x_{1n} & x_{2p} & x_{2n} \end{array}$$
$$\begin{bmatrix} -6 & 6 & 0 & 0 & 1 & 0 & -1 & 6 \\ 0 & 0 & 0 & 0 & 1 & 1 & 4 & 22 \\ 0 & 0 & 1 & -1 & \frac{1}{6} & 0 & \frac{5}{6} & 3 \\ 0 & 0 & 0 & 0 & -\frac{1}{6} & 0 & -\frac{23}{6} & -9 \end{bmatrix}$$

The answer: $x_{1p}=0$, $x_{1n}=1$, $x_{2p}=3$, $x_{2n}=0$, $y=9$; that is, $x_1=-1$, $x_2=3$, $y=9$.
Problem 2: Minimize $y=3x_1+4x_2$ subject to $5x_1-x_2 \geq -8$, $x_1-5x_2 \leq 8$, $x_1+x_2 \leq 2$.
Note that this problem is *not* the dual of the previous problem.
Solution:

$$\begin{bmatrix} -5 & 5^* & 1 & -1 & 1 & 0 & 0 & 8 \\ 1 & -1 & -5 & 5 & 0 & 1 & 0 & 8 \\ 1 & -1 & 1 & -1 & 0 & 0 & 1 & 2 \\ -3 & 3 & -4 & 4 & 0 & 0 & 0 & 0 \end{bmatrix}$$

$$\begin{bmatrix} -5 & 5 & 1 & -1 & 1 & 0 & 0 & 8 \\ 0 & 0 & -\frac{24}{5} & \frac{24}{5}^* & \frac{1}{5} & 1 & 0 & \frac{48}{5} \\ 0 & 0 & \frac{6}{5} & -\frac{6}{5} & \frac{1}{5} & 0 & 1 & \frac{18}{5} \\ 0 & 0 & -\frac{23}{5} & \frac{23}{5} & -\frac{3}{5} & 0 & 0 & -\frac{24}{5} \end{bmatrix}$$

$$\begin{array}{cccc} x_{1p} & x_{1n} & x_{2p} & x_{1n} \end{array}$$
$$\begin{bmatrix} -5 & 5 & 0 & 0 & \frac{25}{24} & \frac{5}{24} & 0 & 16 \\ 0 & 0 & -\frac{24}{5} & \frac{24}{5} & \frac{1}{5} & 1 & 0 & \frac{48}{5} \\ 0 & 0 & 0 & 0 & \frac{1}{4} & \frac{1}{4} & 1 & 6 \\ 0 & 0 & 0 & 0 & 0 & -\frac{23}{24} & 0 & -14 \end{bmatrix}$$

The answer: $x_{1p}=0$, $x_{1n}=2$, $x_{2p}=0$, $x_{2n}=2$, $y=4$; that is, $x_1=-2$, $x_2=-2$, $y=-14$.
13. The given minimization problem has no feasible solution. The dual maximization problem is

Maximize $y = 7x_1 + 8x_2 + 5x_3$ subject to $x_2 \geq 0$, $x_3 \geq 0$, $x_2 - x_3 = 2$, $x_1 - x_2 + x_3 \leq -3$, $x_1 + 2x_2 - x_3 \leq 3$.

This problem has feasible but no optimal solutions.

15. The answer to the given maximization problem is $x_1=2$, $x_2=1$, $x_3=0$, $y=0$. It is feasible since $2+2-0=4\geq 2$, $6-2+0=4\leq 4$, $-2-2+0=-4\leq -4$; also $y=2-2+0=0$.

The dual minimization problem is

Minimize $y=-2x_1+4x_2-4x_3$ subject to $x_1\geq 0$, $x_2\geq 0$, $x_3\geq 3$, and $-x_1+3x_2-x_3\geq 1$, $-2x_1-2x_2-2x_3\geq -2$, $x_1+2x_2+4x_3\geq 2$.

The answer to the problem is $x_1=0$, $x_2=\frac{1}{2}$, $x_3=\frac{1}{2}$, $y=0$. It is feasible since $0+\frac{3}{2}-\frac{1}{2}=1\geq 1$, $0-1-1=-2\geq -2$, $0+1+2=3\geq 2$; also $y=0+2-2=0$.

17. The answer to the given maximization problem is $x_1=-12$, $x_2=0$, $x_3=7$, and $y=-3$. It is feasible since $0+7=7$, $12+0-14=-2\leq 8$, $12+0-7=5\geq 5$; also $y=-24-0+21=-3$.

The dual minimization problem is

Minimize $7x_1+8x_2-5x_3$ subject to $x_2\geq 0$, $x_3\geq 0$, and $-x_2+x_3=2$, $x_1+x_2-x_3\geq -3$, $x_1-2x_2+x_3\geq 3$.

The answer is $x_1=1$, $x_2=0$, $x_3=2$, $y=-3$. This answer is feasible since $0+2=2$, $1+0-2=-1\geq -3$, $1-0+2=3\geq 3$; also $y=7+0-10=-3$.

19. The answer to the given maximization problem is $x_1=0$, $x_2=3$, $x_3=-3$, $y=3$. This answer is feasible since $0+3-3=0\geq 8$, $0-3+9=6\leq 6$, $0+3+3=6\leq 6$; also $y=0-3+6=3$.

The dual minimization problem is

Minimize $y=8x_1+6x_2-6x_3$ subject to $x_1\geq 0$, $x_2\geq 0$, $x_3\geq 0$, $-x_1+2x_2+3x_3\geq -3$, $-x_1-x_2-x_3\geq -1$, $-x_1-3x_2+x_3\geq -2$.

The answer to this problem is $x_1=0$, $x_2=\frac{3}{4}$, $x_3=\frac{1}{4}$, $y=3$. It is feasible since $0+\frac{3}{2}+\frac{3}{4}=\frac{9}{4}\geq -3$, $0-\frac{3}{4}-\frac{1}{4}=-1$, $0-\frac{9}{4}+\frac{1}{4}=-2$; also $y=0+\frac{18}{4}-\frac{6}{4}=3$.

21. Kraye's best offer is to give away type-A coal and charge $625 for 100 tons of type-B coal and $291\frac{2}{3}$ for 100 tons of type-C coal. Their daily income will be $30,416\frac{2}{3}$.

22. Let $x_1=$ the price he sets for powdered protein, $x_2=$ the price of carbohydrate, $x_3=$ the price of calcium. At these prices it would cost

$$8x_1+3x_3$$

cents to duplicate the food value in one ounce of hamburger,

$$20x_1+35x_2+870x_3$$

cents to duplicate the food value in one cup of powdered milk, and

$$6x_1+27x_3$$

cents to duplicate the food value in one egg.

I will not buy anything unless $8x_1+3x_3\leq 6$, $20x_1+35x_2+870x_3\leq 15$, $6x_1+27x_3\leq 7$. On the other hand, given my needs, his profit will be

$$y=60x_1+126x_2+3{,}180x_3.$$

His problem is to maximize $y=60x_1+126x_2+3{,}180x_3$ subject to $x_1\geq 0$, $x_2\geq 0$, $x_3\geq 0$, and $8x_1+3x_3\leq 6$, $20x_1+35x_2+870x_3\leq 15$, $6x_1+27x_3\leq 7$.

This is the dual problem to my problem of minimizing cost. (But not the dual to exercise 12 of Section 5.5, p. 359.)

23. Since Taint It Pork? gets $x_1$ dollars per pound at Secaucus and pays $x_3$ dollars per pound at Winesburg, they lose

$$x_3 - x_1$$

dollars per pound (but get free shipping). So they do not care as long as this is less than the usual transportation cost of $2 per pound per shipments from Secaucus to Winesburg. Thus we must have

$$x_3 - x_1 \leq 2.$$

Similarly, for each of the other transportation costs:

$$x_4 - x_1 \leq 5$$
$$x_3 - x_2 \leq 3$$
$$x_4 - x_2 \leq 4.$$

The 10-4 company buys 40 pounds of pork at Secaucus and 40 pounds of pork at Gary. They lose $40x_1 + 40x_2$. When they sell it back in Winesburg and the Ozarks, they get only $30_3 + 50x_4$ since that is what these two markets demand. Their net profit is

$$y = -40x_1 - 40x_2 + 30x_3 + 50x_4$$

The problem for 10-4 is

Maximize $y = -40x_1 - 40x_2 + 30x_3 + 50x_4$ subject to $x_1 \geq 0$, $x_2 \geq 0$, $x_3 \geq 0$, $x_4 \geq 0$,
$-x_1 + x_3 \leq 2$, $-x_1 + x_4 \leq 5$, $-x_2 + x_3 \leq 3$, $-x_2 + x_4 \leq 4$.
This is the dual of the Taint It Pork? transportation cost minimization problem.
The answer is:

$$x_1 = 0,\ x_2 = 1,\ x_3 = 2,\ x_4 = 5.$$

Thus, 10-4 should pay nothing for the pork it picks up at Secaucus and one dollar a pound for the pork it picks up at Gary. It resells this pork at the rate of 2 dollars a pound in Winesburg and 5 dollars a pound in the Ozarks. Of course, since these problems are dual to one another, the profit of 10-4, $270, is the same as the cost to Taint It Pork?.

Chapter 5
Review Exercises
page 382

1. (a)                                    (b)

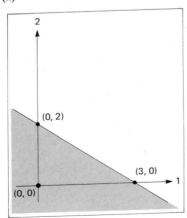
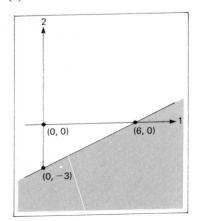

(c)

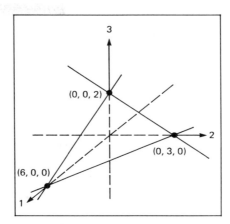

The region consists of all points on or below the plane that contains $(6,0,0)$, $(0,3,0)$, and $(0,0,2)$.

2. $x_1 = 3$, $x_2 = 1$, $y = 13$.

3. There is no maximum. The minimum is $y = -4$ when $x_1 = 0$, $x_2 = -2$.

4. Maximum: $y = 18$ when $x_1 = -1$, $x_2 = 3$.
   Minimum: $y = -22$ when $x_1 = 4$, $x_2 = -2$.

5. (a) $x_1 = \frac{12}{7}$, $x_2 = \frac{3}{7}$, $y = \frac{66}{7}$.
   (b) There is no feasible solution.

6. $x_1 = \frac{3}{2}$, $x_2 = 0$, $x_3 = \frac{1}{4}$, $x_4 = 0$, $y = \frac{11}{2}$.

7. Minimize $y = 4x_1 + 5x_2 + 3x_3 + 4x_4$ subject to $x_1 \geq 0$, $x_2 \geq 0$, $x_3 \geq 0$, $x_4 \geq 0$, $2x_1 + 3x_2 + 2x_3 + x_4 \geq 3$, $4x_1 + 2x_2 + 2x_3 + x_4 \geq 3$, $4x_1 + x_2 + 2x_4 \geq 4$, $2x_1 + 3x_3 + x_4 \geq 2$. Answer: $x_1 = 1$, $x_2 = 0$, $x_3 = \frac{1}{2}$, $x_4 = 0$, $y = \frac{11}{2}$.

8. Let $x_1$ = number of days Supergas, $x_2$ = number of days Exxtrabig. Minimize $y = 11x_1 + 7x_2$ subject to $x_1 \geq 0$, $x_2 \geq 0$, $4x_1 + 6x_2 \geq 9$, $8x_1 + 3x_2 \geq 7$, to obtain $x_1 = \frac{5}{12}$, $x_2 = \frac{11}{9}$, $y = \frac{473}{36}$. The xs are in units of 10,000 gallons, while the requirements are in units of one million gallons; thus we multiply $x_1$ and $x_2$ by 100 days and y by \$1,000,000 to obtain the answer: order 41.7 days production from Supergas, 122.2 days from Exxtrabig. Cost: about \$13,138,889.

9. Make 1,000 type-A boxes, 2,000 type-C boxes, and none of the other types. The profit will be \$900.

10. The answer to the given problem is $x_1 = 10$, $x_2 = -8$, $x_3 = 0$, $y = 18$. This answer is feasible: $10 - 8 + 0 = 2 \geq 0$, $20 - 8 = 12 \leq 12$, $10 + 0 = 10 = 10$; also $y = 10 + 8 + 0 = 18$. The dual problem is
    Minimize $y = -12x_2 + 10x_3$ subject to $x_1 \geq 0$, $x_2 \geq 0$, $x_1 - 2x_2 + x_3 \leq 1$, $x_1 - x_2 = -1$, $x_1 + x_3 \leq 4$.
    The answer to this problem is $x_1 = 0$, $x_2 = 1$, $x_3 = 3$. This answer is feasible: $-2 + 3 = 1 \leq 1$, $0 - 1 = -1$, $0 + 3 \leq 4$; also $y = -12 + 30 = 18$.

Chapter 5
Supplementary
Exercises
page 383

1. $x_1 = \frac{9}{7}$, $x_2 = 0$, $y = 9$

3. $x_1 = x_2 = 0$, $x_3 = 1$, $y = 7$

5. $x_1 = x_4 = x_5 = 0$, $x_2 = 13$, $x_3 = \frac{8}{3}$, $y = 55$

7. $x_1 = 5$, $x_2 = x_3 = 0$, $y = 20$

9. $x_1 = \frac{17}{5}$, $x_2 = 0$, $y = \frac{102}{5}$

11. $x_1 = \frac{7}{4}$, $x_2 = \frac{3}{2}$, $x_3 = x_4 = 1$, $y = \frac{89}{4}$

13. $x_1 = \frac{7}{3}$, $x_2 = \frac{4}{9}$, $x_3 = \frac{16}{27}$, $x_4 = \frac{64}{81}$, $y = \frac{1,672}{81}$

15. Operate mine I 28 times and mine II 30 times for a profit of $11,840.

17. Take 1 teaspoon of I and 7 tsps. of II for 80¢. (Recall 1 tablespoon = 3 teaspoons.)

19. There are no feasible, and therefore no optimal, solutions.

21. $x_1 = 0$, $x_2 = 1$, $x_3 = 0$, $x_4 = 3$, $y = 10$.

23. $x_1 = 0$, $x_2 = \frac{14}{3}$, $x_3 = \frac{2}{3}$, $y = 26$.

25. $x_1 = \frac{7}{2}$, $x_2 = \frac{5}{2}$, $y = \frac{19}{2}$.

27. $x_1 = 0$, $x_2 = \frac{13}{7}$, $x_3 = 0$, $x_4 = \frac{4}{7}$, $y = \frac{62}{7}$.

29. $x_1 = \frac{1}{2}$, $x_2 = \frac{4}{3}$, $x_3 = 0$, $y = \frac{31}{6}$.

31. Answer for the given maximization problem: $x_1 = 10$, $x_2 = x_3 = 0$, $x_4 = 18$, $y = 92$.
    Answer for the dual minimization problem: $x_1 = 0$, $x_2 = 3$, $x_3 = 7$, $y = 92$.

33. (a) Yes, it is reasonable to use a linear model.

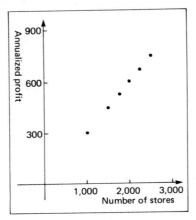

33. (b) No, it is not reasonable to use a linear model.

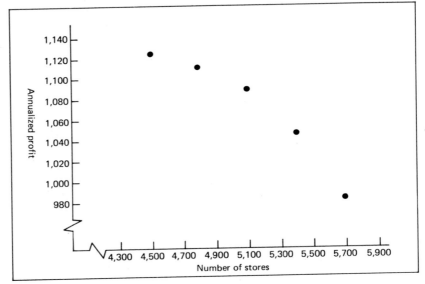

Note: To save space we have deleted parts of each axis.

35. Yes.

1. (a) $\frac{1}{17} \doteq 0.059$   (b) $\frac{4}{221} \doteq 0.018$    3. $\frac{15}{392} \doteq 0.038$    5. $\frac{264}{13.685} \doteq 0.193$
7. 11 (For instance: A, 2, 3, 4 of hearts, 6, 7, 8, 9 of clubs, J, Q, K of spades.)
9. 3 to 2 in favor     11. 315
13. Odds for A, p to q. $P(A) = p/(p+q)$. Odds for A, $(p+q)-p$ to q; that is, p to q, as expected.

1. No, the $(2, 1)$-entry is 1 instead of 0.

3. $\begin{bmatrix} \frac{1}{2} & 0 \\ 0 & \frac{1}{3} \end{bmatrix}$    5. $\begin{bmatrix} \frac{1}{2} & -\frac{2}{3} \\ 0 & \frac{1}{3} \end{bmatrix}$    7. $\begin{bmatrix} \frac{3}{14} & -\frac{2}{7} \\ \frac{5}{14} & -\frac{1}{7} \end{bmatrix}$    9. $\begin{bmatrix} -\frac{15}{31} & \frac{105}{124} \\ -\frac{28}{31} & -\frac{70}{93} \end{bmatrix}$

11. No inverse     13. No inverse

15. $\begin{bmatrix} -1 & 22 & -8 \\ 0 & -5 & 2 \\ 1 & -19 & 7 \end{bmatrix}$    17. No inverse    19. $\frac{1}{18}\begin{bmatrix} -5 & 7 & 1 \\ 1 & -5 & 7 \\ 7 & 1 & -5 \end{bmatrix}$

20. $\begin{bmatrix} -\frac{27}{32} & \frac{9}{32} & -\frac{3}{16} \\ -\frac{3}{4} & \frac{1}{4} & -\frac{3}{2} \\ \frac{69}{64} & \frac{9}{64} & -\frac{3}{32} \end{bmatrix}$    21. $\frac{1}{226}\begin{bmatrix} -14 & 28 & 49 & 15 \\ -34 & 68 & 6 & -12 \\ 64 & 98 & 2 & -4 \\ -4 & 8 & 14 & -28 \end{bmatrix}$

22. $\frac{1}{5}\begin{bmatrix} -115 & 145 & -64 & -18 \\ 50 & -60 & 26 & 7 \\ 5 & -10 & 6 & 2 \\ 10 & -10 & 3 & 1 \end{bmatrix}$    23. $\begin{bmatrix} -17 & 14 \\ 17 & -13 \end{bmatrix}$

25. No solution     27. No solution

29. $\frac{1}{76}\begin{bmatrix} 69 & -135 & -21 & 73 & 126 \\ -20 & 92 & 16 & -52 & -96 \\ -26 & 74 & -2 & -22 & -64 \\ 3 & -29 & 9 & 23 & 22 \\ 24 & -80 & -4 & 32 & 100 \end{bmatrix}$

30. (a) $x+2z$ and $3x+6z$, respectively

(b) $\begin{bmatrix} x+2z=1 \\ 3x+6z=0 \end{bmatrix}$

(c) No solution
(d) It has no inverse.

31. Inverse does not exist if $ad-bc=0$. If $ad\text{-}bc \neq 0$, inverse is

$$\frac{1}{ad-bc}\begin{bmatrix} d & -b \\ -c & a \end{bmatrix}.$$

33. $x_1 = 51$, $x_2 = 32$    35. $x_1 = 4$, $x_2 = 7$, $x_3 = 2$
37. (a) $x_1 = 28$, $x_2 = -12$, $x_3 = -2$, $x_4 = -1$    (b) $x_1 = \frac{3}{5}$, $x_2 = \frac{2}{5}$, $x_3 = -\frac{6}{5}$, $x_4 = \frac{18}{5}$
38. The inverse for the system is

$$\begin{bmatrix} 0 & 5 & -7 & 1 \\ -2 & 0 & 0 & 1 \\ 1 & -2 & 3 & -1 \\ 1 & -1 & 1 & 0 \end{bmatrix}$$

39. $x_1 = 5$, $x_2 = -2$, $x_3 = -1$, $x_4 = 0$

41. $x_1 = -1$, $x_2 = -1$, $x_3 = 1$, $x_4 = 1$

43. $x_1 = 1$, $x_2 = 1$, $x_3 = -1$, $x_4 = 0$

45.

| Order # | 1 | 2 | 3 | 5 | 7 | 8 | 9 |
|---|---|---|---|---|---|---|---|
| No. of type-I boxes | 0 | 1 | 18 | 3 | 1087 | 1 | 0 |
| No. of type-II boxes | 3 | 1 | 12 | 61 | 2190 | 0 | 1 |

Orders 4 and 6 cannot be filled without opening boxes.

46. Multiply orders by

$$\begin{bmatrix} -6 & -6 & 7 \\ \frac{11}{5} & 2 & -\frac{12}{5} \\ \frac{24}{5} & 5 & -\frac{28}{5} \end{bmatrix}$$

47. (a) $x_1 = 4$, $x_2 = 11$, $x_3 = 0$ (b) $x_1 = 0$, $x_2 = 0$, $x_3 = 50$
(c) $x_1 = 16$, $x_2 = 48$, $x_3 = 0$ (d) $x_1 = 72$, $x_2 = 0$, $x_3 = 0$

49.

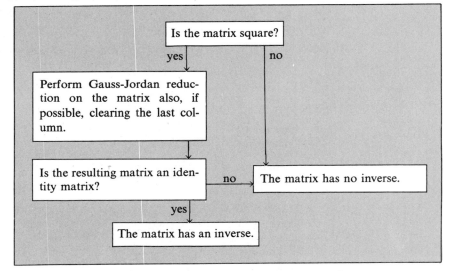

51.
$$\begin{bmatrix} 2 & -1 & 3 & 4 & 0 & 2 \\ 3 & 1 & -1 & 2 & 4 & 2 \end{bmatrix} \begin{bmatrix} 1 & -\frac{1}{2} & \frac{3}{2} & 2 & 0 & 1 \\ 0 & \frac{5}{2} & -\frac{11}{2} & -4 & 4 & -1 \end{bmatrix}$$

$$\begin{bmatrix} 1 & 0 & \frac{2}{5} & \frac{6}{5} & \frac{4}{5} & \frac{4}{5} \\ 0 & 1 & -\frac{11}{5} & -\frac{8}{5} & \frac{8}{5} & -\frac{2}{5} \end{bmatrix}$$

Solutions are, respectively,

$$\left(\frac{6}{5} - \frac{2}{5}x_3, -\frac{8}{5} + \frac{11}{5}x_3, x_3\right), \left(\frac{4}{5} - \frac{2}{5}x_3, \frac{8}{5} + \frac{11}{5}x_3, x_3\right), \left(\frac{4}{5} - \frac{2}{5}x_3, -\frac{2}{5} + \frac{11}{5}x_3, x_3\right),$$

where $x_3$ is free.

53. Manufacturing must produce $3,660 worth of goods. The other sector must produce $1,290 worth.

55. The extractive sector should produce $180 worth of goods, manufacturing $167, and services $173.

57. $(I-A)^{-1} = \frac{10}{583} \begin{bmatrix} 70 & 18 & 11 \\ 17 & 71 & 11 \\ 13 & 20 & 77 \end{bmatrix}$

The answer: Produce $4,300 worth of typing, $7,550 worth of personnel placement and $2,430 worth of copying.

59. Make $156.5 million worth of Saturday night specials, $412 million worth of automatic rifles, and $223.3 worth of grenades.

60.

| Used by | Questions | Rhymes | Reasons |
|---|---|---|---|
| **Obtained from** | | | |
| Questions | .2 | .1 | .3 |
| Rhymes | .3 | 0 | .1 |
| Reasons | .1 | .1 | .4 |

Let

$$A = \begin{bmatrix} .2 & .1 & .3 \\ .3 & 0 & .1 \\ .1 & .1 & .4 \end{bmatrix},$$

then

$$(I-A)^{-1} = \frac{10}{414} \begin{bmatrix} 59 & 9 & 31 \\ 19 & 45 & 17 \\ 13 & 9 & 77 \end{bmatrix}$$

$$(I-A)^{-1}D = \frac{10}{414} \begin{bmatrix} 59 & 9 & 31 \\ 19 & 45 & 17 \\ 13 & 9 & 77 \end{bmatrix} \begin{bmatrix} 4,140 \\ 0 \\ 8,280 \end{bmatrix} = \begin{bmatrix} 12,100 \\ 5,300 \\ 16,700 \end{bmatrix}$$

They need to come up with 12,100 questions, 5,300 rhymes, 16,700 reasons. Fortunately, it takes them a long time to get home.

**Section 6.3**
**page 439**

1. There is a saddle point at (2, 1). Player A should always use strategy 2, and player B should always use strategy 1. The value of the game is 3. This game can also be solved by eliminating dominated strategies.

3. Player A should mix strategies: $\frac{3}{8}$ strategy 1, $\frac{5}{8}$ strategy 2. Player B should mix strategies: $\frac{1}{4}$ strategy 1, $\frac{3}{4}$ strategy 2. The value of the game is $\frac{11}{4}$.

4. There are two saddle points. Player A should always use strategy 2. However, player B can use any mixture of strategies 1 and 2. The value of the game is 4.

5. It is necessary to add 3 to every entry of the payoff matrix. The simplex method involves the following sequence of matrices:

$$\begin{bmatrix} 2^* & 1 & 1 & 0 & 1 \\ 0 & 4 & 0 & 1 & 1 \\ 1 & 1 & 0 & 0 & 0 \end{bmatrix}$$

$$\begin{bmatrix} 1 & \frac{1}{2} & \frac{1}{2} & 0 & \frac{1}{2} \\ 0 & 4^* & 0 & 1 & 1 \\ 0 & \frac{1}{2} & -\frac{1}{2} & 0 & -\frac{1}{2} \end{bmatrix}$$

$$\begin{bmatrix} 1 & 0 & \frac{1}{2} & -\frac{1}{8} & \frac{3}{8} \\ 0 & 1 & 0 & \frac{1}{4} & \frac{1}{4} \\ 0 & 0 & -\frac{1}{2} & -\frac{1}{8} & -\frac{5}{8} \end{bmatrix}$$

Since $\frac{1}{2} + \frac{1}{8} = \frac{5}{8}$, we obtain the mixed strategy for A by multiplying each answer by $\frac{8}{5}$. Thus, A should mix strategies: $\frac{4}{5}$ strategy 1 and $\frac{1}{5}$ strategy 2. Similarly, B should mix strategies: $\frac{3}{5}$ strategy 1, $\frac{2}{5}$ strategy 2. The value of the game is $\frac{8}{5} - 3 = -\frac{7}{5}$.

7. The payoff matrix is $\begin{bmatrix} 0 & -1 & 2 \\ -1 & 0 & -1 \\ 2 & -1 & 0 \end{bmatrix}$. Both players should mix strategies: $\frac{1}{6}$ strategy 1, $\frac{2}{3}$ strategy 2, and $\frac{1}{6}$ strategy 3. Player B should pay player A $\$\frac{1}{3}$ to make the game fair.

9. A: $(\frac{1}{3}, \frac{2}{3}, 0)$, B: $(\frac{2}{3}, 0, \frac{1}{3})$, value: $\frac{4}{3}$.

11. Removal of dominant strategies 1, 2, and 3 for A and 1, 4, and 6 for B leaves the matrix

$$\begin{bmatrix} 1 & 0 & 4 \\ 1 & 4 & 3 \\ 4 & 0 & 3 \end{bmatrix},$$

which has the solution

$$\text{A: } \left(\frac{4}{7}, \frac{3}{7}, 0\right), \quad \text{B: } \left(0, \frac{4}{7}, \frac{3}{7}\right).$$

Thus, A should use strategy 5, $\frac{4}{7}$ of the time and strategy 6, $\frac{3}{7}$ of the time, while B should use strategy 2, $\frac{4}{7}$ of the time and strategy 3, $\frac{3}{7}$ of the time. The value is $\frac{16}{7}$.

12. The payoff matrix is:
$$\begin{array}{c} \\ \text{rock} \\ \text{paper} \\ \text{scissors} \end{array} \begin{array}{ccc} \text{r} & \text{p} & \text{s} \\ \left[\begin{array}{ccc} 0 & -1 & 1 \\ 1 & 0 & -1 \\ -1 & 1 & 0 \end{array}\right] \end{array}.$$

13. $\begin{bmatrix} 6 & 3 & 1 & 0 & 1 \\ 2 & 5 & 0 & 1 & 1 \\ 1 & 1 & 0 & 0 & 0 \end{bmatrix}$ $\begin{bmatrix} 1 & 0 & - & - & \frac{1}{12} \\ 0 & 1 & - & - & \frac{1}{6} \\ 0 & 0 & -\frac{1}{8} & -\frac{1}{8} & -\frac{1}{4} \end{bmatrix}$ PHE should air hard sell $\frac{1}{2}$ of the time and soft sell $\frac{1}{2}$ of the time; McD should air hard sell $\frac{1}{3}$ of the time and soft sell $\frac{2}{3}$ of the time. PHE will then get $4 million of McD business.

15. (a) Each player should: never write 1; write 2, $\frac{2}{5}$ of the time; write 3, $\frac{1}{5}$ of the time; and write 4, $\frac{2}{5}$ of the time. The game is fair.

(b) Each player should write 1, $\frac{1}{16}$ of the time; 2, $\frac{5}{16}$ of the time; 3, $\frac{4}{16}$ of the time; 4, $\frac{5}{16}$ of the time; and 5, $\frac{1}{16}$ of the time. The game is fair. N.B.: this is the correct strategy for Low Number for *any* set of 5 or more consecutive integers beginning with 1, even for the set of *all* such integers. No integer greater than 5 should ever be written!

16. We label the board

| 1 | 2 | 3 |
|---|---|---|
| 4 | 5 | 6 |
| 7 | 8 | 9 |

and state the following rule.

> THE RULE
>
> Move as follows:
> (i) Win if possible; if not
> (ii) Block if possible; if not
> (iii) Move in any open space.

Here is a strategy for A (player X) which guarantees at least a draw.

Move 1: Play in 1.

Move 2: Play in 5 (if possible), otherwise
play in 3 and then use The Rule.

Move 3: If possible, move in 9 to win. Otherwise, move according to the following
tabulation.

| If 0 is in | Play in |
|---|---|
| 2 | 7; win with next move |
| 3 | 6; then use The Rule to win or draw |
| 4 | 3; win with next move |
| 6 | 3; win with next move |
| 7 | 8; use The Rule to win or draw |
| 8 | 7; win with next move. |

Here is a strategy for a player B (player 0) which also guarantees at least a draw.

Move 1: 0 in 5 if possible. Otherwise 0 in 1.

Move 2: Case 1. 0 is in 5. Move according to the following tabulation.

| If X is in | 0 should |
|---|---|
| 1,2; 1,4; 2,3; 3,6; 4,7; 6,9; 7,8; 8,9; 1,3; 1,7; 3,9; 7,9 | Apply The Rule |
| 2,4; 2,7; 3,4: | Move in 1; then apply The Rule to win or draw |
| 2,6; 2,9; 1,6; | Move in 3; then apply The Rule to win or draw |
| 4,8; 1,8; 4,9; | Move in 7; then apply The Rule to win or draw |
| 6,8; 6,7; 3,8; | Move in 9; then apply The Rule to win or draw |
| 2,8; 4,6; | Move in 9; then apply The Rule to win |
| 1,9; 3,7; | Move in 6; then apply The Rule to win or draw |

Case 2: X is in 5; 0 is in 1. Move according to the following tabulation.

| If X is in | 0 should |
|---|---|
| 3,6,7,8 | Apply The Rule to win or draw |
| 2 | Move in 8 |
| 4 | Move in 6 |
| 9 | Move in 3; then use The Rule |

Move 3: Case 1. X is in 2,5; 0 is in 1,8.
If X is in 3,4,6,7 use The Rule.
If X is in 9, move in 3, then use The Rule.
Case 2. X is in 4,5; 0 is in 1,6.
If X is in 2,3,7,8 use The Rule.
If X is in 9, move in 7, then use The Rule.

Since each player has a strategy which guarantees at least a draw, the game has a saddle point which involves both the strategies mentioned above. Of course, there are other strategies for each player which also guarantee at least a draw. Thus, there are many saddle points.

17. (a) If Sam hires 4 instructors, it costs $1,600 and he can handle 400 people. If 400 show up they pay $2,000 and Sam makes $400. If 200 show up, they pay $1,000 and Sam loses $600. If he hires 3 instructors, it costs $1,200. If 400 show up,

only 300 pay. Sam pays $100 to the others. Thus Sam makes $1,500 - 1,200 - 100 = $200. On the other hand if 200 show up, they pay $1,000. So Sam loses $200. Finally, if he hires 2 instructors it costs $800. If 400 show up only 200 pay. Sam pays $200 to the others and his net is $1,000 - 800 - 200 = $0. If 200 show up they pay $1,000 and Sam nets $1,000 - 800 = $200.

(b) Solution one: Never hire 4 instructors; $\frac{1}{3}$ of the time hire 3; $\frac{2}{3}$ of the time hire 2. The value of the game is $\frac{2}{3}$ hundred dollars or about $67 for Sam. We tell Sam that the best he can expect is to average about $67 a week and suggest that he give up the ski-slope since this together with his profit on concessions, parking, and the ski-tow will not meet his expenses. However, if he persists we suggest that he roll a balanced die and hire 3 instructors if it comes up 1 or 2 and 2 instructors if it comes up 3, 4, 5, or 6.

Solution two: $\frac{1}{6}$ of the time hire 4 instructors; never hire three instructors; $\frac{5}{6}$ of the time hire 2 instructors. Sam still averages about $67 a week. Note that whenever a game has two solutions it has infinitely many all with the same value. All the solutions for this game are given by the formula: $\frac{1}{6}t$ of the time use strategy 1; $\frac{1}{3}s$ of the time use strategy 2; $\frac{5}{6}t + \frac{2}{3}s$ of the time use strategy 3; where s and t are numbers such that $s \geq 0$, $t \geq 0$ and $s + t = 1$.

**Section 6.4**
**page 447**

1. $q/p = 3$, $\dfrac{1-3}{1-3^2} = \dfrac{2}{8} = \dfrac{1}{4}$.

3. $\frac{2}{3}$

5. $\dfrac{1-9^3}{1-9^4} = \dfrac{728}{6,560} = \dfrac{91}{820} \doteq 0.111$

7. $\dfrac{1-9^4}{1-9^5} = \dfrac{6,560}{59,048} = \dfrac{820}{7,381} \doteq 0.111$

9. $\frac{1}{6}$

11. Omit $R_1$ and $R_6$. In *one step* use $R_2$ to clear $C_2$ and $R_5$ to clear $C_5$, obtaining:

$$\begin{bmatrix} -\frac{1}{3} & 1 & -\frac{2}{3} & 0 & 0 & 0 & 0 \\ \frac{1}{9} & 0 & -\frac{7}{9} & \frac{2}{3} & 0 & 0 & 0 \\ 0 & 0 & \frac{1}{3}* & -\frac{7}{9} & 0 & \frac{4}{9} & 0 \\ 0 & 0 & 0 & -\frac{1}{3} & 1 & -\frac{2}{3} & 0 \end{bmatrix}$$

$$\begin{bmatrix} -\frac{1}{3} & 1 & 0 & -\frac{14}{9} & 0 & \frac{8}{9} & 0 \\ \frac{1}{9} & 0 & 0 & -\frac{31}{27}* & 0 & \frac{28}{27} & 0 \\ 0 & 0 & 1 & -\frac{7}{3} & 0 & \frac{4}{3} & 0 \\ 0 & 0 & 0 & -\frac{1}{3} & 1 & -\frac{2}{3} & 0 \end{bmatrix}$$

$$\begin{bmatrix} -\frac{15}{31} & 1 & 0 & 0 & 0 & -\frac{16}{31} & 0 \\ -\frac{3}{31} & 0 & 0 & 1 & 0 & -\frac{28}{31} & 0 \\ -\frac{7}{31} & 0 & 1 & 0 & 0 & -\frac{24}{31} & 0 \\ -\frac{1}{31} & 0 & 0 & 0 & 1 & -\frac{30}{31} & 0 \end{bmatrix}$$

Restore $R_1$ and $R_6$, switch $R_3$ and $R_4$, read the answer, and write matrix **3**.

13. $\checkmark$

15. $\left(1-(q/p)^2\right)/\left(1-(q/p)^3\right)=(p^3-pq^2)/(p^3-q^3)=$
$$p(p-q)(p+q)/(p-q)(p^2+pq+q^2)=p/(p^2+pq+q^2)=$$
$$p/\left[(p+q)^2-pq\right]=p/(1-pq).$$

17. $p/(1-pq)=(\tfrac{1}{2})/\left(1-(\tfrac{1}{2})(\tfrac{1}{2})\right)=(\tfrac{1}{2})/(\tfrac{3}{4})=\tfrac{2}{3}.$

18. The flow chart begins with

$$\begin{bmatrix} 1 & 0 & 0 & 0 & 0 & 0 \\ 0 & -1 & p & 0 & 0 & 0 \\ 0 & q & -1 & p & 0 & -0 \\ 0 & 0 & q & -1 & 0 & p \\ 0 & 0 & 0 & 0 & 1 & 1 \end{bmatrix}$$

Gauss-Jordan reduction leads to

$$\begin{bmatrix} 1 & 0 & 0 & 0 & 0 & 0 \\ 0 & 1 & 0 & 0 & 0 & \dfrac{p^3}{1-2pq} \\ 0 & 0 & 1 & 0 & 0 & \dfrac{p^2}{1-2pq} \\ 0 & 0 & 0 & 1 & 0 & \dfrac{p(1-pq)}{1-2pq} \\ 0 & 0 & 0 & 0 & 1 & 1 \end{bmatrix}$$

If $p\neq\tfrac{1}{2}$ then, since $p-q\neq0$, $p+q=1$, and $p^2+q^2=p^2+(1-p)^2=p^2+1-2p+p^2=1-2p(1-p)=1-2pq$, we have

$$\frac{p^3}{1-2pq}=\frac{p^3}{p^2+q^2}=\frac{p^3(p-q)}{(p^2+q^2)(p-q)(p+q)}=\frac{p^4-p^3q}{p^4-q^4}$$

$$=\frac{\dfrac{p^4-p^3q}{p^4}}{\dfrac{p^4-q^4}{p^4}}=\frac{1-q/p}{1-(q/p)^4},$$

$$\frac{p^2}{1-2pq}=\frac{p^2(p^2-q^2)}{(p^2+q^2)(p^2-q^2)}=\frac{p^4-p^2q^2}{p^4-q^4}=\frac{1-(q/p)^2}{1-(q/p)^4},$$

$$\text{and}\quad\frac{p(1-pq)}{1-2pq}=\frac{p(p-q)(p^2+q^2+pq)}{(p-q)(p^2+q^2)(p+q)}=\frac{p(p^3-q^3)}{p^4-q^4}=\frac{1-(q/p)^3}{1-(q/p)^4};$$

so **7** holds. If $p=1/2$, then $q=1/2$ and

$$\frac{p^3}{1-2pq}=\frac{1}{4},\quad\frac{p^2}{1-2pq}=\frac{1}{2}=\frac{2}{4},\quad\text{and}\quad\frac{p(1-pq)}{1-2pq}=\frac{3}{4};$$

so **8** holds.

19. (a) If none of A is present they cannot dominate; hence $p_0=0$. If n of A are present then none of B is present; hence $p_n=1$.

(b) $p_i=P((A\text{ increases by }1\cap A\text{ dominates})\cup(A\text{ decreases by }1\cap A\text{ dominates}))$

$= P(A \text{ increases by } 1) \cdot P(A(\text{now with } i+1 \text{ members}) \text{ dominates}) +$

$P(A \text{ decreases by } 1)P(A(\text{now with } i-1) \text{ dominates}) = pp_{i+1} + qp_{i-1}.$

21. $pp_{i+1} + qp_{i-1} = p(1-(q/p)^{i+1})/(1-(q/p)^n) + q(1-(q/p)^{i-1})/(1-(q/p)^n) =$

$[p - q^{i+1}/p^i + q - q^i/p^{i-1}]/(1-(q/p)^n) = [(p+q) - q(q/p)^i - p(q/p)^i]/(1-(q/p)^n)$

$= [(p+q) - (p+q)(q/p)^i]/(1-(q/p)^n) = (1-(q/p)^i)/(1-(q/p)^n) = p_i.$

23. $p = P(A_1) = P(A_1|A_1A_1)P(A_1A_1) + P(A_1|A_1A_2)P(A_1A_2) = a_{11} + (\frac{1}{2})a_{12}.$ $q = 1-p = (a_{11} + a_{12} + a_{22}) - (a_{11} + (\frac{1}{2})a_{12}) = a_{22} + (\frac{1}{2})a_{12}.$

25. $n(\text{genotypes}) = n(\text{genotypes with both forms the same}) + n(\text{genotypes with different forms}) = n + C_2^n = n + \dfrac{n(n-1)}{2} = (2n + n^2 - n)/2 = (n^2 + n)/2 = n(n+1)/2 = C_2^{n+1}.$

27. $a_{11} = 0.30$, $a_{12} = 0.45$, $a_{22} = 0.25$, $p = 0.30 + 0.45/2 = 0.525$, $q = 0.475$. In next generation $p^2 = 0.275625$, $2pq = 0.49875$, $q^2 = 0.225625$: 27.5625% red, 49.875% pink, 22.5625% white.

29. A male must have a Y chromosome; hence $P_1(G_1|\text{male}) = P_0(G_1|\text{female}) = 30\%$, and $P_1(G_2|\text{male}) = 70\%$. $P_1(G_1G_1|\text{female}) = P_0(G_1|\text{male})P_0(G_1|\text{female}) = (0.40)(0.30) = 12\%$; $P_1(G_1G_2|\text{female}) = P_0(G_1|\text{male})P_0(G_2|\text{female}) + P_0(G_2|\text{male})$. $P(G_1|\text{female}) = (0.40)(0.70) + (0.60)(0.30) = 46\%$. $P_1(G_2G_2|\text{female}) = (0.60)(0.70) = 42\%$.

*30. $P_2(G_1G_1 \text{ female}) = P_1(G_1 \text{ male})P_1(G_1 \text{ female}) = (0.30)(P_1(G_1G_1)P_1(G_1G_1) + P(G_1|G_1G_2)P(G_1G_2)) = (0.30)((1)(0.12) + (0.5)(0.46)) = (0.30)(0.35) = 10.5\%.$

$P_2(G_1G_2) = P_1(G_1|\text{male})P_1(G_2|\text{female}) + P_1(G_2|\text{male})P_1(G_1|\text{female}) = (0.30)(1-0.35) + (0.70)(0.35) = 44\%.$ $P_2(G_2G_2) = (0.70)(0.65) = 45.5\%.$

31. In the next generation the Hardy-Weinberg law would give $p^2$, $2pq$, $q^2$. Adjusting for fitness gives $\dfrac{s_1p^2}{s_1p^2 + 2s_2pq + s_3q^2}$, $\dfrac{2s_2pq}{s_1p^2 + 2s_2pq + s_3q^2}$, $\dfrac{s_3q^2}{s_1p^2 + 2s_2pq + s_3q^2}$, respectively.

**Section 6.5**
**page 470**

1. 82 wagonloads.
3. A maximal flow is 130; a minimal cut consists of the edges from $\text{(s)}$ to $\text{(1)}$, $\text{(s)}$ to $\text{(2)}$, and $\text{(s)}$ to $\text{(3)}$.
5. A maximal flow is 125; a minimal cut consists of all the edges into $\text{(t)}$.
7. A maximal flow is 95; a minimal cut consists of the edges from $\text{(3)}$ to $\text{(11)}$, $\text{(7)}$ to $\text{(12)}$, $\text{(8)}$ to $\text{(12)}$, $\text{(10)}$ to $\text{(13)}$, and $\text{(9)}$ to $\text{(14)}$.
9. (a) 190
   (b) Build a pipeline from $\text{(5)}$ to $\text{(4)}$ with capacity 130.
10. Let the variables $x_1, \ldots, x_8$ denote the quantities listed in the following tabulation.

| Variable | Amount shipped between |
|---|---|
| $x_1$ | $\text{(s)}$ and $\text{(1)}$ |
| $x_2$ | $\text{(s)}$ and $\text{(2)}$ |
| $x_3$ | $\text{(s)}$ and $\text{(3)}$ |
| $x_4$ | $\text{(1)}$ and $\text{(2)}$ |
| $x_5$ | $\text{(3)}$ and $\text{(2)}$ |
| $x_6$ | $\text{(1)}$ and $\text{(t)}$ |
| $x_7$ | $\text{(2)}$ and $\text{(t)}$ |
| $x_8$ | $\text{(3)}$ and $\text{(t)}$ |

The edge capacities yield the following inequalities:

$$x_1 \le 50, \quad x_2 \le 40, \quad x_3 \le 60, \quad x_4 \le 30,$$
$$x_5 \le 20, \quad x_6 \le 20, \quad x_7 \le 80, \quad x_8 \le 30.$$

Since we may not ship more into a vertex than out, we also obtain the following equalities:

at vertex ①: $x_1 = x_4 + x_6$
at vertex ②: $x_2 + x_4 + x_5 = x_7$
at vertex ③: $x_3 = x_5 + x_8$

Finally we are to maximize the flow into ⓣ: $y = x_6 + x_7 + x_8$. Mathematically formulated, our problem becomes:

Maximize $y = x_6 + x_7 + x_8$ subject to

$x_1 \ge 0, x_2 \ge 0, x_3 \ge 0, x_4 \ge 0, x_5 \ge 0, x_6 \ge 0, x_7 \ge 0, x_8 \ge 0$, and $x_1 \le 50, x_2 \le 40, x_3 \le 60$, $x_4 \le 30, x_5 \le 20, x_6 \le 20, x_7 \le 80, x_8 \le 30, x_1 - x_4 - x_6 = 0, x_2 + x_4 + x_5 - x_7 = 0$, $x_3 - x_5 - x_8 = 0$. The simplex method is applied as follows:

$$\begin{bmatrix}
1 & 0 & 0 & 0 & 0 & 0 & 0 & 0 & 1 & 0 & 0 & 0 & 0 & 0 & 0 & 0 & 50 \\
0 & 1 & 0 & 0 & 0 & 0 & 0 & 0 & 0 & 1 & 0 & 0 & 0 & 0 & 0 & 0 & 40 \\
0 & 0 & 1 & 0 & 0 & 0 & 0 & 0 & 0 & 0 & 1 & 0 & 0 & 0 & 0 & 0 & 60 \\
0 & 0 & 0 & 1 & 0 & 0 & 0 & 0 & 0 & 0 & 0 & 1 & 0 & 0 & 0 & 0 & 30 \\
0 & 0 & 0 & 0 & 1 & 0 & 0 & 0 & 0 & 0 & 0 & 0 & 1 & 0 & 0 & 0 & 20 \\
0 & 0 & 0 & 0 & 0 & 1 & 0 & 0 & 0 & 0 & 0 & 0 & 0 & 1 & 0 & 0 & 20 \\
0 & 0 & 0 & 0 & 0 & 0 & 1 & 0 & 0 & 0 & 0 & 0 & 0 & 0 & 1 & 0 & 80 \\
0 & 0 & 0 & 0 & 0 & 0 & 0 & 1 & 0 & 0 & 0 & 0 & 0 & 0 & 0 & 1 & 30 \\
1^* & 0 & 0 & -1 & 0 & -1 & 0 & 0 & 0 & 0 & 0 & 0 & 0 & 0 & 0 & 0 & 0 \\
0 & 1^* & 0 & 1 & 1 & 0 & -1 & 0 & 0 & 0 & 0 & 0 & 0 & 0 & 0 & 0 & 0 \\
0 & 0 & 1^* & 0 & -1 & 0 & 0 & -1 & 0 & 0 & 0 & 0 & 0 & 0 & 0 & 0 & 0 \\
0 & 0 & 0 & 0 & 0 & 1 & 1 & 1 & 0 & 0 & 0 & 0 & 0 & 0 & 0 & 0 & 0
\end{bmatrix}$$

$$\begin{bmatrix}
0 & 0 & 0 & 1 & 0 & 1 & 0 & 0 & 1 & 0 & 0 & 0 & 0 & 0 & 0 & 0 & 50 \\
0 & 0 & 0 & -1 & -1 & 0 & 1 & 0 & 0 & 1 & 0 & 0 & 0 & 0 & 0 & 0 & 40 \\
0 & 0 & 0 & 0 & 1 & 0 & 0 & 1 & 0 & 0 & 1 & 0 & 0 & 0 & 0 & 0 & 60 \\
0 & 0 & 0 & 1 & 0 & 0 & 0 & 0 & 0 & 0 & 0 & 1 & 0 & 0 & 0 & 0 & 30 \\
0 & 0 & 0 & 0 & 1 & 0 & 0 & 0 & 0 & 0 & 0 & 0 & 1 & 0 & 0 & 0 & 20 \\
0 & 0 & 0 & 0 & 0 & 1^* & 0 & 0 & 0 & 0 & 0 & 0 & 0 & 1 & 0 & 0 & 20 \\
0 & 0 & 0 & 0 & 0 & 0 & 1 & 0 & 0 & 0 & 0 & 0 & 0 & 0 & 1 & 0 & 80 \\
0 & 0 & 0 & 0 & 0 & 0 & 0 & 1 & 0 & 0 & 0 & 0 & 0 & 0 & 0 & 1 & 30 \\
1 & 0 & 0 & -1 & 0 & -1 & 0 & 0 & 0 & 0 & 0 & 0 & 0 & 0 & 0 & 0 & 0 \\
0 & 1 & 0 & 1 & 1 & 0 & -1 & 0 & 0 & 0 & 0 & 0 & 0 & 0 & 0 & 0 & 0 \\
0 & 0 & 1 & 0 & -1 & 0 & 0 & -1 & 0 & 0 & 0 & 0 & 0 & 0 & 0 & 0 & 0 \\
0 & 0 & 0 & 0 & 0 & 1 & 1 & 1 & 0 & 0 & 0 & 0 & 0 & 0 & 0 & 0 & 0
\end{bmatrix}$$

$$\begin{bmatrix}
0 & 0 & 0 & 1 & 0 & 0 & 0 & 0 & 1 & 0 & 0 & 0 & 0 & -1 & 0 & 0 & 30 \\
0 & 0 & 0 & -1 & -1 & 0 & 1^* & 0 & 0 & 1 & 0 & 0 & 0 & 0 & 0 & 0 & 40 \\
0 & 0 & 0 & 0 & 1 & 0 & 0 & 1 & 0 & 0 & 1 & 0 & 0 & 0 & 0 & 0 & 60 \\
0 & 0 & 0 & 1 & 0 & 0 & 0 & 0 & 0 & 0 & 0 & 1 & 0 & 0 & 0 & 0 & 30 \\
0 & 0 & 0 & 0 & 1 & 0 & 0 & 0 & 0 & 0 & 0 & 0 & 1 & 0 & 0 & 0 & 20 \\
0 & 0 & 0 & 0 & 0 & 1 & 0 & 0 & 0 & 0 & 0 & 0 & 0 & 1 & 0 & 0 & 20 \\
0 & 0 & 0 & 0 & 0 & 0 & 1 & 0 & 0 & 0 & 0 & 0 & 0 & 0 & 1 & 0 & 80 \\
0 & 0 & 0 & 0 & 0 & 0 & 0 & 1 & 0 & 0 & 0 & 0 & 0 & 0 & 0 & 1 & 30 \\
1 & 0 & 0 & -1 & 0 & 0 & 0 & 0 & 0 & 0 & 0 & 0 & 0 & 1 & 0 & 0 & 20 \\
0 & 1 & 0 & 1 & 1 & 0 & -1 & 0 & 0 & 0 & 0 & 0 & 0 & 0 & 0 & 0 & 0 \\
0 & 0 & 1 & 0 & -1 & 0 & 0 & -1 & 0 & 0 & 0 & 0 & 0 & 0 & 0 & 0 & 0 \\
0 & 0 & 0 & 0 & 0 & 0 & 1 & 1 & 0 & 0 & 0 & 0 & -1 & 0 & 0 & -20
\end{bmatrix}$$

$$\begin{bmatrix}
0 & 0 & 0 & 1 & 0 & 0 & 0 & 0 & 1 & 0 & 0 & 0 & 0 & -1 & 0 & 0 & 30 \\
0 & 0 & 0 & -1 & -1 & 0 & 1 & 0 & 0 & 1 & 0 & 0 & 0 & 0 & 0 & 0 & 40 \\
0 & 0 & 0 & 0 & 1 & 0 & 0 & 1 & 0 & 0 & 1 & 0 & 0 & 0 & 0 & 0 & 60 \\
0 & 0 & 0 & 1 & 0 & 0 & 0 & 0 & 0 & 0 & 0 & 1 & 0 & 0 & 0 & 0 & 30 \\
0 & 0 & 0 & 0 & 1 & 0 & 0 & 0 & 0 & 0 & 0 & 0 & 1 & 0 & 0 & 0 & 20 \\
0 & 0 & 0 & 0 & 0 & 1 & 0 & 0 & 0 & 0 & 0 & 0 & 0 & 1 & 0 & 0 & 20 \\
0 & 0 & 0 & 1 & 1 & 0 & 0 & 0 & 0 & -1 & 0 & 0 & 0 & 0 & 1 & 0 & 40 \\
0 & 0 & 0 & 0 & 0 & 0 & 0 & 1^* & 0 & 0 & 0 & 0 & 0 & 0 & 0 & 1 & 30 \\
1 & 0 & 0 & -1 & 0 & 0 & 0 & 0 & 0 & 0 & 0 & 0 & 0 & 1 & 0 & 0 & 20 \\
0 & 1 & 0 & 0 & 0 & 0 & 0 & 0 & 0 & 1 & 0 & 0 & 0 & 0 & 0 & 0 & 40 \\
0 & 0 & 1 & 0 & -1 & 0 & 0 & -1 & 0 & 0 & 0 & 0 & 0 & 0 & 0 & 0 & 0 \\
0 & 0 & 0 & 1 & 1 & 0 & 0 & 1 & 0 & -1 & 0 & 0 & 0 & -1 & 0 & 0 & -60
\end{bmatrix}$$

$$\begin{bmatrix}
0 & 0 & 0 & 1 & 0 & 0 & 0 & 0 & 1 & 0 & 0 & 0 & 0 & -1 & 0 & 0 & 30 \\
0 & 0 & 0 & -1 & -1 & 0 & 1 & 0 & 0 & 1 & 0 & 0 & 0 & 0 & 0 & 0 & 40 \\
0 & 0 & 0 & 0 & 1 & 0 & 0 & 0 & 0 & 0 & 1 & 0 & 0 & 0 & -1 & 0 & 30 \\
0 & 0 & 0 & 1^* & 0 & 0 & 0 & 0 & 0 & 0 & 0 & 1 & 0 & 0 & 0 & 0 & 30 \\
0 & 0 & 0 & 0 & 1 & 0 & 0 & 0 & 0 & 0 & 0 & 0 & 1 & 0 & 0 & 0 & 20 \\
0 & 0 & 0 & 0 & 0 & 1 & 0 & 0 & 0 & 0 & 0 & 0 & 0 & 1 & 0 & 0 & 20 \\
0 & 0 & 0 & 1 & 1 & 0 & 0 & 0 & 0 & -1 & 0 & 0 & 0 & 0 & 1 & 0 & 40 \\
0 & 0 & 0 & 0 & 0 & 0 & 0 & 1 & 0 & 0 & 0 & 0 & 0 & 0 & 0 & 1 & 30 \\
1 & 0 & 0 & -1 & 0 & 0 & 0 & 0 & 0 & 0 & 0 & 0 & 0 & 1 & 0 & 0 & 20 \\
0 & 1 & 0 & 0 & 0 & 0 & 0 & 0 & 0 & 1 & 0 & 0 & 0 & 0 & 0 & 0 & 40 \\
0 & 0 & 1 & 0 & -1 & 0 & 0 & 0 & 0 & 0 & 0 & 0 & 0 & 0 & 0 & 1 & 30 \\
0 & 0 & 0 & 1 & 1 & 0 & 0 & 0 & 0 & -1 & 0 & 0 & -1 & 0 & -1 & & -90
\end{bmatrix}$$

$$\begin{bmatrix}
0 & 0 & 0 & 0 & 0 & 0 & 0 & 0 & 1 & 0 & -1 & 0 & -1 & 0 & 0 & 0 \\
0 & 0 & 0 & 0 & -1 & 0 & 1 & 0 & 0 & 1 & 0 & 1 & 0 & 0 & 0 & 0 & 70 \\
0 & 0 & 0 & 0 & 1 & 0 & 0 & 0 & 0 & 0 & 1 & 0 & 0 & 0 & -1 & 0 & 30 \\
0 & 0 & 0 & 1 & 0 & 0 & 0 & 0 & 0 & 0 & 0 & 1 & 0 & 0 & 0 & 0 & 30 \\
0 & 0 & 0 & 0 & 1 & 0 & 0 & 0 & 0 & 0 & 0 & 0 & 1 & 0 & 0 & 0 & 20 \\
0 & 0 & 0 & 0 & 0 & 1 & 0 & 0 & 0 & 0 & 0 & 0 & 0 & 1 & 0 & 0 & 20 \\
0 & 0 & 0 & 0 & 1^* & 0 & 0 & 0 & 0 & -1 & 0 & -1 & 0 & 0 & 1 & 0 & 10 \\
0 & 0 & 0 & 0 & 0 & 0 & 0 & 1 & 0 & 0 & 0 & 0 & 0 & 0 & 0 & 1 & 30 \\
1 & 0 & 0 & 0 & 0 & 0 & 0 & 0 & 0 & 0 & 0 & 1 & 0 & 1 & 0 & 0 & 50 \\
0 & 1 & 0 & 0 & 0 & 0 & 0 & 0 & 0 & 1 & 0 & 0 & 0 & 0 & 0 & 0 & 40 \\
0 & 0 & 1 & 0 & -1 & 0 & 0 & 0 & 0 & 0 & 0 & 0 & 0 & 0 & 0 & 1 & 30 \\
0 & 0 & 0 & 0 & 1 & 0 & 0 & 0 & 0 & -1 & 0 & -1 & 0 & -1 & 0 & -1 & -120
\end{bmatrix}$$

Without doing any more clearing we can read the answer (which would be obtained in one more step):

$$x_1 = 50, \quad x_2 = 40, \quad x_3 = 40, \quad x_4 = 30, \quad x_5 = 10,$$
$$x_6 = 20, \quad x_7 = 80, \quad x_8 = 30,$$
$$\text{and } y = 130.$$

11. It is possible to assign only 9 applicants. For example: A—9, B—6, C—2, D—4, E—1, F—5, G—3, H—8, and J—10. In this particular scheme, I is unemployed.

**Section 6.6**
**page 490**

1.

| Number of Martians | 31 | 56 | 78 | 95 | 109 |
|---|---|---|---|---|---|
| Probability that at least 2 were hatched on the same day | 0.5 | 0.9 | 0.99 | 0.999 | 0.9999 |

(Note: These asnwers are unchanged if the more accurate estimate of 668.6 Martian mean solar days per Martian tropical year is used.)

3. $-22,105.827 \begin{bmatrix} 4 & 4 \\ 4 & 4 \end{bmatrix}$

5. $x_1 = -3.21, \ x_2 = 1.23$

7. After the second clearing the third column has a positive bottom entry but no other positive entries.

9. The exact answer is $x_1 = 2.8, \ x_2 = 0, \ x_3 = 0, \ x_4 = 0.2, \ x_5 = 0, \ y = 9.8$. Not bad!

11. I realized at once that this was an LP minimization problem. I let $x_1$ be the number of number-1 tents to be purchased, and so forth. The total cost to be minimized was then

$$70x_1 + 105x_2 + \cdots \text{(etc.)} \cdots + 142x_{18} + 159x_{19}$$

I isolated six conditions:

(1) There must be enough tent space for all 85 people. Thus,

$$y_1 = 2x_1 + \cdots + 3x_{19} \geq 85$$

(2) There must be room for at least 17 AC executives in AC tents:

$$y_2 = 2x_1 + 2x_2 + 2x_3 + 2x_4 \geq 17$$

(3) There must be room for at least 15 AK executives in AK tents:

$$y_3 = 2x_5 + 2x_6 + 3x_7 + 2x_8 + x_9 \geq 15$$

(4) Similarly, for the 13 PP executives:

$$y_4 = 2x_{10} + 2x_{11} + 3x_{12} + 6x_{13} + 2x_{14} + 2x_{15} \geq 13$$

(5) The total volume must not exceed 15 cubic feet, that is, 25,920 cubic inches:

$$y_5 = 804x_1 + \cdots + 1011x_{19} \leq 25,920$$

(6) Finally, the total number of AC, AK, and PP tents must exceed all others:

$$x_1 + \cdots + x_{15} \geq x_{16} + x_{17} + x_{18} + x_{19},$$

that is,

$$y_6 = x_1 + \cdots + x_{15} - x_{16} - \cdots - x_{19} \geq 0$$

I punched the cards, submitted them, and obtained the following output:

| NAME | VKMCLUB | |
|------|---------|---|
| **COLUMNS** | | |
| X1 | Z | 70.000 000 |
| X1 | Y1 | 2.000 000 |
| X1 | Y2 | 2.000 000 |
| X1 | Y5 | 804.000 000 |
| X1 | Y6 | 1.000 000 |
| X2 | Z | 105.000 000 |
| X2 | Y1 | 2.000 000 |
| X2 | Y2 | 2.000 000 |
| X2 | Y5 | 616.000 000 |
| X2 | Y6 | 1.000 000 |
| X3 | Z | 100.000 000 |
| X3 | Y1 | 2.000 000 |
| X3 | Y2 | 2.000 000 |
| X3 | Y5 | 565.000 000 |
| X3 | Y6 | 1.000 000 |
| X4 | Z | 80.000 000 |
| X4 | Y1 | 2.000 000 |
| X4 | Y2 | 2.000 000 |
| X4 | Y5 | 565.000 000 |
| X4 | Y6 | 1.000 000 |
| X5 | Z | 70.000 000 |
| X5 | Y1 | 2.000 000 |
| X5 | Y5 | 565.000 000 |
| X5 | Y6 | 1.000 000 |
| X5 | Y3 | 2.000 000 |
| X6 | Z | 98.000 000 |
| X6 | Y1 | 2.000 000 |
| X6 | Y5 | 650.000 000 |
| X6 | Y6 | 1.000 000 |
| X6 | Y3 | 2.000 000 |
| X7 | Z | 150.000 000 |
| X7 | Y1 | 3.000 000 |
| X7 | Y5 | 285.000 000 |
| X7 | Y6 | 1.000 000 |
| X7 | Y3 | 3.000 000 |
| X8 | Z | 125.000 000 |
| X8 | Y1 | 2.000 000 |
| X8 | Y5 | 678.000 000 |
| X8 | Y6 | 1.000 000 |
| X8 | Y3 | 2.000 000 |
| X9 | Z | 35.000 000 |
| X9 | Y1 | 1.000 000 |
| X9 | Y5 | 275.000 000 |
| X9 | Y6 | 1.000 000 |
| X9 | Y3 | 1.000 000 |
| X10 | Z | 110.000 000 |
| X10 | Y1 | 2.000 000 |
| X10 | Y5 | 427.000 000 |
| X10 | Y6 | 1.000 000 |

| | | |
|---|---|---|
| X10 | Y4 | 2.000000 |
| X11 | Z | 150.000000 |
| X11 | Y1 | 2.000000 |
| X11 | Y5 | 553.000000 |
| X11 | Y6 | 1.000000 |
| X11 | Y4 | 2.000000 |
| X12 | Z | 142.000000 |
| X12 | Y1 | 3.000000 |
| X12 | Y5 | 554.000000 |
| X12 | Y6 | 1.000000 |
| X12 | Y4 | 3.000000 |
| X13 | Z | 195.000000 |
| X13 | Y1 | 6.000000 |
| X13 | Y5 | 1428.000000 |
| X13 | Y6 | 1.000000 |
| X13 | Y4 | 6.000000 |
| X14 | Z | 100.000000 |
| X14 | Y1 | 2.000000 |
| X14 | Y5 | 396.000000 |
| X14 | Y6 | 1.000000 |
| X14 | Y4 | 2.000000 |
| X15 | Z | 125.000000 |
| X15 | Y1 | 2.000000 |
| X15 | Y5 | 565.000000 |
| X15 | Y6 | 1.000000 |
| X15 | Y4 | 2.000000 |
| X16 | Z | 165.000000 |
| X16 | Y1 | 2.000000 |
| X16 | Y5 | 565.000000 |
| X16 | Y6 | −1.000000 |
| X17 | Z | 43.000000 |
| X17 | Y1 | 2.000000 |
| X17 | Y5 | 285.000000 |
| X17 | Y6 | −1.000000 |
| X18 | Z | 142.000000 |
| X18 | Y1 | 2.000000 |
| X18 | Y5 | 906.000000 |
| X18 | Y6 | −1.000000 |
| X19 | Z | 159.000000 |
| X19 | Y1 | 3.000000 |
| X19 | Y5 | 1011.000000 |
| X19 | Y6 | −1.000000 |

BOUNDS

| | | |
|---|---|---|
| FR BOUND | Z | |
| LO BOUND | Y1 | 85.000000 |
| LO BOUND | Y2 | 17.000000 |
| UP BOUND | Y5 | 25920.000000 |
| LO BOUND | Y6 | 0.000000 |
| LO BOUND | Y3 | 15.000000 |
| LO BOUND | Y4 | 13.000000 |

ENDATA

| LP SOLUTION ITERATION NUMBER | VALUE OF 'Z | NUMBER INFEAS | SUM OF INFEAS |
|---|---|---|---|
| 0 | 0.000 | 4 | 60.003 |
| 6 | 2402.500 | 0 | 0.000 |
| SOLUTION OPTIMUM | | | |
| ERROR BELOW TOLERANCE | | 0.000000 | |

VKMCLUB

| VARIABLE | TYPE | ENTRIES | SOLUTION ACTIVITY | UPPER BOUND | LOWER BOUND |
|---|---|---|---|---|---|
| X1 | B* | 5 | 8.500 | *899000.000 | 0.000 |
| Z | B* | 0 | 2402.500 | *899000.000 | *899000.000 |
| Y1 | LL | 0 | 85.000 | *899000.000 | 85.000 |
| Y2 | LL | 0 | 17.000 | *899000.000 | 17.000 |
| Y5 | B* | 0 | 19837.999 | 25920.000 | 0.000 |
| Y6 | LL | 0 | 0.000 | *899000.000 | 0.000 |
| X2 | LL | 5 | 0.000 | *899000.000 | 0.000 |
| X3 | LL | 5 | 0.000 | *899000.000 | 0.000 |
| X4 | LL | 5 | 0.000 | *899000.000 | 0.000 |
| X5 | B* | 5 | 5.667 | *899000.000 | 0.000 |
| Y3 | LL | 0 | 15.000 | *899000.000 | 15.000 |
| X6 | LL | 5 | 0.000 | *899000.000 | 0.000 |
| X7 | LL | 5 | 0.000 | *899000.000 | 0.000 |
| X8 | LL | 5 | 0.000 | *899000.000 | 0.000 |
| X9 | B* | 5 | 3.667 | *899000.000 | 0.000 |
| X10 | LL | 5 | 0.000 | *899000.000 | 0.000 |
| Y4 | LL | 0 | 13.000 | *899000.000 | 13.000 |
| X11 | LL | 5 | 0.000 | *899000.000 | 0.000 |
| X12 | LL | 5 | 0.000 | *899000.000 | 0.000 |
| X13 | B* | 5 | 2.167 | *899000.000 | 0.000 |
| X14 | LL | 5 | 0.000 | *899000.000 | 0.000 |
| X15 | LL | 5 | 0.000 | *899000.000 | 0.000 |
| X16 | LL | 4 | 0.000 | *899000.000 | 0.000 |
| X17 | B* | 4 | 20.001 | *899000.000 | 0.000 |
| X18 | LL | 4 | 0.000 | *899000.000 | 0.000 |
| X19 | LL | 4 | 0.000 | *899000.000 | 0.000 |

The answer is $z = \$2,402.50$, and

$$x_1 = 8.500$$
$$x_5 = 5.667$$
$$x_9 = 3.667$$
$$x_{13} = 2.167$$
$$x_{17} = 20.001$$

with all other variables zero.

When I returned to the club and showed them the answer, they were not impressed. "How can we possibly buy $8\frac{1}{2}$ tents? $8\frac{1}{2}$ is a movie or a shoe size; it's not a whole number. Take it back and do it right."

Luckily for me, George, our mathematical programming expert, was in the computer room when I returned. I explained my problem, showed him this book, and the following dialogue ensued.

*GEORGE: This book is only an introduction. It has failed to explain several things that I feel could have been included, but perhaps the authors felt this would be too much for a beginning student.*

*ME: But what has this to do with tents?*

*GEORGE: Nothing. I thought I should warn you that you can't expect to learn everything from a one-semester introductory course. What's more, they've barely mentioned sensitivity analysis, branch and bound for integer programming, and several other important topics.*

*ME: But what should I do now?*

*GEORGE: Based on your experience with this course, what do you think?*

*ME: Well, I guess I'll have to round off. I'll try rounding some up, some down. I don't know. Maybe we can find more room in the truck or convince somebody not to go.*

*GEORGE: Mmm. Your problem is that you've gotten yourself into an integer programming situation. You realize, of course, that the network flow problems are integer programming problems. However, it happens that the Ford-Fulkerson labeling method, which is just a version of the simplex method, always yields integer answers.*

*ME: That's lucky. But my problem is not a network flow problem.*

*GEORGE: Several techniques have been developed for more general situations; there are even computer programs available.*

*ME: Could we try some of them on this problem?*

*GEORGE: Unfortunately, this particular computing facility only purchased LPS. The integer programs were felt to be too specialized and not entirely satisfactory.*

*ME: Will rounding off work?*

*GEORGE: Generally not. Rounding off might destroy feasibility. It is unfortunate that the optimal integer feasible solution is not simply the rounded off noninteger optimum. It can happen that restricting the problem to integers radically alters the answer. The integer optimum can be very different indeed.*

*ME: What about in my case?*

*GEORGE: Oh, you're probably OK if you round off. Especially since your constraints can surely be stretched a little, and it appears that most of the tents are absolutely ruled out on account of size or price.*

*ME: OK. I'll take $x_1 = 9$, $x_5 = 6$, $x_9 = 4$, $x_{13} = 2$, $x_{17} = 20$, and refigure z by hand...$2,440. That should be acceptable.*

*GEORGE: Good. You know, you really should consider studying more LP. With your background from this course, it shouldn't be hard to get into more subtle aspects.*

*ME: I haven't got the time now. I just wanted to solve this one problem for the club. Oh, by the way, did you notice that this conversation we're having right now is recorded word for word in the answer section of the book I used for the course?*

*GEORGE: No!*

1. (a) If "at least three of a kind" means "a hand at least as good as a three-of-a-kind poker hand," the answer is $624/74{,}628 = 52/6{,}319 \doteq 0.0084$. If it means "at least 3 cards of the same denomination," the answer is $624/C_1^{13}C_3^4C_2^{49} = 1/98 \doteq 0.0102$.

(b) 510 to 3,001; or about 1 to 6.

2. (b) $\frac{652}{2{,}598{,}960} = \frac{163}{649{,}740}$.

3. (a) $\frac{936}{18{,}657} \doteq 0.0502$  (b) $\frac{4{,}576}{6{,}219} \doteq 0.7358$

5. $\frac{1{,}625}{4{,}998} \doteq 0.3251$    7. $\frac{35{,}673}{54{,}145} \doteq 0.6588$

9. Flush and straight are each disjoint from all the others.

10. $\dfrac{p/n}{p/n+q/n} = \dfrac{p}{p+q}$    11. $\frac{5}{24}$    13. 71,693 to 4

15. $\frac{1}{2}\begin{bmatrix} -102 & 100 \\ 101 & -99 \end{bmatrix}$    17. $\frac{72}{2465}\begin{bmatrix} -64 & -81 \\ 81 & 64 \end{bmatrix}$

19. $\frac{1}{6}\begin{bmatrix} 23 & 24 & -17 \\ -19 & -18 & 13 \\ -5 & -6 & 5 \end{bmatrix}$    21. $\frac{1}{4}\begin{bmatrix} -5 & 1 & 4 \\ -1 & 1 & 0 \\ 17 & -5 & -8 \end{bmatrix}$

23. No inverse    25. $\begin{bmatrix} 5 & -6 & -13 \\ -4 & 5 & 11 \\ -2 & 2 & 5 \end{bmatrix}$

27. $\frac{1}{102}\begin{bmatrix} 58 & -15 & 25 \\ -32 & 3 & -5 \\ 8 & 12 & 14 \end{bmatrix}$    28. $\frac{1}{126}\begin{bmatrix} -16 & -2 & 35 \\ -20 & -34 & 28 \\ 34 & 20 & -35 \end{bmatrix}$

29. $\frac{1}{150}\begin{bmatrix} 81 & -77 & 48 \\ -60 & 70 & -30 \\ 18 & -6 & -6 \end{bmatrix}$    30. $\frac{1}{477}\begin{bmatrix} 4 & -76 & 29 \\ 26 & -17 & -50 \\ 51 & -15 & 12 \end{bmatrix}$

31. $\begin{bmatrix} 1 & -1 & -6 & 5 \\ -1 & 0 & 10 & -8 \\ 0 & -2 & 1 & 0 \\ 0 & 2 & -2 & 1 \end{bmatrix}$

33. Let $\begin{bmatrix} x_1 \\ x_2 \end{bmatrix}$ be the first column of **X**. We must have $-x_1+x_2+3=3$ and $x_1-x_2-1=4$, i.e., $\begin{bmatrix} -x_1+x_2=0 \\ x_1-x_2=5 \end{bmatrix}$. This system has no solution; hence there is no such matrix **X**.

35. If $X\begin{bmatrix} -1 & 1 \\ 1 & -1 \end{bmatrix}$ is defined, it will be a matrix with only two columns. Hence this exercise has no answer.

37. Using the answer to Exercise 19

$$X = \frac{1}{6}\begin{bmatrix} 12 & 4 & 0 \\ 2 & 2 & 2 \\ -3 & 1 & 3 \end{bmatrix}\begin{bmatrix} 23 & 24 & -17 \\ -19 & -18 & 13 \\ -5 & -6 & 5 \end{bmatrix} = \begin{bmatrix} \frac{100}{3} & 36 & -\frac{76}{3} \\ -\frac{1}{3} & 0 & \frac{1}{3} \\ -\frac{103}{6} & -18 & \frac{79}{6} \end{bmatrix}$$

39. $x_1 = -\frac{227}{24},\ x_2 = -\frac{15}{8},\ x_3 = \frac{119}{24},\ x_4 = \frac{23}{12}$.

41. $x_1 = \frac{4}{5},\ x_2 = \frac{3}{5},\ x_3 = \frac{3}{5},\ x_4 = -\frac{2}{15},\ x_5 = \frac{1}{3}$.

43. $17x_1 + 18x_2 + 19x_3 + 20x_4 = 23$

44. $\begin{bmatrix} 4 & -3 & -4 \\ -\frac{3}{2} & \frac{5}{4} & \frac{5}{4} \\ -3 & 2 & 3 \end{bmatrix}$   45. $\begin{bmatrix} 4 & 1 & 3 & -6 & -1 \\ 5 & 2 & 1 & -4 & 2 \\ -1 & 0 & 3 & -4 & -4 \end{bmatrix}$

46. $\begin{bmatrix} 3x_1 - \frac{9}{2}x_2 + 6x_3 = \frac{3}{2} \\ \frac{4}{3}x_1 - 2x_2 + \frac{8}{3}x_3 = \frac{2}{3} \\ -\frac{16}{5}x_1 + \frac{24}{5}x_2 - \frac{32}{5}x_3 = -\frac{8}{5} \end{bmatrix}$

47. Services 720; other 410

48.

$$(I-A)^{-1} = \frac{1}{255} \begin{bmatrix} 765 & 510 & 255 \\ 629 & 816 & 323 \\ 289 & 306 & 493 \end{bmatrix}$$

49.

$$(I-A)^{-1} = \frac{10}{774} \begin{bmatrix} 342 & 135 & 144 & 117 \\ 78 & 153 & 60 & 81 \\ 32 & 33 & 104 & 63 \\ 70 & 48 & 34 & 162 \end{bmatrix}$$

A: 19,890; B: 8,510; C: 6,410; D: 6,040

51. $x_1 = 3$, $x_2 = -\frac{5}{2}$; $x_1 = 1$, $x_2 = -\frac{1}{2}$; $x_1 = -1$, $x_2 = \frac{3}{2}$.

53. $x_1 = \frac{5}{2} + x_3$, $x_2 = -\frac{1}{2}$, $x_3$ free; no solution.

55. Mixed strategy for A: $\frac{2}{9}, \frac{4}{9}, \frac{3}{9}$; for B: $\frac{3}{9}, \frac{2}{9}, \frac{4}{9}$; value: $\frac{1}{9}$.

57. $\frac{1}{5}$

59. Move 1. A(1, 3)

Move 2. A(3, 1) to win, if possible. Otherwise A(2, 3)

Move 3. A(2, 1) to win, if possible. Otherwise A(3, 3) to win.

(There are other correct answers. See pages 566–567.)

61. $\dfrac{4^{15} - 1}{4^{20} - 1} = \dfrac{1}{4^5} \doteq 0.001$

63. $\dfrac{\text{hetero}}{\text{homo}} = \dfrac{2\left(\frac{1}{n}\right)^2 - C_2^n}{\left(\frac{1}{n}\right)^2 \cdot n} = \dfrac{2}{n} \cdot \dfrac{n(n-1)}{2} = n - 1.$

64. All individuals can be assigned jobs; for example: A—7, B—4, C—6, D—9, E—8, F—3, G—5, H—2.

65. Only nine individuals can be assigned jobs; for example: A—2, B—1, C—3, D—9, E is unemployed, F—5, G—4, H—6, I—8, J is unemployed, K—11.

66. The maximal flow is 190. A minimal cut consists of the edges from ⑧ to ⓣ, ⑦ to ⑨, and ⑩ to ⓣ.

67. The maximal flow is 290. A minimal cut consists of the edges into ⓣ.

68. The maximal flow is 320. A minimal cut consists of the following edges: ① to ②, ① to ⑤, ① to ③, ⑤ to ⑧, ⑪ to ⑦, ⑪ to ⑳, ⑰ to ⑳, ⑲ to ⓣ.

69. Let $x_1$ be the number of hamburgers to be made, $x_2$ the cheeseburgers,..., $x_{11}$ the

large colas, $x_{12}$ the burger snacks,..., and $x_{16}$ the number of fishfeasts to be made. Let $z$ be the profit, $y_1$ the constraint on hamburger patties, $y_2$ the constraint on cheese slices, $y_3$ the upper constraint on potatoes,..., $y_{10}$ the lower constraint on potatoes, $y_{11}$ the upper constraint on short hotdog buns, $y_{12}$ the upper constraint on long hotdog buns, $y_{13}$ the constraint on dogfeasts, and $y_{14}$ on fishfeasts. Here's the input and results.

| NAME | PHE | |
|------|-----|---|
| COLUMNS | | |
| X1 | Z | 7.000000 |
| X1 | Y1 | 1.000000 |
| X1 | Y7 | 1.000000 |
| X2 | Z | 10.000000 |
| X2 | Y1 | 1.000000 |
| X2 | Y7 | 1.000000 |
| X2 | Y2 | 1.000000 |
| X3 | Z | 17.000000 |
| X3 | Y1 | 2.000000 |
| X3 | Y2 | 1.000000 |
| X3 | Y8 | 1.000000 |
| X4 | Z | 6.000000 |
| X4 | Y3 | 3.000000 |
| X4 | Y10 | 3.000000 |
| X5 | Z | 8.000000 |
| X5 | Y3 | 5.000000 |
| X5 | Y10 | 5.000000 |
| X6 | Z | 9.000000 |
| X6 | Y5 | 1.000000 |
| X6 | Y9 | 1.000000 |
| X7 | Z | 11.000000 |
| X7 | Y6 | 1.000000 |
| X7 | Y11 | 1.000000 |
| X8 | Z | 14.000000 |
| X8 | Y8 | 1.000000 |
| X8 | Y12 | 1.000000 |
| X9 | Z | 10.000000 |
| X9 | Y4 | 4.000000 |
| X10 | Z | 15.000000 |
| X10 | Y4 | 6.000000 |
| X11 | Z | 20.000000 |
| X11 | Y4 | 8.000000 |
| X12 | Z | 19.000000 |
| X12 | Y1 | 1.000000 |
| X12 | Y7 | 1.000000 |
| X12 | Y4 | 4.000000 |
| X13 | Z | 35.000000 |
| X13 | Y1 | 1.000000 |
| X13 | Y7 | 1.000000 |
| X13 | Y2 | 1.000000 |
| X13 | Y3 | 3.000000 |
| X13 | Y10 | 3.000000 |
| X13 | Y4 | 6.000000 |
| X14 | Z | 52.000000 |

| | | |
|---|---|---|
| X14 | Y1 | 2.000000 |
| X14 | Y2 | 1.000000 |
| X14 | Y8 | 1.000000 |
| X14 | Y3 | 5.000000 |
| X14 | Y10 | 5.000000 |
| X14 | Y4 | 8.000000 |
| X15 | Z | 35.000000 |
| X15 | Y3 | 5.000000 |
| X15 | Y10 | 5.000000 |
| X15 | Y6 | 1.000000 |
| X15 | Y11 | 1.000000 |
| X15 | Y4 | 8.000000 |
| X15 | Y13 | 1.000000 |
| X16 | Z | 42.000000 |
| X16 | Y8 | 1.000000 |
| X16 | Y3 | 5.000000 |
| X16 | Y10 | 5.000000 |
| X16 | Y12 | 1.000000 |
| X16 | Y4 | 8.000000 |
| X16 | Y14 | 1.000000 |

BOUNDS

| | | |
|---|---|---|
| FR BOUND | Z | |
| FX BOUND | Y1 | 342.000000 |
| UP BOUND | Y7 | 284.000000 |
| UP BOUND | Y2 | 194.000000 |
| UP BOUND | Y8 | 178.000000 |
| UP BOUND | Y3 | 460.000000 |
| LO BOUND | Y10 | 320.000000 |
| UP BOUND | Y5 | 244.000000 |
| UP BOUND | Y9 | 244.000000 |
| UP BOUND | Y6 | 110.000000 |
| UP BOUND | Y11 | 130.000000 |
| UP BOUND | Y12 | 180.000000 |
| UP BOUND | Y4 | 8320.000000 |
| LO BOUND | Y13 | 70.000000 |
| FX BOUND | Y14 | 22.000000 |

ENDATA

| VARIABLE | TYPE | ENTRIES | SOLUTION ACTIVITY | UPPER BOUND | LOWER BOUND |
|---|---|---|---|---|---|
| X1 | LL | 3 | 0.000 | *899000.000 | 0.000 |
| Z | B* | 0 | 29962.001 | *899000.000 | *899000.000 |
| Y1 | EQ | 0 | 342.000 | 342.000 | 342.000 |
| Y7 | UL | 0 | 284.000 | 284.000 | 0.000 |
| X2 | B* | 4 | 165.001 | *899000.000 | 0.000 |
| Y2 | UL | 0 | 194.000 | 194.000 | 0.000 |
| X3 | B* | 4 | 29.000 | *899000.000 | 0.000 |
| Y8 | UL | 0 | 178.000 | 178.000 | 0.000 |
| X4 | LL | 3 | 0.000 | *899000.000 | 0.000 |
| Y3 | UL | 0 | 460.000 | 460.000 | 0.000 |
| Y10 | B* | 0 | 460.001 | *899000.000 | 320.000 |

| | | | | | |
|---|---|---|---|---|---|
| X5 | LL | 3 | 0.000 | *899000.000 | 0.000 |
| X6 | B* | 3 | 244.001 | *899000.000 | 0.000 |
| Y5 | B* | 0 | 244.000 | 244.000 | 0.000 |
| Y9 | UL | 0 | 244.000 | 244.000 | 0.000 |
| X7 | B* | 3 | 40.001 | *899000.000 | 0.000 |
| Y6 | UL | 0 | 110.000 | 110.000 | 0.000 |
| Y11 | B* | 0 | 110.000 | 130.000 | 0.000 |
| X8 | B* | 3 | 127.001 | *899000.000 | 0.000 |
| Y12 | B* | 0 | 149.001 | 180.000 | 0.000 |
| X9 | B* | 2 | 1777.001 | *899000.000 | 0.000 |
| Y4 | UL | 0 | 8320.000 | 8320.000 | 0.000 |
| X10 | LL | 2 | 0.000 | *899000.000 | 0.000 |
| X11 | LL | 2 | 0.000 | *899000.000 | 0.000 |
| X12 | B* | 4 | 119.000 | *899000.000 | 0.000 |
| X13 | B* | 7 | 0.000 | *899000.000 | 0.000 |
| X14 | LL | 7 | 0.000 | *899000.000 | 0.000 |
| X15 | B* | 7 | 70.000 | *899000.000 | 0.000 |
| Y13 | LL | 0 | 70.000 | *899000.000 | 70.000 |
| X16 | B* | 7 | 22.000 | *899000.000 | 0.000 |
| Y14 | EQ | 0 | 22.000 | 22.000 | 22.000 |

Answer: $x_2 = 165.001$, $x_3 = 29.000$, $x_6 = 244.001$, $x_7 = 40.001$, $x_8 = 127.001$, $x_9 = 1,777.001$, $x_{12} = 119.000$, $x_{15} = 70.000$, $x_{16} = 22.000$, with all other variables equal to zero. Then $z = 29,962.001$.

Thus, they should make only the following items in the following quantities.

165 cheeseburgers
29 superburgers
244 hot dogs
40 foot-long hot dogs
127 fishburgers
1,777 small colas
119 burger snacks
70 dogfeasts
22 fishfeasts

The profit will be $29,962¢ = \$299.62$.

**Appendix A
page 512**

1. (a) 27  (b) 1024  (c) $\frac{1}{8}$  (d) 1  (e) $\frac{27}{64}$  (f) 1  (g) 32  (h) 49  (i) $\frac{16}{81}$  (j) 1
2. (a) 4  (b) 6  (c) 11  (d) $-\frac{3}{10}$  (e) $-\frac{133}{60}$  (f) $-\frac{1}{3}$  (g) $-\frac{47}{24}$
3. (e) $-2\frac{13}{60}$  (g) $-1\frac{23}{24}$
4. (a) $\frac{1}{6}$  (b) $-\frac{1}{8}$  (c) $-\frac{1}{8}$  (d) $\frac{3}{2}$  (e) $\frac{5}{3}$  (f) $-\frac{6}{5}$  (g) $\frac{3}{4}$
5. 18: $\frac{5}{6} = \frac{15}{18}$, $-\frac{7}{9} = -\frac{14}{18}$
6. (a) $-7.16$  (b) 6.96
7. 12.5%
8. (a) $\frac{13}{24}$  (b) $-\frac{13}{24}$
9. (a) 1,2,3,4  (b) 1,2,3,4,5,6,7  (c) 1,2,3,4,5,6,7,8,9
   (d) 3,4,5,6,7,8,9,10  (e) 1,2,3,4  (f) 8,9,10  (g) 6,7,8,9,10
   (h) 3,4,5,6,7,8,9,10
10. $\frac{3}{4}$, 70, 4, 0, 3, and 4
11. $-x_1 - 2x_3 + 2x_4 \le 7$
12. $\frac{12}{35}$

# Index

Page references to terms discussed in the marginal notes are in italics.

Absolute value, 510–511
Absorbing Markov chain, 184,
    192–202
  absorbing state of, 184
  determining long-range distribu-
      tion, 192–202
  flowcharts, 197, 199
Abstract mathematics, 350
Accuracy, false, 261–262
Addition of fractions, 507
  inequalities, 510
  matrices, 111–113
Address of an entry, 70
Alan's neighborhood (problems),
    40–41, 155–156, 165–166
Algebra, review of, 503–512
Allele, *445*
Analysis
  input-output, 415–420
  sensitivity, 486
Answer
  dual variable check, 363–365
  multiple. *See* Multiple answers
  reading. *See* Reading the answer
Arithmetic average, 257
Arithmetic, matrix, 107–135
Assignment problem, 463–470
Associativity of matrix multiplication,
    530
Average, arithmetic, 257
Axis (axes), 56, 102–103

Bar graph, 238
Base, 504
Bayes, Rev. Thomas (d. 1761), *166*
Bayes' formula, 166–167
Bayes' theorem, 160–168
Bell-shaped curve, *283*
Bernoulli, Jacques (1654–1705), *265*
Bernoulli trials, 264–272, 276–278
  expectation, 276
  experiment, 264–272, *265*, 276–278
  formula, 269, 271
  mean, 278

standard deviation, 278
  variance, 278
Binomial, 275
Binomial coefficients, *275*
Binomial distribution, 270, *275*,
    276–278
  expectation, 276
  mean, 278
  normal approximation to, 279–286
  Poisson approximation to, 288–291
  standard deviation, 278
  variance, 278
Binomial expansion, 273–275
Binomial theorem, 275
Biological applications, 441–448
  competition of species, 441–444
  distribution of genotypes, 444–448
Birthday problem, 34–36, 476, 490
  classical, 36
    with calculator, 476
  day of month, 34
  day of week, 34–35
  day of year, 36
  for Martians, 490
Bound, 315
  lower, 479
  upper, 479
Bound matrix for an LP problem,
    315–316

$C_r^n$
  formula for, 30
  how to calculate by hand, 32
Calculators (hand, pocket), 475–477
Calculus, *54*, *86*, *377*
Cancellation, 505
Cantor, Georg (1845–1918), *12*
Capacity of a cut, 461
Cardan, Jerome (1501–1576), *12*
Cards, playing, 387–392
Carroll, Lewis (1832–1898), 519
Cayley, Arthur (1821–1895), *65*
Central moment (nth), 263
Certain event, 11

Chain
  absorbing, 192–202
  ergodic, 210, 215–220
  Markov, 170, 169–225; *see also*
      Markov chain
  periodic, 202–207
  regular, 185–192
Chasing errors, 99–101
Check
  dual variable, 363–365
  LP maximization answer, 321
  simplex method, 325–326
Chromosomes, 448
Clark, Colin, *415*
Clear (a column in a matrix), 79
Cleared columns, locating, 321
Closed sets of states, 207–209
  determining limit matrix in terms
      of, 210
Coefficient(s)
  binomial, *275*
  matrix, 119, 413
Column matrix, *114*
Combination, 30–32
Common denominator, least, 507
Common divisor, greatest, 213
Commutative, matrix multiplication
    is *not*, 125, 530
Comparing fractions, 510
Competition of species, 441–444
*Compleat Strategyst, The*, 428
Complement, 13
Computer(s), 477–490
  programming, *297*, 478, 491
Conditional probability, *37*, 37–47
  definition, 38
  in equally likely distribution, 39
Conditions for application of the
    simplex method for standard
    maximization problems, 316
Constraint(s), 300
  equality, 342–347
    flow chart, 344
  matrix for an LP problem, 315
  mixed, 316, 334–341, 346
  redundant, 340

Constraint(s), *cont.*
  standard format, *347*, 511
Coordinates, 55–57
  of a point in space, 102–103
  of a point in the plane, 56–57
  of a point on a line, 55–56
Corner point, 304
  theorem. *See* Extreme point theorem
Counting, 3–6, 28–35, 389–393
  poker hands, 389–392
  principle of division in, 30
  principle of multiplication in, 5
  starting sets for Scrabble® Brand
    Crossword Game, 392–393
Coxeter, H. S. M., *31*
Cross-multiplication, 506
Crossover point, 526
Cube (third power) 504
Curve
  bell-shaped, *283*
  normal, 283
Cut (in a network), 461
  capacity, 461
  minimal, 461
    finding, 462–463
Cycle, 207
Cycling in the simplex method, 347

Dandolos, Nicholas (Nick the Greek)
    (1882–1966), 394–397
Dantzig, George, 297
Decimals, 508–509
Decision making, 54
Deficiencies in mathematical models,
    378–382
Demands, 416
De Moivre, Abraham (1667–1754),
    282–283
De Morgan, Augustus (1806–1871),
    *16*
De Morgan's laws, *16*
Denominator, 505
  least common, 507
Dependent events, *41*
Descartes, René (1596–1650), 56
Deviation
  mean absolute, 294
  standard, 261; *see also* Standard
    deviation
Diagonal, main, 127, 399
Diagram
  tree, 149–153
  Venn, *16*, 519
Dice, realistic probability distribution,
    20, 33
Die (dice), *2*

Difference equations, 444
Disjoint events, 21
Distribution
  binomial, 270, *275*, 276–278; *see
    also* Binomial distribution
  equally likely, 26
  geometric, 272
  normal, 279–286, 283
    table, 516–517
  of genotypes, 444–448
  Poisson, 288–291
    table, 517
  probability, 20, 17–24, *240*
    rules for, 18, 19
Distribution matrix, 174
  obtaining final
    for absorbing chain, 192–199
    for ergodic chain, 210, 215–220
    for regular chain, 185–192
Distributive laws, of set theory, *16*
Division
  fraction, 506
  matrix, *119*, 397–409
    defined, 400
    *see also* Inverse of a matrix
Divisor, greatest common, 213
Dodgson, Charles L. (1832–1898), 519
Dominant strategies, 433
  eliminating, 433–434
Dual LP problem, 360, 361, 367
  general, 367
  standard, 361
  variable check, 363–365
Duality, economic interpretation of,
    372–374

Edge
  of network, 449
  of region of feasibility, 315
Element, of a set, 11
*Elements of Input-Output Analysis,
    The*, 419
Elimination, Gaussian, *93*, 95
Empty region of feasibility, 305
Empty set, 11
Entry, in a matrix, *70*, 70
  address, 70
  position, 70
Equality constraints, 342–346
  flow chart, 344
Equality of matrices, 403, 411
Equally likely
  outcomes, 26–36
  probability distribution, 26
    conditional probability in, 39
  probability of an event, how to
    calculate, 27

Equation(s)
  difference, 444
  of a line, finding, 143
  linear. *See* Linear equation
  solving, 512
Ergodic Markov chain, 202, 215,
    215–220
Error chasing, 99–101
Euler, Leonard (1707–1783), *16*
Event(s), 8–17
  certain, 11
  dependent, *41*
  determining probability of, 18
  disjoint, 21
  impossible, 11
  independence of three, 295–296
  independent, 41–47, 267; *see also*
    Independent events
  joint, 244; *see also* Joint event
  mutually exclusive, 21
  odds, *394*; *see also* Odds
  probability of. *See* Probability of
    events
Exclusive or, *13*
Expansion, binomial, 275
Expectation(s), 249–255
  for Bernoulli trials experiment, 276
  for binomial distribution, 276
  properties of, 252–255
  of product of two random variables, 255
  related to mean, 261
  of sum and difference of random
    variables, 253
  of two comparable random variables, 254
  used to simplify game, 437–439
Experiment(s), 8, *150*
  Bernoulli trials, 264–272, 265,
    276–278
Exponents, 504
Extreme point, *304*
Extreme point theorem, 306

Factorial, *30*
Fair game, 433
Fair odds, *394*
False accuracy, 261–262
Feasibility, region of, 303
  edge, 315
  empty, 305
  graphing, 303–305
  unbounded, 304
Feasible solution, 303
de Fermat, Pierre (ca. 1601–1665), *12*,
    56
Filling orders, 409–412

Filling orders, *cont.*
  a straight, 397
Final distribution, computing
  for absorbing chains, 192–199
  for ergodic chains, 215–220
  for regular chains, 185–192
First quadrant, *304*
Fitness of genotype, 447
Fixed variable, 479
Flow (in a network), 450
  finding maximal, 452–463
Flow charts
  absorbing chain
    limit matrix, 197
    long-range distribution, 199
  calculating $C_r^n$, 32
  equality constraints, 344
  Ford-Fulkerson, outline, 452
  Gauss-Jordan reduction, 80–81
  graphing $ax_1 + bx_2 = c$, 60
  independence of random variables,
    245
  inverse of matrix
    existence, 564
    finding, 407
  limit matrix, in terms of closed sets
    of states, 210
  linear programming, geometric, 307
  Markov chain, regular or periodic,
    213
  matrix multiplication
    matrix times column, 117
    matrix times matrix, 122
    row matrix times column matrix,
      115
  network flow, 452
  phase I, 338
  regular Markov chain, final distri-
    bution, 189
  saddle point, 432
  simplex method, 318
  strategy, best mixed, 436
  systems of equations, two by two,
    70
  vertex labelling (outline), 454
Ford-Fulkerson labeling method,
    450–463
  outline flow chart, 452
Ford, L. R., 450
Form, linear, 301
Format, standard
  constraint, *347*, 511
  for LP problem, 299
Formula, Bayes', 166
Fractions, 505–508
  addition, 507; *see also* Addition, of
    fractions
  avoiding, 94–95
  cancellation, 505

common denominator, least, 507
comparing, 510
division, 506
equality, 506
exponents, 506
mixed, 505
multiplication, 505
subtraction, 507
Free variable, 81, 479
Fulkerson, D. R., 450
Functional notation, *19*

Gale, David, *429*, 439
Game theory, 428–441
Games and expectations, 437–439
Game(s)
  chess, 49, 429
  fair, 433
  Low Number, 429, 440
  matrix, *430*
  maze, 153
  Monopoly®, *8*
  Morra, 440, 486–490
  multiple solutions, 439
  1, 2, 3 game, 438–439
  poker, 387–392
  pool, 46
  rock, paper, scissors, 440
  Scrabble® Brand Crossword Game,
    392–393
  solving, 435–439
  tennis, 153, 230
  tick tack toe, 50, 440, 566–567
  two-person zero-sum, 428
  value, 431
  zero-sum, 428
Gauss, C. F. (1777–1855), 64
Gaussian elimination, *93*, 95
Gaussian reduction, 64, *93*, 95
  defined, 95
  relative efficiency, *93*
Gauss-Jordan reduction, 64–102
  flow chart, 80–81
  larger systems, 77–102
  reading the answer, 81
  shortcuts in, 93–102
  small systems, 64–71
  substitution, compared with, 75
  two equations, 64–75
General LP problem, 366
  dual, 367
Genotype(s), 445
  distribution of, 444–448
  heterozygous, *498*
  homozygous, *498*
  sex-linked, 447–448
Geometric distribution, 272

Geometrical method for LP problems,
    297–310
Geometry of linear equations,
    102–106
Goodwin, Harvey, 30
Graph, 57
  bar, 238
Graphing
  a linear equation
    in three variables, 103–104, *323*
    in two variables, 58–60
  $ax_1 + bx_2 = c$, flow chart, 60
  inequalities, 301–303
    region of feasibility, 303–305
Greater than, 509
Greatest common divisor, 213

Half-plane
  lower, 301
  right, 303
  upper, 301
Half-space, 314
Hardy, G. H. (1877–1947), 446
Hardy-Weinberg law, *446*
Heterozygous genotype, *498*
Histogram, 238–242
Homozygous genotype, *498*
*How to Lie with Statistics*, 240
How to read the answer after Gauss-
    Jordan reduction, 81
Huff, Darrel, 240
Hyperplane, 102

Identical lines, 69
Identical planes, 104
Identity matrix, 127, 399
Impossible event, 11
Inclusive "or", 13–14
Independent events, 41–47, 267
  definition, 41
  necessary condition, 44
  sufficient condition, 44
  three, 295–296
Independent random variables,
    245–247
  flow chart, 245
Inequalities
  addition of, 510
  graphing, 301–304
  multiplication by −1, 335–336, 511
  working with, 511
Initial state matrix, 173
Input-output analysis, 415–420
*Intermediate Algebra*, 272
Intersection, 13
Inventory control, *86*

Inverse
  of a matrix
    applications, 409–412, 416–419
    calculation of, 397–409
    defined, 399
    flow chart, 407
    and Leontief models, 416–419
    notation, 401
    shortcuts in calculating, 409
    uniqueness, 401
    when calculation method fails,
      403
  multiplicative, 506
  of a nonsquare matrix, 402
  of a number, 506
Irreducible Markov chain, 213
Isolated absorbing state, 185, 194–195
Iteration, 482


Johnson, Samuel (1709–1784), 449
Joint event, 244
  probabilities, matrix of, 244
  probability, 244–247
Jordan, W. (1819–1904), 64


Kuhn, H., *430*
Kurtosis, *263*


Labeling method, 450–463
  outline flow chart, 452
Labeling vertices, outline flow chart,
  454
LaPlace, Pierre Simon (1749–1827),
  *166*, 282
Least common denominator, 507
Least squares, method of, 76
Leontief, Wassily, *416*
Leontief models, 415–420
Less than, 509
Limit matrix determination
  for absorbing chains, 192–202
  for ergodic chains, 215–220
  for regular chains, 185–192
  in terms of closed sets of states, 210
Line(s)
  finding equation for, 143
  graphing, 57–60
  identical, 69
  intersecting, 60–71
  parallel, 69
  point of intersection, 60–77
Linear, definition of, *54*, 378–382
Linear equations, 57–106
  general definition, 58, 77–78, 135

geometry of, 102–106
graphing, 57–60
systems of, 60–106, 409–415
  coefficient matrix, 119, 413
  flow charts, 70, 80–81
  matrix form, 119, 413–415
  and matrix inversion, 409–415
  requirement matrix, 119, 413
  two, 64–77
  unknown matrix, 119, 413
three variable, 102–106
  graphing, 103–104, *323*
two variable, 57–60
  graphing, 58–60
Linear form, 301
Linear model, 54, 135–136, 378–382,
  *381*
Linear programming, 88, 297–310,
  315–326, 336–340, 342–347,
  366–372
  dual LP problems, 360, 361, 366,
    367; *see also* Dual LP prob-
    lems
  general LP problems, 366; *see also*
    General LP problems
  geometric approach, 297–310
    flow chart, 307
  maximization problems, 315–326,
    336–340, 342–347, 366–372,
    *see also* Maximization LP
    problems
  meaning of words, *297*, 298
  minimization problems, 340–342,
    366; *see also* Minimization LP
    problems
  standard LP problems, 361; *see also*
    Standard LP problems
  *see also* Simplex method
Locating cleared columns, 321
Long-range distribution, determination
  for absorbing chain, 192–199
  for ergodic chain, 215–220
  for regular chain, 185–192
Lower bound, 479
  half-plane, 301
Low Number (game), 429, 440


Main diagonal, 127, 399
Markov, A. A. (1856–1922), 170
Markov chain, 170, 169–225
  absorbing, 192–202
  application to biology, 442–444
  ergodic, 202, 210, 215–220
  final distribution, computing
    absorbing, 192–199
    ergodic, 210, 215–220
    regular, 183, 185–192

irreducible, 213
isolated absorbing state, 185,
  194–195
limit matrix, determining
  absorbing, 192–199
  ergodic, 215–220
  regular, 185–192
periodic, 202–207
regular, 183, 185–192
states, 170
transition percentages, 170
transition probabilities, 180
washing out, 188
Markov matrix, *171*
Martian birthday problem, 490
Mathematical models, deficiencies
  in, 378–382
Matrix (matrices), *65*
  addition of, 111–113
  application of inverse, 409–412,
    416–419
  arithmetic, 107–135
  bound, 315–316
  coefficient, 119, 413
  column, *114*
  constraint, 315
  distribution, 174
  division, *119*, 397–409
    defined, 400
  equality, 403, 411
  game, *430*
  identity, 127, 399
  initial state, 173
  inverse, 399
    using to fill orders, 409–412
    *see also* Inverse of a matrix
  inversion, 397–409
    flow chart, 407
    notation, 401
    shortcuts, 409
    uniqueness, 401
  of joint probabilities, 244
  Markov, *171*
  multiplication, 113–127
    associativity, 530
    by a number, 108–109
    flow charts, 115, 117, 122
    *not* commutative, 125, 530
    size of answer, 124–125
    and systems of equations, 119,
      413–415
  objective, 316
  of a system, 65
  1 × 1, 114–115
  partitioned, *145*
  payoff, 429
  power of, 175
  preference, *165*
  requirement, 119, 413

Matrix (matrices), *cont.*
row, *114*
size of, 78
square, *127*
submatrix, *145*
subtraction of, 111–113
transition, 173
transpose, 188, 360–361
unknown, 119, 413
zero, 529

*Matrix Methods in Finite Mathematics,* 321, *347, 409, 439, 470*
Maximal flow (in networks), finding, 452–463
Maximization LP problem, 315–326, 336–340, 342–347, 366–372
checking the answer, 321
dual variable check, 363, 365
equality constraints, 342–347
flow charts, 318, 338, 344
general problem, 366–372
locating cleared columns, 321
multiple answers, 309, 321
phase I, 336–340
shortcuts, 365–366
simplex method, 297, 313–326, 340–342, 368–372, 435–438
standard problems, 315–326
Maximize, 299
Mean, 257–258
absolute deviation, 294
for Bernoulli trials experiment, 278
for binomial distribution, 278
related to expectation, 261
Median, 262
Mendelsohn, N. S., *429*
Method
geometrical for LP, 306, 297–310
flow chart, 307
labeling (for networks), 450–463
outline flowchart, 452
simplex, 297, 313–326, 342–347, 368–372; *see also* Simplex method
Miernyk, William H., 419
Minimal cut, 461
finding, 462–463
Minimax strategies, 431
Minimization LP problems, 305–310, 340–342
geometrical method, 305–310
reading the answer from dual maximization problem, 366
Minimize, 307
Minus, rules for, 508
Mixed constraints, 316, 334–336
Mixed fractions, 505
Mixed strategy, 434
determining best, 434–439

flow chart, 436
Model(s),
Leontief, 415–420
linear, 54, 135–136, 378–382, *381*
probability, 54
deMoivre, Abraham (1667–1754), 282–283
Moment, nth central, 263
Monopoly®, *8*
Morgenstern, Oscar, 428
Morra
three-finger, 486–490
two-finger, 440
Multiple answers
in linear programming, 309, 321
for matrix games, 439
Multiple sinks, 463
Multiple sources, 463
Multiplication
associativity of matrix, 530
cross, 506
fraction, 505
matrix, 108–110, 113–127; *see also* Matrix multiplication
notations, 503
principle in counting, 5
Multiplicative inverse, 506
Multistage process, 149–231
Mutually exclusive events, 21

Necklaces, 51–52
Negative (number), 510
Network, 449
von Neumann, John (1903–1957), 428
von Neumann's minimax strategy, 431
*n*-factorial, *30*
Nick the Greek. *See* Dandolos, Nicholas
*Nick the Greek, King of the Gamblers,* 394–397
Nonnegative, 510
Normal approximation to binomial, 279–286
Normal curve, 283
distribution, 279–286, 283
table, 516–517
nth central moment, 263
Numerator, 505

Objective matrix (for LP), 316
Objective variable, 299
Octant, positive, 314
Odds, 394
against, *394*
converting to probability, 394
fair, *394*

on an event, *394*
Olney, Thomas (1600–1682), 177
1-axis, 56
$1 \times 1$ matrix, 114–115
1, 2, 3 game, 438–439
Operation, row, 78
Operations research, *1*
Optimum (solution), 298
Or
exclusive, *13*
inclusive, *13*–14
Order filling, 409–412
Ordered pair, *8*, 56
Ordered triple, *10*
Origin, 55
Outcomes, *8*–14
possible, 8

Pair
ordered, *8*, 56
Paradox, St. Petersburg, 549
Parallel lines, 69
Parallel planes, 104
Parentheses, 503
Partition, 154–159
equation, 166
Partitioned matrix, *145*
Pascal, Blaise (1623–1662), *12*
Payoff matrix, 429
Peacock, George, *31*
Peano, Giuseppe (1858–1932), *13*
Percent, 508–509
Periodic Markov chain, 202–207
Persistence of transition percentages, 171
Person-hour, *298*
Phase 1, 336–340
flow chart, 338
PHE exercises,

$$\begin{bmatrix} 5,6 & 20 & 23 & 15,17 & 18 & \\ 27 & 21 & 38 & 4 & 9 & 29,82,83 \\ 12 & 18 & 6 & 13 & & \\ 12 & 9 & 23 & & 31 & 6 \\ 35 & 35 & 3 & 35 & 7 & \\ & 29,47 & 13 & & & \end{bmatrix}$$

The (i,j)-entry of this matrix gives the number of the PHE exercise in Chapter i, Section j. *Also* Review Exercise 1, Chapter 3; Supplementary Exercises 60, 75, Chapter 2; Supplementary Exercise 33, Chapter 3.

Plane(s), 103
identical, 104
in space, possibilities, 104–105

Plane(s) *cont.*
  intersecting, 104–106
  parallel, 104
Playing cards, 387–392
Plus and minus, rules for, 508
Poem, 427
Point
  corner, 304
  crossover, 526
  extreme (theorem), 306
  saddle, 431; *see also* Saddle point
Poisson, Simeon-Denis (1781–1840), *288*
Poisson approximation to binomial distribution, 288–289
Poisson distribution, 288–291
  table, 517
Poker,
  draw, 389
  five-card stud, 388
  hands, 388
  probability of hands, 389–390
  seven-card stud, 388
  straight, 388
Position of an entry, 70
Positive number, 510
Positive octant, 314
Positive quadrant, 304
Power, 504
Powers of a square matrix, 175
Preference matrix, *165*
Preliminary row operation, 97
Principle of division, in counting, 30
Principle of multiplication, 5–8
  in counting, 5
Probability
  conditional, *37*, 37–47
    definition, 38; *see also* Conditional probability
  converting to odds, 394
  distribution, 17–24, 20, *240*
    equally likely, 26
    rules for, 18, 19
    two dice, 20
  of events, 18–26
    relationship between, complement, 24
    relationship between union and intersection, 22
  history of, *12*
  introduction to, 2–3
  joint, 244–247
  measure, *20*
  model, 54
  philosophy of, 47–48
  of poker hands, 389–390
  transition, 180
Problems. *See* Assignment problem; Birthday problem; Dual

LP problems; General LP problems; Maximization LP problems; Minimization LP problems; Standard LP problems
Process, multistage, 150, 149–231
Programming
  computer, *297*, 478, 491
  linear. *See* Linear programming

Quadrant
  first, *304*
  positive, 304
Quesnay, Francois (1694–1774), 416

Random variables, 234, 232–242
  expectations, 249–255
  independent, 245–247
  not comparable, *254*
Reading the answer in
  Gauss-Jordan reduction, 181
  in the Simplex method, 319–320
  in small systems, 71
Reciprocal, 506
Reduction
  Gaussian, 64, *93*, 95
  Gauss-Jordan, 64–102
Redundant constraint, 340
Region of feasibility, 303
  edge, 315
  empty, 305
  graphing, 303–306
  unbounded, 304
Regular Markov chain, 183, 185–192
  final distribution, 189
Requirement matrix, 119, 413
Rice, Cy, 394–395
Right half-plane, 303
Right-hand side, 315
Rock, paper, scissors, 440
Root, square, 507
  table, 514
Rothstein, Arnold, 394–397
Rounding off, *477*, 577
Row matrix, *114*
  multiplication by column matrix, 114–116
Row operations, 68, 78
  preliminary, 97
Row switching, 68, 78, 143
Rules for probability distribution, 18, 19
Russell, Bertrand (1872–1970), *13*

Saddle point, 431
  determining, 431–433
    flow chart, 432
St. Petersburg paradox, 549
Sample space, 8–14
  *a*, 9
  *the*, 9
Scrabble® Brand Crossword Game, 392–393
Sensitivity analysis, 486
Set(s)
  empty, 11
  partition of a, 154–159
  of states, closed, 207; *see also* Closed sets of states
Set theory, 9–17, 21
  arithmetic of, 16
  definitions in probability, summary, 48
  distributive laws, *16*
  summary, 48
Sex-linked, genotype, 447–448
Shoemaker problem, 312
Shortcuts
  in Gauss-Jordan reduction, 93–102
    general advice, 98
  for matrix inversion, 409
  for the simplex method, 325–326
  for standard LP problems, 365–366
Simplex method, 297
  algebra of, 328–334
  common errors, 325–326
  conditions 1, 2, and 3, 316
  cycling in, 347
  dual variable check, 363–365
  equality constraints, 342–346
    flow chart, 344
  flow chart, 318
  games, solving, 435–439
  general problems, 368–372
  geometric intepretation, 313–315
  maximization problems, 313–326, 336–340, 342–347, 366–372
    checking the answer, 321
    flow chart, 318
    locating cleared columns, 321
    reading the answer, 319
  minimization problems, 340–342, 366
  misapplication, 378–382
  phase I, 336–340
    flow chart, 338
  practical problems, 349–356
  shortcuts, 325–326
  unrestricted variables, 368–372
  warning, 321 *See also* Linear programming
Sink, 451
  multiple, 463

Size
  of answer
    matrix addition, 112
    matrix multiplication, 124–125
    matrix subtraction, 112
  of a matrix, 78
Slack variable, 329
  reading the final values, 330
Solution
  feasible, 303
  small system of equations, 70
Sorting, 3–8
  mental, 3
Source, 451
  multiple, 463
Space
  half, 314
  sample, 8–14
Species, competition, 441–444
Square, 504
  matrix, *127*
    powers of, 175
  power, 504
  root, 507–508
  table, 514–516
Standard deviation, 261
  for Bernoulli trials, 278
  for binomial distribution, 278
Standard format constraint, *347*, 511
Standard LP problem, 361
  dual, 361
  format for, 299
Starting sets for Scrabble® Brand
    Crossword Game, 392–393
State(s) (in a Markov chain), 170
  absorbing, 184
  closed set of, 207–209
  isolated absorbing, 185, 194–195
  transient, 209
Statistics, 18, 54, 232
Strategy, 429
  dominated, 433
    eliminating, 433–434
  mixed, 434; *see also* Mixed strategy
Submatrix, *145*
Subset, 12
Substitution, Gauss-Jordan reduction
    compared, 75
Subtraction
  of fractions, 507
  of matrices, 111–113
Switching rows, 68, 78, 143
*Symbolic Logic*, 519
System
  of equations, 60–109, 119, 413–415
    applications, 71–75, 89–92,
      141–142
    coefficient matrix, 119, 413
    matrix form, 119, 413–415

matrix multiplication, 119,
    413–415
requirement matrix, 119, 413
solution of, 60–106
unknown matrix, 119, 413
  *see also* Gauss-Jordan reduction
of two linear equations, 64–77
  flow chart, 70
  reading the answer, 71

Tables, 514–517
  normal distribution, 516–517
  Poisson probabilities, 517
  square root, 514–516
Theorem
  Bayes', 160–168
  binomial, 275
  extreme point, 306
*Theory of Games and Economic Be-*
    *havior*, 428
*Theory of Linear Economic Models,*
    *The*, *429*, 439
Three-finger Morra, 486–490
Tick tack toe, 50, 440
  strategy, 566–567
Transient state, 209
Transition-matrix, 173
Transition percentages, 170
  persistence, 171
Transition probabilities, 180
Transpose of a matrix, 188, 360–361
Tree diagram, 149–153
Trial(s), 264
  Bernoulli, 264–272; *see also*
    Bernoulli trials
Triple, ordered, *10*
Tufts, Sonny (1911–1970), 7
Turpo, 426
2-axis, 56
Two-finger Morra, 440
Two-person zero-sum game, 428

Unbounded region of feasibility, 304
Uncleared columns, *369*
Union, 13–14
Unit point, 55
Unknown matrix, 119, 413
Unrestricted variables, 316, *366*,
    368–372
  rule for, 368
Upper bound, 479
  half-space, 301

Value
  absolute, 510–511
  of game, 431

Variable
  fixed, 479
  free, 81, 479
  objective, 299
  random, 234, 232–242
    expectation, 250, 249–255
  slack, 329
    reading final values, 330
  unrestricted, 316, *366*, 368–372
  rule for, 368
Variable check, dual, 363–365
Variance, 259–261
  as an expectation, 261
  for Bernoulli trials, 278
  for binomial distribution, 278
Venn, John (1834–1923), *16*
Venn diagram
  for four sets, 519
  for three sets, 17
Vertex labeling, outline flow chart,
    454
Vertices, 449

Wallis, John (1616–1703), 56
Warning for simplex check, 321
Washing-out (of Markov chain), 188
Weinberg, Wilhelm (1862–1937), 446
Wendy's Old Fashioned Hamburgers,
    52–53
Whitehead, Alfred (1861–1947), *13*
Whitworth, W. A., *30*, *31*
Williams, J. D., 428
Word, in probability, *51*
Worn die, 21, *250*

x-axis, *56*

y-axis, *56*
y-line, 306

z, formula for, 282
z-score, 282
Zero, 504–505
Zero matrix, 529
Zero-sum game, 428
Zuckerman, Martin, *272*

# Symbols and Abbreviations

| | (absolute value), 510–511
A (ace), 387
AC (Appalachian Creations), 1
$\doteq$ (is approximately equal to), 18, *509*
\* (hard exercise, answered in Appendix C), xi, 6
$^C$(exercise that is commented on in Appendix C), xi, 6
C (column of a matrix), 123
$C_r^n$ (combinations), 30
D (decimal), 35
e, *282*
$\varnothing$ (empty set or impossible event), 11
! (factorial), *30*
$\geq$ (greater than or equal to), 509
$\cap$ (intersection), 13
"It can be shown that…", xi

J (jack), 387
K (king), 387
$\leq$ (less than or equal to), 509
LP (linear programming), 298
LPS (linear programming system), 478
n(A) (number in A), *27*
nCr (combinations), 30
$\sim$ (not), 13
nPr (permutations), 30
n(S) (number in S), 26
OR (operations research), *1*
$\pi$(pi), *282*
p (probability of success), 269
$P_r^n$ (permutations), 30
P(A) (probability of event A), 19
P(A|B) (conditional probability), 37

PHE (Petaluma Hamburger Emporium), *6–7*
PHEM (Petaluma Hamburger Emporium Model), 130
PP (Pocono Productions), 7–8
P(x) (probability of outcome x), 19
Q (Queen), 387
R (row of a matrix), 66, 123
S (sample space or certain event), 12
SARB (Sporting and Recreation of Boston), x, 192
$>$ (strictly greater than), 509
$<$ (strictly less than), 509
3D (accurate to three decimals), 35
$\cup$ (union), 14